*MATH*FOCUS 7

Nelson

MATH FOCUS 7

Senior Author and
Senior Consultant
Marian Small

Authors
Jack Hope
Carolyn Martin
Marian Small
Joyce Tonner
Michèle Wills
David Zimmer

Assessment Consultants
Sandra Carl Townsend
Gerry Varty

Australia Canada Mexico Singapore Spain United Kingdom United States

Nelson Math Focus 7

Senior Author and Senior Consultant
Marian Small

Authors
Jack Hope, Carolyn Martin, Marian Small, Joyce Tonner, Michèle Wills, David Zimmer

Contributing Author
Kathleen Kacuiba

Assessment Consultants
Sandra Carl Townsend
Gerry Varty

Director of Publishing
Beverley Buxton

General Manager, Mathematics, Science & Technology
Lenore Brooks

Publisher, Mathematics
Colin Garnham

Associate Publisher, Mathematics
Sandra McTavish

Managing Editor, Development
David Spiegel

Product Manager
Linda Krepinsky

Program Managers
Colin Bisset
Tony Rodrigues

Project Editor
First Folio Resource Group, Inc.:
Robert Templeton

Developmental Editors
First Folio Resource Group, Inc.:
Alasdair Graham
Wendi Morrison
Bradley T. Smith

Assistant Editors
Linda Watson, First Folio Resource Group, Inc.
Carmen Yu

Editorial Assistant
Caroline Winter

Executive Director, Content and Media Production
Renate McCloy

Director, Content and Media Production
Linh Vu

Senior Content Production Editor
Debbie Davies-Wright

Copy Editor/Proofreader
Paula Pettitt-Townsend

Indexer
James Leahy

Production Manager
Cathy Deak

Senior Production Coordinator
Sharon Latta Paterson

Design Director
Ken Phipps

Interior Design
Allan Moon
Kyle Gell

Cover Design
Wil Bache

Cover Image
Horst Neumann/Getty Images

Illustrators
Steve Corrigan
Deborah Crowle
Kyle Gell
Kathy Karakasidis
Allan Moon
Dave Whamond

Compositor
Allan Moon

Photo/Permissions Researcher
Lisa Brant

Photo Shoot Coordinator
Lynn McLeod

Set-up Photos
Dave Starrett

Printer
Transcontinental Printing Inc.

ISBN-13: 978-0-17-632464-3
ISBN-10: 0-17-632464-X

Printed and bound in Canada
1 2 3 4 10 09 08 07

For more information contact Thomson Nelson, 1120 Birchmount Road, Toronto, Ontario, M1K 5G4. Or you can visit our Internet site at http://www.nelson.com

Advisory Panel

The authors and publisher gratefully acknowledge the contributions of the following educators:

Gerry-Lynn Borys
Teacher
St. Francis of Assisi
Red Deer Catholic Regional Division
Red Deer, Alberta

Bob Boyechko
Teacher
St. Elizabeth Seton School
Edmonton Catholic Schools
Edmonton, Alberta

Shona Dobrowolski
Mathematics Consultant
Okotoks, Alberta

Marj Farris
Teacher
Hill Crest Community School
Fort Vermilion School Division
La Crete, Alberta

Lenée Fyfe
Teacher
Park Meadows School
Lethbridge School Division No. 51
Lethbridge, Alberta

Allan Hnatiuk
Teacher
A.E. Cross Junior High School
Calgary Board of Education
Calgary, Alberta

Allan Macdonald
Teacher
Lakeland Ridge Junior High School
Elk Islands Public Schools
Sherwood Park, Alberta

Bernard MacGregor
Assistant Principal
St. Maria Goretti
Elementary School
Edmonton Catholic Schools
Edmonton, Alberta

Moyra Martin
Principal
Cardinal Newman Elementary/Junior
High School
Calgary Catholic School District
Calgary, Alberta

Kathy McCabe
Principal
Edith Rogers School
Edmonton Public Schools
Edmonton, Alberta

Dave McCann
Vice Principal
Stettler Middle School
Clearview School Division #71
Stettler, Alberta

Kevin McGoey
Teacher
St. Elizabeth Seton School
Edmonton Catholic Schools
Edmonton, Alberta

Mike Morrison
Teacher
St. Bonaventure School
Calgary Catholic Separate
School Division
Calgary, Alberta

D.S. Moss
Teacher
Father Michael Troy
Catholic School
Edmonton Catholic Schools
Edmonton, Alberta

Meagan Mutchmor
K-8 Mathematics Consultant
Winnipeg School Division #1
Winnipeg, Manitoba

Sean O'Connell
Teacher
St. Elizabeth Seton School
Edmonton Catholic Schools
Edmonton, Alberta

Rita Paquette
Math Coordinator/Teacher
Sherwood Heights
Junior High School
Elk Island Public Schools
Sherwood Park, Alberta

Vicki Park
Teacher
Crossing Park School
Calgary Board of Education
Calgary, Alberta

Dane Sadownyk
Teacher
St. Elizabeth Seton School
Edmonton Catholic Schools
Edmonton, Alberta

Gerry Varty
AISI/Math Coordinator
Wolf Creek Public Schools
Ponoka, Alberta

Tracy Welke
Mathematics Teacher
Vegreville, Alberta

Aboriginal Consultants

Jennifer Hingley
Project Leader, First Nation and
Métis Content and Perspectives
Okiciyapi Partnership
Saskatoon Public Schools and
Saskatoon Tribal Council

Susie Robinson
Cree Language Consultant
Aboriginal Learning Services
Edmonton Catholic Schools
Edmonton, Alberta

Michael D. Thrasher—Kawhywaweet
Elder
Victoria, British Columbia

Literacy Consultants

Vicki McCarthy
Language and Literacy Consultant
Vancouver School District
Vancouver, British Columbia

Melanie Quintana
Teacher
St. Julia Catholic
Elementary School
Dufferin-Peel Catholic
District School Board
Mississauga, Ontario

Equity Consultant

Mary Schoones
Teacher (Retired)
and Educational Consultant
Ottawa-Carleton District
School Board
Ottawa, Ontario

Contents

Chapter 2: Fractions 40

Chapter 3: Decimal Numbers 96

Chapter 4: Percent 150

Chapter 5: Measurement 190

Chapter 6: Addition and Subtraction of Integers 236

Chapter 7: 2-D Geometry 280

Chapter 9: Linear Relations and Linear Equations 372

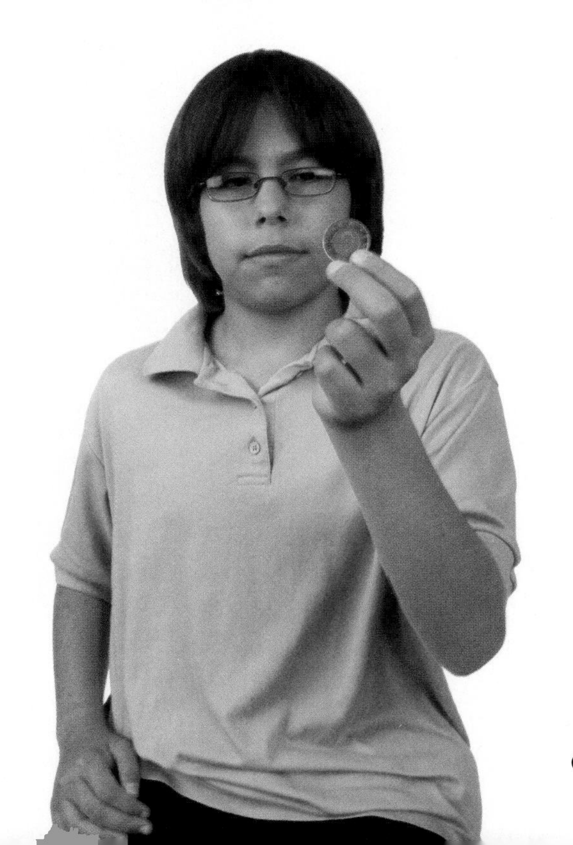

Chapter 10: Probability 426

Chapter 11: Circle Graphs 464

STOP

Chapter 1

Number Relationships

GOAL

You will be able to

- use divisibility rules to identify factors of whole numbers
- determine factors, common factors, and the greatest common factor of whole numbers
- determine multiples, common multiples, and the least common multiple of whole numbers
- explain what happens when you try to divide a number by 0
- identify and extend number patterns to solve problems

Many real-life objects are arranged in rectangular arrays. Create a problem about the cars. How could you use factors or multiples to solve your problem?

Getting Started

YOU WILL NEED
- a hundred chart

Mystery Campsite Number

Star and her family are camping at Lakelse Lake Provincial Park near Terrace, British Columbia.

How can Sam find Star's campsite?

A. How do you know that the campsite number is even? Where are the even numbers located in a hundred chart?

B. Where are the numbers that have 5 as a factor located in a hundred chart? Explain your thinking.

C. Shade the numbers in a hundred chart that have both 2 and 5 as factors.

D. Circle the shaded numbers that also have 3 as a factor. Explain your strategy.

E. How can you tell if a number is a **multiple** of 4?

F. What is Star's campsite number? How do you know?

What Do You Think?

Decide whether you agree or disagree with each statement.
Be ready to explain your decision.

1. You can decide if 10 is a factor of a whole number without dividing the entire number by 10.
2. Every whole number has at least two factors.
3. If 2 and 4 are factors of a whole number, then 8 must also be a factor of the number.
4. If 12 is a multiple of a number, then 24 must also be a multiple of the number.
5. A factor of two numbers is always a factor of their sum. For example, 2 is a factor of both 4 and 8, so 2 is a factor of $4 + 8 = 12$.

1.1 Divisibility by 10, 5, and 2

YOU WILL NEED
- a place value chart

GOAL

Create and use divisibility rules to determine if 10, 5, or 2 is a factor of a whole number.

LEARN ABOUT the Math

Three schools co-hosted the district soccer championships. Each school sold a different type of gift card to raise money for the event.

School	Amount raised
Mountain Heights	$1995
Lavallée	$1020
Plains View	$1634

How can you determine which type of card each school sold?

A. Represent each amount raised on a place value chart.

B. How does regrouping 1020 into 102 tens and 0 ones show that 1020 is divisible by 10, 5, and 2?

C. How does regrouping 1995 into tens and ones show that 1995 is divisible by 5? Is 2 or 10 a factor of 1995? Explain.

Communication | Tip

Every whole number is divisible by its factors. For example, "1020 is divisible by 10" means the same as "10 is a factor of 1020."

$1020 \div 10 = 102$

$102 \times 10 = 1020$

D. How does regrouping 1634 into tens and ones show that 1634 is divisible by 2? Is 5 or 10 a factor of 1634? Explain.

E. Which type of card did each school sell? How do you know?

Reflecting

F. How does regrouping a whole number into tens and ones help you determine the remainder when you divide the number by 10, 5, or 2?

G. What are the possible ones digits if a number is divisible by 10? What if a number is divisible by 5 or by 2?

H. Describe the **divisibility rules** you would use to determine whether 10, 5, and 2 are factors of a number.

divisibility rule

a way to determine if one whole number is a factor of another whole number without actually dividing the entire number

WORK WITH the Math

Example | Using divisibility rules for 10, 5, and 2

Without dividing the entire number, determine if 10, 5, or 2 is a factor of 34 648.

Ryan's Solution

34 648 = 3464 tens + 8 ones Any number of tens is divisible by 10, 5, and 2.	When I divide and there is no remainder, the divisor is a factor.
8 is not divisible by 10.	When I divide 34 648 by 10, the remainder is the ones digit, 8.
8 is not divisible by 5.	When I divide 34 648 by 5, the remainder is 3 because the 3464 tens are divisible by 5 and the remainder when I divide 8 by 5 is 3.
8 is divisible by 2. 2 is a factor of 34 648, but 5 and 10 are not.	When I divide 34 648 by 2, the remainder is 0 because the 3464 tens are divisible by 2 and 8 is divisible by 2.

A Checking

1. Use divisibility rules to decide if 10, 5, or 2 is a factor of each number. If 10, 5, or 2 is not a factor, determine the remainder.
   a) 375 **b)** 1987 **c)** 12 456 **d)** 1 000 000

2. Write all the possibilities for the missing digit.
   a) 136■ is divisible by 10, 5, and 2.
   b) 456■ is divisible by 2, but not by 10 or 5.
   c) 786■ has a remainder of 2 when divided by 5.
   d) 943■ is divisible by 5, but not by 10 or 2.

B Practising

3. Why do you think a divisibility rule for 1 is not needed?

4. Write a four-digit number that is divisible by 5, but not by 10. Explain how you know.

5. A truck is loaded with 1645 kg of potatoes in bags that have the same mass. Are the bags 1 kg, 2 kg, 5 kg, or 10 kg bags? Explain.

6. How many ways can you pay each amount using only one type of Euro coin shown? Explain how you know.
   a) 456 cents **c)** 2445 cents
   b) 1430 cents **d)** 6843 cents

7. **a)** Is your year of birth divisible by 10, 5, or 2? Explain.
   b) How old will you be in the next year that is divisible by 10, 5, and 2?

8. **a)** Which numbers between 1000 and 1100 are divisible by 20?
   b) Use your answer in part (a) to create a divisibility rule for 20. Use a four-digit number as an example to help you explain your rule.

Number Trick
- Multiply your age by 2.
- Multiply this product by 5.
- Remove the last digit.
- The answer is your age.

9. Try the number trick at the left. Then explain why it works.

10. What are the greatest and least numbers between 900 and 1000 that are divisible by 10, 5, and 2? Explain your thinking.

11. How are the divisibility rules for 10, 5, and 2 similar? How are they different?

1.2 Divisibility by 3 and 9

GOAL

Apply divisibility rules to determine if 3 or 9 is a factor of a whole number.

LEARN ABOUT the Math

In the game Divide and Conquer, players use a spinner to create a four-digit number. They have 1 min to identify as many factors as possible.

How can you show that the divisibility rules for 3 and 9 make sense?

Example 1 | Investigating divisibility rules for 3 and 9

Without dividing the entire number, decide if 3 or 9 is a factor of the number.

Sarah's Solution

I thought of my number as 2523 counters in a case.

I looked at the place values, and then put as many counters as I could into bags that hold 999, 99, or 9.

999 999 2 thousands

99 99 99 99 99 5 hundreds

9 9 2 tens

3 ones

The number of counters in each bag is divisible by 3 and by 9. If the counters left over can be put in groups of 3 or 9, then the number of counters left over is also divisible by 3 or 9. This means that the total number of counters is divisible by 3 or 9 too.

I have 2 + 5 + 2 + 3 = 12 ones left over.

12 is divisible by 3, but not by 9, so 2523 is divisible by 3, but not by 9.

12 is also the sum of the digits of 2523!

Denis's Solution

I renamed my number, 7352, as 7 thousands + 3 hundreds + 5 tens + 2 ones.

If I divide by 3 or 9:
7 thousands will have 7 left over.
3 hundreds will have 3 left over.
5 tens will have 5 left over.
2 ones will have 2 left over.

Each thousand will have 1 left over when I divide it by 3 or 9.

$$1000 \div 3 = 333 \text{ R } 1 \qquad 1000 \div 9 = 111 \text{ R } 1$$

So will hundreds and tens.

Total left over: 7 + 3 + 5 + 2 = 17.
17 ÷ 3 = 5 R2

17 and 7352 have a remainder of 2 when divided by 3, so 7352 is not divisible by 3. This means that it can't be divisible by 9 either.

Reflecting

A. How did Denis know that 7352 is not divisible by 9?

B. If a number is divisible by 9, is it always divisible by 3? Explain.

C. Do the divisibility rules for 3 and 9 work for numbers with more than four digits? Explain.

WORK WITH the Math

Example 2 | Applying divisibility rules for 3 and 9

Use divisibility rules to determine the remainder when you divide 4434 by 3 or 9.

Megan's Solution

4 + 4 + 3 + 4 = 15

I calculated the sum of the digits.

15 ÷ 3 = 5 R0
15 ÷ 9 = 1 R6

The number and the sum of the digits have the same remainder when you divide by 3 or 9.

4434 ÷ 3 has remainder 0.
4434 ÷ 9 has remainder 6.

Ⓐ Checking

1. Use divisibility rules to determine if 3 or 9 is a factor of each number. If 3 or 9 is not a factor, explain how to use the rules to determine the remainder.

a) 657 **b)** 3278 **c)** 4002 **d)** 37 782

2. Each number below is divisible by 9. Identify all the possibilities for the missing digit.
   a) 533▒ b) ▒678 c) 30▒6 d) 3▒27

B Practising

3. Use a divisibility rule to solve each problem.
   a) 1117 trees are planted in 9 rows. Is it possible for each row to have an equal number of trees?
   b) A dairy has 5529 kg of cheese to be made into 3 kg packages. Will any cheese be left over?

4. Use divisibility rules to determine if 3 or 9 is a factor of each number. If 3 or 9 is not a factor, explain how to use the rules to determine the remainder.
   a) 6957 b) 5273 c) 44 442 d) 68 073

5. What are the greatest and least four-digit numbers that are divisible by 9?

Reading Strategy

Read the problem in question 6. What inferences can you make? How can they help you solve the problem?

6. A three-digit number is divisible by 10, and its middle digit is 5. Can you determine what the number is if you know that it is also divisible by 3? What if it is divisible by 9? Show your work.

7. Choose any four-digit number. Rearrange its digits to create another four-digit number. Explain why both numbers have the same remainder when you divide by 9.

8. Create a four-digit number for each description. Explain how you created one of the numbers.
   a) a number not divisible by 3 and not divisible by 2
   b) an even number divisible by 9
   c) a number divisible by 3 and 10
   d) a number divisible by 9 and 5

9. What is the least number that is greater than 3876 and divisible by 3? Explain your strategy.

10. Would you rather divide 18 927 and 17 658 by 9, or use a divisibility rule to see if 9 is a factor? Justify your choices.

11. How are the divisibility rules for 3 and 9 the same as the divisibility rules for 2, 5, and 10? How are they different?

CURIOUS MATH

Casting Out Nines

You already know that when you divide a number by 9, the remainder is equal to the sum of its digits divided by 9. When you are calculating the sum of the digits, you can cast out (or throw away) any combination of digits that adds to a multiple of 9. The remainder will stay the same.

Example 1 Is 978 246 divisible by 9?

- 978 246 Cross out 9.
- 978 246 Cross out 2 and 7 because 2 + 7 = 9.
- 978 246 Cross out 8, 4, and 6 because 8 + 4 + 6 = 18 and 18 is a multiple of 9.

The remainder is 0, so 978 246 is divisible by 9.

Example 2 Is 35 675 divisible by 9?

- 35 675 3 + 6 = 9
- 35 675 8 5 + 7 + 5 = 17 = 9 + 8, so cast out the 9 and replace the 5, 7, and 5 with an 8.

When you divide 35 675 by 9, the remainder is 8.

So 35 675 is not divisible by 9.

1. Use casting out nines to determine the remainder when each number is divided by 9. Show your work.

a) 1206 **c)** 36 171 **e)** 77 777
b) 11 728 **d)** 123 981 **f)** 678 123

2. Why do you think that casting out nines results in the same remainder as dividing the sum of the digits by 9?

1.3 Divisibility by 6

YOU WILL NEED

- grid paper

GOAL

Create and use a rule to determine if 6 is a factor of a whole number.

LEARN ABOUT the Math

When customers log on to a music website, they are randomly assigned a number. If the number is divisible by 6, they win a free download.

Is Eva's number a winner?

1	2	3	4	5	6
7	8	9	10	11	12
13	14	15	16	17	18

A. Create a chart with numbers from 1 to 30 in six columns on grid paper. Circle every second number. Cross out every third number.

B. In which columns are the numbers divisible by 2? In which columns are the numbers divisible by 3? Where are the numbers that are divisible by both 2 and 3?

C. Is 197 436 divisible by both 2 and 3? Use divisibility rules to help you decide.

D. In which column would 197 436 be located if you extended your chart? Explain.

E. Did Eva win? Explain.

Reflecting

F. Why do you think a number that is divisible by both 2 and 3 is also divisible by 6?

G. If a number is divisible by 6, must it also be divisible by 2 and 3? Explain your thinking.

H. Use the divisibility rules for 2 and 3 to create a divisibility rule for 6. Use your rule to decide if 8574 is divisible by 6.

WORK WITH the Math

Example | Using the divisibility rule for 6

Without dividing the entire number, decide if 6 is a factor of 3376.

Oshana's Solution

The last digit, 6, is even, so 2 is a factor of 3376.	I used the divisibility rule for 2.
3 + 3 + 7 + 6 = 19 3 is a not factor of 19, so it is not a factor of 3376.	Then I used the divisibility rule for 3.
6 is a not a factor of 3376.	According to the divisibility rule for 6, a number is divisible by 6 if it is divisible by both 2 and 3.

A Checking

1. Which numbers are divisible by 6? Show your work.

a) 348 **b)** 2987 **c)** 5630 **d)** 46 524

2. Each number below is divisible by 6. Identify all the possibilities for the missing digit. Show your work for one number.

a) 243■ **b)** 56■22

B Practising

3. Use a divisibility rule to decide if each number is divisible by 6.

a) 758 **b)** 4908 **c)** 75 084 **d)** 64 856

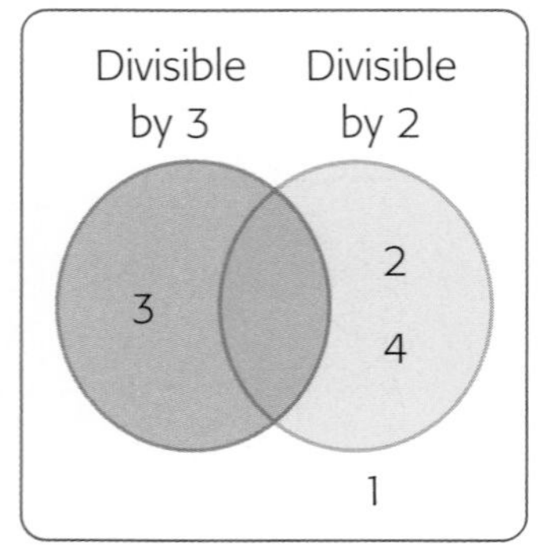

4. Brennan has 21 hockey games to play this season. Every second game is out of town, and every third game is on a school night. How often does Brennan have an out-of-town game on a school night? Use the Venn diagram at the left to help you solve the problem, and then explain how you used it.

5. Explain how you would use a divisibility rule to solve each problem.

a) 6 L containers are being filled from a tank that contains 3258 L of detergent. Will any detergent be left over?

b) A 9355 cm length of wire is cut into 6 equal parts. Will each part have a whole number length in centimetres?

		2 is a factor	
		Yes	No
3 is a factor	Yes	6	3
	No	2, 4	1, 5

6. a) Complete the Carroll diagram at the left to help you sort the numbers from 1 to 24.

b) How does your diagram help you see that every multiple of 6 is divisible by 2 and 3?

7. Will a four-digit number that ends in 6 always be divisible by 6? Use an example to help you explain.

8. Explain why 14■13 cannot be divisible by 6 for any possible hundreds digit.

9. Give an example of a four-digit number that matches each description, or explain why no four-digit number matches.

a) an even number divisible by 3

b) a number divisible by 6 and by 5

c) a number divisible by 6 and by 10

10 a) Oshana wonders if a number is divisible by 12 when it is divisible by 2 and 6. Use examples to help her decide.

b) If a number is divisible by 12, is it divisible by 2 and 3? Explain.

11. If a number is divisible by 2, 3, and 6, what else must be true about it?

1.4 Divisibility by 4 and 8

GOAL

Explain and apply divisibility rules to decide if 4 or 8 is a factor of a whole number.

LEARN ABOUT the Math

Nayana and Jacob found these divisibility rules.

How can you show that the divisibility rules for 4 and 8 make sense?

Example 1 | Explaining the divisibility rule for 8

Explain the divisibility rule for 8 using 4696 as an example.

Nayana's Solution

I renamed 4696 as 4 thousands + 6 hundreds + 9 tens + 6 ones.
Then I looked at each part separately.

$1000 \div 8 = 125\ R0$

Any number of thousands will have 0 left over when I divide by 8.

$100 \div 8 = 12\ R4$
6 hundreds will have $6 \times 4 = 24$ left over.

For each hundred, there will be 4 left over when I divide by 8.

$10 \div 8 = 1\ R2$
9 tens will have $9 \times 2 = 18$ left over.

For each ten, there will be 2 left over when I divide by 8.

The total left over is $6 \times 4 + 9 \times 2 + 6 = 48$.
48 is divisible by 8, so 4696 is divisible by 8.

I didn't look at the ones digit, so I included it in the total.

The divisibility rule for 8 makes sense because it looks at the amount left over when you divide each place value by 8.

Example 2 | Explaining the divisibility rule for 4

Explain the divisibility rule for 4 using 4696 as an example.

Jacob's Solution

Any number of hundreds will have no remainder when I divide by 4,
so I looked at the tens and ones.

$10 \div 4 = 2\ R2$
9 tens will have $9 \times 2 = 18$ left over.

Each ten will have 2 left over when I divide by 4.

The total left over is $9 \times 2 + 6 = 24$.

I included the ones in the total.

24 is divisible by 4, so 4696 is also divisible by 4.	The divisibility rule for 4 makes sense because it looks at the amount left over when the place values are divided by 4.

Reflecting

A. Why is every place value greater than 100 divisible by 4 and every place value greater than 1000 divisible by 8?

B. After Nayana showed that 4696 is divisible by 8, did Jacob need to use the divisibility rule for 4? Explain.

WORK WITH the Math

Example 3 | Applying divisibility rules for 4 and 8

Is 47 724 divisible by 4 or 8? If it is not, determine the remainder.

Ryan's Solution

47 724 $7 \times 4 + 2 \times 2 + 4 = 36$	I used the divisibility rule for 8 on the last three digits.
$36 \div 8 = 4$ R4 $47\ 724 \div 8$ has a remainder of 4.	Since 36 is not divisible by 8, I divided it by 8 to determine the remainder.
47 724 $2 \times 2 + 4 = 8$	I used the divisibility rule for 4 on the last two digits.
8 is divisible by 4, so 47 724 is divisible by 4.	I knew that 8 is divisible by 4, so I didn't have to divide.

A Checking

1. Use divisibility rules to determine if 4 or 8 is a factor. If 4 or 8 is not a factor, determine the remainder.

a) 3466 **b)** 1288 **c)** 39 804 **d)** 64 684

2. Each four-digit number below is divisible by 4. Identify all the possibilities for each missing digit.

a) 533■ **b)** 167■ **c)** 306■ **d)** 32■4

B Practising

3. Use a divisibility rule to solve each problem.

a) A nursery planted 3448 seeds in 8 rows. Can each row have an equal number of seeds?

b) The Reel of Four and the Reel of Eight are Métis dances for 4 and 8 people. Can a school district of 1736 students form groups of 4 without any students left over? What about groups of 8?

4. Use divisibility rules to determine if 4 or 8 is a factor. If 4 or 8 is not a factor, determine the remainder. Show your work.

a) 6958 **b)** 44 008 **c)** 68 072

5. If a number is divisible by 2 and 4, will it always be divisible by 8? Use an example to help you explain.

6. How can you arrange these five number cards to create the greatest number divisible by 4 and 8? Explain your strategy.

A whole number is divisible by 8 if the number formed by the last three digits is divisible by 8.

7. Maddy found another rule for deciding if a number is divisible by 8. The rule she found is shown at the left.

a) Use a four-digit number to test the rule.

b) Explain why you only need to divide the number formed by the last three digits to decide if a number is divisible by 8.

c) Create a similar rule for deciding if a number is divisible by 4. Explain why your rule makes sense.

8. Emily divided 3648 by 2 three times in a row. Explain how her division shows that 3648 is also divisible by 4 and 8.

9. How might the divisibility rules for 2, 4, and 8 help you create a divisibility rule for 16?

1.5 Divisibility by 0

GOAL

Determine whether or not a number can be divided by 0.

How can you use the meaning of division to explain the error when you try to divide by 0?

Mid-Chapter Review

Frequently Asked Questions

Q: How can you use divisibility rules to decide if a number is divisible by 10, 5, or 2?

A: Because 10, 5, and 2 are factors of any number of tens, you need to look at the ones digit only. For example, in 2426, 2 is a factor because the ones digit is even.

Q: ... by 3 or 9?

A: The sum of the digits tells you the total left over when each place value is divided by 3 or 9. If 3 or 9 is a factor of the sum of the digits, 3 or 9 is a factor of the entire number. For example, in 6129, the sum of the digits is 18, so 3 and 9 are factors.

Q: ... by 6?

A: You can use the divisibility rules for 2 and 3, because 6 is a factor of a number if both 2 and 3 are factors.

Q: ... by 4 or 8?

A: When you divide each place value by 8, the total left over is $h \times 4 + t \times 2 + o$.

When you divide each place value by 4, the total left over is $t \times 2 + o$.
(h = hundreds digit , t = tens digit, o = ones digit)

If 8 or 4 is a factor of the total left over, it is a factor of the entire number.

For example, in 9756: $7 \times 4 + 5 \times 2 + 6 = 44$
- 8 is not a factor because 8 is not a factor of 44.
  $5 \times 2 + 6 = 16$
- 4 is a factor because 4 is a factor of 16.

Practice

Lesson 1.1

1. Use a divisibility rule to decide if each number is divisible by 10, 5, or 2. If it is not divisible by 10, 5, or 2, explain how to use the rule to determine the remainder.

a) 4601 **b)** 46 050 **c)** 148 088

Lesson 1.2

2. Matti is using exactly 1405 linking cubes to build a wall behind his model roller coaster. Which of the heights shown at the left can he use? Use divisibility rules to help you explain.

3. Determine the greatest three-digit number that is divisible by 3, 5, and 9. Show your work.

4. The number ▒2 077 is divisible by 9. Determine all the possibilities for the missing digit. Explain your strategy.

5. Can you arrange 2043 plants in 3 equal rows? Can you arrange them in 9 equal rows? Use divisibility rules to explain.

Lesson 1.3

6. Use a divisibility rule to decide which numbers are divisible by 6. Show your work for one answer.

a) 2376 **b)** 4863 **c)** 9192 **d)** 45 420

7. Can a stadium have 3348 seats in 6 equal rows? Can it have these seats in 9 equal rows? Use divisibility rules to explain.

Lesson 1.4

8. Use a divisibility rule to decide which numbers are divisible by 4 or 8. If a number is not divisible by 4 or 8, use the rule to determine the remainder.

a) 4608 **b)** 35 280 **c)** 146 089

9. What is the greatest four-digit number that is divisible by 8? Show your work. Use a divisibility rule to help you explain.

10. Explain why the four-digit number ▒048 is divisible by 4 and 8 for any number of thousands.

1.6 Determining Common Multiples

Identify multiples, common multiples, and least common multiples of whole numbers.

LEARN ABOUT *the Math*

Denis's school is planning a hot dog lunch to raise money for sports equipment. Based on the last hot dog lunch, the students expect to sell at least 100 hot dogs. Wieners come in packages of 12, and buns come in packages of 8.

How many packages of wieners and buns should the students buy to ensure that the numbers of wieners and buns are equal?

A. Calculate the possible sums of wieners by listing multiples of 12.
12, 24, 36, ...

B. Calculate the possible sums of buns by listing multiples of 8.
8, 16, 24, ...

common multiple

a number that is a **multiple** of two or more given numbers; for example, 12, 24, and 36 are common multiples of 4 and 6

least common multiple (LCM)

the least whole number that has two or more given whole numbers as **factors**; for example, 12 is the least common multiple of 4 and 6

C. Circle the numbers that are common to the lists in parts A and B. These are **common multiples** of 8 and 12.

D. Write the least of the circled multiples. This is the **least common multiple,** or **LCM.**

E. How can you use the LCM you identified in part D to determine other common multiples of 8 and 12?

F. Explain how your answer in part E helps you solve the problem of how many packages of wieners and buns to buy.

Reflecting

G. Why do you think the problem would be easier to solve if buns came in packages of 6 and wieners came in packages of 12?

H. How can you tell if a number is a common multiple of two numbers? Use an example to help you explain.

WORK WITH *the Math*

Example 1 | Determining common multiples

What is the LCM of 10 and 12? Identify three other common multiples.

Oshana's Solution

10, 20, 30, 40, 50, (60)
The LCM of 10 and 12 is 60.

I listed the multiples of 10 first because it's easy to count by 10s. I stopped at the first number that was divisible by 12.

2 x 60 = 120
3 x 60 = 180
4 x 60 = 240
120, 180, and 240 are three other common multiples of 10 and 12.

Any multiple of the LCM, 60, is also a common multiple of 10 and 12.

Example 2 | Verifying a common multiple

Is 31 620 a common multiple of 3, 4, and 5?

Denis's Solution

$3 + 1 + 6 + 2 + 0 = 12$

I used divisibility rules. The sum of the digits is divisible by 3, so 3 is a factor of 31 620.

31 620

4 is a factor of 20, so 4 is also a factor of 31 620.

31 620

The last digit is 0, so 5 is a factor of 31 620.

3, 4, and 5 are all factors, so 31 620 is a common multiple of 3, 4, and 5.

Example 3 | Solving a problem using common multiples

One afternoon, Star skied the Squirrel Loop cross-country trail and her mother skied the Marmot Loop trail. If they travelled the same distance, how many complete loops did each of them ski?

Sarah's Solution

Star skied 9 km in each loop, so her total distance is a multiple of 9 km. Her mother skied 6 km in each loop, so her mother's total distance is a multiple of 6 km. I need to find a common multiple of 6 and 9.

6, 12, (18)
18 is the LCM of 6 and 9.

I listed multiples of 6 and stopped at the first number that was divisible by 9.
The next common multiple is $2 \times 18 = 36$, but I think 36 km is too far to ski in an afternoon.

$18 \div 6 = 3$ loops
$18 \div 9 = 2$ loops

I divided 18 by each distance to determine the number of loops.

Star skied two loops, and her mother skied three loops.

A Checking

1. List the first five multiples of each number.
   a) 2 **b)** 5 **c)** 6

2. Determine the LCM of 2, 5, and 6 by continuing the patterns in question 1.

3. Show that 67 440 is a common multiple of 3 and 5 using divisibility rules.

B Practising

4. Determine the LCM of each set of numbers. Show your work.
   a) 9, 12 **b)** 3, 4, 6 **c)** 6, 10 **d)** 2, 3, 5, 20

5. How many packages of buns and soy patties should the school buy to sell in the cafeteria each week?
   - Buns are sold in packages of 6.
   - Soy patties are sold in packages of 8.
   - The school expects to sell between 80 and 100 soy burgers.
   - They want equal numbers of buns and burgers.

6. Identify the numbers that are common multiples of 5 and 8 using divisibility rules. Show your work.
   a) 195 **b)** 10 000 **c)** 13 731 **d)** 10 018

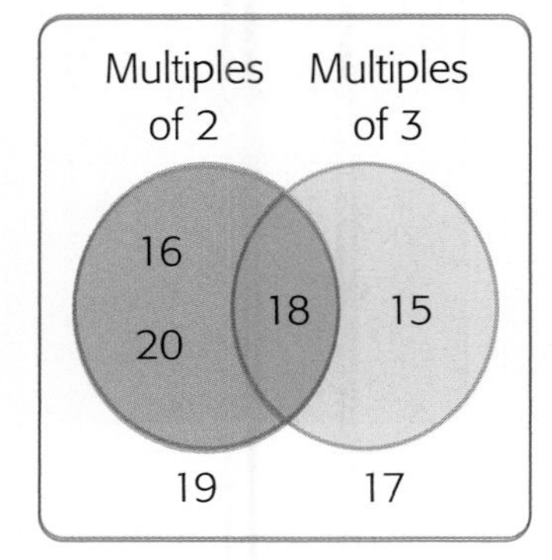

7. **a)** Complete the Venn diagram for the numbers 15 to 30.
   b) How can you describe the numbers that belong in the overlap?

8. Stephen is training for a triathlon. He runs every second day, swims every third day, and cycles every fifth day. How many times during the month of April will he practise all three events on the same day?

9. Max wrote an entry about the LCM in his math portfolio. Do you think his method is always correct? Use an example to help you explain.

> You can calculate the LCM of any two numbers by multiplying them together. For example, 2 x 3 = 6, so 6 is the LCM of 2 and 3.

1.7 Determining Common Factors

Determine factors, common factors, and the greatest common factor of whole numbers.

LEARN ABOUT the Math

Dogrib

Beaver

Okanagan

The Quilt of Belonging is made of 263 square blocks. Each block represents one of the 71 Aboriginal and 192 immigrant groups found in Canada.

Several students have decided to create a collage representing the heritage of the students in their school. They will use an array of cardboard squares, all the same size, to fill a 135 cm $\times$ 120 cm bulletin board completely, without any overlapping.

What is the side length of the largest square that can be used in the array?

Example 1 | Identifying common factors

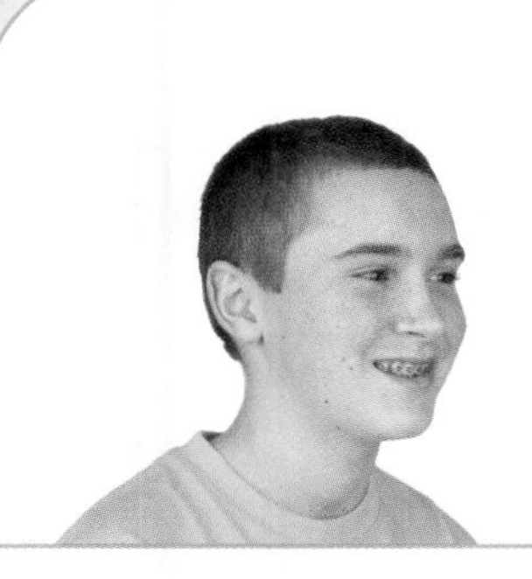

Determine the size of the largest square that can be used for the collage by examining the **common factors** of 135 and 120.

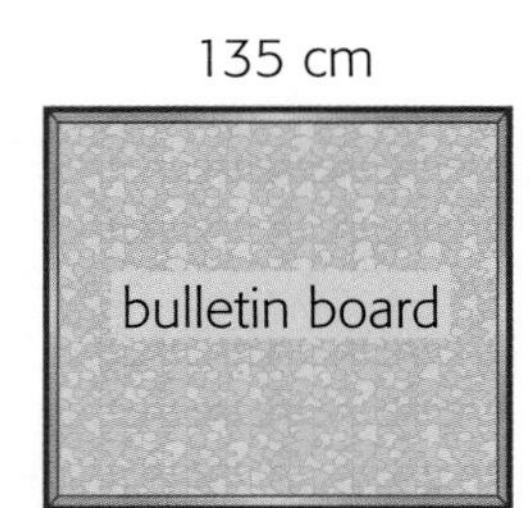

Jacob's Solution: Using lists

common factor

a whole number that divides into two or more other whole numbers with no remainder; for example, 4 is a common factor of 12 and 24

The side lengths of the squares across the rectangle will total 135 cm. The side lengths of the squares up and down will total 120 cm. So, the side length of each square must be a factor of both 120 and 135.

120		135	
1	120	1	135

I listed the factor partners of each number in order. 1 is a factor of every whole number.
$120 = 1 \times 120 \quad 135 = 1 \times 135$

120		135	
1	120	1	135
2	60		

I used a divisibility rule to determine that 2 is a factor of 120, but not 135. Then I found the factor partner of 2 by dividing: $120 \div 2 = 60$, so $120 = 2 \times 60$.

120		135	
(1)	120	(1)	135
2	60		
(3)	40	(3)	45
4	30		
(5)	24	(5)	27
6	20		
8	(15)		
		9	(15)
10	12		

I continued until I could tell there were no more factors. Then I circled the factors that appeared in both lists. These are the common factors.

The greatest side length possible will be the **greatest common factor (GCF)**.

The greatest circled factor, 15, is the GCF of 120 and 135.

A 15 cm × 15 cm square is the largest square that can be used to fill the rectangle without any overlapping.

greatest common factor (GCF)

the greatest whole number that is a factor of two or more whole numbers; for example, 4 is the greatest common factor of 8 and 12

Reflecting

A. Why do you think there is always at least one common factor for any two numbers?

B. How can divisibility rules help you identify the common factors of two numbers? Use 45 and 60 to help you explain.

WORK WITH the Math

Example 2 | Determining common factors and the GCF

Determine the common factors and the greatest common factor (GCF) of 36 and 24.

Solution A: Listing factors

36		24	
(1)	36	(1)	24
(2)	18	(2)	(12)
(3)	(12)	(3)	8
(4)	9	(4)	6
(6)	6		

Make a list of factor partners for each number.

Use divisibility rules to help you identify the factors of 36 and 24. Once you identify a factor, divide to determine its partner.

Circle the common factors.

Solution B: Using a Venn diagram

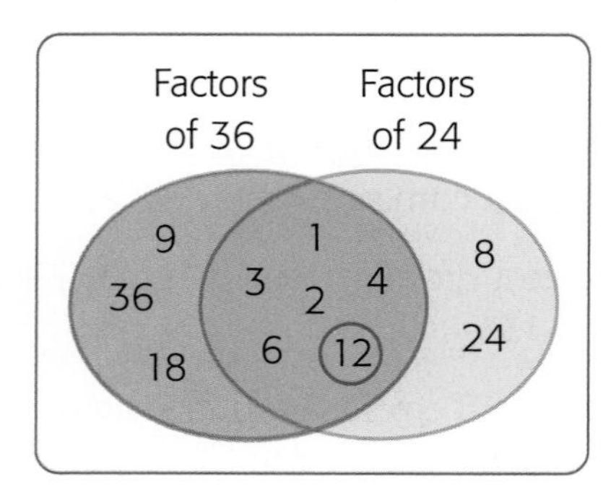

Label two overlapping circles, and make lists of the factors of 24 and 36.

As you identify factors, write them in the section where they belong.

The common factors are in the overlap.

The common factors from least to greatest are 1, 2, 3, 4, 6, and 12.

The greatest common factor is 12.

Ⓐ Checking

1. Identify the common factors and GCF of each pair of numbers. For one pair, describe the divisibility rules you used.
   a) 15, 35 **b)** 42, 54 **c)** 100, 65 **d)** 144, 240

2. Riel wants to use squares to tile a floor that measures 240 cm by 300 cm. What is the side length of the largest square he can use?

Ⓑ Practising

3. Use divisibility rules to identify three common factors of each pair of numbers. Show your work for one answer.
   a) 6690, 9900 **b)** 4848, 4000 **c)** 9990, 3465

4. Use divisibility rules to decide if each number is a common factor of 144 and 1296. Show your work for one answer.
   a) 3 **b)** 4 **c)** 5 **d)** 6 **e)** 8

150		200	
1	150	1	200
2	75	2	✸
3	50	4	50
✸	30	✸	40
6	25	8	25
10	✸	10	✸

5. **a)** Ink dripped on the work shown at the left. What are the hidden factors of 150 and 200?
   b) What is the GCF of 150 and 200?

6. Both 2 and 5 are factors of a number. The number is between 101 and 118. What is the number? Give a reason for your answer.

7. What is the GCF of two different **prime numbers**? Explain your reasoning.

8. The LCM of two different numbers is 24, and the GCF is 12. What are the numbers? Explain your thinking.

9. 48 students arrived in an auditorium, where 54 chairs were arranged in equal rows. Suppose that the same number of students sat in each row. How were the chairs arranged? Explain.

10. Meg wants to install square tiles in a rectangular room. How can identifying common factors help her decide if any tiles will need to be cut? Use numbers to help you explain.

1.8 Solve Problems by Identifying and Extending a Pattern

GOAL

Identify and extend number patterns to solve problems.

LEARN ABOUT the Math

Oshana wants to create passwords for her computer. The passwords will be her first name followed by a number between 1000 and 1050. She decides that every number will have a remainder of 1 when divided by 2 and when divided by 3. She wonders how many passwords she can create.

How can you use a pattern to determine the number of possible passwords?

1 Understand the Problem

Oshana says, "I need to know how many numbers between 1000 and 1050 have a remainder of 1 when divided by both 2 and 3."

2 Make a Plan

Oshana decides, "It will take too long to divide all 49 numbers between 1000 and 1050 by 2 and 3 to see which have a remainder of 1. Instead, I'll figure out the first possible number. Then I'll use divisibility rules to find the next few numbers. Then I'll look for a pattern to find other possible numbers."

3 Carry Out the Plan

I know by using divisibility rules that 1002 is divisible by both 2 and 3. So 1003 will be the first number that has a remainder of 1 when divided by 2 and by 3. I'll list the odd numbers greater than 1003 to determine other password numbers.

Number	1003	1005	1007	1009	1011	1013	1015
Remainder when divided by 3	1	0	2	1	0	2	1

There is a pattern. Every password number is 1003 plus a multiple of 6.
The 7th multiple of 6 is 42, so the password number is $1003 + 42 = 1045$. This is just less than 1050.
The 8th multiple of 6 is 48, so $1003 + 48 = 1051$, which is too high.
Therefore, in addition to 1003, there are seven other numbers. I can create eight passwords altogether.

Reflecting

A. How can you tell that 1003 is the first possible password number?

B. How can you check Oshana's solution?

C. How did identifying and extending a pattern help Oshana solve the problem?

WORK WITH the Math

Example | Extending a pattern to solve a problem

Barrett wrote numbers between 5000 and 6000 in the following pattern: 5010, 5025, 5040, 5055, ….

What is the last number in his pattern?

Ryan's Solution

1 Understand the Problem

I have to determine a number just less than 6000 that fits Barrett's pattern.

2 Make a Plan

I noticed that the numbers go up by 15 each time, and that they are all divisible by 5. Then I noticed that each number is also divisible by 3. I will use this information to determine a number that is divisible by 3 and 5, and just less than 6000.

3 Carry Out the Plan

I know by using divisibility rules that 6000 is divisible by both 3 and 5.
So if I subtract 15 from 6000, the answer will be divisible by both 3 and 5.
$6000 - 15 = 5085$
5085 is the last number in Barrett's pattern.

4 Look Back

I can use divisibility rules to check my answer.
5085 is divisible by 5 because the last digit is divisible by 5.
5085 is divisible by 3 because the sum of the digits, 18, is divisible by 3.

A Checking

1. How many numbers between 1000 and 1100 have a remainder of 1 when divided by 3 and by 4? Show your work.

B Practising

2. Maddy wrote numbers between 4000 and 5000 in the following pattern:
   4014, 4032, 4050, 4068, ...
   What is the last number in her pattern?

3. A bag contains between 1000 and 1100 beads. If you divide the beads into 2 or 5 equal groups, you have 1 bead left over each time. How many beads might be in the bag? Show your work.

4. How many numbers in the form 12■■ are divisible by 3 and 4? Show your work.

5. What is the sum of the first 100 odd numbers? Show your work.

6. What is the ones digit in the product of the first 100 counting numbers? Show your work.

7. What is the ones digit when you multiply 100 nines together? Show your work.

8. To calculate the digital root of a product, add the digits of the product. Then add the digits of this sum and repeat until you get a one-digit number. For example,
   $747 \times 9 = 6723$
   $6 + 7 + 2 + 3 = 18$
   $1 + 8 = 9$
   9 is the digital root of 747×9.
   a) What are the digital roots of the product of any number and 9? Show your work.
   b) Use your answer to part (a) to predict the digital root of the product of any number and 3. Is your prediction correct? Explain.

MATH GAME

GCF Showdown

Number of players: 2 to 4

YOU WILL NEED

- 10 number cards for each player

0 1 2 3 4 5 6 7 8 9

How to Play

1. For each round, all the players shuffle their 10 cards, and then place their cards face down.
2. The players select four cards to create 2 two-digit numbers.
3. The players determine the GCF of the two numbers.
4. The player with the greatest GCF scores 1 point.
5. The first player to reach 10 points wins.

Ryan's Turn

I turned over 2, 4, 7, and 8.
I made 72 and 48.

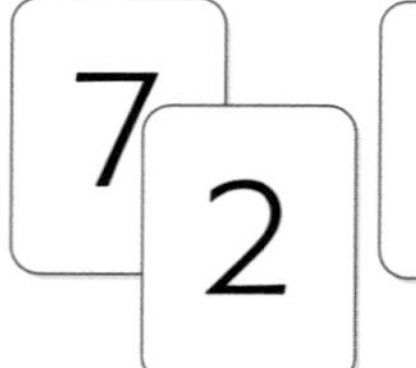

The common factors of 48 and 72 are 1, 2, 3, 4, 6, 8, 12, and 24.
With her cards, Oshana chose 1, 2, 6, and 8. She made 28 and 16 with a GCF of 4.
My GCF was greatest, so I score 1 point.

Chapter Self-Test

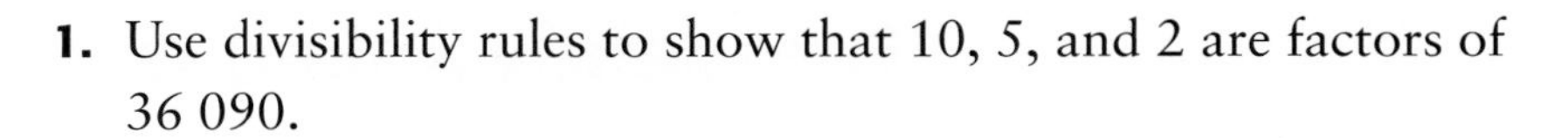

1. Use divisibility rules to show that 10, 5, and 2 are factors of 36 090.

2. If 3 and 9 are factors of 12 34■, identify the missing digit. Show your work.

3. Peter has a collection of 2232 hockey cards. How can you tell without dividing 2232 that he can arrange the cards into either 4 or 8 equal piles?

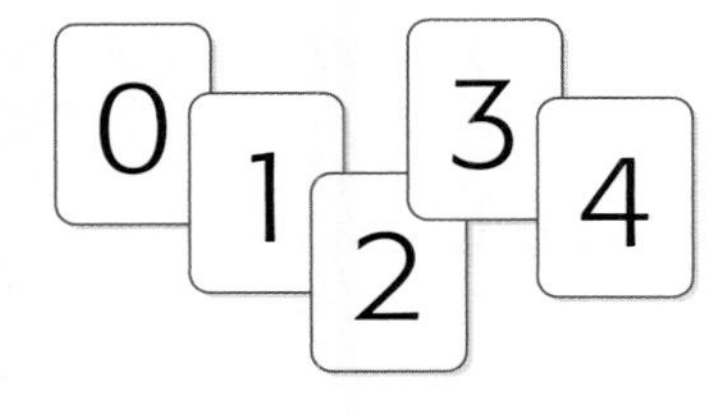

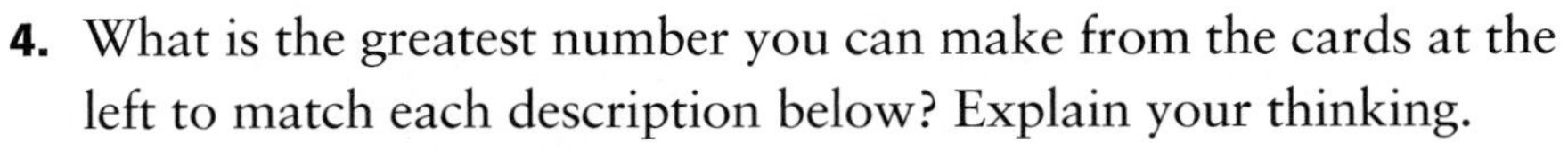

4. What is the greatest number you can make from the cards at the left to match each description below? Explain your thinking.
   a) divisible by 10, 5, and 2
   b) divisible by 3 and 9

5. Which statements are true? If a statement is true, explain why. If a statement is not true, use an example to show why not.
   a) A number divisible by 10 is also divisible by 2 and 5.
   b) A number divisible by 4 is also divisible by 8.
   c) A number divisible by 6 is also divisible by 2 and 3.
   d) A number divisible by 9 is also divisible by 3.

6. **a)** What is the LCM of 15 and 25?
   b) Determine three other common multiples of 15 and 25.
   c) Identify all of the common factors of 15 and 25.
   d) What is the GCF of 15 and 25?

7. The rocks in a pouch can be divided into 2, 3, or 5 equal groups.
   a) Explain how identifying common multiples can help you determine the possible number of rocks in the pouch.
   b) What is the least number of rocks that can be in the pouch? How do you know?

What Do You Think Now?

Revisit What Do you Think? on page 3. How have your answers and explanations changed?

Chapter Review

Frequently Asked Questions

Q: How do you determine common multiples and the least common multiple (LCM) of two numbers?

A: To determine the LCM of two numbers, list the multiples of one number in order from least to greatest. The LCM is the first number you write that is also a multiple of the other number.

For example, to determine the LCM of 15 and 20, list the multiples of 20: 20, 40, 60, ...

15 is not a factor of 20 or 40, but it is a factor of 60.

So, 60 is the LCM of 15 and 20.

Any multiple of 60, such as 120, 180, and 240, is also a common multiple of 15 and 20.

Q: How do you determine common factors and the greatest common factor (GCF) of two numbers?

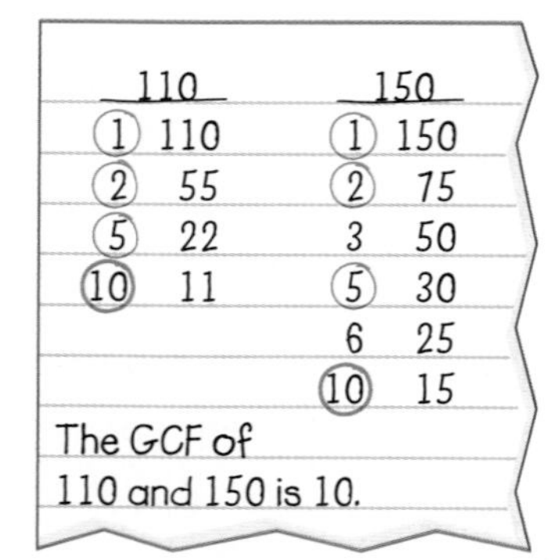

A1: Use divisibility rules to help you list all the factors of both numbers. Then circle the factors that appear in both lists. The greatest of these circled factors is the GCF.

A2: You can use a Venn diagram to help you sort the factors of the two numbers. The common factors are in the overlap. The greatest number in the overlap is the GCF. In the example below, 10 is the greatest number in the overlap, so 10 is the GCF of 110 and 150.

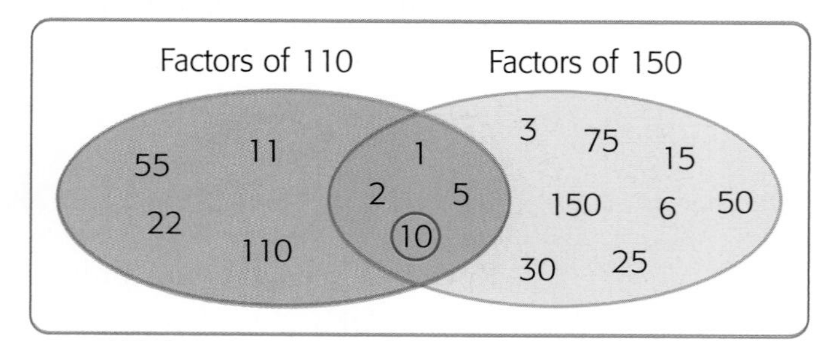

Practice

Lesson 1.1

1. List the first number that is greater than 10 000 and divisible by 10, 5, and 2. Explain your strategy.

2. If you multiply any whole number by 10, will the product always be divisible by 5 and 2? Explain.

Lesson 1.2

3. **a)** Explain why 3 is a factor of a number if 9 is a factor.
b) If 3 is a factor of a number, is 9 also a factor? Use an example to help you explain.

4. Use divisibility rules to solve each problem. Explain your thinking.
a) If you use 1035 wheels to build tricycles, will any wheels be left over?
b) Can 1230 people sit in 9 equal rows at a rock concert?

5. 43 ■ 55 is divisible by 3 and 9. Identify the missing digit.

Lesson 1.3

6. Use a divisibility rule to show that 6 is a factor of 21 456.

Lesson 1.4

7. The number 61 7■8 is divisible by 4. What are the possibilities for the missing digit? Explain.

8. Can 2232 juice containers be packaged in groups of 4 or 8 without any containers left over? Use divisibility rules to solve this problem.

Lesson 1.5

9. **a)** Explain why you can calculate $0 \div 3$ but not $3 \div 0$.
b) Explain why 0 has only one multiple, while other whole numbers have an unlimited number of multiples.

Lesson 1.6

10. Every third car on an assembly line is green. Every fourth car is a convertible.

a) What is the position of the first green convertible on the assembly line?

b) How many cars out of the first 100 will be green convertibles? Show your work.

c) How did common multiples help you solve this problem?

11. Identify the LCM and three other common multiples of each pair of numbers.

a) 20, 16 **b)** 40, 50 **c)** 15, 12 **d)** 60, 120

Lesson 1.7

12. Which pair of numbers has the greatest GCF?

A 45, 70 **B** 120, 270 **C** 135, 270 **D** 480, 640

13. Brennan has one rope that is 90 cm long and another rope that is 120 cm long. He wants to cut both ropes so that all the pieces are the same length. What is the longest piece he can make? Explain.

Chapter Task

Task | *Checklist*

- ✔ Did you show all the steps you used?
- ✔ Did you use correct math language?
- ✔ Did you explain your thinking?

Creating Divisibility Rules

The divisibility rules you have learned in this chapter can be used to create other divisibility rules.

How can you create your own divisibility rules?

A. Explain how you can use the divisibility rules for 3 and 5 to create a divisibility rule for 15. Use several four-digit numbers to show how it works.

B. Use other combinations of divisibility rules to create more divisibility rules. Use several examples to make sure that your divisibility rules work.

C. Research more divisibility rules on the Internet. Report your findings to the class. Use examples to illustrate how each rule works.

NEL

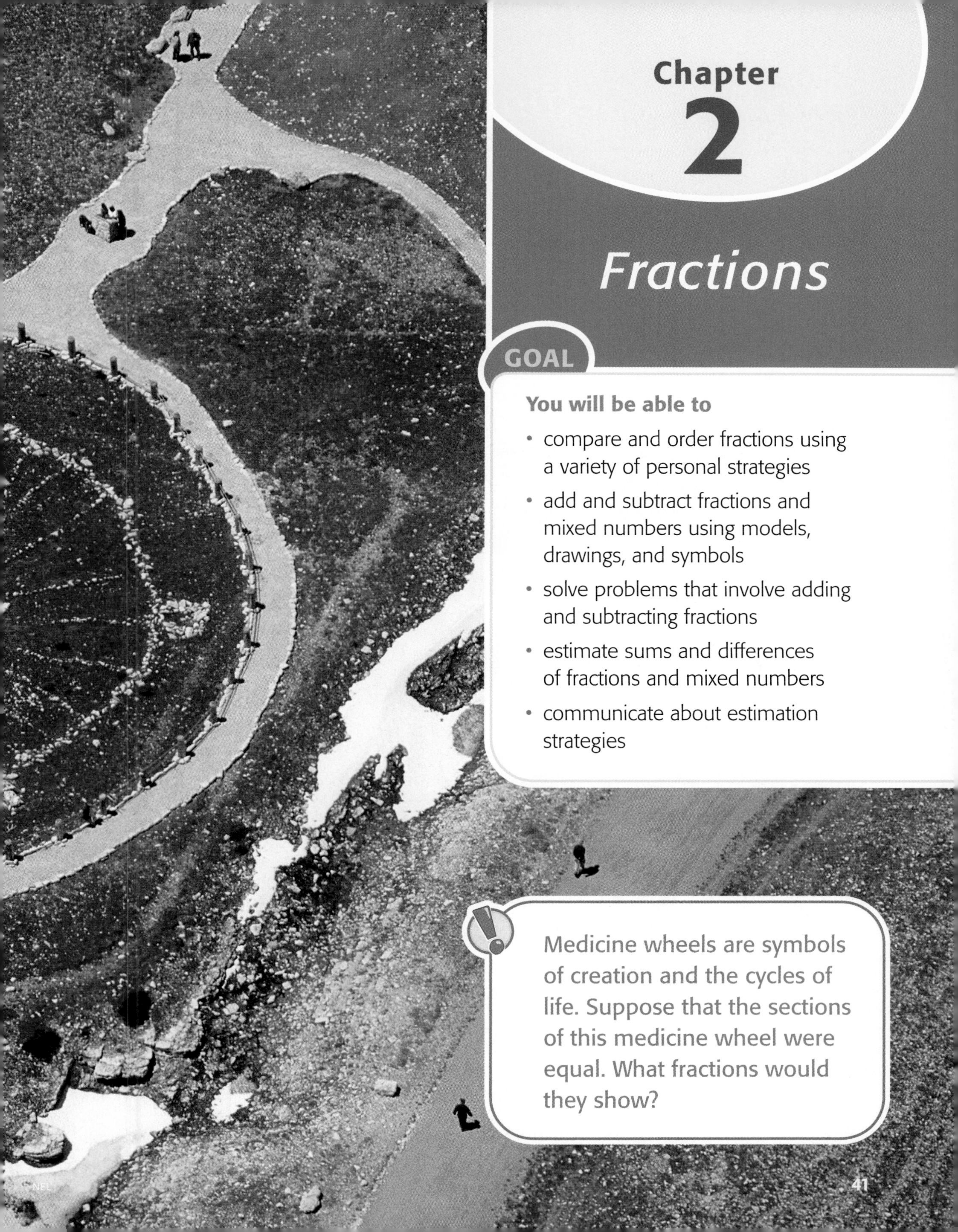

Chapter 2

Fractions

GOAL

You will be able to

- compare and order fractions using a variety of personal strategies
- add and subtract fractions and mixed numbers using models, drawings, and symbols
- solve problems that involve adding and subtracting fractions
- estimate sums and differences of fractions and mixed numbers
- communicate about estimation strategies

Medicine wheels are symbols of creation and the cycles of life. Suppose that the sections of this medicine wheel were equal. What fractions would they show?

Chapter 2

Getting Started

YOU WILL NEED
- pattern blocks
- triangle dot paper

Sweatshirt Sales

The members of a track team are selling sweatshirts to raise money so they can go to an out-of-town meet.

How many different fractions or mixed numbers can you use to represent the sweatshirts?

A. What is true about $\frac{6}{12}$ of the sweatshirts?

B. Why does $\frac{1}{2}$ also describe the sweatshirts in part A?

C. What is true about $\frac{1}{3}$ of the sweatshirts?

D. What other fraction describes the sweatshirts in part C?

E. Joe said that $\frac{3}{2}$ of the tables are being used. Explain why he said this.

F. Describe the picture on page 42 using at least five other fractions. Explain what each fraction represents.

G. Suppose that a double hexagon represents 1. You could represent $\frac{1}{6}$ with a blue rhombus, since 6 blue rhombuses would cover the double hexagon.

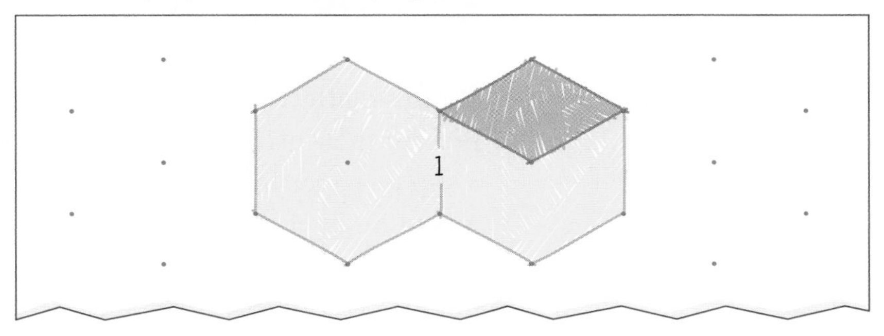

Model each of your fractions in part F, using a double hexagon to represent 1. Draw your models on dot paper.

What Do You Think?

Decide whether you agree or disagree with each statement. Be ready to explain your decision.

1. There are equivalent fractions for $\frac{2}{3}$ and $\frac{1}{4}$ that have the same denominator.
2. The fraction $\frac{6}{8}$ is in lowest terms.
3. This shape could represent $\frac{1}{2}$, $\frac{1}{3}$, or $\frac{2}{5}$.

4. When you add two fractions, the sum is always less than 1.

2.1 Comparing Fractions

YOU WILL NEED
- coloured pencils
- a number line

GOAL

Compare and order fractions using benchmarks and equivalent fractions.

LEARN ABOUT the Math

Sarah's math teacher has a new way to decide which students will present their projects first. In groups of 10, each student pulls a slip of paper from a jar. A fraction or **mixed number** is written on each slip. The student with the fourth greatest number will present first.

In Sarah's group, the slips were

$2\frac{1}{3}$ $\frac{8}{9}$ $\frac{12}{5}$ $\frac{2}{9}$ $\frac{15}{18}$ $\frac{7}{9}$ $\frac{2}{3}$ $\frac{4}{6}$ $\frac{2}{5}$ $\frac{4}{5}$

Sarah chose $\frac{8}{9}$.

The students decided to place the fractions on a number line to help them see the order.

lowest terms

an equivalent form of a fraction with a numerator and a denominator that have no common factors other than 1; for example, $\frac{3}{4}$ is the lowest term form of $\frac{12}{16}$, since $\frac{3}{4} = \frac{12}{16}$, and 3 and 4 have no common factors other than 1

common denominator

a common multiple of two or more denominators; for example, a common denominator for $\frac{2}{3}$ and $\frac{3}{6}$ would be any multiple of 6. If you use the least common multiple of the denominators, the common denominator is called the least common denominator

Will Sarah present first in her group?

A. How do you know that $\frac{2}{5}$ is to the left of $\frac{4}{5}$ on the number line?

B. How would you decide where $\frac{2}{9}$ goes?

C. How would writing $\frac{4}{6}$ in **lowest terms** help you place it on the number line?

D. How would renaming $\frac{12}{5}$ as a mixed number help you place it on the number line?

E. How would writing $\frac{4}{6}$ and $\frac{15}{18}$ as equivalent fractions with a **common denominator** help you place $\frac{15}{18}$ on the number line?

F. Place all the fractions from Sarah's group on the number line.

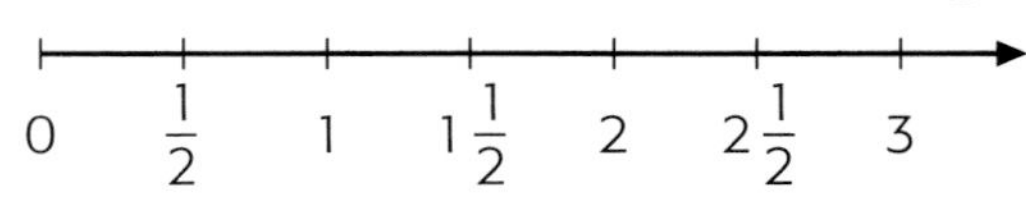

G. Which fraction is fourth greatest? Will Sarah present first in her group?

Reflecting

H. Before you placed the numbers on the number line, how might you have known that the student holding $\frac{2}{9}$ or $\frac{2}{5}$ had no chance of presenting first?

I. What strategies did you use to place the numbers on the number line?

WORK WITH the Math

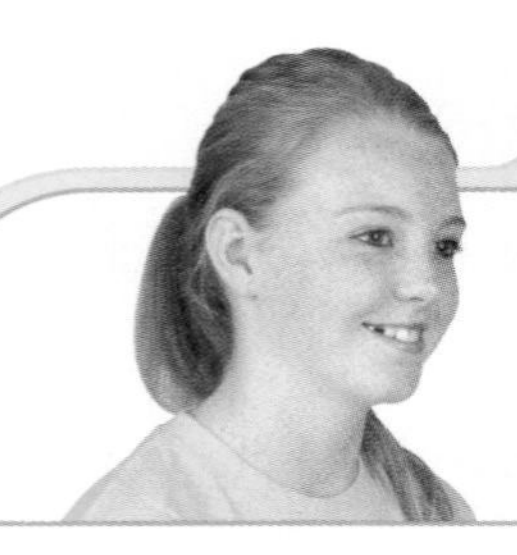

Example 1 | Ordering numbers on a number line

Place these numbers on a number line: $\frac{5}{6}, 2\frac{3}{5}, \frac{31}{8}, \frac{2}{8}, \frac{3}{9}$.

Sarah's Solution

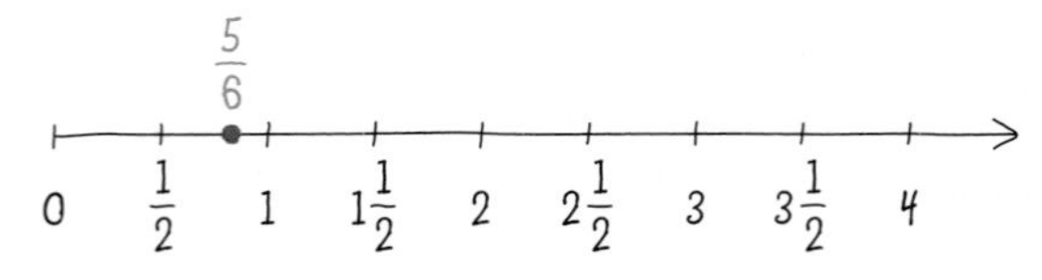

I went through the numbers from left to right.

I know that $\frac{5}{6}$ is more than $\frac{1}{2}$ but less than 1.

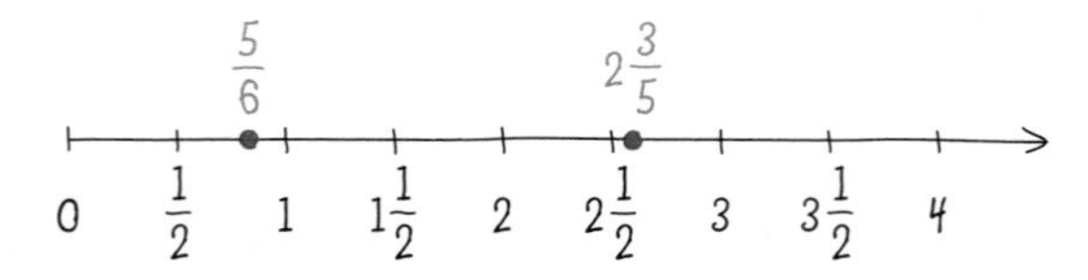

I know that $2\frac{3}{5}$ is a bit more than $2\frac{1}{2}$, since $\frac{3}{6} = \frac{1}{2}$ and $\frac{3}{5} > \frac{3}{6}$. I know this since each fifth is more than each sixth.

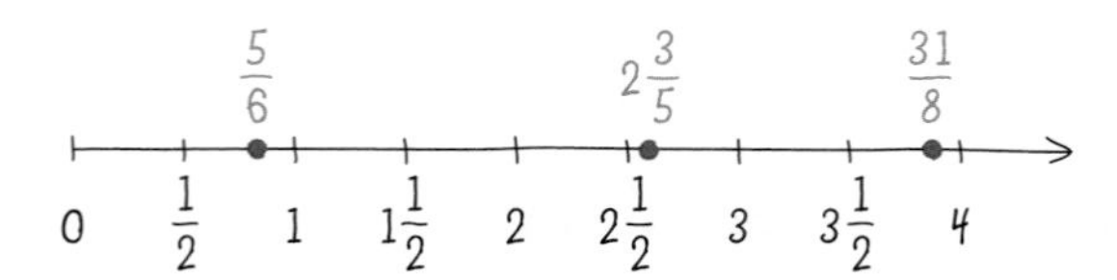

I know that $\frac{32}{8} = 4$, so $\frac{31}{8}$ is a little less than 4.

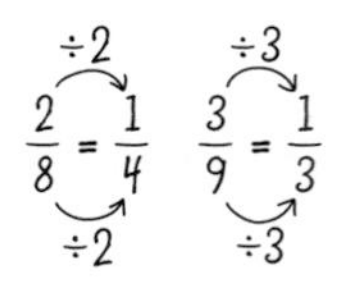

I divided $\frac{2}{8}$ and $\frac{3}{9}$ by common factors to rename them in lower terms.

I know that 1 fourth piece is less than 1 third piece, so $\frac{1}{4} < \frac{1}{3}$.

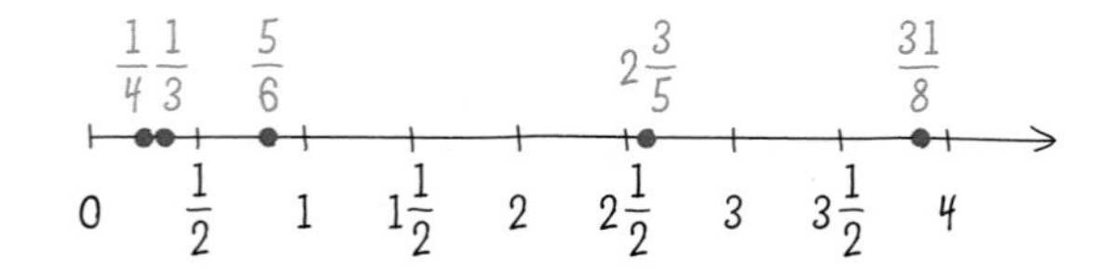

I know that both $\frac{1}{4}$ and $\frac{1}{3}$ are less than $\frac{1}{2}$, since 1 piece out of 4 or 1 piece out of 3 is less than 1 piece out of 2.

Example 2 | Locating a fraction between fractions

Name some fractions that are between $\frac{1}{2}$ and $\frac{2}{3}$.

Ryan's Solution

$\frac{1}{2} = \frac{3}{6}$ (×3) $\frac{2}{3} = \frac{4}{6}$ (×2)

I renamed $\frac{1}{2}$ and $\frac{2}{3}$ using a common denominator. I couldn't think of a fraction between $\frac{3}{6}$ and $\frac{4}{6}$, so I used equivalent fractions with a common denominator of 24 so that the numerators were farther apart.

$\frac{1}{2} = \frac{12}{24}$ (×12) $\frac{2}{3} = \frac{16}{24}$ (×8)

Some fractions between $\frac{1}{2}$ and $\frac{2}{3}$ are $\frac{13}{24}$, $\frac{14}{24}$ or $\frac{7}{12}$, and $\frac{15}{24}$ or $\frac{5}{8}$.

A Checking

1. Write each pair of fractions as equivalent fractions with a common denominator.

a) $\frac{3}{5}$ and $\frac{2}{4}$

b) $\frac{5}{8}$ and $\frac{3}{4}$

c) $\frac{2}{10}$ and $\frac{1}{15}$

d) $\frac{2}{3}$ and $\frac{1}{8}$

2. a) Place $1\frac{2}{3}$, $\frac{3}{4}$, $\frac{3}{5}$, and $\frac{7}{5}$ on the number line.

0 $\frac{1}{2}$ 1 $1\frac{1}{2}$ 2 $2\frac{1}{2}$ 3

b) List the fractions in order from least to greatest.

3. Compare each pair of fractions using a strategy of your choice.

a) $\frac{3}{7}$ and $\frac{2}{3}$ **b)** $\frac{2}{5}$ and $\frac{1}{2}$ **c)** $\frac{8}{6}$ and $\frac{4}{8}$

B Practising

4. Rewrite each fraction in lowest terms.

a) $\frac{4}{8}$ **b)** $\frac{10}{15}$ **c)** $\frac{15}{6}$ **d)** $\frac{10}{6}$

5. a) Place $\frac{15}{4}$, $2\frac{2}{5}$, $\frac{34}{10}$, $\frac{5}{8}$, and $\frac{6}{9}$ on the number line.

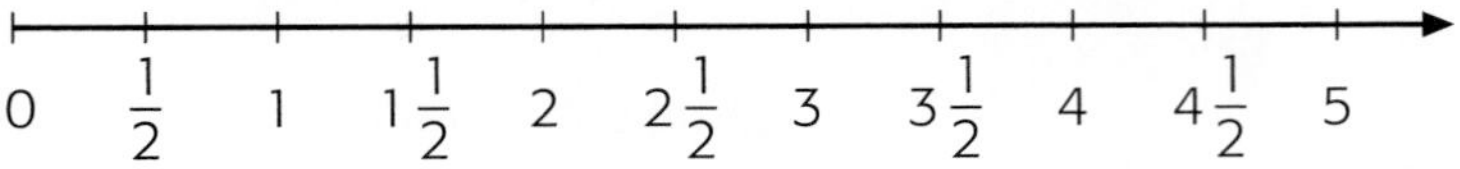

b) List the fractions in order from least to greatest.

6. a) Place $2\frac{2}{5}$, $3\frac{1}{2}$, $\frac{8}{7}$, $\frac{7}{8}$, and $\frac{4}{5}$ on the number line.

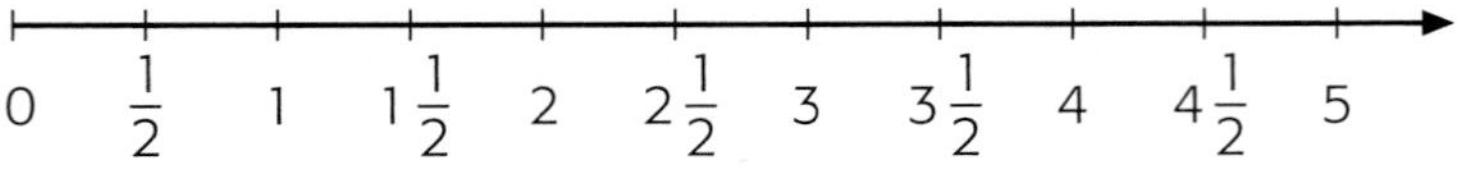

b) List the fractions in order from greatest to least.

7. Compare each pair of fractions using different strategies.

a) $\frac{4}{9}$ and $\frac{5}{6}$ **b)** $\frac{4}{5}$ and $\frac{1}{6}$ **c)** $\frac{8}{3}$ and $\frac{13}{15}$

8. Which number in each list is out of order?

a) $\frac{1}{6}, \frac{2}{5}, \frac{4}{9}, \frac{3}{8}, \frac{9}{5}$

b) $\frac{12}{5}, \frac{11}{3}, 2\frac{1}{2}, \frac{11}{4}, \frac{11}{2}$

c) $\frac{1}{10}, \frac{4}{7}, \frac{7}{6}, \frac{2}{3}, \frac{8}{5}$

d) $\frac{3}{4}, \frac{2}{10}, \frac{11}{12}, \frac{6}{5}, \frac{3}{2}$

9. Which fraction is in the wrong location?

a)

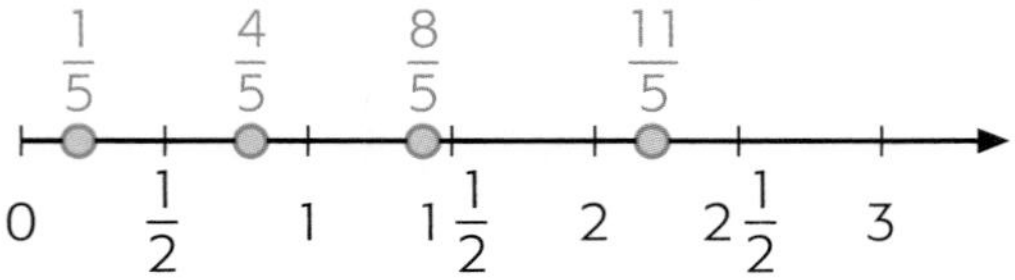

b)

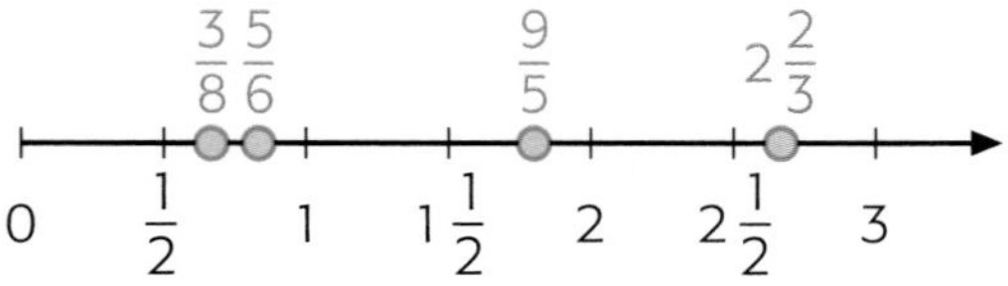

c)

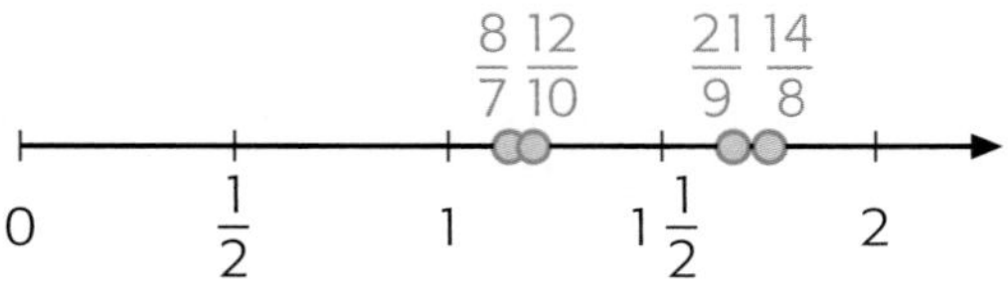

10. On which quiz did Jane do best?

Quiz	A	B	C
Score	$\frac{31}{40}$	$\frac{25}{30}$	$\frac{20}{25}$

11. Mike's test marks kept going up by 2, but so did the total possible score on the tests. Were his marks improving? Explain.

> ***Reading Strategy***
>
> Look for the important information in this problem.
> Record your ideas.

12. Alasdair, Briana, and Lesya played a series of chess games. They reported what fraction of the games they won:

- Alasdair said that he won less than $\frac{1}{2}$ of his games.
- Briana said that she won between $\frac{1}{2}$ and $\frac{5}{8}$ of her games.
- Lesya said that she won between $\frac{5}{8}$ and $\frac{5}{6}$ of her games.

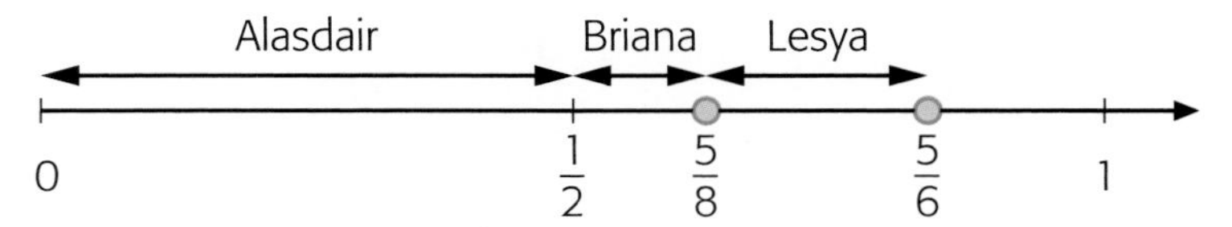

Name two possible fractions for each student.

13. Choose two fractions in which the numerators and denominators are both more than 2 apart; for example, $\frac{3}{5}$ and $\frac{7}{10}$.

- Create a new fraction by using a numerator between the two numerators and a denominator between the two denominators; for example, $\frac{5}{8}$.
- How does the new fraction compare with the original two fractions?
- Try some more examples. Does this result always seem to be true?

14. How can you tell whether a fraction is greater than $\frac{1}{2}$?

15. Why is it easier to compare $\frac{2}{3}$ with $\frac{2}{7}$ than it is to compare $\frac{2}{3}$ with $\frac{4}{7}$ using mental strategies?

2.2 Exploring Adding and Subtracting Fractions with the Same Denominator

YOU WILL NEED
- coloured tiles
- grid paper
- pencil crayons

GOAL

Describe fraction addition and subtraction models with equations.

EXPLORE the Math

Nayana filled a 3×4 grid with coloured tiles. She wrote two fraction equations to describe how the different colours filled the space.
$\frac{2}{12} + \frac{10}{12} = \frac{12}{12}$ and $\frac{12}{12} - \frac{2}{12} = \frac{10}{12}$

What fraction equations can you write to describe a grid covered with coloured tiles?

MATH GAME

Super Sixes

Number of players: 2 to 4

YOU WILL NEED
- 2 dice

How to Play

1. Roll the dice twice to create two pairs of numbers.
2. Add the numbers in one pair. Multiply the numbers in the other pair.
3. Calculate the least common multiple (LCM) of the two results.
4. Score 1 point if you calculate the LCM correctly.
5. Score 1 more point if one digit of your LCM is 6.
6. Score 2 more points if your LCM is a multiple of 6.
7. The first player to reach 12 points wins.

Jacob's Turn

I rolled a 3 and a 5. Then I rolled a 2 and a 2.

I decided to multiply 3 and 5, and add 2 and 2.

$3 \times 5 = 15$ $\qquad$ $2 + 2 = 4$

15, 30, 45, 60

The LCM for 15 and 4 is 60, since 60 is the first multiple of 15 with 4 as a factor.

I get 4 points:
- 1 point for calculating the 60 correctly
- 1 point for the 6 in 60
- 2 points since 60 is a multiple of 6

2.3 Adding Fractions with Fraction Strips

YOU WILL NEED

- Fraction Strips (Blackline Master)

GOAL

Add fractions less than 1 using fraction strips.

LEARN ABOUT the Math

Denis is reading a book. Last weekend, he read $\frac{1}{3}$ of the book. Yesterday, he read $\frac{1}{4}$ more of it.

What fraction of the book has Denis read?

Example 1 | Estimating sums using fraction strips

Estimate $\frac{1}{3} + \frac{1}{4}$ using fraction strips.

Denis's Solution

I modelled the two fractions using fraction strips.

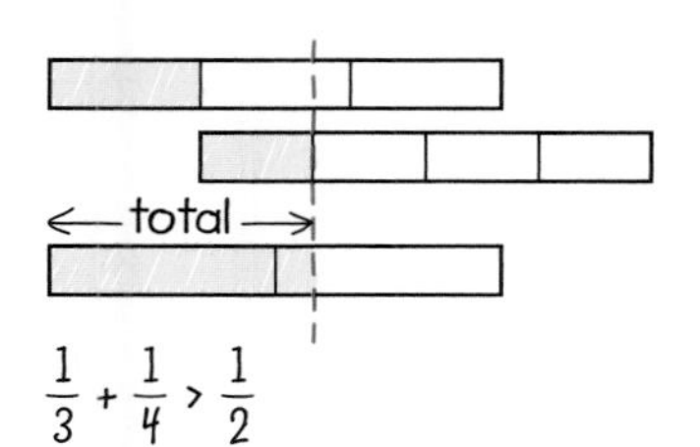

First, I made a $\frac{1}{3}$ strip and a $\frac{1}{4}$ strip.

To add, I put the $\frac{1}{4}$ strip at the end of the $\frac{1}{3}$ strip.

I compared the total with the $\frac{1}{2}$ strip. The sum is a bit more than $\frac{1}{2}$.

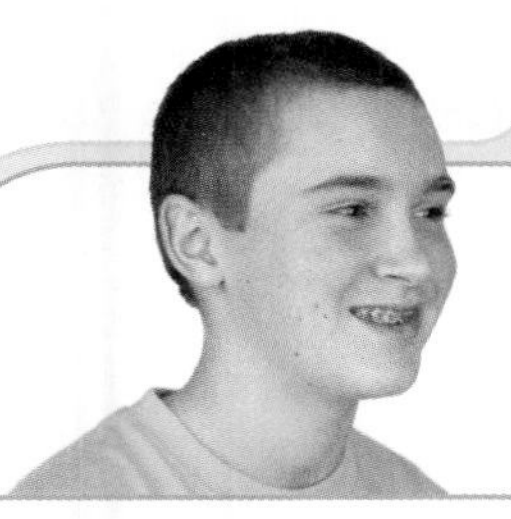

Example 2 | Adding using fraction strips

Add $\frac{1}{3} + \frac{1}{4}$ using fraction strips.

Jacob's Solution

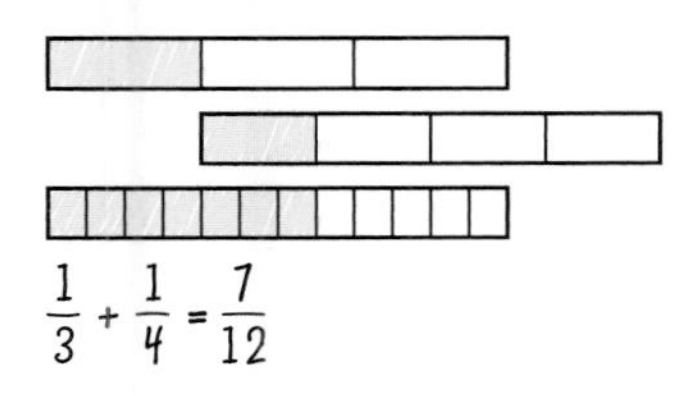

First, I added a $\frac{1}{4}$ strip to the end of a $\frac{1}{3}$ strip.

Then, I looked for a strip to match the total length. Since 12 is a common multiple of 3 and 4, I looked for a 12ths strip.

$\frac{7}{12}$ is as long as $\frac{1}{3}$ and $\frac{1}{4}$ together.

Since $\frac{1}{3} = \frac{4}{12}$ and $\frac{1}{4} = \frac{3}{12}$, it makes sense that the $\frac{7}{12}$ strip matched the total length.

Reflecting

A. How does Denis's estimate show that Jacob's answer is probably correct?

B. How could you have predicted that Jacob's answer might involve a 12ths strip?

WORK WITH the Math

Example 3 | Adding using models

Estimate and then add $\frac{2}{3} + \frac{5}{6}$.

Solution

2 whole fraction strips:

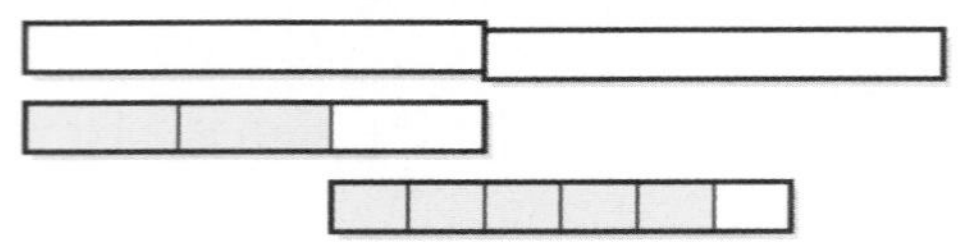

$\frac{2}{3} + \frac{5}{6} > 1 \quad \frac{2}{3} + \frac{5}{6} < 2$

Estimate: The answer is more than 1, since the shaded part is more than 1 whole strip. The shaded part is less than 2 whole strips, however. It's about $1\frac{1}{2}$.

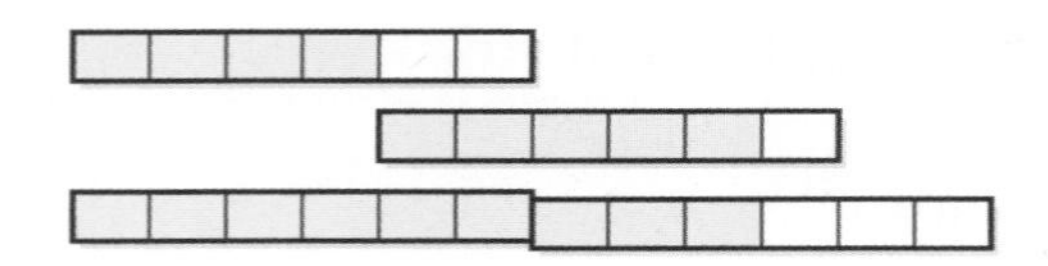

To add $\frac{2}{3}$ and $\frac{5}{6}$, use strips with a common denominator of 6.

$\frac{4}{6} + \frac{5}{6} = \frac{9}{6}$

$\frac{2}{3} = \frac{4}{6}$

$\frac{9}{6} = 1\frac{3}{6}$

$\frac{2}{3} + \frac{5}{6} = 1\frac{3}{6}$

Since $\frac{3}{6} = \frac{1}{2}$, $1\frac{1}{2}$ was a good estimate for $\frac{2}{3} + \frac{5}{6}$.

A Checking

1. Write the addition that each model represents.

a)

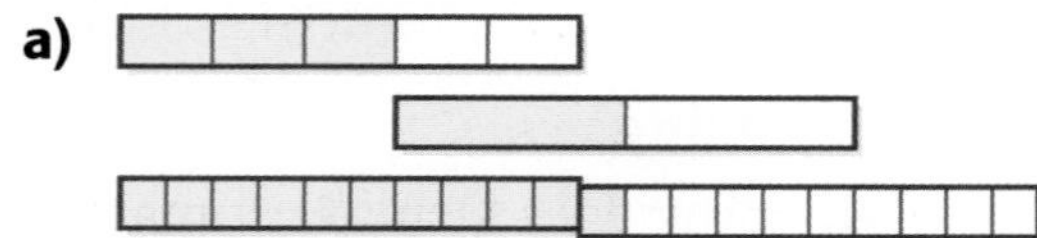

b)

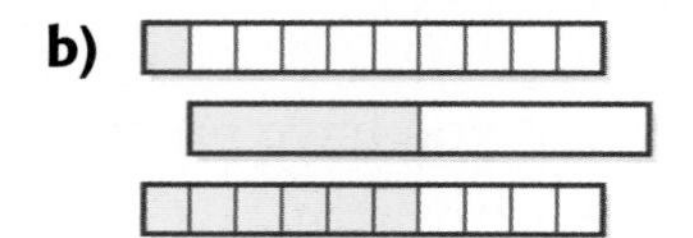

2. **a)** How do you know that $\frac{3}{4} + \frac{1}{6} < 1$?

   b) Calculate $\frac{3}{4} + \frac{1}{6}$ using fraction strips. Show your work.

B Practising

3. Estimate. Show your work.

   a) $\frac{2}{3} + \frac{1}{10}$ **b)** $\frac{1}{4} + \frac{9}{10}$ **c)** $\frac{2}{3} + \frac{1}{2}$ **d)** $\frac{5}{6} + \frac{3}{4}$

4. Calculate.

   a) $\frac{3}{5} + \frac{1}{5}$ **c)** $\frac{1}{6} + \frac{1}{4}$ **e)** $\frac{5}{6} + \frac{1}{3}$

   b) $\frac{2}{3} + \frac{2}{3}$ **d)** $\frac{1}{3} + \frac{7}{12}$ **f)** $\frac{5}{6} + \frac{1}{4}$

5. Yesterday, Jacques read $\frac{1}{3}$ of the novel *Les beaux jours*. Today, he read $\frac{1}{6}$ of the novel. Use a fraction to describe how much of the novel Jacques has read so far.

6. Francis added fractions with different denominators using fraction strips. His total was one whole strip. List six pairs of fractions he might have been adding.

7. Abby watched one television program for $\frac{1}{4}$ of an hour and then watched another program for 20 min. For what fraction of an hour did Abby watch television?

8. A fraction with a denominator of 4 is added to a fraction with a denominator of 6. What denominator might the answer have? Explain.

9. Yan poured sand into three identical pails. Will all the sand fit in one of these pails? Explain.

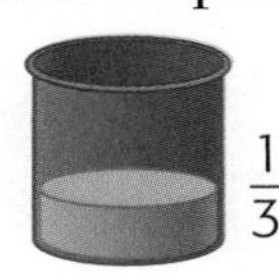

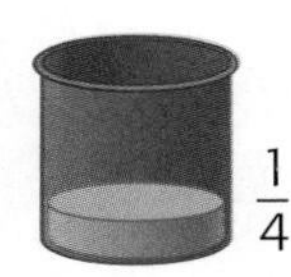

10. When you add any two counting numbers (such as 1, 2, 3, ...), the answer is always greater than either number. Is the same true when you add any two fractions? Explain.

11. Why is it quicker to add $\frac{5}{12}$ and $\frac{11}{12}$ than to add $\frac{5}{12}$ and $\frac{3}{4}$?

2.4 Subtracting Fractions with Fraction Strips

YOU WILL NEED
- Fraction Strips (Blackline Master)

Subtract fractions less than 1 using fraction strips.

LEARN ABOUT the Math

The student council will make a profit on a dance if $\frac{1}{4}$ of the students buy tickets. So far, only $\frac{1}{6}$ of the students have bought tickets.

What fraction of the students still need to buy tickets for the student council to make a profit?

A. Is the fraction probably greater than $\frac{1}{10}$ or less than $\frac{1}{10}$? Explain.

B. How can you use fraction strips to model the problem?

C. What fraction of the students still need to buy tickets for the student council to make a profit?

Reflecting

D. What strategy did you use to answer part A?

E. Why might you subtract two fractions to answer part C?

F. Explain how you can use fraction strips to subtract a different pair of fractions, such as $\frac{2}{3} - \frac{1}{4}$.

WORK WITH the Math

Example 1 | Subtracting from a fraction less than 1

Estimate and then subtract $\frac{11}{12} - \frac{1}{2}$.

Ryan's Solution

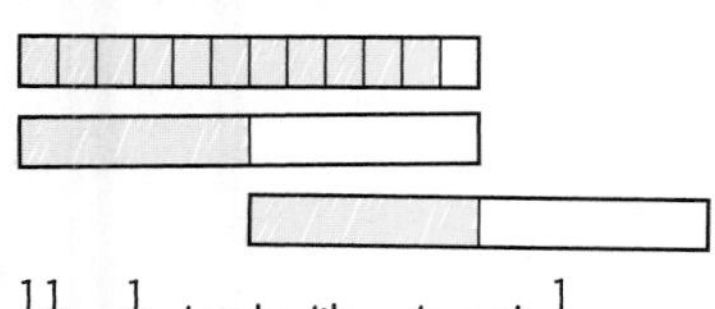

$\frac{11}{12} - \frac{1}{2}$ looks like almost $\frac{1}{2}$.

I modelled both fractions.

The greater fraction is greater by about $\frac{1}{2}$.

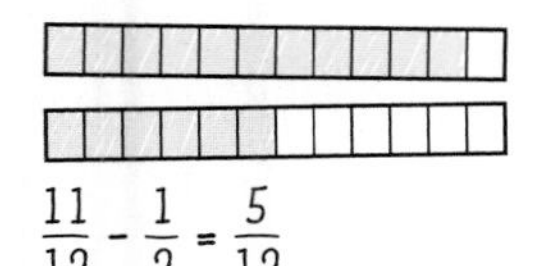

$\frac{11}{12} - \frac{1}{2} = \frac{5}{12}$

Then, I modelled equivalent fractions with the same denominator. I used $\frac{1}{2} = \frac{6}{12}$.

The $\frac{11}{12}$ strip is $\frac{5}{12}$ longer than the $\frac{6}{12}$ strip. Since $\frac{5}{12}$ is close to $\frac{1}{2}$, the answer makes sense.

Example 2 | Subtracting from a fraction greater than 1

Subtract $\frac{2}{3}$ from $\frac{7}{6}$.

Megan's Solution

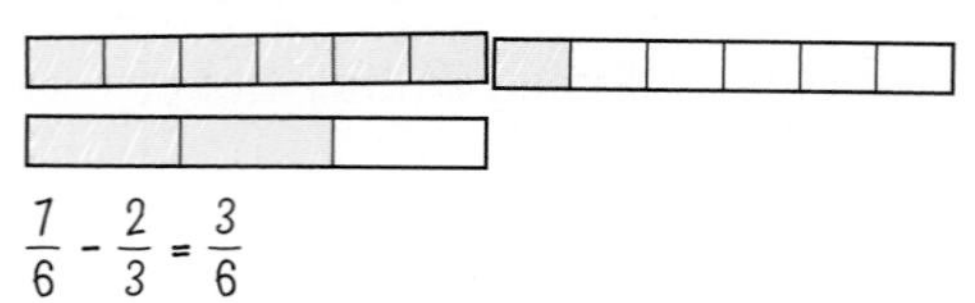

$\frac{7}{6} - \frac{2}{3} = \frac{3}{6}$

I modelled both fractions. To model $\frac{7}{6}$, I used a $\frac{6}{6}$ strip and another $\frac{1}{6}$ strip.

When I put the $\frac{2}{3}$ strip next to the $\frac{7}{6}$ strip, I saw that $\frac{7}{6}$ is $\frac{3}{6}$ longer.

I can also write the difference as $\frac{1}{2}$, since I can write $\frac{3}{6}$ in lowest terms as $\frac{1}{2}$.

A Checking

1. a) Why is $\frac{4}{5} - \frac{2}{5}$ equal to $\frac{2}{5}$?

b) Estimate $\frac{4}{5} - \frac{1}{3}$.

c) Calculate $\frac{4}{5} - \frac{1}{2}$ using fraction strips.

2. Suppose that $\frac{3}{4}$ of the students in your class have pets and that $\frac{1}{6}$ have more than one pet. Calculate the fraction of the students with only one pet.

B Practising

3. Calculate.

a) $\frac{5}{6} - \frac{2}{6}$ **b)** $\frac{5}{8} - \frac{2}{8}$ **c)** $\frac{5}{12} - \frac{2}{12}$

4. What pattern do you notice in question 3? Why does this pattern make sense?

5. Estimate each difference.

a) $\frac{7}{12} - \frac{1}{5}$ **b)** $\frac{7}{10} - \frac{1}{4}$ **c)** $\frac{11}{12} - \frac{1}{5}$

6. Calculate.

a) $\frac{3}{5} - \frac{1}{10}$ **c)** $\frac{8}{3} - \frac{3}{4}$ **e)** $\frac{3}{10} - \frac{1}{5}$

b) $\frac{5}{2} - \frac{9}{12}$ **d)** $\frac{7}{4} - \frac{4}{6}$ **f)** $\frac{5}{4} - \frac{5}{12}$

7. **a)** Draw a shape. Colour the shape so that $\frac{2}{3}$ is blue and $\frac{1}{6}$ is yellow.

b) What fraction tells how much more of the total shape is blue than yellow?

c) What fraction tells how much is neither blue nor yellow?

8. Rosa wrote $\frac{1}{2}$ of her book report on Tuesday and another $\frac{1}{5}$ on Wednesday.

a) What fraction of her book report does she still have left to write?

b) How do you know that your answer makes sense?

9. Aiden said that he calculated $\frac{3}{4} - \frac{2}{3}$ by calculating $1 - \frac{2}{3}$ and then subtracting $\frac{1}{4}$. Do you agree with what he did? Why or why not?

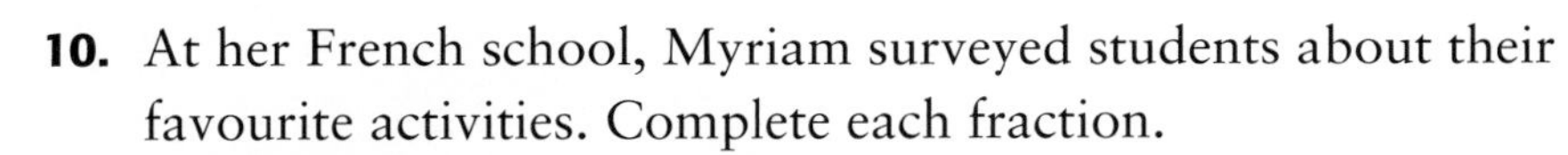

10. At her French school, Myriam surveyed students about their favourite activities. Complete each fraction.

Activity	Fraction of students who prefer activity
radio étudiante	$\frac{1}{4}$
jazz band	$\frac{1}{6}$
journal étudiant	$\frac{1}{12}$
art dramatique	$\frac{1}{3}$

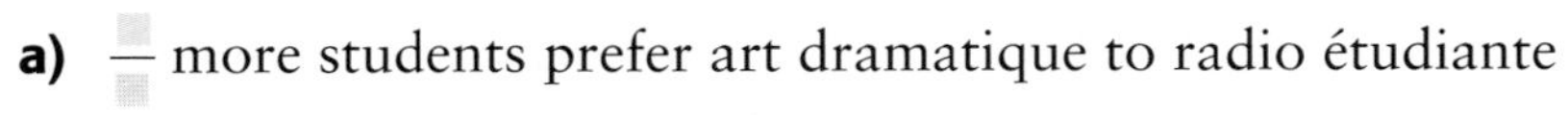

a) $\frac{\square}{\square}$ more students prefer art dramatique to radio étudiante

b) $\frac{\square}{\square}$ more students prefer radio étudiante to journal étudiant

c) $\frac{\square}{\square}$ more students prefer jazz band to journal étudiant

11. To calculate $\frac{4}{3} - \frac{3}{4}$, Ann adds $\frac{1}{4}$ to $\frac{1}{3}$.

a) Model $\frac{4}{3}$ and $\frac{3}{4}$.

b) Explain Ann's method.

c) What is $\frac{4}{3} - \frac{3}{4}$?

12. The Labrador block in the Canadian Quilt of Belonging is shown below.

a) Estimate what fraction of the block is green.

b) Estimate what fraction of the block is grey.

c) About how much more of the block is green than grey?

13. The Ukrainian Bilingual School is holding a talent show. Between $\frac{1}{4}$ and $\frac{1}{2}$ of the performers will dance. At least $\frac{1}{2}$ will read poetry. The rest will play music. What fraction of the performers will play music? Explain your thinking.

14. a) Choose two fractions. Model them with fraction strips.

b) Add your fractions.

c) Subtract one fraction from the other.

d) Is the denominator of the sum the same as the denominator of the difference? Explain.

15. How is subtracting fractions like adding them?

2.5 Exploring Fraction Addition on Grids

YOU WILL NEED
- grid paper
- counters
- chart paper

GOAL

Add fractions with grids and counters.

EXPLORE the Math

Denis served a tray of spring rolls.
Jacob ate $\frac{1}{3}$ of the spring rolls, and Ryan ate $\frac{2}{5}$ of them.

How can you calculate, using a grid and counters, what fraction of the spring rolls Jacob and Ryan ate?

2.6 Subtracting Fractions with Grids

YOU WILL NEED
- grid paper
- counters

Subtract fractions concretely.

LEARN ABOUT the Math

Ryan is awake for $\frac{2}{3}$ of every day. He spends $\frac{1}{4}$ of every school day either at school or on the bus.

What fraction of a school day is left for other activities?

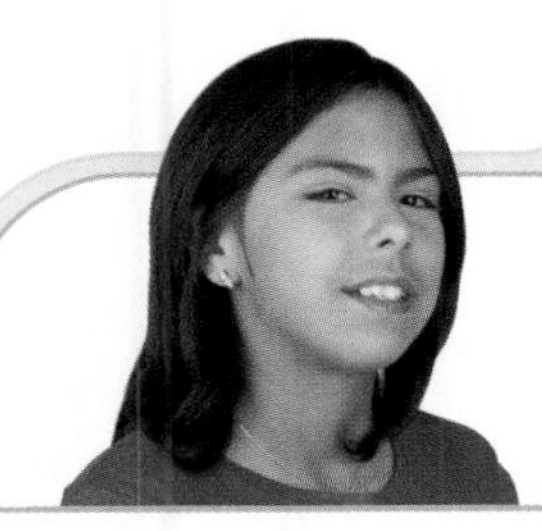

Example 1 | Subtracting with grid paper

Subtract $\frac{2}{3} - \frac{1}{4}$ using a grid and counters.

Oshana's Solution

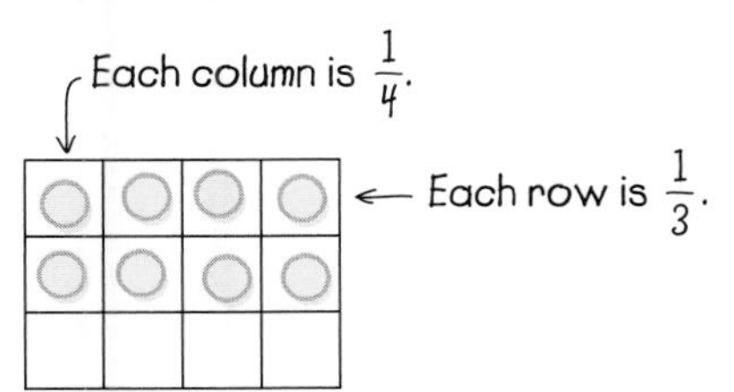

I used a 3 × 4 grid, so I could easily show thirds and fourths.

To show $\frac{2}{3}$, I filled in two rows of the grid.

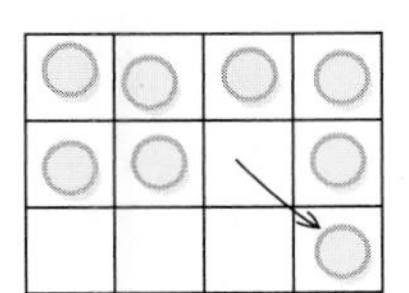

$\frac{1}{4}$ is one column, so I knew that I'd need to remove counters from one whole column.
I moved a counter to fill a column.

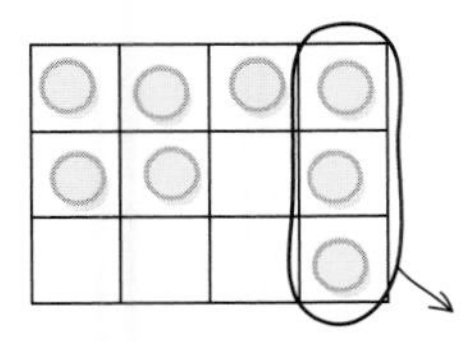

I removed all the counters in this column and counted how many counters were left. There were 5 counters left.

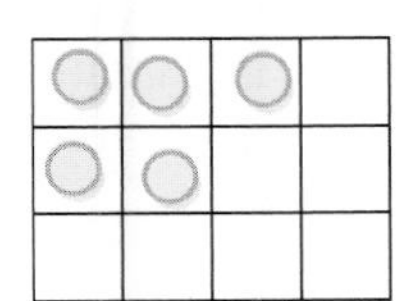

There are 12 sections in the grid. Each section is $\frac{1}{12}$.

$\frac{2}{3} - \frac{1}{4} = \frac{5}{12}$

Since there were 5 counters left, $\frac{5}{12}$ of a school day is left for other activities.

Reflecting

A. How did Oshana's grid give her equivalent fractions for $\frac{2}{3}$ and $\frac{1}{4}$ with a common denominator?

B. What size of grid would you use to calculate $\frac{3}{4} - \frac{1}{2}$? Explain how you would use counters to model the subtraction.

WORK WITH the Math

Example 2 | Subtracting from a whole

Darby mowed $\frac{1}{3}$ of a lawn before lunch and another $\frac{2}{5}$ after lunch. How much of the lawn is left to mow?

Solution

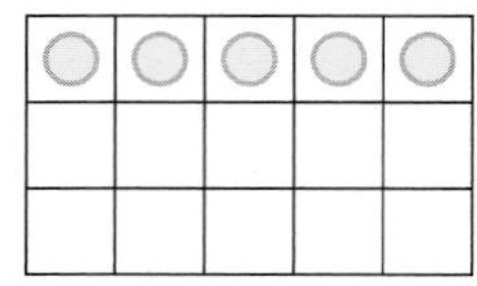

Use a 3×5 grid to show thirds and fifths.

Model $\frac{1}{3}$ using one row of counters.

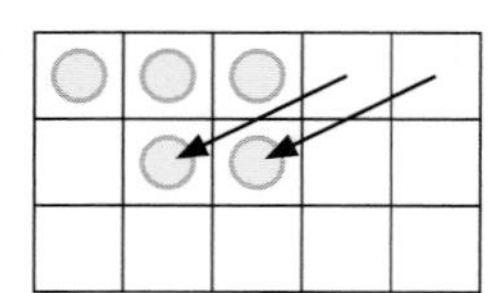

Now prepare to model adding $\frac{2}{5}$.

Each column is $\frac{1}{5}$, so clear 2 columns to make room for counters to be added.
Move 2 counters.

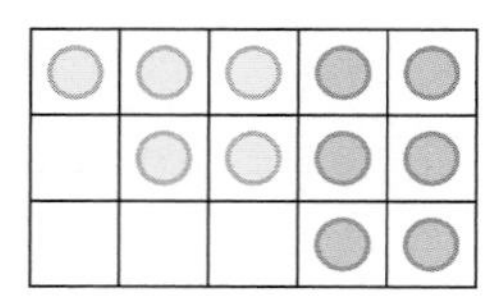

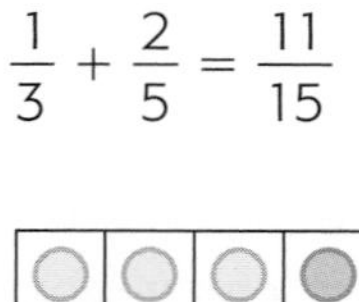

$$\frac{1}{3} + \frac{2}{5} = \frac{11}{15}$$

Now add 2 columns of counters.

That adds $\frac{2}{5}$. There are 11 counters, so $\frac{11}{15}$ of the lawn has been mowed.

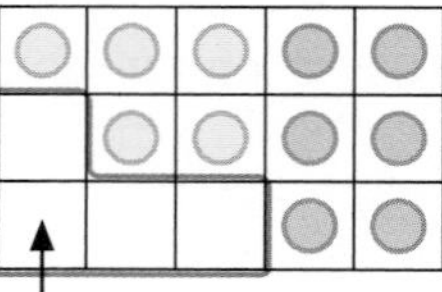

The amount left to mow

$$1 - \left(\frac{1}{3} + \frac{2}{5}\right) = \frac{4}{15}$$

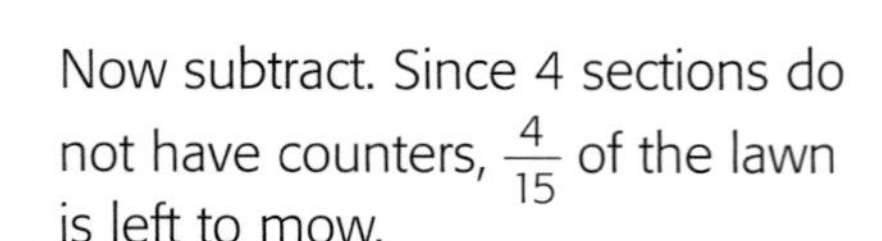

Now subtract. Since 4 sections do not have counters, $\frac{4}{15}$ of the lawn is left to mow.

Example 3 | Determining what was removed

There was $\frac{3}{4}$ of a pie left, and Dan ate some of it. After he finished, $\frac{5}{8}$ of the pie was left. How much of the pie did Dan eat?

Solution

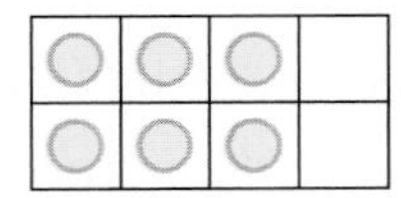

You could use a 4 × 8 grid, but fourths and eighths can also be shown on a 2 × 4 grid.
Each square is $\frac{1}{8}$ of the grid.
Each column is $\frac{1}{4}$.
Three columns of counters are $\frac{3}{4}$, or $\frac{6}{8}$, of the grid.

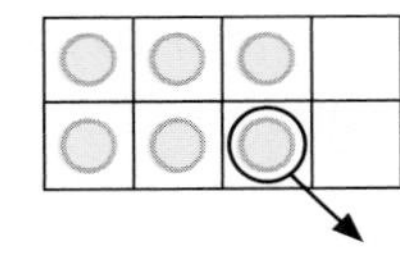

To have $\frac{5}{8}$ left, remove 1 of the 6 counters. Subtract $\frac{1}{8}$.

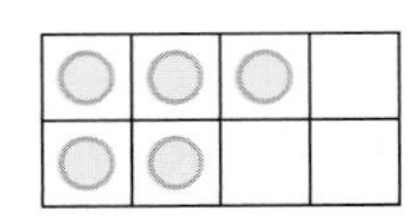

$$\frac{3}{4} - \frac{■}{■} = \frac{5}{8}$$
$$\frac{6}{8} - \frac{■}{■} = \frac{5}{8}$$
$$\frac{■}{■} = \frac{1}{8}$$

Each counter represents $\frac{1}{8}$ of the pie.
Since 1 counter was taken away,
Dan ate $\frac{1}{8}$ of the pie.

A Checking

1. Calculate each difference using a grid and counters. Show your work.

a) $\frac{2}{3} - \frac{1}{5}$ **b)** $\frac{5}{6} - \frac{1}{4}$

2. $\frac{7}{12}$ of the flowers in a garden have bloomed, and $\frac{1}{3}$ of these flowers are geraniums. Use a model to show what fraction of the flowers that have bloomed are other flowers.

B Practising

3. Calculate each difference. Show your work.

a) $\frac{4}{5} - \frac{2}{3}$

b) $\frac{1}{3} - \frac{1}{4}$

c) $\frac{1}{3} - \frac{2}{7}$

d) $\frac{7}{8} - \frac{2}{3}$

e) $\frac{3}{5} - \frac{1}{4}$

f) $\frac{3}{4} - \frac{2}{5}$

4. Ella phoned $\frac{1}{3}$ of the track team members on her list last weekend. She phoned $\frac{1}{5}$ of the members on Saturday.

a) Did she phone more team members on Saturday or on Sunday? How do you know?

b) What fraction of the team did she phone on Sunday?

5. André and his mom drove from Saint-Norbert to Brandon and back. When they left, the gas tank was $\frac{3}{4}$ full. When they returned, the gas tank was $\frac{1}{8}$ full. What fraction of a tank of gas did they use on the trip? How do you know that your answer is reasonable?

6. Make up your own problem that is similar to question 5, and then solve it.

7. Suppose that you subtract one fraction between $\frac{1}{2}$ and 1 from another fraction between $\frac{1}{2}$ and 1. Is each statement always true, sometimes true, or never true? Explain your thinking.

A. The difference is less than $\frac{1}{2}$.

B. The difference is greater than $\frac{1}{4}$.

8. These musical notes are like fractions. The total of the fractions in each measure is 1. What notes can you add to complete the second measure?

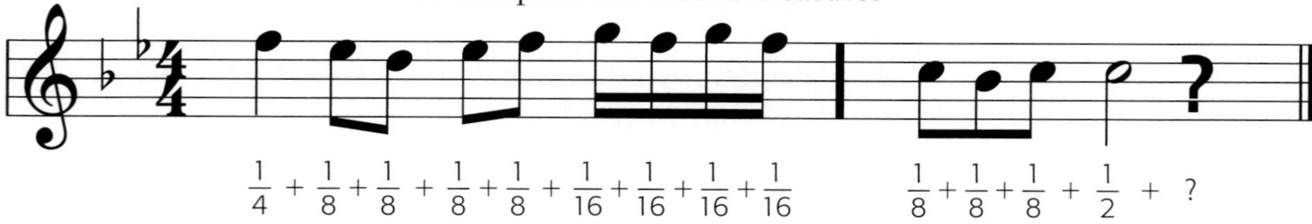

9. Why might it be easier to subtract fractions with a grid and counters than with fraction strips?

MATH GAME

Fraction Tic-Tac-Toe

In this game, you will use unit fractions to play tic-tac-toe.

Number of players: 2

YOU WILL NEED
- 9 square index cards
- 2 dice
- 2 colours of counters

How to Play

1. Place nine cards on a table to form a square.
   Write "0" on the middle card.
   Write fractions on the other cards.

For numerators, use	For denominators, use
1, 2, 3, 4, 5, or 6	2, 3, 4, 5, 6, 8, 10, 12, 15, 18, 20, or 30

2. Roll the dice. Use the numbers you roll as the denominators of two fractions. Use 1 as the numerator of the two fractions.
3. If the sum or difference of your two fractions is on a card, put one of your counters on the card.
4. Take turns rolling and calculating. Check each other's work.
5. The winner is the first player who has three counters in a horizontal, vertical, or diagonal line.

Oshana's Turn

These were our cards. I rolled a 6 and a 5.
The difference between $\frac{1}{5}$ and $\frac{1}{6}$ is $\frac{1}{30}$,
so I put a counter on that card.

$\frac{2}{20}$	$\frac{4}{15}$	$\frac{6}{18}$
$\frac{3}{5}$	0	$\frac{5}{12}$
$\frac{3}{8}$	$\frac{1}{30}$	$\frac{5}{6}$

Mid-Chapter **Review**

Frequently Asked Questions

Q: How do you compare two fractions, such as $\frac{3}{5}$ and $\frac{1}{8}$?

A1: You can compare each fraction to a benchmark, such as $\frac{1}{2}$. Since $\frac{3}{5}$ is greater than $\frac{1}{2}$ and $\frac{1}{8}$ is less than $\frac{1}{2}$, $\frac{3}{5} > \frac{1}{8}$.

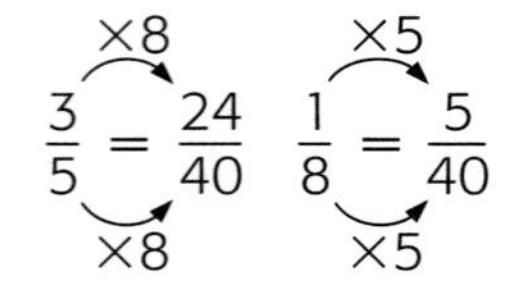

A2: You can use equivalent fractions with a common denominator. The least common multiple of 5 and 8 is 40. Rename the fractions. $\frac{24}{40} > \frac{5}{40}$, so $\frac{3}{5} > \frac{1}{8}$.

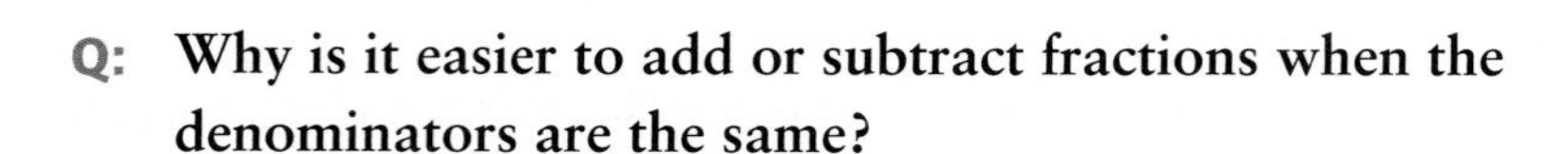

Q: Why is it easier to add or subtract fractions when the denominators are the same?

A: When the denominators are the same, then all the pieces are the same size. You can just add or subtract the numerators to count the pieces.

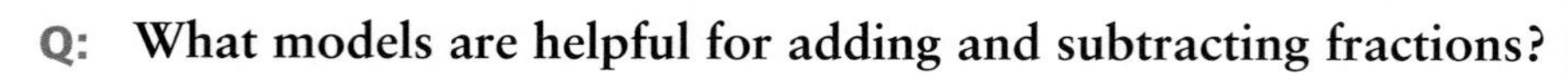

Q: What models are helpful for adding and subtracting fractions?

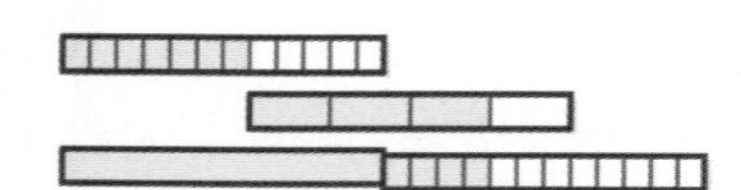

A1: You can use fraction strips that show different numbers of sections. For example, $\frac{7}{12} + \frac{3}{4} = 1\frac{4}{12}$.

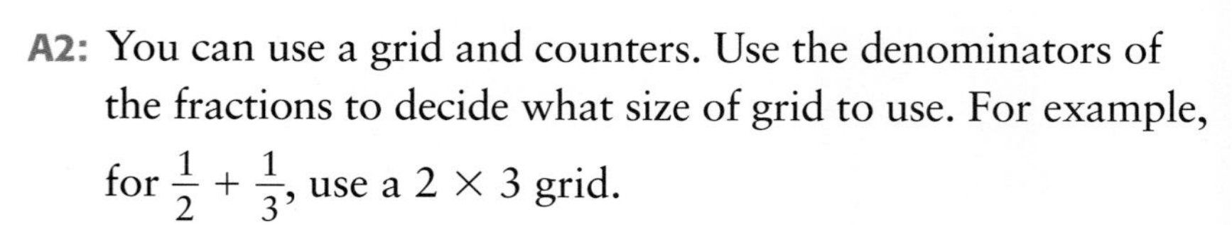

A2: You can use a grid and counters. Use the denominators of the fractions to decide what size of grid to use. For example, for $\frac{1}{2} + \frac{1}{3}$, use a 2×3 grid.

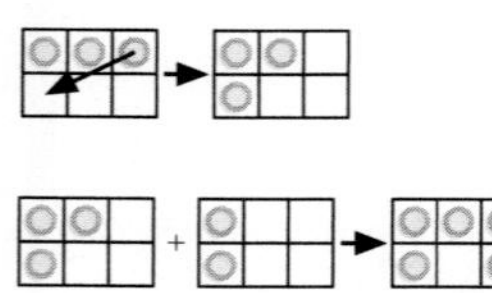

Start with $\frac{1}{2}$. Move 1 counter so you can add $\frac{1}{3}$.

Add $\frac{1}{3}$. There are 5 counters, so $\frac{1}{2} + \frac{1}{3} = \frac{5}{6}$.

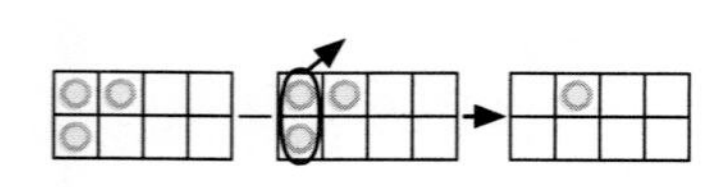

For $\frac{3}{8} - \frac{1}{4}$, use a 2×4 grid or a 4×8 grid.

$$\frac{3}{8} - \frac{1}{4} = \frac{1}{8}$$

Practice

Lesson 2.1

1. Write each pair of fractions as equivalent fractions with a common denominator.

a) $\frac{3}{5}$ and $\frac{2}{6}$ **b)** $\frac{3}{5}$ and $\frac{2}{10}$ **c)** $\frac{3}{10}$ and $\frac{4}{15}$

2. Write an equivalent fraction in lower terms.

a) $\frac{4}{6}$ **b)** $\frac{12}{18}$ **c)** $\frac{21}{15}$

3. Order from least to greatest: $3\frac{1}{4}, \frac{5}{6}, \frac{1}{9}, \frac{2}{3}, \frac{8}{5}, \frac{7}{3}$.

Lesson 2.3

4. Estimate each sum and then calculate. Show your work.

a) $\frac{3}{5} + \frac{4}{5}$ **b)** $\frac{7}{12} + \frac{1}{2}$ **c)** $\frac{7}{10} + \frac{2}{5}$ **d)** $\frac{2}{3} + \frac{11}{12}$

5. At a powwow, $\frac{1}{6}$ of the people were fancy dancers and $\frac{1}{4}$ were traditional ladies. What fraction were fancy dancers or traditional ladies?

Lesson 2.4

6. Calculate.

a) $\frac{4}{10} - \frac{1}{10}$ **b)** $\frac{7}{4} - \frac{5}{12}$ **c)** $\frac{11}{10} - \frac{4}{5}$ **d)** $\frac{3}{4} - \frac{1}{12}$

7. In the Yukon Territory, about $\frac{3}{4}$ of the people are from 15 to 65 years old. About $\frac{1}{5}$ of the people are 14 years old or younger. Use a fraction to describe the difference between the two age groups.

8. Which of these expressions have answers between $\frac{1}{2}$ and $1\frac{1}{2}$? How do you know?

A. $\frac{3}{4} + \frac{1}{5}$ **B.** $\frac{3}{4} + \frac{5}{6}$ **C.** $\frac{3}{8} + \frac{1}{2}$ **D.** $\frac{1}{4} + \frac{2}{3}$

Lesson 2.6

9. What size of grid would you use to model each calculation? Why?

a) $\frac{5}{6} - \frac{1}{2}$ **b)** $1 - \frac{2}{5}$ **c)** $\frac{4}{5} + \frac{2}{3}$ **d)** $\frac{3}{8} + \frac{3}{4}$

2.7 Adding and Subtracting Fractions with Number Lines

YOU WILL NEED
- number lines
- dice

GOAL

Add and subtract fractions using a pictorial model.

LEARN ABOUT the Math

In 2004, about $\frac{2}{3}$ of the Canadian tourists who visited Alberta were from either Saskatchewan or British Columbia. About $\frac{2}{5}$ of Canadian tourists were from British Columbia.

What fraction tells how many more tourists came from British Columbia than from Saskatchewan?

A. Why might you subtract to solve the problem?

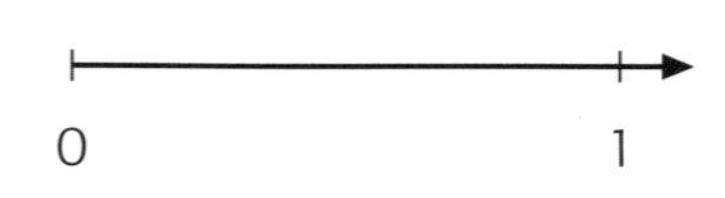

B. Think of a number line as a thin fraction strip. How could you use a number line to solve the problem?

C. What fraction tells about how many more tourists were from British Columbia than from Saskatchewan?

Reflecting

D. What subtraction did you complete? How did you show it on a number line?

E. How can you check your answer by adding on your number line?

WORK WITH the Math

Example 1 | Adding using a number line

Add $\frac{1}{3} + \frac{1}{4}$ using a number line.

Denis's Solution

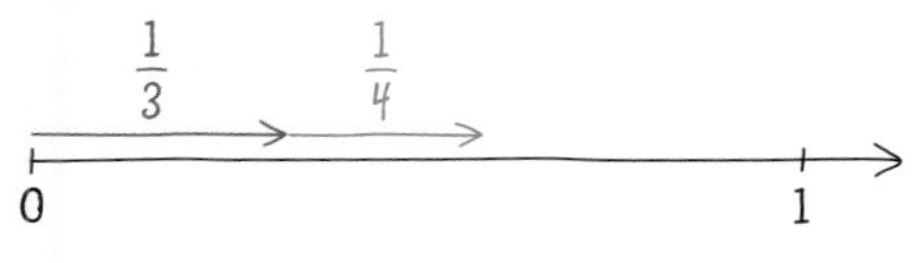

I made a number line and drew $\frac{1}{3}$ and $\frac{1}{4}$.
I could see that the total was a bit more than $\frac{1}{2}$, but I wanted the actual answer.

$\frac{0}{12}$ $\frac{1}{12}$ $\frac{2}{12}$ $\frac{3}{12}$ $\frac{4}{12}$ $\frac{5}{12}$ $\frac{6}{12}$ $\frac{7}{12}$ $\frac{8}{12}$ $\frac{9}{12}$ $\frac{10}{12}$ $\frac{11}{12}$ $\frac{12}{12}$

I used equivalent fractions with a common denominator to make the answer easier to read. Since 12 is the least common denominator for $\frac{1}{3}$ and $\frac{1}{4}$, I used a number line marked in 12ths.

$\frac{1}{3} = \frac{4}{12}$ (×4) $\frac{1}{4} = \frac{3}{12}$ (×3)

I renamed $\frac{1}{3}$ and $\frac{1}{4}$ in 12ths.

$\frac{4}{12}$ $\frac{3}{12}$

$\frac{0}{12}$ $\frac{1}{12}$ $\frac{2}{12}$ $\frac{3}{12}$ $\frac{4}{12}$ $\frac{5}{12}$ $\frac{6}{12}$ $\frac{7}{12}$ $\frac{8}{12}$ $\frac{9}{12}$ $\frac{10}{12}$ $\frac{11}{12}$ $\frac{12}{12}$

I started the $\frac{3}{12}$ arrow at the end of the $\frac{4}{12}$ arrow to add, just as I did with fraction strips.

The sum is $\frac{7}{12}$.

$$\frac{1}{3} + \frac{1}{4}$$
$$= \frac{4}{12} + \frac{3}{12}$$
$$= \frac{7}{12}$$

Example 2 | Subtracting using a number line

Calculate $\frac{9}{8} - \frac{3}{4}$ using a number line.

Megan's Solution

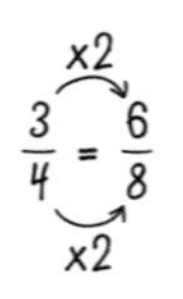

The least common multiple of 8 and 4 is 8. I renamed $\frac{3}{4}$ using an equivalent fraction with a denominator of 8.

I knew that $\frac{9}{8}$ is $\frac{1}{8}$ more than 1 $\left(\frac{8}{8}\right)$.

I drew arrows to show $\frac{9}{8}$ and $\frac{6}{8}$.

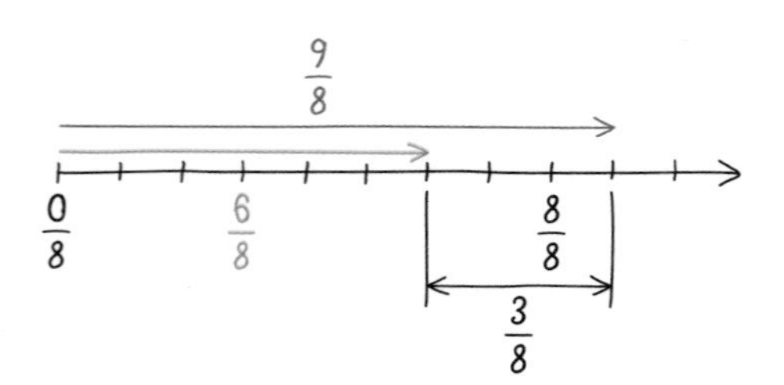

There are 3 eighths from $\frac{6}{8}$ to $\frac{9}{8}$.

$$\frac{9}{8} - \frac{3}{4} = \frac{3}{8}$$

A Checking

1. Calculate. Show your work.
   - **a)** $\frac{3}{4} + \frac{1}{6}$
   - **b)** $\frac{6}{5} - \frac{2}{3}$

2. About $\frac{1}{5}$ of the members of the Vancouver Symphony Orchestra play a woodwind. About $\frac{1}{4}$ play the violin.
   - **a)** What total fraction of the orchestra do these members represent?
   - **b)** What fraction tells how many more members play the violin than a woodwind?

B Practising

3. Calculate.

a) $\frac{2}{3} + \frac{1}{2}$ **b)** $\frac{11}{12} + \frac{1}{4}$ **c)** $\frac{8}{9} - \frac{2}{3}$ **d)** $\frac{6}{7} - \frac{1}{3}$

4. Jake ate $\frac{3}{8}$ of a pan of lasagna, and his dad ate $\frac{1}{4}$ of the pan. Marie and Leah ate the rest. How much lasagna did the girls eat?

5. Leanne put some of her allowance into her bank account to save for a bicycle. After making the deposit, she had $\frac{2}{5}$ of her allowance left. At the end of the week, she still had $\frac{1}{7}$ of her allowance left. What fraction of her allowance did she spend during the week?

6. A Chinese restaurant makes $\frac{1}{3}$ of its income on Friday and Saturday nights and $\frac{2}{5}$ from lunches during the work week. What fraction of its income is from other meals?

7. Roll a pair of dice twice. Use the numbers you roll to create two fractions.

a) Can you roll numbers so that the sum of the two fractions is $\frac{5}{6}$? Explain.

b) Can you roll numbers so that the difference is $\frac{5}{6}$? Explain.

8. Jarod calculated $\frac{3}{4} - \frac{1}{3}$ using the number line below. How does this number line show that his answer is the same as the answer for $\frac{2}{3} - \frac{1}{4}$?

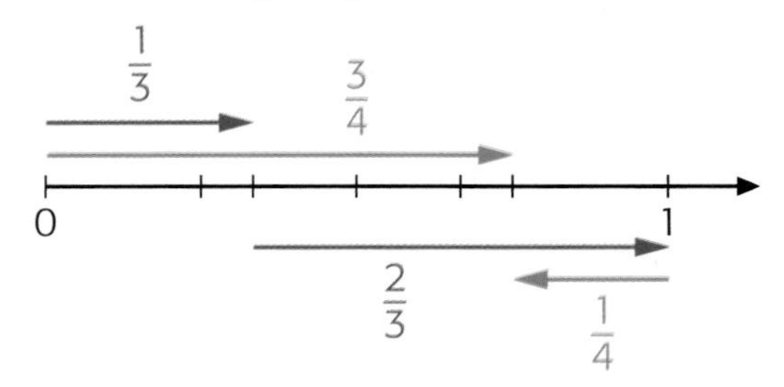

9. In this chapter, you have added and subtracted fractions with fraction strips, a grid and counters, and a number line. Which method do you prefer? Why?

2.8 Exploring Fraction Patterns

GOAL

Investigate fraction patterns that involve addition and subtraction.

EXPLORE the Math

Nayana and Jacob are creating fraction patterns.
This is the start of Nayana's pattern.

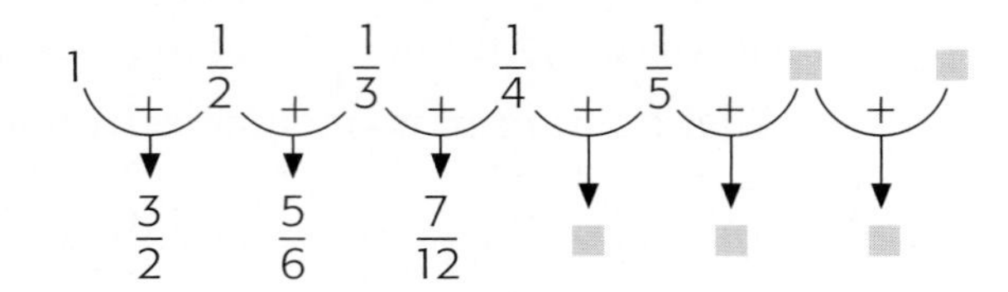

This is the start of Jacob's pattern.

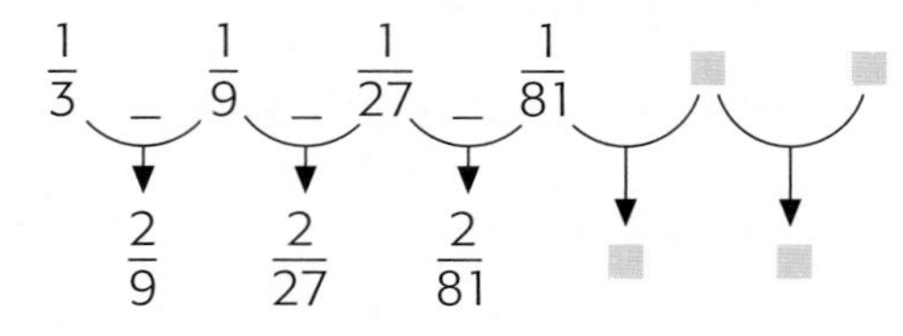

What patterns can you create using addition or subtraction of fractions?

2.9 Adding and Subtracting Fractions

Add and subtract fractions less than 1 symbolically.

LEARN ABOUT the Math

Canadian Students' Internet Connections at Home

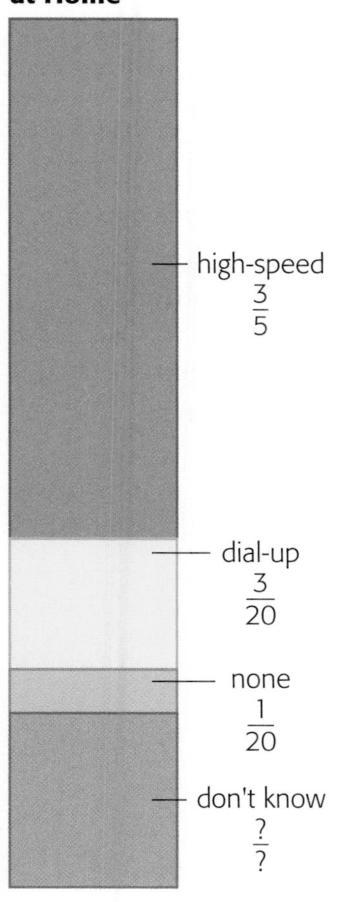

What kind of Internet connection do you have at home? In 2005, Canadian students from Grades 4 to 11 were asked this question. The graph at the left shows the results.

What fraction of the students said "don't know"?

A. List the fractions that describe the students who said high-speed, dial-up, and none.

B. Calculate each sum.
a) high-speed + dial-up
b) high-speed + dial-up + none

C. What fraction of the students said "don't know"? How do you know?

Reflecting

D. Why is there more than one way to calculate the fraction for "don't know"?

E. Why did you choose the denominator you did in part B to add the fractions?

F. How can you add or subtract two fractions without a model?

WORK WITH the Math

Example 1 | Adding using equivalent fractions

Madeleine's recycling bin is already $\frac{2}{3}$ full. She fills another $\frac{1}{4}$ of the bin. How full is the bin now?

Nayana's Solution

$\frac{2}{3} + \frac{1}{4} = \frac{\blacksquare}{\blacksquare}$

I had to add the two fractions.

$\frac{2}{3} = \frac{8}{12}$ (×4) $\quad \frac{1}{4} = \frac{3}{12}$ (×3)

The least common multiple of 3 and 4 is 12.
I used equivalent fractions with 12 as the denominator.

$\frac{8}{12} + \frac{3}{12} = \frac{11}{12}$

The bin is now $\frac{11}{12}$ full.

Example 2 | Subtracting using equivalent fractions

In Jay's class, $\frac{3}{4}$ of the students were born in Richmond and $\frac{1}{7}$ were born in Surrey. How many more students were born in Richmond than in Surrey?

Jacob's Solution

$\frac{3}{4} - \frac{1}{7} = \frac{\blacksquare}{\blacksquare}$

I had to subtract the two fractions.

$\frac{3}{4} = \frac{21}{28}$ (×7) $\quad \frac{1}{7} = \frac{4}{28}$ (×4)

The least common multiple of 4 and 7 is 28.
I used equivalent fractions with 28 as the denominator.

$\frac{21}{28} - \frac{4}{28} = \frac{17}{28}$

If I subtract 4 parts from 21 parts and the parts are all 28ths, there are 17 parts left. In Jay's class, $\frac{17}{28}$ more students were born in Richmond than in Surrey.

A Checking

1. Calculate.

a) $\frac{3}{5} - \frac{1}{5}$ **b)** $\frac{3}{6} + \frac{2}{3}$ **c)** $\frac{7}{8} - \frac{3}{4}$ **d)** $\frac{2}{7} + \frac{2}{3}$

2. At a school party, $\frac{2}{3}$ of the students wore T-shirts and $\frac{1}{5}$ wore long-sleeved shirts. Which fraction is greater? By how much?

B Practising

3. Which of these expressions are equal to $\frac{1}{2}$?

A. $\frac{5}{12} - \frac{1}{3}$ **B.** $\frac{5}{12} + \frac{1}{3}$ **C.** $\frac{3}{7} + \frac{1}{14}$ **D.** $\frac{3}{5} - \frac{1}{10}$

4. In a Grade 7 class, $\frac{1}{5}$ of the students have two pets and $\frac{1}{20}$ have three or more pets.

a) Estimate the fraction of the class with two or more pets.

b) How many students do you think are in the class? Explain.

5. Complete this equation: $\frac{2}{3} + \frac{3}{5} + \frac{■}{15} = \frac{■}{15}$.

6. Which of these expressions are greater than 1? How do you know?

A. $\frac{2}{3} + \frac{1}{6}$ **B.** $\frac{1}{2} + \frac{3}{5}$ **C.** $\frac{3}{2} - \frac{3}{7}$ **D.** $2 - \frac{3}{4}$

7. Four students added $\frac{3}{4} + \frac{5}{6}$ and got these answers: $\frac{38}{24}$, $1\frac{14}{24}$, $1\frac{7}{12}$, and $\frac{19}{12}$. Are they all correct? How do you know?

8. Calculate using equivalent fractions.

a) $\frac{2}{3} + \frac{3}{7}$ **b)** $\frac{3}{5} + \frac{4}{7}$ **c)** $\frac{3}{4} + \frac{7}{9}$ **d)** $\frac{3}{4} - \frac{1}{3}$

9. Kristen poured water into this pail until it was $\frac{3}{4}$ full. How much water did she add?

10. Two fractions add to $\frac{1}{4}$. Is each statement true or false? Explain.

A. Both fractions are less than $\frac{1}{8}$.

B. One fraction might be $\frac{1}{5}$.

C. One fraction might be $\frac{2}{5}$.

D. The denominators might be 10 and 20.

Reading Strategy

What questions can you ask to help you understand the question?

11. An estimate of the area of each territory is shown as a fraction of Canada's area. About how much of Canada do all three territories cover?

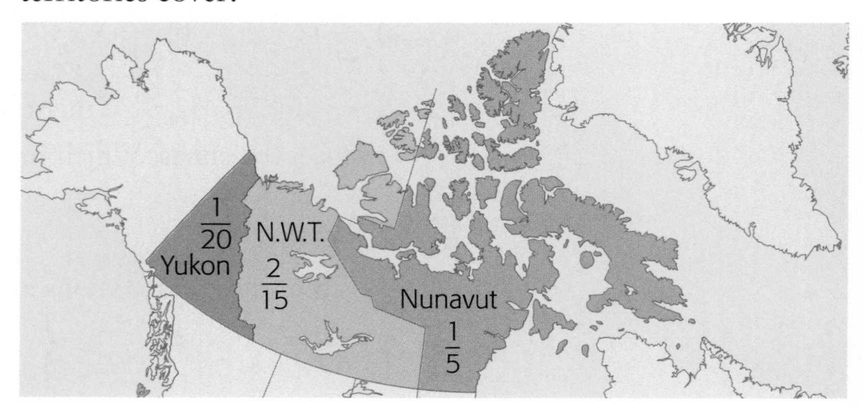

12. Which of these expressions is closest to $\frac{1}{2}$ in value? How close is it?

A. $\frac{3}{4} - \frac{2}{10}$

B. $\frac{4}{5} - \frac{1}{3} + \frac{1}{15}$

C. $\frac{1}{3} + \frac{1}{5} + \frac{1}{10}$

D. $\frac{2}{9} + \frac{1}{6} + \frac{1}{3}$

13. Describe a situation in which you might add $\frac{1}{3} + \frac{1}{4} + \frac{1}{2}$.

How often do you read news online?

- regularly
- rarely
- never

14. About $\frac{1}{3}$ of Canadians read news online regularly. Another $\frac{1}{8}$ read news online rarely. About what fraction of Canadians never read news online?

15. Your friend wants to calculate how much more $\frac{3}{4} + \frac{4}{5}$ is than $\frac{2}{3} + \frac{2}{5}$. How would you explain what to do?

CURIOUS MATH

Egyptian Fractions

The ancient Egyptians used only fractions with a numerator of 1 (called unit fractions).

They used parts of the "eye of Horus" to represent these fractions, as shown below.

They wrote other fractions as sums of the unit fractions.

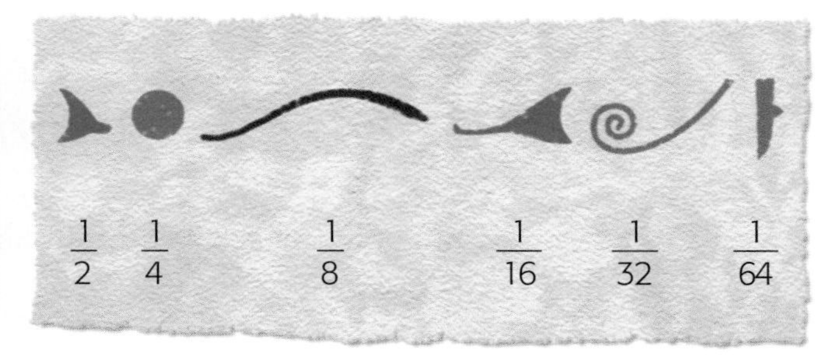

1. Show that $\frac{2}{3}$ equals $\frac{1}{2} + \frac{1}{6}$.

2. Write each fraction as a sum of unit fractions with different denominators.

a) $\frac{3}{4}$ **b)** $\frac{8}{15}$ **c)** $\frac{19}{24}$

3. Complete the table to show that you can write any unit fraction as the difference of two other unit fractions.

$\frac{1}{3}$	$= \frac{1}{2} - \frac{1}{6}$
$\frac{1}{4}$	$= \frac{1}{\blacksquare} - \frac{1}{\blacksquare}$
$\frac{1}{5}$	$= \frac{1}{\blacksquare} - \frac{1}{\blacksquare}$
$\frac{1}{6}$	$= \frac{1}{\blacksquare} - \frac{1}{\blacksquare}$
$\frac{1}{7}$	$= \frac{1}{\blacksquare} - \frac{1}{\blacksquare}$
...	...
$\frac{1}{50}$	$= \frac{1}{49} - \frac{1}{2450}$
$\frac{1}{100}$	$= \frac{1}{99} - \frac{1}{9900}$

4. Describe a pattern in the table.

5. Use your pattern to write another fraction as the difference of unit fractions.

2.10 Adding and Subtracting Mixed Numbers

Solve problems by adding or subtracting mixed numbers and fractions.

LEARN ABOUT the Math

Oshana is working on a Bear Claw quilt. She has $25\frac{1}{2}$ large blue squares.

Suppose that Oshana makes 3 quilt sections. How many blue squares will she have left?

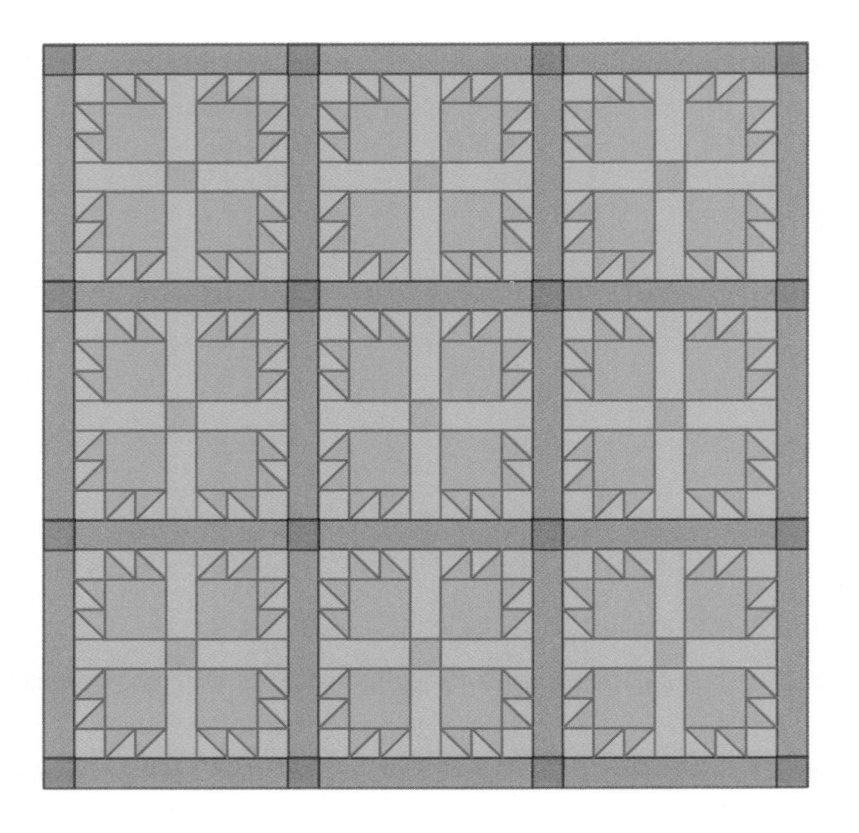

Example 1 | Adding wholes and fractions separately

I'll determine how many blue squares are used in each section. Then I'll calculate how many blue squares are in three sections. Then I'll subtract the total from $25\frac{1}{2}$.

Oshana's Solution

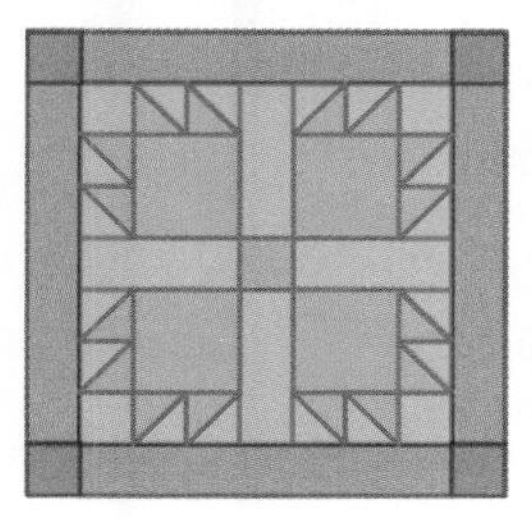

This is one section. It has 4 large blue squares.

It has 16 small triangles, which can be cut out of 2 large squares.

It has 1 small blue square, which is $\frac{1}{4}$ of a large square.

$4 + 2 + \frac{1}{4} = 6\frac{1}{4}$

Each section uses $6\frac{1}{4}$ large blue squares.

$6\frac{1}{4} + 6\frac{1}{4} + 6\frac{1}{4} = 6 + 6 + 6 + \frac{1}{4} + \frac{1}{4} + \frac{1}{4}$

I added to determine how many blue squares are in 3 sections.

$6 + 6 + 6 = 18$

I added the whole numbers.

$\frac{1}{4} + \frac{1}{4} + \frac{1}{4} = \frac{3}{4}$

I added the fractions.

$18 + \frac{3}{4} = 18\frac{3}{4}$

I added the two sums.

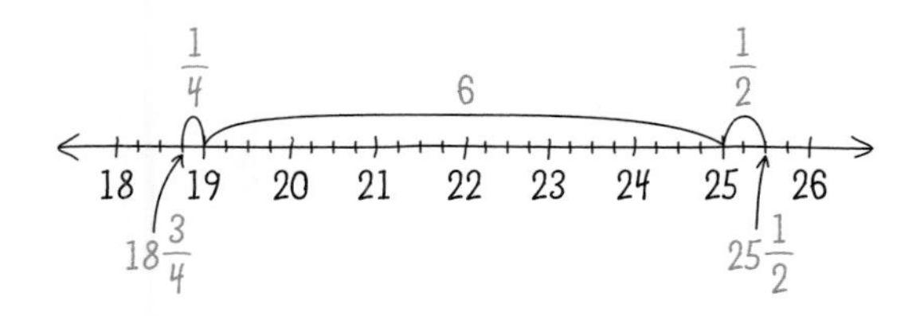

I had to subtract $18\frac{3}{4}$ from $25\frac{1}{2}$.

I thought about the difference between $18\frac{3}{4}$ and $25\frac{1}{2}$ on a number line.

$\frac{1}{4} + 6 + \frac{1}{2} = 6\frac{3}{4}$

I'll have $6\frac{3}{4}$ squares left.

Example 2 | Calculating using improper fractions

I'll add $6\frac{1}{4}$ three times and subtract the total from $25\frac{1}{2}$.

Ryan's Solution

$6\frac{1}{4} = \frac{24}{4} + \frac{1}{4}$ or $\frac{25}{4}$

I renamed $6\frac{1}{4}$ as an improper fraction.
Each whole is $\frac{4}{4}$, so 6 wholes is $\frac{24}{4}$.

$\frac{25}{4} + \frac{25}{4} + \frac{25}{4} = \frac{75}{4}$

I added $\frac{25}{4}$ three times, once for each section.

$\frac{25}{1} = \frac{100}{4}$ (×4) $\frac{1}{2} = \frac{2}{4}$ (×2)

$\frac{100}{4} + \frac{2}{4} = \frac{102}{4}$

To subtract from $25\frac{1}{2}$, I renamed both the 25 and the $\frac{1}{2}$ as fourths.

$\frac{102}{4} - \frac{75}{4} = \frac{27}{4}$

I subtracted.

$\frac{27}{4} = \frac{24}{4} + \frac{3}{4}$

I renamed the difference as a mixed number.

$= 6\frac{3}{4}$

$\frac{24}{4}$ is 6 wholes. Oshana will have $6\frac{3}{4}$ squares left.

Reflecting

A. If a number line is marked only with whole numbers, why is it easier to estimate a difference using mixed numbers rather than improper fractions?

B. How are the two methods alike? How are they different?

WORK WITH *the Math*

Example 3 | Adding and subtracting mixed numbers

Caleb mixed $1\frac{1}{2}$ cans of yellow paint with $2\frac{3}{4}$ cans of blue paint.
He used $3\frac{4}{5}$ of these cans to paint a room. How much paint is left?

Solution A: Using mixed numbers

$1\frac{1}{2} = 1 + \frac{1}{2}$ and $2\frac{3}{4} = 2 + \frac{3}{4}$

Add $1\frac{1}{2} + 2\frac{3}{4}$ to determine how much paint Caleb started with.

$1 + 2 = 3$ $\qquad \frac{1}{2} + \frac{3}{4} = \frac{2}{4} + \frac{3}{4} = \frac{5}{4}$

Add the whole numbers, and then add the fractions.

$3 + \frac{5}{4} = 3 + 1 + \frac{1}{4} = 4\frac{1}{4}$

Add the whole numbers and the fractions.

Caleb started with $4\frac{1}{4}$ cans of paint.

$4\frac{1}{4} - 3\frac{4}{5}$

Subtract to determine how much paint is left.

Since $\frac{4}{5} > \frac{1}{4}$, regroup $4\frac{5}{20}$ to get $3\frac{25}{20}$.

Rename $\frac{1}{4}$ and $\frac{4}{5}$ using a common denominator of 20.

$3 - 3 = 0$ $\qquad \frac{25}{20} - \frac{16}{20} = \frac{9}{20}$

Subtract the whole numbers, and then subtract the fractions.

There is $\frac{9}{20}$ of a can left.

Solution B: Using improper fractions

$1\frac{1}{2} = \frac{2}{2} + \frac{1}{2} = \frac{3}{2}$ $\qquad 2\frac{3}{4} = \frac{8}{4} + \frac{3}{4} = \frac{11}{4}$ $\qquad 3\frac{4}{5} = \frac{15}{5} + \frac{4}{5} = \frac{19}{5}$

Write the mixed numbers as improper fractions.

$\frac{3}{2} + \frac{11}{4} = \frac{6}{4} + \frac{11}{4} = \frac{17}{4}$

Rename $\frac{3}{2}$ and $\frac{11}{4}$ using a common denominator of 4. Add to determine how much paint Caleb started with. He started with $\frac{17}{4}$ cans of paint.

$\frac{17}{4} - \frac{19}{5} = \frac{85}{20} - \frac{76}{20} = \frac{9}{20}$

Rename $\frac{17}{4}$ and $\frac{19}{5}$ using a common denominator of 20. Subtract to determine how much paint is left.

There is $\frac{9}{20}$ of a can left.

Example 4 | Subtracting on a number line

Lang just turned 12. His sister is $8\frac{3}{4}$. How much older is he?

Solution

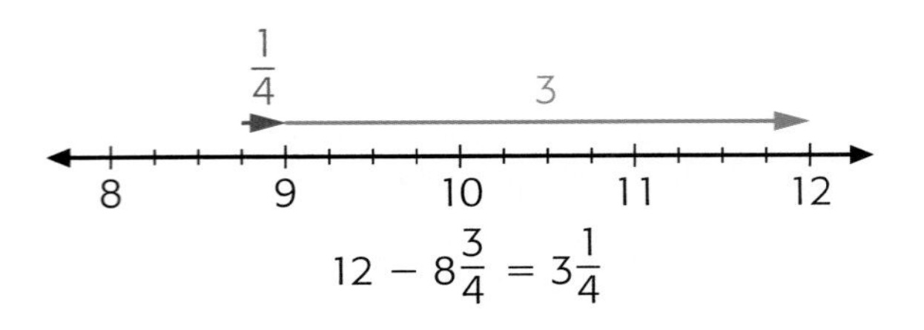

It is $\frac{1}{4}$ from $8\frac{3}{4}$ to 9.

It is 3 from 9 to 12.

It is $3\frac{1}{4}$ from $8\frac{3}{4}$ to 12.

Lang is $3\frac{1}{4}$ years older than his sister.

A Checking

1. Calculate.

a) $5\frac{1}{4} + \frac{3}{8}$ **b)** $5\frac{2}{3} - 3\frac{1}{4}$ **c)** $3 - 1\frac{3}{4}$ **d)** $5\frac{7}{8} + 2\frac{5}{6}$

2. Jane is helping Oshana make her Bear Claw quilt. Suppose that Jane had 18 blue squares and made 2 quilt sections. How many blue squares would she have left?

B Practising

3. Calculate.

a) $3\frac{1}{4} + \frac{2}{3}$ **b)** $5\frac{1}{3} + \frac{3}{5}$ **c)** $4 - 2\frac{1}{5}$ **d)** $2\frac{2}{3} - \frac{3}{4}$

4. Calculate.

a) $3\frac{2}{3} - 1\frac{1}{3}$ **b)** $4\frac{2}{5} - 2\frac{4}{5}$ **c)** $3\frac{2}{5} + 5\frac{1}{6}$ **d)** $6\frac{3}{5} + 2\frac{3}{4}$

5. Ethel had $10\frac{1}{2}$ white squares before she made this star blanket. How many white squares does she have now?

6. Jasleen goes to bed 3 h after dinner. Yesterday, after dinner, she spent $1\frac{1}{2}$ h on her homework and $\frac{2}{3}$ h on the phone. How much time did she have left before bedtime? How do you know that your answer is reasonable?

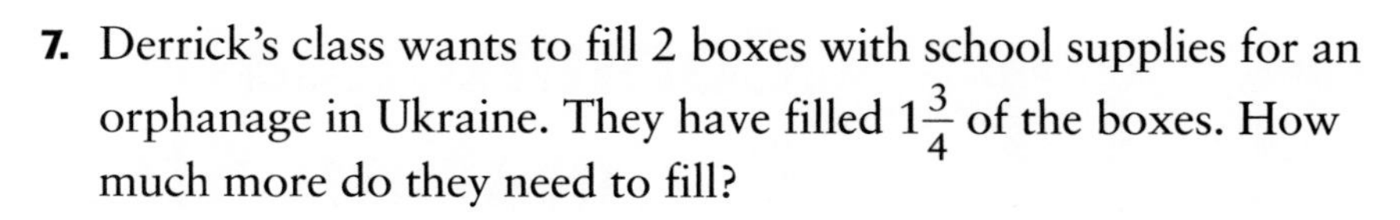

7. Derrick's class wants to fill 2 boxes with school supplies for an orphanage in Ukraine. They have filled $1\frac{3}{4}$ of the boxes. How much more do they need to fill?

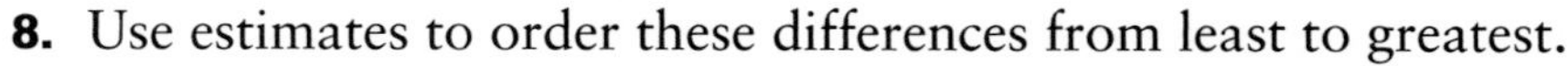

8. Use estimates to order these differences from least to greatest.

A. $5\frac{1}{3} - 4\frac{1}{2}$

B. $6\frac{1}{2} - 3\frac{2}{9}$

C. $12\frac{3}{8} - 9\frac{4}{5}$

D. $7\frac{2}{3} - 2\frac{6}{8}$

9. This week, Anita practised piano for $3\frac{1}{2}$ h, played soccer for $6\frac{1}{4}$ h, and talked on the phone for $4\frac{1}{3}$ h.

a) How many hours did Anita spend practising piano and playing soccer?

b) How many more hours did Anita spend playing soccer than talking on the phone?

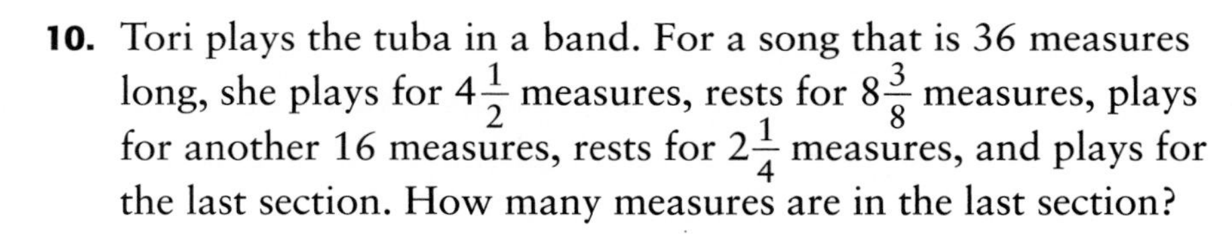

10. Tori plays the tuba in a band. For a song that is 36 measures long, she plays for $4\frac{1}{2}$ measures, rests for $8\frac{3}{8}$ measures, plays for another 16 measures, rests for $2\frac{1}{4}$ measures, and plays for the last section. How many measures are in the last section?

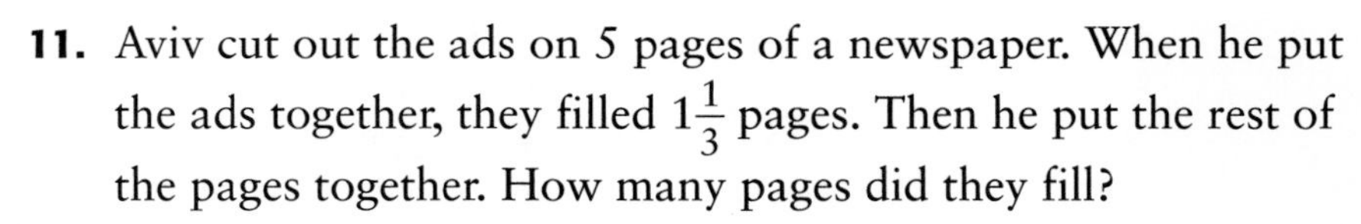

11. Aviv cut out the ads on 5 pages of a newspaper. When he put the ads together, they filled $1\frac{1}{3}$ pages. Then he put the rest of the pages together. How many pages did they fill?

12. Describe a situation in which you might calculate $3\frac{1}{4} - 1\frac{1}{2}$.

13. When can the sum of two mixed numbers be a whole number? Explain.

14. Kevin added $4\frac{\square}{\square} + 3\frac{\square}{\square}$. What could the whole number part of the answer be? Why?

15. To calculate $7\frac{1}{8} - 2\frac{2}{3}$, Lee added $\frac{1}{3}$ to $4\frac{1}{8}$. Why do you think Lee did this?

16. Explain the reasoning for each statement.

a) It is easier to estimate $12\frac{1}{5} - 2\frac{1}{3}$ as mixed numbers than as improper fractions.

b) To calculate $2\frac{1}{2} + 3\frac{2}{3}$, add 4 to $2\frac{1}{2}$ and then subtract $\frac{1}{3}$.

17. Describe three strategies you can use to calculate $4\frac{1}{2} - 2\frac{5}{6}$.

2.11 Communicate about Estimation Strategies

Explain how to estimate sums and differences of fractions and mixed numbers.

LEARN ABOUT the Math

Megan ordered 7 pizzas for a math class party. The students ate all but $2\frac{1}{3}$ pizzas. Megan says, "We ate almost 5 pizzas." Jacob says, "How do you know?"

Megan explains, "When I estimate with fractions, I like to use whole numbers. We started with 7 pizzas. There are about 2 left, and 7 – 2 = 5."

How can Megan improve her explanation?

Megan can show more detail in her explanation.

I drew 7 circles to represent the pizzas.

I coloured 2 pizzas to show that they are left.

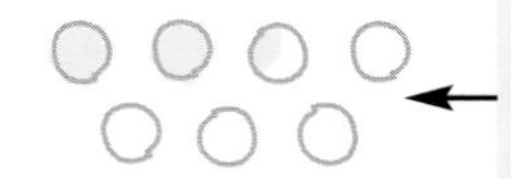

I coloured $\frac{1}{3}$ of the next pizza to show that it is also left. Almost 5 pizzas are gone, so we ate more than $4\frac{1}{2}$ pizzas, but less than 5. I think a good estimate is all we need.

Communication Checklist

- ✔ Did you show all the necessary steps?
- ✔ Were your steps clear?
- ✔ Did you include words to describe your model, as well as pictures?
- ✔ Did your words support your use of the models?

A. Use the Communication Checklist to explain how Megan improved her explanation.

B. Edit Megan's explanation. Explain how your changes improve it.

Reflecting

C. Why was it reasonable for Megan to estimate, rather than calculate? Explain.

D. Why does a visual model help to explain an estimation strategy?

WORK WITH the Math

Example | Estimating a total

Ryan is building a birdhouse. He needs $2\frac{2}{3}$ boards for one part of the birdhouse and $3\frac{1}{2}$ boards for another part. About how many boards does Ryan have to buy? Why does he just need an estimate?

Ryan's Solution

I just need an estimate because I have to buy either 6 or 7 boards. I can't buy part of a board.

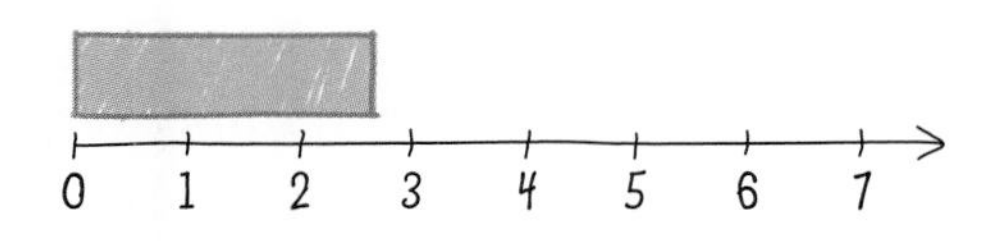

$2\frac{2}{3}$ is a little more than $2\frac{1}{2}$.

0 1 2 3 4 5 6 7

If I added $2\frac{1}{2}$ and $3\frac{1}{2}$, I'd get 5 wholes and 2 halves. That's 6 whole boards. The total is a little more than 6 boards, since $2\frac{2}{3}$ is a little more than $2\frac{1}{2}$. I have to buy 7 boards.

A Checking

1. Mia has $4\frac{1}{4}$ packages of modelling clay. She wants to estimate how many packages of clay will be left if her brother uses $2\frac{1}{2}$ packages. Here is the beginning of her explanation to her brother: "$4\frac{1}{4}$ is a little more than 4. The distance from $2\frac{1}{2}$ to 3 is $\frac{1}{2}$." Complete her explanation. Use the Communication Checklist.

B Practising

2. George's family had $5\frac{1}{2}$ packages of noodles. One Sunday, George used $1\frac{5}{6}$ packages to make a casserole. About how many packages are left? Why is an estimate all he needs?

3. Karen's grandmother has 10 scoops of flour. One batch of bannock uses $2\frac{1}{3}$ scoops of flour. About how many batches can she bake? Why is an estimate all she needs?

4. Braydon and Winnie are each building a bridge with straws for a science project. They have 9 bags of straws. Braydon thinks that he will use $3\frac{4}{5}$ bags of straws. Winnie thinks that she will use $2\frac{3}{4}$ bags of straws. About how many bags of straws will be left? Explain.

5. Suki, Lee, and Janice have collected the same number of pencils for the orphanage in Ukraine. When they put their pencils together, they have almost 5 full boxes of pencils. About how many boxes of pencils does each person have? Explain.

Chapter Self-Test

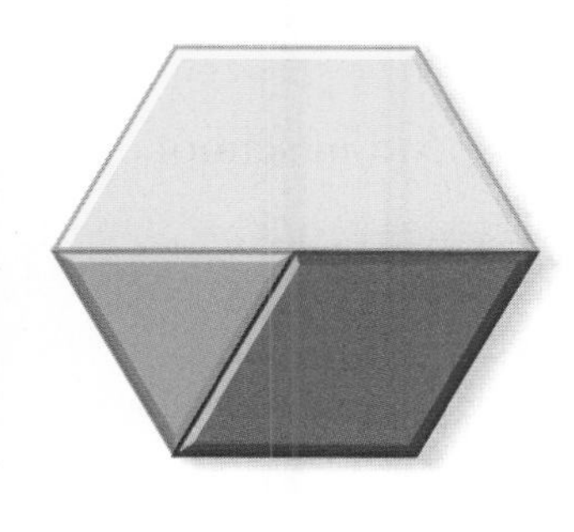

1. Order $\frac{3}{5}$, $\frac{4}{9}$, and $\frac{8}{5}$ from least to greatest.

2. Rename in lowest terms.

a) $\frac{8}{24}$ **b)** $\frac{21}{35}$ **c)** $\frac{36}{15}$

3. Two fractions can be renamed as 18ths. What could their denominators be?

4. **a)** Which part of the pattern block model shows $\frac{1}{3} + \frac{1}{6}$?

b) Calculate $\frac{1}{3} + \frac{1}{6}$.

5. Calculate. Then estimate to show that your answers are reasonable.

a) $\frac{3}{8} + \frac{1}{4}$ **b)** $\frac{2}{5} + \frac{3}{4}$

6. Francis wrote a story on his computer for $\frac{1}{2}$ of an hour and then played computer games for $\frac{1}{4}$ of an hour. Write an equation to describe the fraction of an hour that Francis used his computer.

7. Calculate. Show your work.

a) $\frac{3}{8} - \frac{1}{4}$ **b)** $\frac{4}{5} - \frac{3}{4}$

8. Heather is earning money to buy a new stereo. She has earned $\frac{4}{5}$ of the amount she needs. What fraction of the amount does she still need to earn?

9. Luke drew a picture to show how he spends a typical weekday.

Luke's Typical Weekday

school $\frac{1}{4}$
sleep $\frac{1}{3}$
other $\frac{1}{4}$
homework $\frac{1}{24}$
TV and reading $\frac{1}{8}$

a) What fraction of the day does Luke not spend sleeping or in school?

b) How much more of the day does Luke spend in school than on homework?

c) Use the picture to make up a problem that has $\frac{7}{12}$ as the answer.

10. Calculate $\frac{3}{8} + \frac{2}{5}$. Explain what you did.

11. Calculate. Show your work.

a) $\frac{5}{6} - \frac{4}{9}$

b) $\frac{7}{10} - \frac{3}{8}$

12. Calculate. Show your work.

a) $2\frac{3}{4} + 3\frac{8}{9}$

b) $4 - \frac{1}{10}$

c) $3 - 2\frac{1}{5}$

d) $4 - 2\frac{3}{7}$

13. The difference between two mixed numbers is a whole number. What do you know about the two mixed numbers?

What Do You Think Now?

Revisit What Do You Think? on page 43. How have your answers and explanations changed?

Chapter Review

Frequently Asked Questions

Q: What model is helpful for adding and subtracting fractions?

A: You can use a number line with different numbers of sections. For example, the following number line was used to subtract $\frac{7}{8} - \frac{1}{2}$:

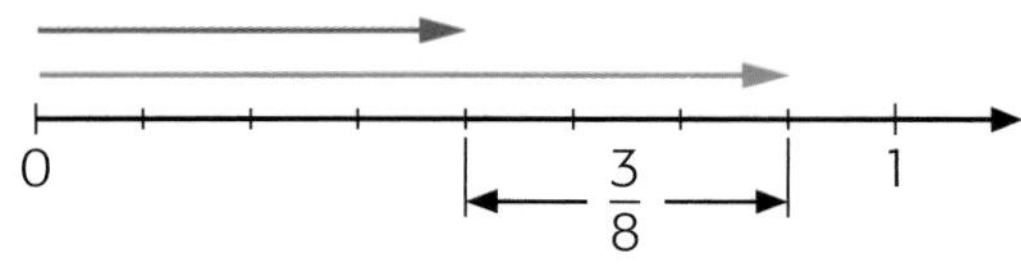

$\frac{7}{8} - \frac{1}{2} = \frac{3}{8}$

Q: How do you add or subtract fractions using equivalent fractions?

A: Choose a common multiple of the two denominators. Then write a new equation, using equivalent fractions that have the common multiple as their denominators. For example, to add $\frac{3}{4} + \frac{3}{5}$, use the common denominator 20, since 20 is a common multiple of 4 and 5.

$\frac{3}{4} = \frac{15}{20}$ (×5) $\quad \frac{3}{5} = \frac{12}{20}$ (×4)

$$\frac{3}{4} + \frac{3}{5} = \frac{15}{20} + \frac{12}{20}$$
$$= \frac{27}{20} \text{ or } 1\frac{7}{20}$$

Q: How do you add mixed numbers, such as $2\frac{3}{4} + 4\frac{1}{2}$?

A1: Add the whole numbers and the fractions separately.

- Add the whole numbers: $2 + 4 = 6$
- Add the fractions: $\frac{3}{4} + \frac{1}{2} = \frac{3}{4} + \frac{2}{4}$, and $\frac{3}{4} + \frac{2}{4} = \frac{5}{4}$ or $1\frac{1}{4}$.
- Then add the whole number sum and fraction sum.

  $6 + 1\frac{1}{4} = 7\frac{1}{4}$

A2: Rename both mixed numbers as improper fractions. Rename the improper fractions with common denominators if you need to, and then add.

$2\frac{3}{4} = \frac{11}{4}$ and $4\frac{1}{2} = \frac{9}{2}$

$$\frac{11}{4} + \frac{9}{2} = \frac{11}{4} + \frac{18}{4}$$
$$= \frac{29}{4} \text{ or } 7\frac{1}{4}$$

Q: How do you subtract a mixed number from a whole number?

A: Use a number line to determine the difference between the numbers. For example, to subtract $7 - 1\frac{3}{5}$, draw jumps that are easy to add from $1\frac{3}{5}$ to 7.

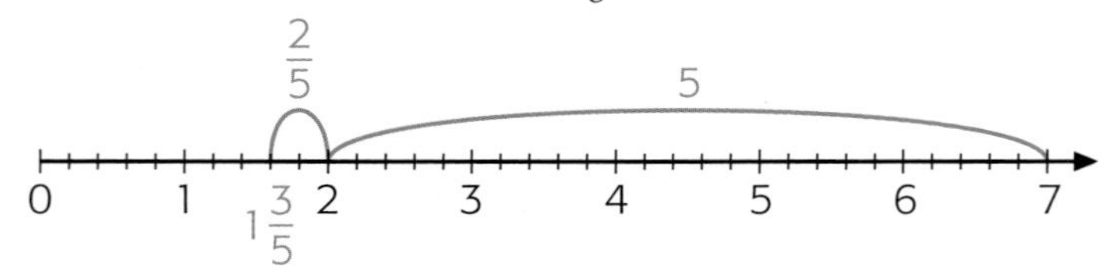

The difference between $1\frac{3}{5}$ and 2 is $\frac{2}{5}$. The difference between 2 and 7 is 5. The total difference is $\frac{2}{5} + 5$, or $5\frac{2}{5}$. So, $7 - 1\frac{3}{5} = 5\frac{2}{5}$.

Q: How do you subtract mixed numbers, such as $7\frac{1}{3} - 2\frac{3}{4}$?

A1: Subtract the fractions and whole numbers separately. Rename the fractions using fractions with a common denominator. If the fraction being subtracted is greater than the original fraction, regroup one whole. For example, you can subtract $7\frac{1}{3} - 2\frac{3}{4}$ by regrouping:

Since $\frac{1}{3} < \frac{3}{4}$, regroup. $7\frac{1}{3} = 6\frac{4}{3}$ $\quad 2\frac{3}{4} = 2\frac{9}{12}$

$= 6\frac{16}{12}$

Subtract. $6\frac{16}{12} - 2\frac{9}{12} = 4\frac{7}{12}$

A2: Rename both mixed numbers as improper fractions. Rename the improper fractions with common denominators if you need to, and then subtract.

$7\frac{1}{3} = \frac{22}{3}$ and $2\frac{3}{4} = \frac{11}{4}$

$$\begin{aligned}\frac{22}{3} - \frac{11}{4} &= \frac{88}{12} - \frac{33}{12} \\ &= \frac{55}{12} \\ &= \frac{48}{12} + \frac{7}{12} \\ &= 4\frac{7}{12}\end{aligned}$$

Practice

Lesson 2.1

1. Name three fractions between $\frac{1}{2}$ and $\frac{5}{4}$.

2. a) Place $\frac{8}{7}$, $\frac{2}{3}$, $\frac{1}{5}$, $\frac{2}{5}$, and $\frac{15}{4}$ on the number line.

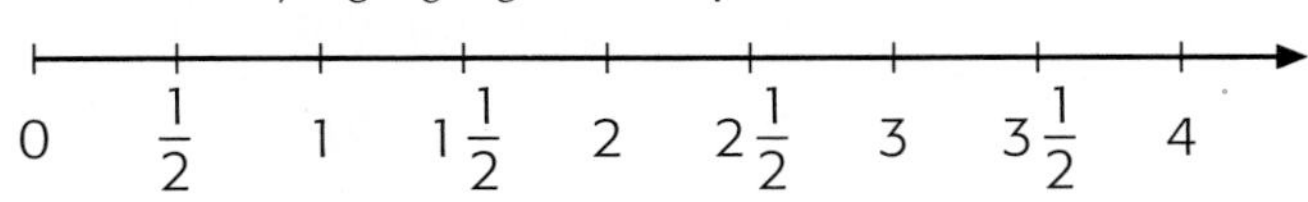

b) List them in order from least to greatest.

3. Rename in lowest terms.

a) $\frac{6}{10}$ **b)** $\frac{12}{36}$ **c)** $\frac{20}{12}$ **d)** $\frac{81}{36}$

Lesson 2.3

4. Calculate.

a) $\frac{6}{12} + \frac{7}{12}$ **b)** $\frac{5}{8} - \frac{1}{4}$ **c)** $\frac{5}{8} + \frac{1}{4}$ **d)** $\frac{3}{5} + \frac{1}{2}$

Lesson 2.4

5. Calculate.

a) $\frac{4}{7} - \frac{1}{3}$ **b)** $\frac{11}{12} - \frac{2}{3}$ **c)** $\frac{5}{6} - \frac{2}{3}$ **d)** $\frac{3}{4} - \frac{3}{5}$

6. a) Marian has $\frac{2}{3}$ of a bag of bagels. She finds another $\frac{1}{4}$ bag of bagels and puts these bagels in the first bag. What fraction of the first bag is now full of bagels?

b) Marian has a third bag of bagels that is $\frac{5}{6}$ full. What fraction describes how many more bagels are in the first two bags combined than in the third bag?

Lesson 2.6

7. Nunavut covers about $\frac{1}{5}$ of Canada's area. Manitoba covers about $\frac{1}{15}$ of Canada's area. What fraction describes how much more of Canada is covered by Nunavut than by Manitoba?

Lesson 2.7

8. Estimate whether each sum is greater than 1. Explain your estimate.

a) $\frac{2}{3} + \frac{5}{7}$ **b)** $\frac{5}{6} + \frac{1}{7}$

9. Calculate each sum in question 8. Use your estimates to verify your calculations.

Lesson 2.9

10. Calculate using equivalent fractions. Show your work.

a) $\frac{3}{5} + \frac{2}{7}$ **b)** $\frac{8}{9} + \frac{2}{3}$ **c)** $\frac{7}{10} - \frac{2}{3}$ **d)** $\frac{2}{3} - \frac{3}{5}$

Lesson 2.10

11. Calculate. Show your work.

a) $\frac{3}{10} + 2\frac{3}{5}$ **b)** $4\frac{5}{9} + \frac{2}{3}$ **c)** $6 - 2\frac{2}{7}$

12. Kyle has 3 h to complete a technology project. He thinks that he will need $1\frac{5}{6}$ h to design and build. How much time will he have to write the report for his project?

Lesson 2.11

13. Estimate whether each sum is between 1 and 3. Explain your estimate.

a) $1\frac{1}{2} + 1\frac{1}{4}$ **b)** $\frac{5}{6} + \frac{1}{10}$ **c)** $1\frac{2}{3} + 2\frac{4}{7}$ **d)** $\frac{3}{5} + 1\frac{9}{13}$

Chapter Task

Task | Checklist

- ✔ Did you explain each step of each calculation?
- ✔ Did you present your combinations clearly?
- ✔ Did your solutions answer the questions?

New Car Lot

Your family has opened a car lot. You need to decide which models and colours of vehicles to buy. You have surveyed visitors to the car lot. Unfortunately, you spilled water on your results, so two fractions are missing.

Preferred model	four-door family car	jeep	truck	sports car
Fraction	$\frac{1}{3}$	$\frac{1}{4}$	$\frac{1}{5}$	

Preferred colour	silver	black	red	green	blue	beige
Fraction	$\frac{1}{4}$	$\frac{1}{10}$		$\frac{3}{10}$	$\frac{3}{20}$	$\frac{1}{20}$

What fraction of each model/colour combination should you order?

A. What fraction of visitors prefer sports cars? Explain.

B. What fraction of visitors prefer red vehicles? Show your work.

C. You ordered 12 cars. Use fractions to describe the models and the colours of the cars. Explain why you ordered these 12 cars.

D. Use addition and subtraction to make your own fraction problem about the car lot. Solve your problem.

MINI-BASKETBALL
MINI-BALLON DE BASKETBALL
NCAA
MINI-BASKETBALL
MINI-BALLON DE BASKETBALL
MINI
NCAA

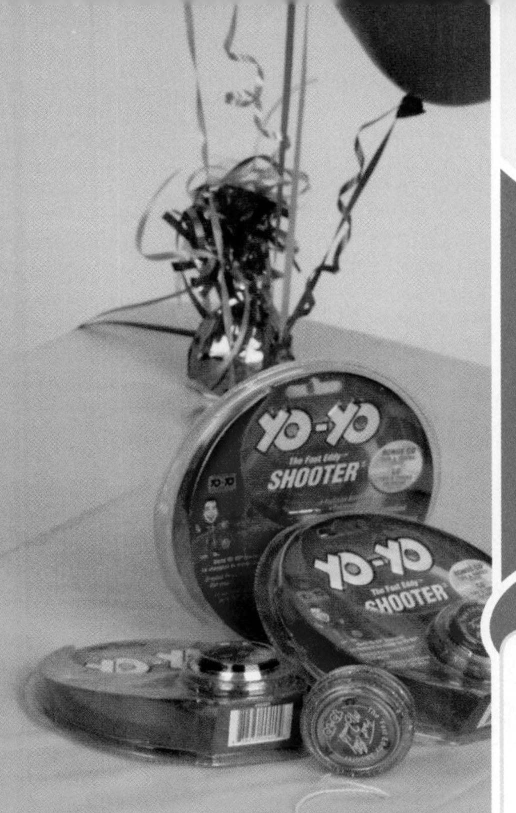

Chapter 3

Decimal Numbers

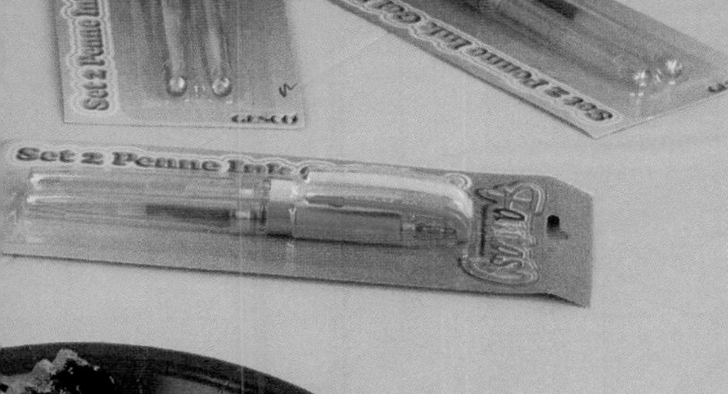

GOAL

You will be able to

- add and subtract decimal numbers
- multiply and divide decimal numbers
- solve real-life problems that invlove decimal numbers
- express fractions as decimal numbers
- order decimal numbers

Decimals are found everywhere. What examples of decimals can you see in this party picture?

Getting Started

Comparing Numbers

Matthew's school has a garden where students can grow vegetables. In this plan of the garden, the white areas show the paths. Each small square is 1 m^2.

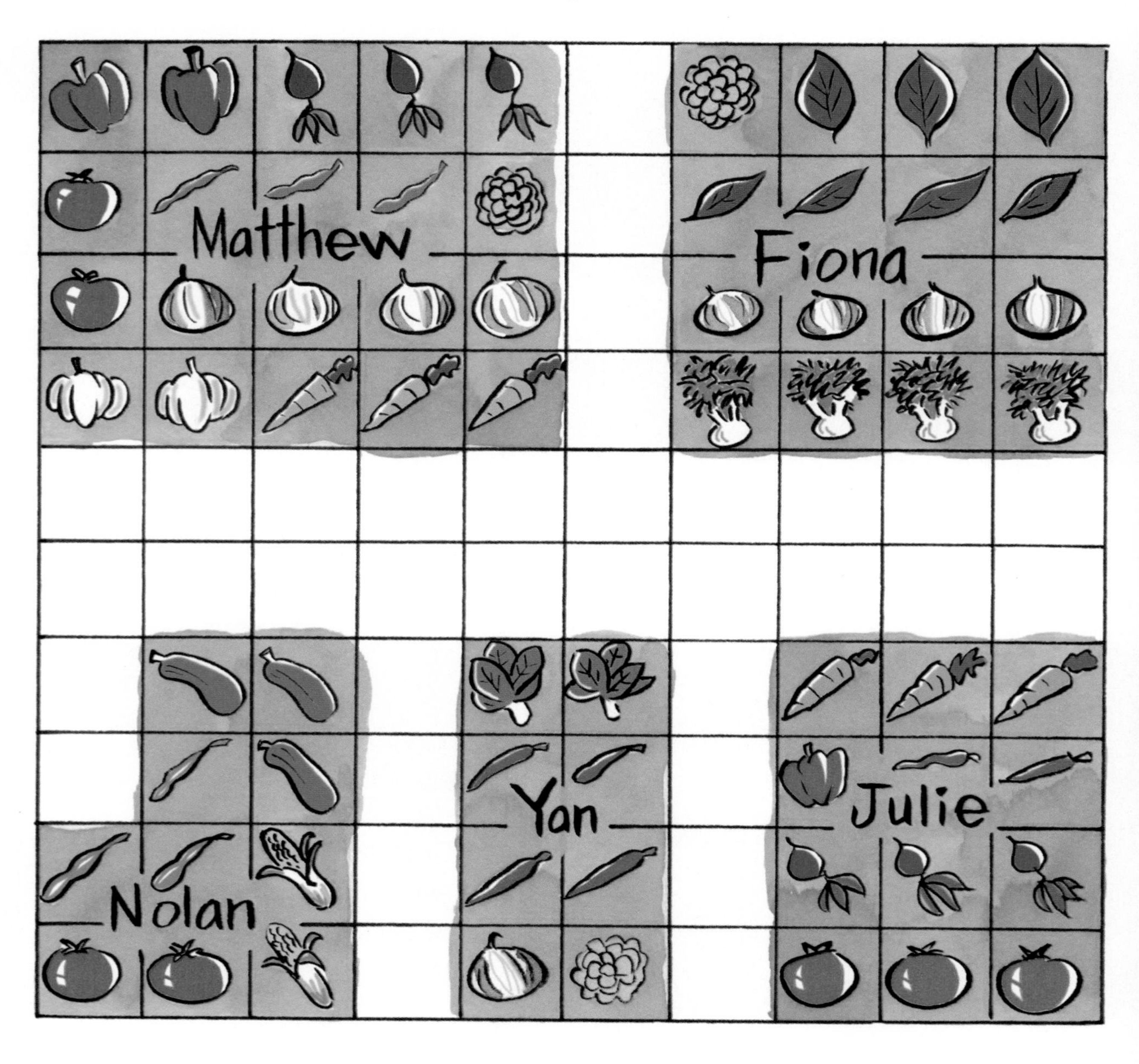

Communication | *Tip*

Decimal numbers can just be called decimals. In this book, they are called decimals.

What decimal describes the total area of the garden that is planted?

A. How many small squares are there in total?

B. What is the area of Matthew's patch?

C. Compare the area of Matthew's patch with the area of the whole garden. Write your answer as a decimal.

D. Compare the area of every other patch with the area of the whole garden. Write each answer as a decimal.

E. What part of the garden is planted? Write your answer as a decimal.

What Do You Think?

Decide whether you agree or disagree with each statement. Be ready to explain your decision.

1. Adding decimals is different from adding whole numbers.

2. Every decimal multiplication is related to a whole number multiplication.

3. $3.2 \div 0.4$ should be less than $3.2 \div 4$.

4. Every decimal is equivalent to more than one fraction.

3.1 Exploring Adding and Subtracting Decimals

Add and subtract decimals using mental math.

EXPLORE the Math

You had \$12.00 for a field trip to the zoo. You spent \$6.50 for the admission fee. You can buy lunch with the money you have left.

With the money you have left, is it better to buy a special or items separately from the menu?

Food	Price
Spring roll	\$0.75
Soup	\$1.25
Buffalo burger	\$3.99
Poutine	\$2.50
Salad	\$2.25
Submarine sandwich	\$3.65

Drinks & dessert	Price
Bottled water	\$0.75
Fruit juice	\$1.25
Milk	\$0.95
Bannock	\$0.50
Carrot cake	\$1.10
Fruit salad	\$0.50

Specials \$4.50 each
1. Salad, fruit juice, carrot cake
2. Buffalo burger, bottled water, bannock
3. Poutine, spring rolls, fruit juice
4. Submarine sandwich, milk, fruit salad

3.2 Adding and Subtracting Decimals

YOU WILL NEED
- a place value mat
- base 10 blocks

GOAL

Develop strategies to add and subtract decimals.

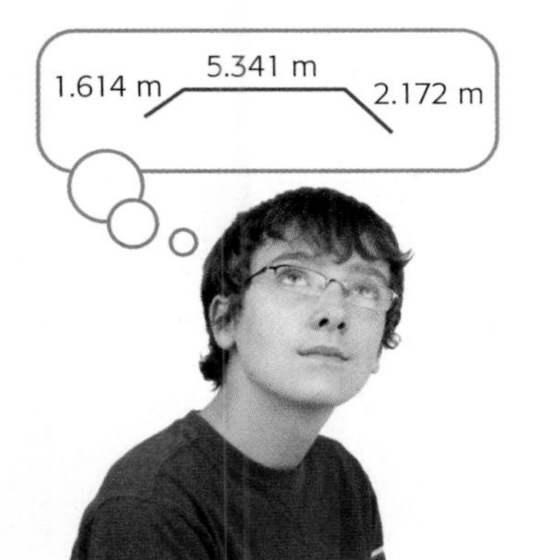

LEARN ABOUT the Math

Matthew and Fiona are cutting a water pipe that is 15.000 m long into sections. Matthew needs sections that are 1.614 m, 5.341 m, and 2.172 m long. Fiona needs a section that is 5.000 m long.

Will there be enough pipe left for Fiona's section?

Example 1 | Estimating a sum and a difference

I estimated the length of pipe I will need using front-end estimation.

Matthew's Solution

$\begin{array}{r} 1.614 \\ 5.341 \\ +\ 2.172 \\ \hline 8 \end{array}$	I added the ones.
$6 + 3 + 1 = 10$ tenths $= 1.0$	Then I added the tenths.
$8 + 1 = 9$	I added the two sums. I'll need about 9 m of pipe for my sections.
$15 - 9 = 6$	I subtracted my estimate from 15 m. I estimate that 6 m of pipe will be left. Since 6 m is greater than 5 m, there will be enough pipe left for Fiona's section.

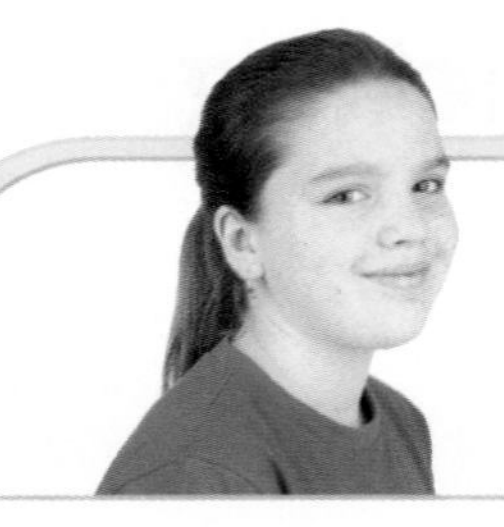

Example 2 | Adding decimals

I calculated the length of pipe that Matthew will need.

Julie's Solution

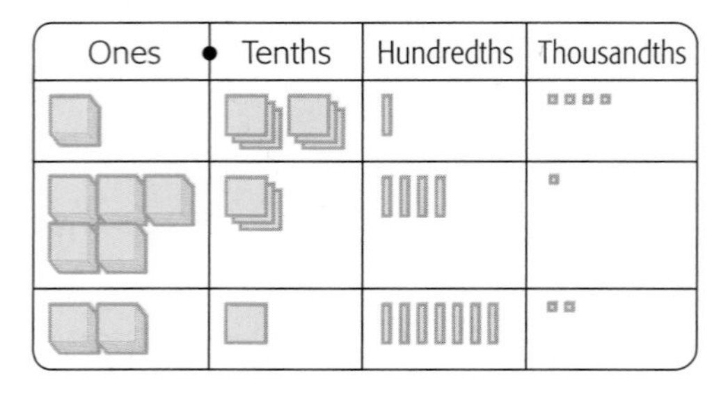

The three sections that Matthew will need are 1.614 m, 5.341 m, and 2.172 m. I modelled the lengths with base ten blocks on a place value mat.
I used the large block to represent 1 so that there would be a block to represent thousandths. The flat represents 0.1, the rod represents 0.01, and the small cube represents 0.001.

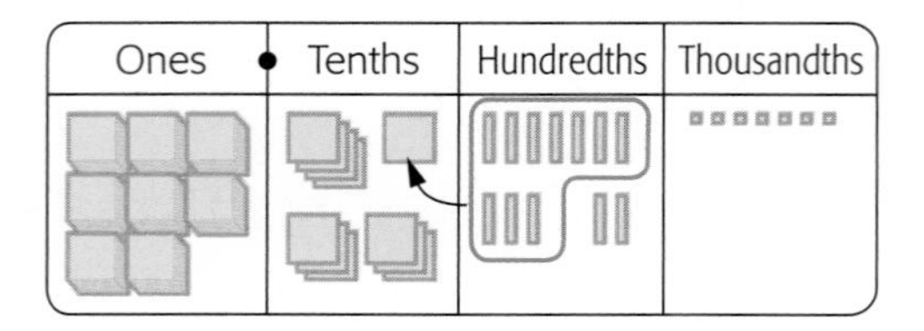

I put blocks that were the same together, and I recorded my addition. There were 7 thousandths. I regrouped 10 of the 12 hundredths as 1 tenth.

$$\begin{array}{r} {\scriptstyle 1} \\ 1.614 \\ 5.341 \\ +\ 2.172 \\ \hline 27 \end{array}$$

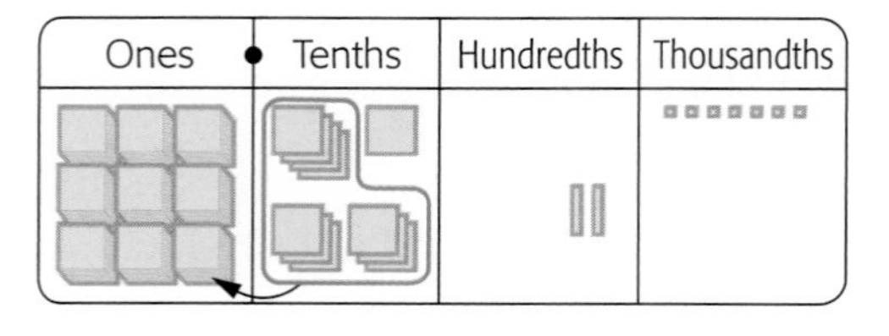

I regrouped 10 of the 11 tenths as a one.

$$\begin{array}{r} {\scriptstyle 1\ \ 1} \\ 1.614 \\ 5.341 \\ +\ 2.172 \\ \hline .127 \end{array}$$

Ones | Tenths | Hundredths | Thousandths

$$\begin{array}{r} {\scriptstyle 1\ \ 1} \\ 1.614 \\ 5.341 \\ +\ 2.172 \\ \hline 9.127 \end{array}$$

Matthew will need 9.127 m of pipe for his sections.

There were 9 ones, 1 tenth, 2 hundredths, and 7 thousandths in total.

Example 3 | Subtracting decimals

To calculate the remaining length, I subtracted the amount that Matthew will need from the total length.

Fiona's Solution

15.000 − 9.127 is about 15 − 9 = 6.	I estimated first.
15 000 = 14 999 + 1 −9 127 −9 127 5 872 + 1 = 5873	I thought of 15.000 as 15 000 thousandths and 9.127 as 9127 thousands and just calculated 15 000 − 9127. I regrouped 15 000 to make the subtraction easier.
I'll have 5.873 m of pipe to work with.	I knew the answer had to be about 6, so I could easily place the decimal point.

Example 4 | Subtracting decimals using mental math

I imagined a number line, and calculated the length of pipe that will be left using mental math.

Liam's Solution

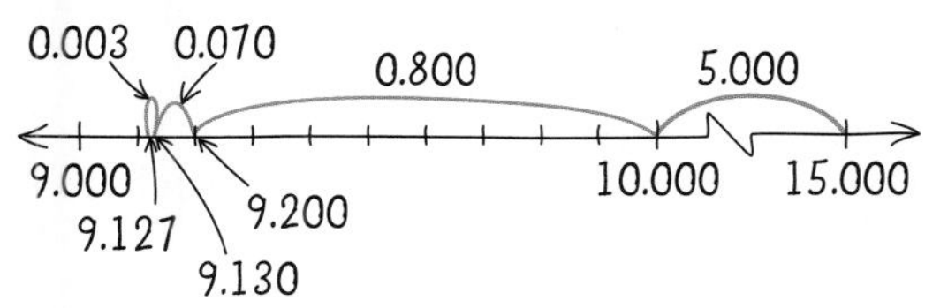

There will be 5.873 m of pipe left.

15.000 − 9.127 means "How far is it from 9.127 to 15.000?"

I calculated the difference in steps that made mental calculation easier.

Reflecting

A. How else could Julie and Fiona have regrouped to calculate their answers?

B. Why do you think Liam added 5, then 0.8, then 0.07, and then 0.003?

C. Which method would you have used for the subtraction? Why?

WORK WITH the Math

Example 5 | Adding and subtracting thousandths

For a science experiment, Amar and William need to add 0.800 g of salt to a beaker of water. Amar has measured 0.345 g of salt, and William has measured 0.406 g. How many more grams of salt do they need?

Solution

$$\begin{array}{r} 0.345 \\ +\ 0.406 \\ \hline 0.751 \end{array}$$

Add the amounts that Amar and William measured. Line up the digits to make sure that you add tenths to tenths, hundredths to hundredths, and thousandths to thousandths.

$$\begin{array}{r} \scriptstyle 7\,9\,10 \\ \not{0.800} \\ -\ 0.751 \\ \hline 0.049 \end{array}$$

Subtract the total amount that Amar and William have from the amount that they need. Line up the tenths digits, the hundredths digits, and the thousandths digits. Regroup so you can subtract.

The difference is 0.049, so Amar and William still need 0.049 g of salt.

A Checking

1. Estimate.

a) 2.321 + 5.309 + 2.100 **b)** 9.623 − 5.061

2. Calculate.

a) 3.05 + 4.26 + 0.63 **b)** 4.563 − 2.937

B Practising

3. Estimate.

a) 2.5 + 12.6 + 20.9

b) 1.32 + 10.55 + 62.41

c) 78.615 − 29.321

d) 426.3 + 252.8 − 139.2

Reading Strategy

Read the problem. In your own words, write what you are being asked to do.

4. Calculate.

a) $1.356 + 0.405 + 22.015$

b) $335.216 + 40.52 + 5.145$

c) $3.162 - 0.123$

d) $261.72 - 30.568$

e) $652.1 - 26.358$

f) $4.123 - 3.200$

5. Zoë is putting a fence around her garden. She needs 14.6 m of wire fence. She has three pieces already cut. These pieces are 6.6 m, 2.1 m, and 7.2 m long. Does she have enough? If so, how much will she have left over? If not, how much more does she need? Explain your reasoning.

6. Jocelyne and Martine ran 400 m. Jocelyne took 74.53 s, and Martine took 89.34 s. How many seconds faster was Jocelyne than Martine?

7. a) Spin the spinner five times to fill in the digits.

■.■■

0.■■

b) Add the two numbers.

c) Subtract the lesser number from the greater number.

d) Repeat nine times. What is the greatest value you calculated? What is the least value?

8. Lucas made punch to sell at a powwow. He combined 1.22 L of ginger ale, 0.76 L of orange juice, 0.89 L of grapefruit juice, and 0.56 L of raspberry juice. Then Lucas spilled some of the punch. He had 2.95 L left. How much did he spill?

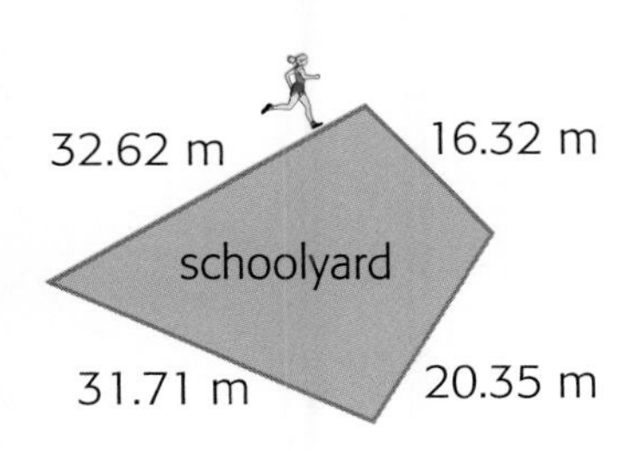

9. Gabrielle is training for a race by running around the schoolyard twice. What might be the distance of the race that she is training for?

10. Why might you be able to solve $3 - 2.04$ by solving $3.00 - 2.04$? Why might you not?

3.3 Multiplying by Numbers Less than 1

YOU WILL NEED
- grid paper
- a calculator

GOAL

Multiply by decimals less than 1.

LEARN ABOUT *the Math*

Yan has a picture that is 80 cm long by 60 cm wide. She is getting a piece of glass cut to cover the picture. She needs to calculate the area of the picture to figure out the price of the glass.

What is the area of the picture in square metres?

A. Draw a model of a square metre on grid paper. Use a 10×10 array of 100 grid squares.

B. What fraction of a square metre does each grid square represent? Write the fraction as a decimal.

C. Represent Yan's picture on your model by colouring grid squares.

D. What is the length of the picture as a fraction of a metre? Write the fraction as a decimal.

E. What is the width of the picture as a fraction of a metre? Write the fraction as a decimal.

F. What expression represents the area of the picture?

G. What is the area of Yan's picture?

Reflecting

H. To determine the area of Yan's picture, you used a 10×10 grid to multiply tenths by tenths. Why does multiplying tenths by tenths always give an answer in hundredths?

I. How is the answer for 0.8×0.6 related to the answer for 8×6?

J. How do you know that when you multiply by a decimal less than 1, the product is less than you started with?

WORK WITH the Math

Example 1 | Multiplying using a grid

Calculate the area of a picture in a frame that is 70 cm long by 50 cm wide. Write the area in square metres.

Yan's Solution

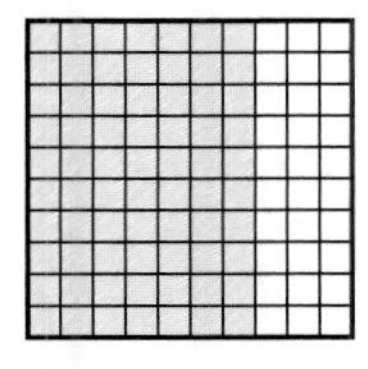

Both the length and the width of the grid represent 1 m. I coloured 7 columns to show 0.7 of the grid.

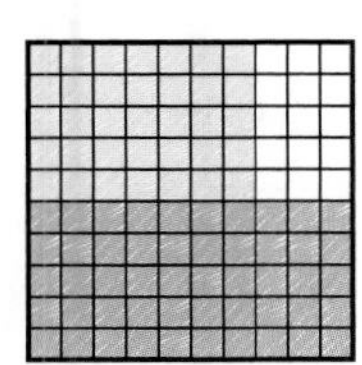

I coloured 5 rows to represent 0.5 of the grid. The area where the blue 0.5 overlaps the yellow 0.7 represents 0.5 of 0.7.

It also represents 0.5×0.7, since it is the area of a 0.5 by 0.7 rectangle. It is 0.35 of the whole grid.

The whole area of the grid represents 1 m^2.

There are 35 squares, so the area is 0.35 m^2.
The area of my frame is 0.35 m^2.

Example 2 | Multiplying thousandths using a calculator

Julie dropped a rubber ball from a height of 8.2 m. Each time the ball bounced, it bounced to 0.355 times its previous height. About how high was the second bounce?

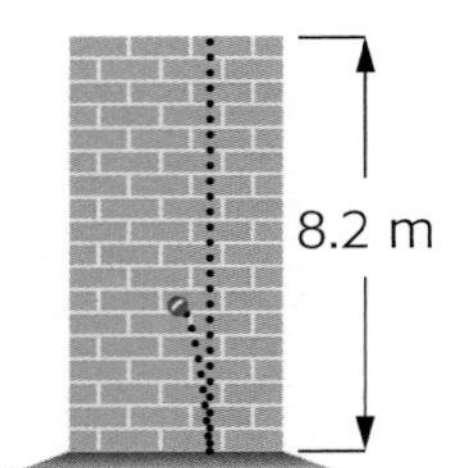

Julie's Solution

8 . 2 [×] 0 . 3 5 5 [=]

2.911

The first bounce was 2.911 m high.

To calculate the height of a bounce, I multiplied the height of the previous bounce by 0.355. I used a calculator.

I know that 0.355 × 8.2 should be close to 0.4 × 8.0. That's 3.2, so my calculation is reasonable.

2 . 9 1 1 [×] 0 . 3 5 5 [=]

1.033405

I multiplied again by 0.355.

1.033 405 is about 1.0.
The second bounce was 1.0 m high.

I expressed my answer to one decimal place, because this is the number of decimal places in the original height.

A Checking

1. Calculate using a 10 × 10 grid.

a) 0.4 × 0.6 **b)** 0.2 × 0.7

2. Calculate, and then estimate to check if your answer is reasonable.

a) What is the cost of 0.38 kg of birdseed at $0.95 for each kilogram?

b) What is the cost of 0.56 kg of rolled oats at $0.88 for each kilogram?

B Practising

3. Calculate.

a) 3.4×0.2 **b)** 7.6×0.8

4. Calculate.

a) 0.2×0.9 **b)** 0.8×0.7

5. Predict the order of these six products from least to greatest. Check your prediction by calculating.

a) 1.3×0.8 **c)** 1.5×0.2 **e)** 5.6×0.2

b) 4.9×0.6 **d)** 10.6×0.3 **f)** 8.4×0.5

6. Place the digits 6, 7, and 8 so that the product is as close to 5 as possible: 0.■ × ▲.◆.

7. In her backyard, Julie has a rabbit run that is 1.2 m long and 0.9 m wide. What is the area of the rabbit run?

8. Joseph Starblanket buys 1.89 kg of beads at $0.85 for each kilogram. Determine how much he pays. Use a calculator.

9. Dora's garden is 2.90 m long and 0.85 m wide. She decides to change her garden so that its length is 1 m less and its width is 1 m greater. What is the change in the area of her garden?

10. Why is it easier to multiply 0.64×0.5 mentally than it is to multiply 0.64×0.7 mentally?

11. Suppose that you multiply 2.34 by a decimal less than 1. What do you know about the answer?

3.4 Multiplying by Numbers Greater than 1

YOU WILL NEED
- a calculator
- base ten blocks

Multiply by decimals greater than 1.

LEARN ABOUT the Math

Max's mother is buying a rug to put in the entrance hall of their home. The area she wants to cover is 2.4 m long and 1.2 m wide.

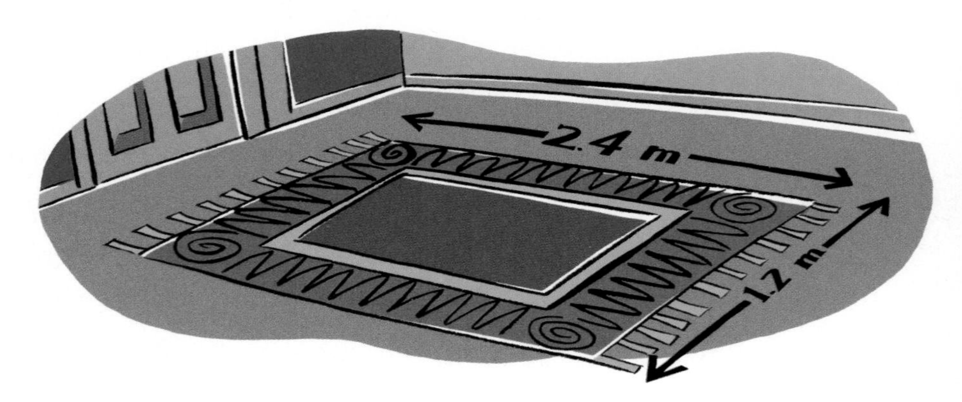

? How big a rug does Max's mother need to cover the hall?

Example 1 | Multiplying decimals using base ten blocks

Determine the area of the rug that Max's mother needs.

Max's Solution

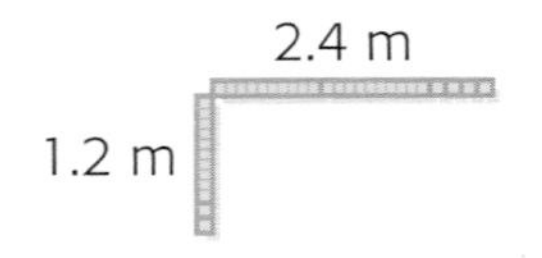

I decided to use base ten blocks to model a rectangle that is 2.4 m long and 1.2 m wide. A rod represents 1.0 m, so the length of a small cube represents 0.1 m. I put down rods and cubes to show the length and width of the rectangle.

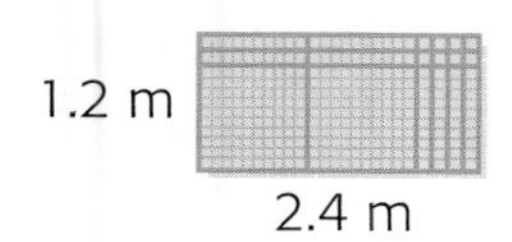

To model the rug, I filled in the rectangle. Each flat represents 1.00 m × 1.00 m = 1.00 m^2.
Since 10 rods make a flat, each rod represents 0.10 m^2.
Since 100 small cubes make a flat, each small cube represents 0.01 m^2.

1.2 m x 2.4 m = 2.88 m^2
The area of the rug that we need is 2.9 m^2.

There are 2 flats, 8 rods, and 8 small cubes.
The area of the rug that we need is
2.00 + 0.80 + 0.08 m^2.

Reflecting

A. Why is the product of two decimals greater than 1 always greater than both factors?

B. How is multiplying by a decimal greater than 1 the same as multiplying by a decimal less than 1?

WORK WITH the Math

Example 2 | Multiplying and dividing by 100

Julie uses 7.2 g of silver to make a small pin. Silver costs about $0.18 for each gram. Calculate the cost of the silver in the pin to the nearest cent.

Solution

0.18 × 7.2 is about 0.2 × 7 = 1.4

Estimate the amount in dollars.

0.18 × 100 = 18

Multiply 0.18 by 100 to get a whole number, so you can avoid having to multiply two decimals.

18 × 7.2 = 129.6

Multiply 18 by 7.2.

129.6 ÷ 100 = 1.296

Divide by 100 to reverse the earlier multiplication by 100.

The cost is $1.30.
This answer is reasonable because it is close to the estimate.

Example 3 | Placing a decimal point in a product

Max entered 6.42×13.5 on his calculator and got 8667.0. Is this result correct?

Solution

6.42×13.5 is about $6 \times 10 = 60$.	The decimal point could go in many places to get answers such as 0.8667, 8.667, 86.67, and 866.7. Estimating helps you determine the answer that is reasonable.
The product must be 86.67.	86.67 is closest to the estimate.

A Checking

1. Place the decimal point correctly in each product.

a) $3.4 \times 2 = 680$ **b)** $26.50 \times 2.2 = 5830$

2. Estimate and then calculate.

a) 4.5×3.6 **b)** 12.23×2.9

B Practising

3. Place the decimal point correctly in each product.

a) $3.13 \times 1.2 = 3756$
b) $15.45 \times 3.2 = 4944$
c) $26.45 \times 2.162 = 571849$
d) $321.06 \times 11.3 = 3627978$

4. Predict the order of these six products from greatest to least. Calculate to check your prediction.

a) 32.25×1.8
b) 0.45×2.6
c) 12.347×0.64
d) 2.2×0.03
e) 3.67×1.01
f) 0.35×10.19

5. The decimal point is in the wrong place in each answer. Put it in the correct place, and explain the strategy you used.

a) $45.66 \times 12.2 = 5570.52$
b) $0.78 \times 1.023 = 79.794$
c) $1.09 \times 30.65 = 334.085$
d) $52.56 \times 11.25 = 5913.0$

Reading Strategy

What does the garden patch look like in your mind?

6. Replace each blank with a number so that the products are in order from least to greatest.

■.4 × 5.■

■.8 × 4. 9

■.562 × ■.12■

7. What is the area of a garden patch that is 3.26 m wide and 5.13 m long?

8. Suppose Annik works 7.5 h each week. After working for a year, she gets a raise from $9.25 for each hour to $9.50 for each hour. How much more money will she earn in a week?

9. Louise wants to integrate the Franco-Albertan flag into the flag for La Conférence de la Francophonie. Her flag will be 2.41 m long and 1.7 m wide. Determine the area of the flag.

10. The adult height of a man is about 1.19 times his height at age 12. The adult height of a woman is about 1.07 times her height at age 12. Miguel is 1.5 m tall, and Romona is 1.6 m tall. Both are 12 years old. Predict how tall they will be as adults.

11. One postage stamp costs $1.85. How much does a book of 25 stamps cost?

12. Suppose that you have $3.00 and jellybeans cost $0.85 for each 100 g. Can you afford to buy 300 g of jellybeans?

13. A butcher sells ground beef for $2.25 for each kilogram. How much will 3.4 kg of ground beef cost?

14. Suki is painting her bedroom ceiling. The ceiling is 4.2 m long and 3.9 m wide. Suki has one can of paint, which will cover 12 m^2. Does she have enough paint to put two coats on the ceiling? Explain.

15. The Hendersons spend about $132.50 on food every week. There are 52 weeks in a year. How much do they spend on food every year?

16. Meagan says that, to multiply 1.3 × 1.3, you can multiply 1 × 1 and 0.3 × 0.3, and then add the products to get 1.09 for the answer. Do you agree? Explain.

3.5 Solve Problems Using Guessing and Testing

YOU WILL NEED
- a calculator

Use guess and test to solve measurement problems.

LEARN ABOUT the Math

The students in Liam's class have drawn some pictures. The teacher puts the pictures in three groups. Group A pictures are 20.3 cm wide, group B pictures are 15.6 cm wide, and group C pictures are 8.4 cm wide. Liam is asked to pin up some of the pictures along the bottom of a bulletin board, from one end to the other, with no space between them.

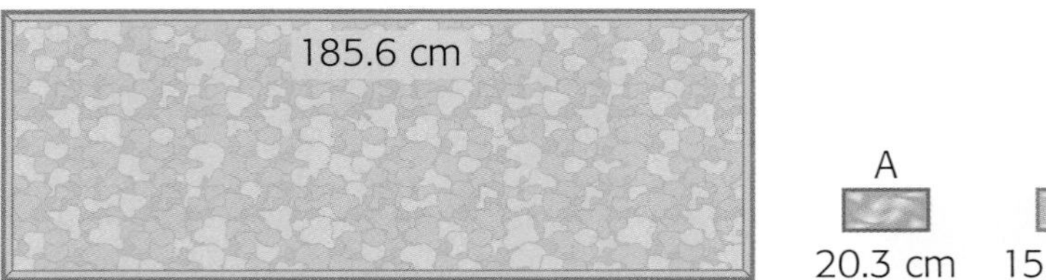

The bulletin board is 185.6 cm wide. Liam has to use about the same number of pictures from each group.

How many pictures from each group should Liam use?

1 Understand the Problem

Liam knows that the bulletin board is 185.6 cm wide. He needs to use pictures from all three groups.

❷ Make a Plan

Liam decides to try different combinations and see which is the right width.

❸ Carry Out the Plan

Liam organizes the combinations he tries in a table.

A	B	C	Total width (cm)	Right width?
1	1	1	20.3 + 15.6 + 8.4 = 44.3	no, too short; try more
2	2	2	44.3 x 2 = 88.6	no, too short; try more
3	3	3	44.3 x 3 = 132.9	no, too short; try more
4	4	4	44.3 x 4 = 177.2	no, too short; try more
5	5	5	44.3 x 5 = 221.5	no, too long; try fewer
5	4	5	101.5 + 62.4 + 42.0 = 205.9	no, too long; try fewer
5	4	4	101.5 + 62.4 + 33.6 = 197.5	no, too long; try fewer
4	4	5	81.2 + 62.4 + 42.0 = 185.6	just right!

Liam can cover the width of the bulletin board with 4 pictures from group A, 4 from group B, and 5 from group C. Since he is using more pictures from group C, he decides to start with C and end with C. His pattern is C, A, B, C, A, B, C, A, B, C, A, B, C.

❹ Look Back

Liam looks at his pattern and thinks it is correct since there are about the same number of drawings from each group. As well, his pattern fits the width of the bulletin board exactly. Liam estimates to check: 4×20.3 is about 80, 4×15.6 is about 60, and 5×8.4 is about 40. $80 + 60 + 40 = 180$, which is close to the width of the bulletin board.

Reflecting

A. How did the guess and test strategy help Liam solve the problem?

B. What other strategy could Liam have used to solve the problem?

WORK WITH *the Math*

Example | Solving a problem using guess and test

A rectangle has an area of 1.44 m^2. Neither the length nor the width is 1.00 m. What might the length and the width of the rectangle be?

Julie's Solution

1 Understand the Problem

Julie knows that the area is 1.44 m^2. She also knows that the formula for the area of a rectangle is length multiplied by width. She knows that there is more than one possible answer, but she needs to determine only one answer.

2 Make a Plan

Julie tries different combinations of the length and width to see which product gives the right area. She keeps track of her guesses in a table.

3 Carry Out the Plan

Length (m)	Width (m)	Area (m^2)	Right area?
1.20	1.10	$1.20 \times 1.10 = 1.32$	too small, try longer width
1.20	1.30	$1.20 \times 1.30 = 1.56$	too big, try shorter width
1.20	1.20	$1.20 \times 1.20 = 1.44$	just right

4 Look Back

Julie checks her calculations. She notices that $12 \times 12 = 144$, so it makes sense that $1.2 \times 1.2 = 1.44$. She thinks she is correct.

Ⓐ Checking

1. Liam had pictures that were 20.3 cm wide, 15.6 cm wide, and 8.4 cm wide. He posted all the pictures along one wall of the class. The pictures made a line that was 318.5 cm long. How many pictures of each width did Liam have?

Ⓑ Practising

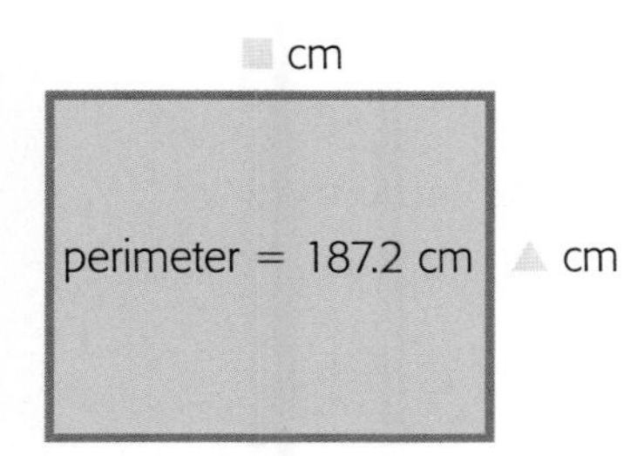

2. Winnie is using the diagram at the left to make a wooden picture frame.
   a) List two different sets of dimensions (length and width) for the picture frame.
   b) Which set results in a greater area?

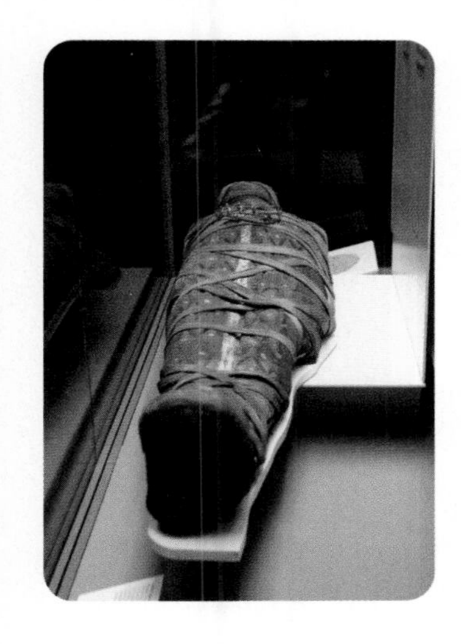

3. An Egyptian mummy is in a case that is 3 m high and has a volume of 24 m^3. The case is half as wide as it is long. What are the length and the width of the case?

4. Poul has 124.8 m of fencing to build a rectangular pen. He wants the pen to have the largest possible area. Calculate the length and width of the pen to one decimal place.

5. A small rectangular box has a width of 18 cm and a volume of 720 cm^3.
   a) Determine the height and the length of the box.
   b) Is there more than one answer? Explain.

6. The Leclaire family is choosing between two swimming pools for their backyard. Model A is almost square. Model B is about twice as long as it is wide. Both pools are 2.0 m deep and hold about 117.6 m^3 of water. Determine a possible length and width for each pool. Express your answers to the nearest tenth.

7. Jessica is helping her grandmother make a quilt with crocheted squares. The area of the material they have is 1.936 m^2. Her grandmother asked her to determine the number of squares they will need to crochet, and the length and width of each square in centimetres. What are two possible choices that Jessica can give her grandmother?

Mid-Chapter Review

Frequently Asked Questions

Q: How can you add or subtract decimals?

A: You can use base ten blocks and a place value mat. For example, this place value mat shows that $5.23 + 3.82 = 9.05$.

	Tens	Ones	Tenths	Hundredths	Thousandths
+					
=					

Q: How can you multiply two decimals?

A1. You can use base ten blocks to represent the length and width of a rectangle. For example, to multiply 1.5 by 1.2, make a rectangle with 1.5 as the length and 1.2 as the width. Use 1 flat and 7 rods, as well as 10 small cubes, which are equal to one rod. So, $1.5 \times 1.2 = 1.8$.

A2: You can multiply related numbers and adjust the answer.

For example, 0.3×4.67 can be compared to 3×467.
$3 \times 467 = 1401$

You can estimate that 0.3×4.67 is about $0.5 \times 4 = 2$, so the answer must be 1.401.

Or, you can multiply 0.3 by 10 to get 3.
$3 \times 4.67 = 14.01$

Then divide by 10 to reverse the multiplication.
$14.01 \div 10 = 1.401$.

Practice

Lesson 3.2

1. Predict the order of the four sums from least to greatest. Calculate to check your prediction.

a) $2.67 + 6.24$ **c)** $55.213 + 26.543 + 38.222$

b) $65.331 + 21.951$ **d)** $0.236 + 1.897$

2. Estimate each difference. What strategy did you use?

a) $22.65 - 11.20$ **c)** $258.688 - 23.126$

b) $159.32 - 62.15$ **d)** $30.265 - 6.697$

3. Anita and Joey have $95. They want to buy a guitar for $75.50, a package of new strings for $16.99, and a pick for $0.69. All prices include taxes.

a) Estimate the total cost. Do Anita and Joey have enough money to buy these items?

b) Calculate either the amount they are short or the amount they would have left over.

Lesson 3.3

4. Calculate using a model.

a) 0.2×0.9 **b)** 0.6×0.4

Lesson 3.4

5. Predict the order of the four products from greatest to least. Calculate to check your prediction.

a) 0.9×3.28 **c)** 1.4×5.3

b) 6.93×0.33 **d)** 6.3×2.1

6. In 2005, gas cost 79.9¢ for each litre. Hector put 40.5 L in his car. How much did he pay? Express your answer to the nearest cent.

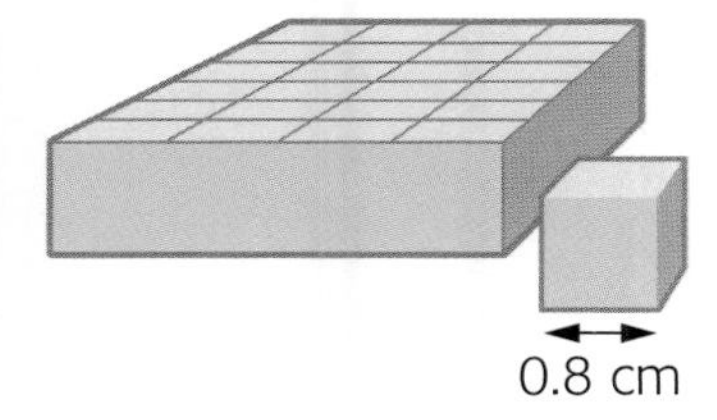

7. This box holds 24 cubes of vegetable stock. Each cube has a side length of 0.8 cm. Determine the area of the bottom of the box.

8. A nickel is 0.185 cm thick. How thick is a roll of nickels worth $2?

9. Suppose that the mass of one egg is 0.065 kg and the mass of an empty egg carton is 16.85 g. One egg carton holds 12 eggs. What is the mass of six cartons of eggs?

3.6 Dividing by Numbers Less than 1

YOU WILL NEED
- number lines
- pencil crayons
- a calculator

GOAL

Divide by one-digit decimals to solve problems.

LEARN ABOUT the Math

Fiona has a ribbon that is 0.84 m long. She is cutting the ribbon into pieces that are 0.07 m long.

How many pieces of ribbon will she have?

A. Estimate how many pieces Fiona can cut.

B. Draw a number line.

C. Show how many pieces of ribbon Fiona can cut using your number line.

Reflecting

D. Why can you solve the problem by dividing 0.84 by 0.07?

E. Why could you have solved $84 \div 7$ instead?

WORK WITH the Math

Example 1 | Dividing decimals

Jean-Luc is pouring maple syrup from a pail into small jars to sell at a market. His pail contains 2.800 L of syrup. Each jar holds 0.350 L of syrup. How many jars can he fill?

Fiona's Solution

2800 ÷ 350 is about 3000 ÷ 300 = 10.
I estimate that he can fill 10 jars.

I estimated how many jars he can fill.
I wrote the amounts in millilitres to avoid dealing with decimals.
2.800 L = 2800 mL and 0.350 L = 350 mL

I drew a number line from 0 to 3000, with spaces of 50 because these numbers were convenient.

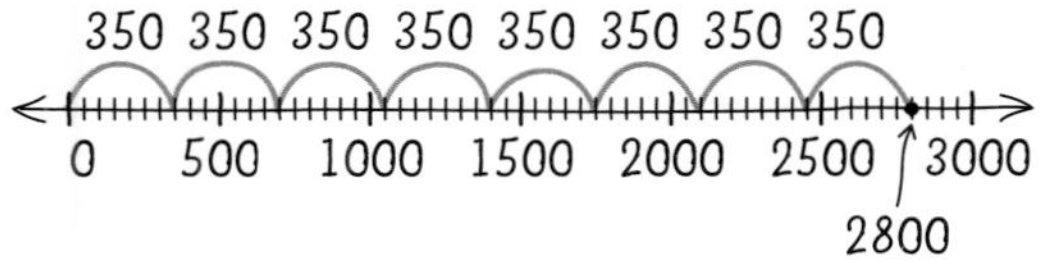

Each "jump" represents 1 jar.
I started at 0 and put a mark on the line for every jump of 350.

2.800 ÷ 0.350 = 8
There are 8 jumps, so Jean-Luc can fill 8 jars.

This answer is close to my estimate, so it is reasonable.

Example 2 | Dividing decimals using a calculator

Calculate 0.6 ÷ 0.125.

Matthew's Solution

0.125 is about 1 tenth, and there are about 6 tenths in 0.6. So 0.6 ÷ 0.125 is about 6.

I estimated.

0 . 6 [÷] 0 . 1 2 5 [=]

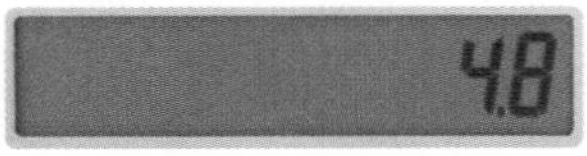

The answer is 4.8.

I divided using a calculator.

The answer is reasonable because it is close to my estimate.

Example 3 | Dividing using a grid

Suppose that Jean-Luc uses a 1.5 L pail of syrup to fill jars that hold 600 mL each. How many jars can he fill?

Yan's Solution

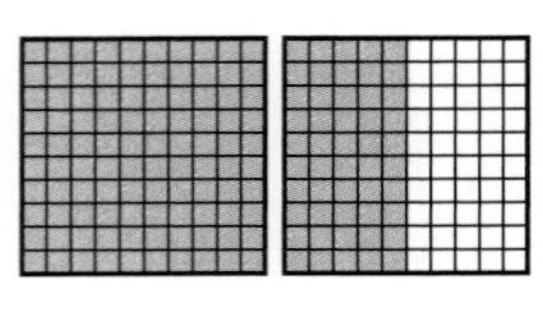

I represented 1.5 L with two 10 × 10 grids. Since 1 L equals 1000 mL, each little square represented 10 mL.

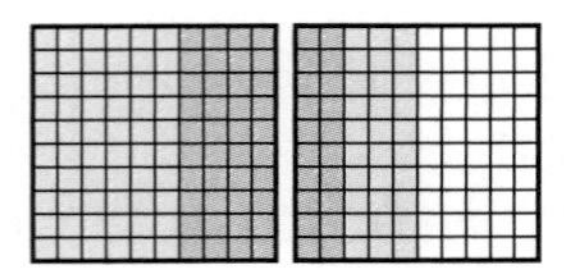

I coloured 150 squares in groups of 60 squares. Each group of 60 squares represented 600 mL, which fills one jar.

There are 2 groups of 60 squares and 30 squares left over. Since 30 squares are another half of a group, the amount left over is 0.5.

1.500 ÷ 0.600 = 2.5

Jean-Luc can fill 2.5 jars.

I knew that 0.6 + 0.6 = 1.2, so the answer is reasonable.

Example 4 | Dividing decimals using equivalents

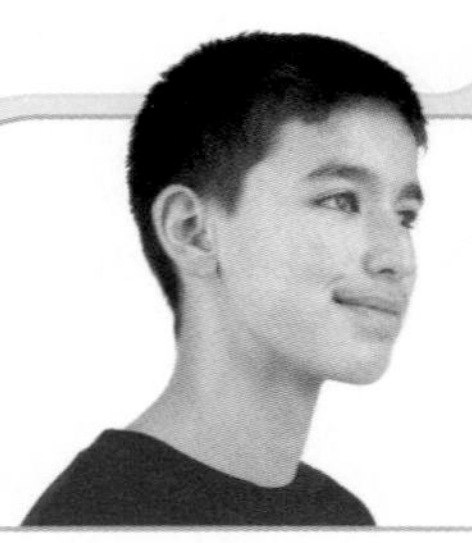

Nolan has $1.75 to spend on pencils. Each pencil costs $0.05. How many pencils can he buy?

Nolan's Solution

1.75 ÷ 0.05 = ?

I needed to divide 1.75 by 0.05.

1.75 ÷ 0.05 is the same as 175 ÷ 5.

I knew that these are the same because the number of 5 hundredths in 175 hundredths is the same as the number of 5s in 175.

175 ÷ 5 = 35

I can buy 35 pencils.

I divided.

A Checking

1. Calculate.

a) $3.6 \div 0.18$ **b)** $7.8 \div 0.3$

2. Estimate each quotient.

a) $3.2 \div 0.4$ **b)** $2.95 \div 0.5$

3. Calculate.

a) $1.65 \div 0.3$ **b)** $4.59 \div 0.9$

B Practising

4. Calculate using mental math or a diagram.

a) $3.6 \div 0.4$ **b)** $2.8 \div 0.4$ **c)** $2.5 \div 0.5$ **d)** $12.4 \div 0.3$

5. Calculate.

a) $2.7 \div 0.45$
b) $3.1 \div 0.05$
c) $10.2 \div 0.14$
d) $14.8 \div 0.18$
e) $0.27 \div 0.04$
f) $1028.34 \div 0.45$

6. Xavier has 8.75 m of rope. He wants to divide it into equal pieces. How many pieces will there be if the pieces are each length below?

a) 0.7 m **b)** half a metre

7. How many 0.35 L glasses can you fill with a 1.65 L bottle of water?

8. Snails travel about 0.013 m each second. A football field is 100.06 m long. How long would a snail take to travel the length of a football field?

9. A small box of craft beads holds 0.44 kg of beads. How many small boxes could you fill with 5.06 kg of beads?

10. Suppose that one side of a die is 0.9 cm. How many dice could you fit in a box with a volume of 36.45 cm^3? Remember that all the sides of a die have the same dimensions.

11. Why is the result for $1.25 \div 0.01$ the same as the result for 1.25×100?

12. Suppose that you divide 2.34 by a decimal less than 1. What do you know about the answer?

3.7 Dividing by Numbers Greater than 1

YOU WILL NEED
- a calculator
- pencil crayons
- a 10 × 10 grid

Divide by decimals greater than 1.

LEARN ABOUT the Math

Max has a piece of lumber that is 2.4 m long. He must cut it into five equal pieces.

How long will each piece of lumber be?

A. Estimate how long each piece will be.

B. Figure out how long each piece will be, using a number line.

Reflecting

C. What strategies did you use to solve this problem?

D. Why is the quotient when you divide by 0.7 greater than if you divide by 1?

E. How did estimating help you check your answer to part B?

WORK WITH the Math

Example 1 | Dividing decimals using base ten blocks

Yan is making a workbench. For the top of the workbench, she plans to use a sheet of wood that has an area of 3.64 m^2 and a width of 1.4 m. How long will the top of the workbench be?

Yan's Solution

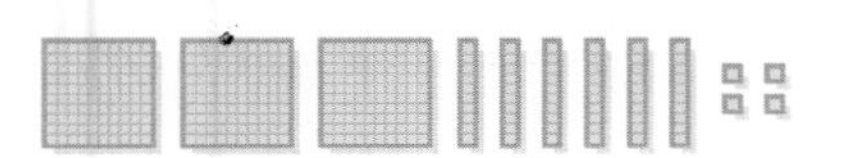

I used base ten blocks to represent the area. The area is 3.64 m^2. I let a flat represent 1 whole.

I knew that 3 flats equal 3 wholes, 6 rods equal 6 tenths, and 4 small cubes equal 4 hundredths.

1.4 m

I needed to arrange the blocks to form a rectangle with a width of 1.4.
I used 1 rod and 4 small cubes to represent the width.

2.6 m

1.4 m

The length of the rectangle was 2 flats and 6 rods, so the top of the workbench will be 2.6 m long.

I arranged the other blocks to complete the rectangle. I needed to regroup some of the blocks. 1 flat became 10 rods, and 2 rods became 20 small cubes. The length is equal to the area divided by the width: $3.64 \div 1.4 = 2.6$.

Example 2 | Dividing decimals using a calculator

The parking lot behind a family restaurant is 91.8 m long. Each parking space is 3.4 m wide. How many cars does the lot hold?

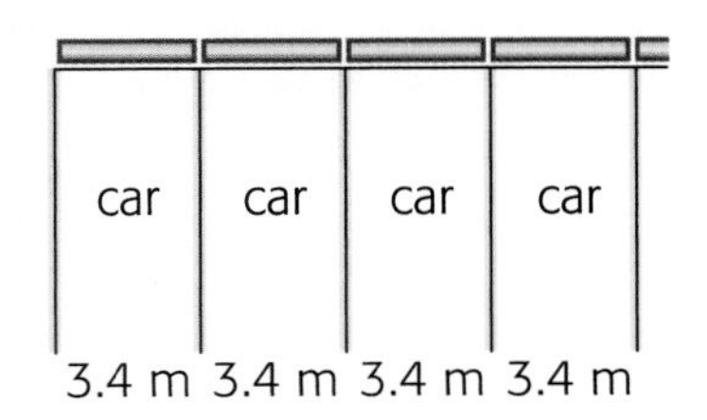

Liam's Solution

I needed to calculate $91.8 \div 3.4$.

The number of spaces is the same as the number of cars the lot will hold. I needed to determine how many 3.4 m spaces are in 91.8 m. That's a division problem.

$91.8 \div 3.4$ is about $90 \div 3 = 30$.
The lot will hold about 30 cars.

I estimated first.

9 1 . 8 [÷] 3 . 4 [=]

The lot will hold 27 cars.

I calculated $91.8 \div 3.4$ on my calculator.
The answer is close to my estimate, so it is reasonable.

Example 3 | Placing a decimal point in a quotient

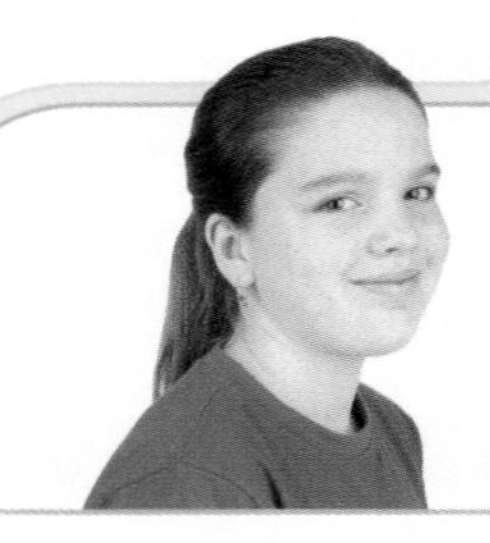

Place the decimal point correctly in this quotient.
11.907 ÷ 2.1 = 567

Julie's Solution

Estimate the quotient. 11.907 ÷ 2.1 is about 12 ÷ 2 = 6.	The decimal point could go in many places. The answer is probably 0.567, 5.67, or 56.7, however. Estimating helps me decide which choice is reasonable.
The product must be 5.67.	5.67 is closer to the estimate of 6 than any other possible number.

A Checking

1. Place the decimal point correctly in each quotient.

a) 5.7 ÷ 1.9 = 30 **b)** 13.2 ÷ 2.4 = 55

2. Calculate. Describe which strategy you used.

a) 2.369 ÷ 1.03 **b)** 50.50 ÷ 5.05

3. Reece worked 13 h at the deli last week. His pay cheque for the week was $97.50. How much is he paid for each hour of work?

B Practising

4. Calculate.

a) 3.6 ÷ 1.2
b) 5.35 ÷ 2.14
c) 2.25 ÷ 0.15
d) 9.72 ÷ 2.7

5. Predict the order of the six quotients from least to greatest. Calculate to test your prediction.

a) 8.4 ÷ 2.4
b) 3.13 ÷ 3.13
c) 10.2 ÷ 1.5
d) 14.04 ÷ 3.12
e) 89.688 ÷ 4.04
f) 3286.976 ÷ 147.2

6. Estimate to check each answer. Correct each incorrect answer.

a) 4.1 ÷ 2.4 = 1.75
b) 6.72 ÷ 2.10 = 3.20
c) 7.12 ÷ 1.20 = 60.0
d) 1.48 ÷ 3.70 = 0.04

7. Kim has \$11.50 in coins. How many coins does she have if all of the \$11.50 is in each type of coin?

a) dimes **b)** nickels **c)** quarters **d)** pennies

8. Nathan has a rope that is 11.4 m long. He wants to divide it into equal pieces. How many equal pieces will there be if the pieces are each length below?

a) 80 cm **b)** 1.4 m **c)** 0.7 m **d)** half a metre

9. Suppose that milk is on sale for 87.5¢ for each litre. How many litres can you buy for \$20?

10. Susan earned \$191.25 last week. She was paid \$8.50 for each hour. How many hours did she work?

11. There are 18 erasers in a box. The total mass of the box of erasers is 229.85 g. The empty box has a mass of 4.85 g. What is the mass of one eraser?

12. The adult height of a man is about 1.19 times his height at age 12. The adult height of a woman is about 1.07 times her height at age 12. Predict how tall each person was at age 12.

a) a man who is 1.8 m tall

b) a woman who is 1.8 m tall

13. Kyle is filling his brother's wading pool. The pool holds 180 L of water, and the hose supplies water at 22.5 L for each minute. How long will it take to fill the pool? Answer to the nearest minute.

14. The mass of a carton of six pizza pockets is 952.0 g. The mass of the empty carton is 72.0 g. Determine the mass of one pizza pocket. Express your answer to three decimal places.

15. Create three division problems that involve decimals. Exchange problems with a classmate, and write the solutions.

16. Suppose that you divide 2.34 by a decimal greater than 1. What do you know about the answer?

3.8 Using the Order of Operations with Decimals

YOU WILL NEED
- a calculator

GOAL

Evaluate expressions using the order of operations.

LEARN ABOUT the Math

order of operations

a set of rules people use when calculating to get the same answer:
Rule 1: Do the operations in brackets first.
Rule 2: Divide and multiply from left to right.
Rule 3: Add and subtract from left to right.
Hint: To remember these rules, think of **BDMAS**: **B**rackets, **D**ivide and **M**ultiply, **A**dd and **S**ubtract.

Max and Fiona are putting wallpaper on one wall of a stage set. Fiona says, "To determine the area of wallpaper we need, we have to calculate $3.8 \times 2.8 - 1.2 \times 0.9$."

Max says, "So we need $3.8 \times 1.6 \times 0.9 = 5.5$ m^2 of wallpaper."

Fiona says, "I don't think that's right. We have to use the correct **order of operations.**"

What area of wallpaper do they need?

Example 1 | Calculating using order of operations

Calculate the area of wallpaper Max and Fiona need.

Fiona's Solution

Area of wallpaper
= area of wall – area of window
= $(3.8 \times 2.8) - (1.2 \times 0.9)$

The area of wallpaper we need is the area of the wall minus the area of the window.
I used brackets to separate the two parts.

Area = $(3.8 \times 2.8) - (1.2 \times 0.9)$
= $10.64 - 1.08$
= 9.56
We need 9.56 m^2 of wallpaper.

I calculated the products in **B**rackets first. They were both **M**ultiplication. There was no **D**ivision or **A**ddition, so I **S**ubtracted from left to right next.

Reflecting

A. Explain why Max calculated the answer the way he did. Why was his calculation wrong?

B. Use the expression $3.2 + 1.5 \times 3.7$ to explain why it is important to have a set of rules for the order of operations that everyone uses.

WORK WITH the Math

Example 2 | Using the rules for the order of operations

Evaluate $32.28 - (1.2 \div 4 + 3.2)$.

Solution

$32.28 - (\underline{1.2 \div 4} + 3.2)$
$= 32.28 - (\underline{0.3 + 3.2})$

Sometimes it helps to underline the operation you need to do in each step. Do the operations inside the brackets first. Divide, and then add.

$= 32.28 - (3.5)$
$= 28.78$

Now do the operations outside the brackets.

Example 3 | Writing an expression with numbers

Write the following word expression as a numerical expression:
Multiply 4.1 by 6. Subtract 2. Divide by 4.

Solution

"Multiply 4.1 by 6" is 4.1×6.	Consider each part separately.
"Subtract 2." $4.1 \times 6 - 2$	Just subtract 2.
"Divide by 4." $(4.1 \times 6 - 2) \div 4$	Brackets are necessary. Without brackets, the expression would be "Multiply 4.1 by 6. Divide 2 by 4. Subtract the result from the product of 4.1 and 6." This is not the same.

A Checking

1. Calculate $15 - 12.6 \div 3 \times 2 - 1.5$ using the order of operations.

2. Which of the following expressions will give the same answer as the expression in question 1?

A. $(15 - 12.6) \div 3 \times 2 - 1.5$
B. $15 - 12.6 \div 3 \times (2 - 1.5)$
C. $15 - 12.6 \div (3 \times 2 - 1.5)$
D. $15 - (12.6 \div 3) \times 2 - 1.5$

3. Calculate.

a) $(4.8 \times 4.8) - 15.02$
b) $7.12 - (4.8 - 2 \times 2)$

B Practising

4. Is each calculation correct? If not, correct it. Show your work.

a) $12 \times 0.8 + 3 = 12.6$
b) $12 + 0.8 \times 3 = 38.4$
c) $5.6 \times 5.6 + 5 - 4.2 \div 2 = 16.08$
d) $6.3 + 5 \times 5 - 4.2 \times 3 = 81.3$
e) $4.2 \times 7 - 10.4 \div 2 + 2.9 \times 3 = 32.9$

5. Press these keys on your calculator:
3 . 8 [×] 2 . 8 [−] 1 . 4 [×] 0 . 9
Does your calculator follow the rules for order of operations? How do you know?

6.

Word expression	Numerical expression
Multiply 6.2 by 2, add 5.8 to this number, and divide the sum by 2.	$6.2 \times 2 + 5.8 \div 2$

a) Explain how the word expression and the numerical expression are different.
b) How can you change the numerical expression to match the word expression?
c) Evaluate the word expression.

7. Evaluate. Show your work.
a) $3.5 \times 10 + 10 \times 3.2$
b) $10.9 + (3.3 \times 3.3 - 1.69) \div 3 - 5.2$
c) $4.2 + 3.1 \times 6.5 \times (4.2 + 5.8)$
d) $6.1 \times (3.3 - 1.1 \times 3) + 8 \div 8$

8. Each solution has one error. Find the error and correct it. Explain what you did.
a)
$$\begin{aligned} 4.2 \times 4.2 - 5 \times 3 &= 17.64 - 5 \times 3 \\ &= 12.64 \times 3 \\ &= 37.92 \end{aligned}$$
b)
$$\begin{aligned} 5.5 - 2.5 \div 0.5 + 3.1 \times 2 + 6 &= 3.0 \div 0.5 + 3.1 \times 2 + 6 \\ &= 6 + 3.1 \times 2 + 6 \\ &= 9.1 \times 2 + 6 \\ &= 18.2 + 6 \\ &= 24.2 \end{aligned}$$

9. Write a numerical expression for each word expression.
a) Add 5.2 to 8.6. Multiply by 6.2.
b) Add 5.24 to 8.6. Multiply by 6. Subtract 5.2.
c) Divide 9.6 by 3.2. Multiply by 6.1. Subtract 8.5.

10. Explain why there are three rules for the order of operations, but there are five letters in BDMAS.

3.9 Expressing Fractions as Decimals

YOU WILL NEED

- a calculator

Use division to express fractions as decimals.

LEARN ABOUT the Math

Julie and her friends are going on a hike. Julie buys 2 kg of trail mix to share.

How much trail mix will each hiker receive?

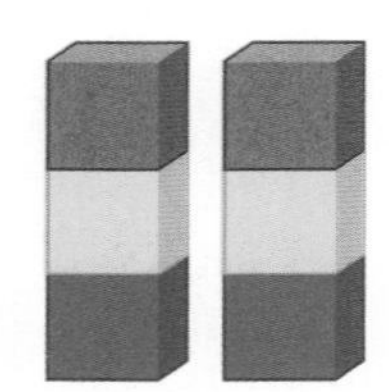

A. Suppose that there are three hikers. How can you use these linking cubes to show that each hiker will get $\frac{2}{3}$ of a kilogram of trail mix?

B. Write a division sentence to describe how each share can be calculated.

C. Calculate $2.000 \div 3$ using pencil and paper. What do you notice about the remainder after each step?

D. When you calculate $2 \div 3$ on your calculator, why does the display show 0.66666667 rather than the **repeating decimal** 0.6666 …, which is the actual answer?

E. Suppose that a different number of hikers go on the hike. Each hiker will receive an equal share of the 2 kg of trail mix. Complete the table on the next page. Write enough digits so that you can either see a pattern or see all the digits if the decimal is **terminating.**

repeating decimal

a decimal in which a block of one or more digits eventually repeats in a pattern; for example, $\frac{25}{99}$ = 0.252 525 ..., $\frac{31}{36}$ = 0.861 111 ..., and $\frac{1}{7}$ = 0.142 857 142 857 .... The dots mean that the numbers continue in the same pattern without stopping.

terminating decimal

a decimal that is complete after a certain number of digits with no repetition; for example, 0.777

Number of hikers	Mass of trail mix each hiker receives (kg)	
	As a fraction	As a decimal
1	$\frac{2}{1}$	
2	$\frac{2}{2}$	
3	$\frac{2}{3}$	
4		
5		
6		
7		
8		
9		
10		

Communication | *Tip*

Some repeating decimals have large groups of repeating digits. This makes them awkward to write out. Instead of writing the repeating digits several times, we use a horizontal bar to mark them. This is called bar notation. For example, write 0.143 514 351 435 … as $0.1\overline{435}$, and write 0.999 … as $0.\overline{9}$.

Reflecting

F. Why can a terminating decimal always be written over a multiple of 10, such as $\frac{■}{10}$, $\frac{■}{100}$, or $\frac{■}{1000}$?

G. Why can't $\frac{1}{3}$ be written in the form $\frac{■}{10}$ or $\frac{■}{100}$? Why can't it be a terminating decimal?

H. Why do you divide the numerator by the denominator to write a fraction as a decimal?

I. Why can a fraction such as $\frac{1}{8}$ or $\frac{1}{25}$ be written as an equivalent fraction with a denominator of 1000?

WORK WITH the Math

Example 1 | Comparing using equivalent decimals

Nolan has three bags of popcorn to share with seven friends. Fiona has four bags of popcorn to share with eight friends. The bags of popcorn are all the same size. Which group will receive larger portions?

Nolan's Solution

3 bags shared among 8 people is $\frac{3}{8}$.
4 bags shared among 9 people is $\frac{4}{9}$.

I included myself and Fiona in our groups. I calculated the size of each share in bags for both groups.
I knew that I could compare these numbers more easily by writing them as decimals.

$3 \div 8 = 0.375$ bags
$4 \div 9 = 0.\overline{4}$ bags

I used my calculator and divided the numerator in each fraction by its denominator.

$0.\overline{4} > 0.375$
Fiona's friends will receive the larger portions.

$0.\overline{4}$ is greater than 0.4, and 0.375 is less than 0.4.

Example 2 | Determining whether a decimal repeats

Determine whether the decimal equivalent of each fraction terminates or repeats. Order the fractions from least to greatest.

a) $\frac{2}{10}$ **b)** $\frac{7}{9}$ **c)** $\frac{8}{42}$ **d)** $\frac{53}{80}$

Max's Solution

If a decimal terminates, I will be able to express it as an equivalent fraction with a denominator that is a multiple of 10, such as 10, 100, or 1000.

a) $\frac{2}{10} = 0.2$; terminates

$\frac{2}{10}$ is already in this form, so I know that it terminates.

b) $\frac{7}{9} = 0.777 \ldots$; repeats

I know that $\frac{1}{9} = 0.111 \ldots$, so I know that $\frac{7}{9}$ must be 7 times as much.

c) $\frac{8}{42} = \frac{4}{21}$; repeats

Since 7 is a factor of 21, but 7 is not a factor of a multiple of 10, such as 1000 or 10 000, the decimal repeats.

I can rewrite $\frac{8}{42}$ as $\frac{4}{21}$. I tried to write $\frac{4}{21} = \frac{\blacksquare}{100}$, but there is no whole number I can multiply 21 by to get 100. I couldn't write the fraction as $\frac{\blacksquare}{1000}$ either.

d) $\frac{53}{80} = \frac{6625}{10\,000}$ or 0.6625; terminates

I tried writing $\frac{53}{80} = \frac{\blacksquare}{100}$, but this didn't work since $100 \div 80$ is not a whole number. Then I tried $\frac{53}{80} = \frac{\blacksquare}{1000}$. This didn't work either. I tried one more time. This worked because $80 = 8 \times 10$ and $10\,000 = 8 \times 125 \times 10$.

I checked my predictions with a calculator.

a) $\frac{2}{10} = 0.2$

b) $\frac{7}{9} = 0.\overline{7}$

c) $\frac{8}{42} = 0.\overline{190\,476}$

d) $\frac{53}{80} = 0.6625$

I was right!

$0.\overline{190\,476}$, 0.2, 0.6625, $0.\overline{7}$

I ordered the decimals from least to greatest.

$\frac{8}{42}, \frac{2}{10}, \frac{53}{80}, \frac{7}{9}$

Then I ordered the fractions from least to greatest.

A Checking

1. Write each repeating decimal in bar notation.

a) 0.555 555 555 … **b)** 0.134 561 345 613 456 …

2. Compare each pair of fractions using equivalent decimals. Replace each ■ with >, <, or =.

a) $\frac{5}{16} \blacksquare \frac{2}{9}$ **b)** $\frac{7}{11} \blacksquare \frac{5}{8}$ **c)** $\frac{17}{20} \blacksquare \frac{11}{14}$

B Practising

3. Decide whether the decimal equivalent of each fraction terminates or repeats.

a) $\frac{3}{4}$ **b)** $\frac{5}{9}$ **c)** $\frac{9}{14}$ **d)** $\frac{19}{20}$

4. Write each decimal as a fraction.

a) 0.1625 **b)** 0.8550

5. If possible, write each fraction as a terminating decimal.

a) $\frac{14}{25}$ **b)** $\frac{5}{8}$ **c)** $\frac{1}{16}$ **d)** $\frac{4}{5}$ **e)** $\frac{19}{20}$ **f)** $\frac{22}{32}$

6. If possible, write each fraction as a repeating decimal.

a) $\frac{1}{6}$ **b)** $\frac{8}{9}$ **c)** $\frac{7}{11}$ **d)** $\frac{7}{15}$ **e)** $\frac{48}{49}$ **f)** $\frac{57}{111}$

7. Sort the fractions based on whether they are equivalent to a terminating decimal or a repeating decimal.

a) $\frac{4}{9}$ **b)** $\frac{3}{5}$ **c)** $\frac{5}{6}$ **d)** $\frac{15}{16}$ **e)** $\frac{5}{18}$ **f)** $\frac{19}{32}$

8. Order the fractions in question 7 from least to greatest.

9. a) Describe the following fraction pattern: $\frac{8}{9}, \frac{8}{99}, \frac{8}{999}, \ldots$. Write the next three fractions in the pattern.

b) Rewrite the pattern using decimal equivalents for each of the six fractions.

c) Describe the decimal pattern. Is the decimal pattern easier or harder to describe than the fraction pattern?

10. Express each fraction as a repeating decimal.

a) $\frac{1}{7}$ **b)** $\frac{2}{7}$ **c)** $\frac{3}{7}$

11. **a)** Describe a pattern in your answers for the previous question.

b) Predict the decimal equivalents of $\frac{4}{7}$ and $\frac{5}{7}$.

12. Replace each ▒ with >, <, or =.

a) 0.2 ▒ $0.\overline{2}$

b) $\frac{45}{99}$ ▒ $0.\overline{45}$

c) $0.\overline{82}$ ▒ $\frac{4}{5}$

d) $\frac{6}{11}$ ▒ $\frac{7}{13}$

e) 0.357 357 357 … ▒ $0.\overline{375}$

f) $\frac{2}{3}$ ▒ 0.633

13. Order the numbers from least to greatest.

a) $\frac{1}{8}$, $\frac{5}{7}$, 0.35, $0.\overline{39}$, $\frac{9}{10}$

b) 0.56, $0.5\overline{6}$, $0.\overline{56}$, $\frac{5}{9}$, $\frac{27}{50}$

14. Predict the decimal equivalent of each fraction, using the fact that $\frac{1}{3} = 0.333....$

a) $\frac{2}{3}$ **b)** $\frac{1}{9}$ **c)** $\frac{1}{30}$ **d)** $\frac{4}{3}$

15. Calculate the decimal equivalent of each fraction.

a) $\frac{1}{12}$ **b)** $\frac{1}{28}$ **c)** $\frac{1}{44}$ **d)** $\frac{1}{52}$

16. Look at your answers for the previous question.

a) How are the decimal equivalents alike?

b) What do the denominators have in common?

17. The cost of a new toy is $1 after taxes. You and two friends want to split the cost evenly.

a) Express each person's share as a fraction.

b) Express the fraction as a decimal.

c) How much should each of you pay? Explain your decision.

d) Create a similar problem with a different fraction and solve it.

18. How can you tell, without calculating, that the decimal equivalent of $\frac{1}{33}$ repeats?

3.10 Expressing Decimals as Fractions

YOU WILL NEED

- a calculator

Write decimals as fractions.

LEARN ABOUT the Math

Fiona says, "I know how to write a fraction as a decimal. I wonder how I can write a decimal as a fraction."

How can you write a repeating decimal as a fraction?

A. Calculate each fraction as a repeating decimal: $\frac{1}{9}, \frac{2}{9}, \frac{3}{9}, \frac{4}{9}$.

B. How could the decimal for $\frac{1}{9}$ have helped you predict the decimals for $\frac{2}{9}, \frac{3}{9}$, and $\frac{4}{9}$?

C. Calculate each fraction as a repeating decimal: $\frac{1}{99}, \frac{5}{99}, \frac{10}{99}, \frac{15}{99}$.

D. How could the decimal for $\frac{1}{99}$ have helped you predict the decimals for $\frac{5}{99}, \frac{10}{99}$, and $\frac{15}{99}$?

E. Predict the decimal equivalent for $\frac{1}{999}$.

F. How could you use what you have just learned to write $0.\overline{123}$ as a fraction?

Reflecting

G. Explain how to convert a repeating decimal to a fraction.

WORK WITH the Math

Example 1 | Expressing some decimals as fractions

Julie forgot her lunch. Yan offered Julie 0.35 of her sandwich. Fiona offered Julie $\frac{1}{3}$ of her sandwich. Who offered more?

Yan's Solution

$0.35 = \frac{35}{100}$

Since 0.35 is 35 hundredths, I wrote 0.35 as $\frac{35}{100}$.

$\frac{35}{100} = \frac{105}{300}$ (×3 in numerator and denominator)

I wanted to compare the two numbers, so I wrote the fractions with the same denominator. I chose a denominator of 300. I multiplied the numerator and the denominator of $\frac{35}{100}$ by 3.

$\frac{1}{3} = \frac{100}{300}$ (×100 in numerator and denominator)

I wrote $\frac{1}{3}$ as an equivalent fraction with a denominator of 300. To do this, I multiplied both the numerator and the denominator by 100.

$\frac{105}{300} > \frac{100}{300}$

$0.35 > \frac{1}{3}$. I offered more.

I compared the fractions.
105 is greater than 100, so $\frac{105}{300}$ is greater than $\frac{100}{300}$.

Example 2 | Writing a repeating decimal as a fraction

Explain how you know that the fraction for $0.\overline{123}$ is greater than the fraction for 0.123.

Liam's Solution

$0.\overline{123} = \frac{123}{999}$ $\quad 0.123 = \frac{123}{1000}$

I wrote the fraction equivalent for each decimal.

$\frac{123}{999} > \frac{123}{1000}$

$\frac{1}{999}$ is greater than $\frac{1}{1000}$.

The fraction for $0.\overline{123}$ is greater than the fraction for 0.123.

Example 3 | Writing a repeating decimal as a fraction

How do you know that $0.\overline{24} = \frac{24}{99}$?

Max's Solution

$0.\overline{01} \times 24 = 0.\overline{24}$

I know that $\frac{1}{99} = 0.\overline{01}$, so $\frac{24}{99}$ is 24 times as much.
I multiplied each $0.\overline{01}$ part by 24.

A Checking

1. Write each decimal as a fraction.

a) 0.162 **b)** 0.0777… **c)** 0.272 727…

2. Write each decimal as a fraction. Then replace each ■ with <, >, or =.

a) $0.375 \ ■ \ \frac{1}{4}$ **b)** $0.23 \ ■ \ \frac{1}{7}$ **c)** $0.844 \ ■ \ \frac{22}{25}$

B Practising

3. Write each decimal as a fraction.

a) $0.\overline{14}$ **c)** 0.0777… **e)** 0.272 727…
b) $0.\overline{273}$ **d)** $4.\overline{17}$ **f)** $0.\overline{767}$

4. Replace each ■ with <, >, or =.

a) $0.416 \ ■ \ \frac{1}{4}$ **c)** $0.\overline{6} \ ■ \ \frac{2}{3}$
b) $0.52 \ ■ \ \frac{1}{2}$ **d)** $0.6 \ ■ \ \frac{2}{3}$

5. Match each fraction with its decimal equivalent.

A. $\frac{4}{7}$ **B.** $\frac{7}{13}$ **C.** $\frac{6}{11}$ **D.** $\frac{2}{21}$

a) $0.\overline{54}$ **b)** $0.\overline{095\,238}$ **c)** $0.\overline{571\,428}$ **d)** $0.\overline{538\,461}$

6. Explain how you know, without using a calculator, that $0.\overline{45}$ is greater than $\frac{9}{20}$.

7. Describe how to write a terminating decimal as a fraction. Give an example.

MATH GAME

Race to 50

YOU WILL NEED
- a deck of 30 cards (3 of each of the digits from 0 to 9)

The goal of this game is to create and multiply decimals to get the greatest product.

Number of payers: 2 or more

How to Play

1. One player shuffles the cards and deals 3 cards to each player.
2. Players use two of their cards to create a decimal that is less than 1.
3. Players then multiply their decimal by the digit on the third card as a one-digit decimal. The digit in the hundredths place of the product is their score for the round.
4. The game continues, with players adding their score for each round to their score for the previous round. The first player to reach 50 points wins.

Yan's Turn

My cards were 7, 9, and 4.
I could multiply $0.49 \times 0.7 = 0.343$.
The answer is 0.343, so I'd get 4 points.
Or, I could multiply $0.97 \times 0.4 = 0.388$.
The answer is 0.388, so I'd get 8 points.
I'll choose the second way, because this gives me more points.

CURIOUS MATH

Repeating Decimal Patterns

Denis noticed that the decimal equivalent of $\frac{1}{13}$ is $0.\overline{076\ 923}$. He put pairs of digits from the decimal into a table. He chose the second digit in the repeat for the *y*-value. Then he plotted the points, starting with (0, 7). Then he connected the points in the order he plotted them. He joined the last point with the first point he plotted.

x	*y*
0	7
7	6
6	9
9	2
2	3
3	0

Denis did this for all the fractions from $\frac{1}{13}$ to $\frac{12}{13}$. All his graphs were one of two shapes. Here are the two shapes:

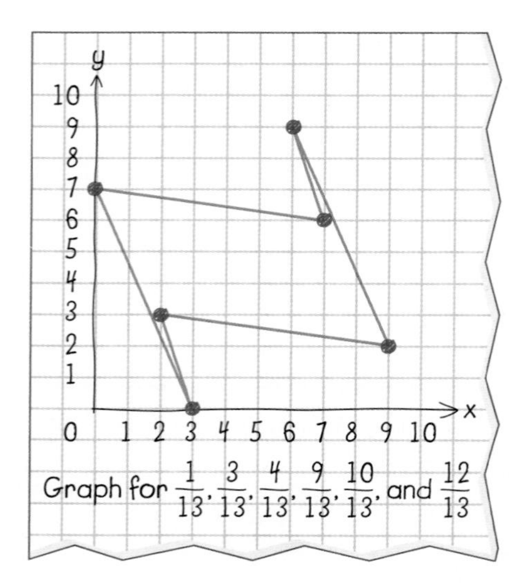

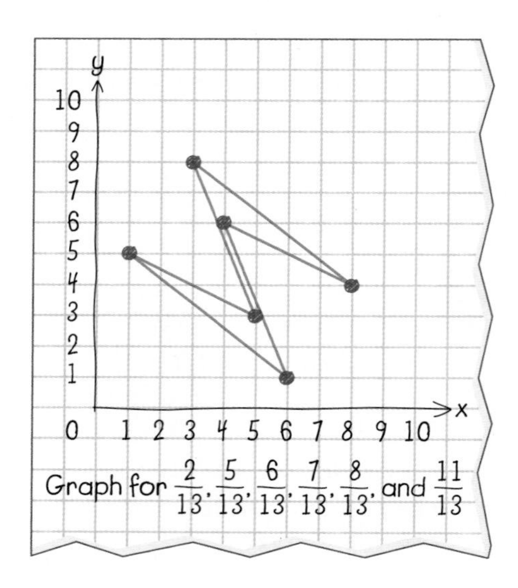

1. Choose one fraction family, such as $\frac{1}{7}, \frac{2}{7}, \ldots, \frac{6}{7}$ or $\frac{1}{14}, \frac{2}{14}, \ldots, \frac{13}{14}$. Write each fraction in the family as a repeating decimal.

2. Graph the pairs of digits in the repeating part of each decimal. Join the points in the order you plotted them.

3. How many different graphs did your fraction family have?

4. What shape of graph do you think you would get for a terminating decimal? (Hint: Recall that 0.375 = 0.375 000….)

Chapter Self-Test

1. Calculate.
   a) $2.14 + 3.72 + 8.93$
   b) $2.032 + 6.352 + 9.986$
   c) $0.69 + 3.13$
   d) $765.43 + 21.2$
2. Replace each ▒ with >, <, or =.
   a) $29.35 - 22.65$ ▒ $44.65 - 39.35$
   b) $9.302 - 6.603$ ▒ $3.695 - 0.385$
3. Ethan has \$2.65, Hannah has \$4.25, and Sybil has \$3.25. They need \$4.95 to rent a video. How many videos can they rent?
4. Jason bought 0.7 kg of tomatoes. The tomatoes sell for \$1.96 for each kilogram. How much did he pay?
5. Calculate.
   a) 1.38×2.7
   b) 2.43×9.15
   c) 18.4×6.55
   d) 69.207×41.5
6. Susan's mother filled her car's gas tank at the gas station. She bought 48.3 L, and her bill was \$37.43. What was the price of the gas in cents for each litre?
7. Calculate.
   a) $6.4 \div 1.6$
   b) $56.482 \div 6.4$
8. Predict whether the decimal equivalent of each fraction will terminate or repeat.
   a) $\frac{17}{20}$ b) $\frac{11}{16}$ c) $\frac{67}{99}$ d) $\frac{2}{7}$
9. Write each fraction in the previous question as a decimal.
10. Write each decimal as a fraction in lowest terms.
    a) 0.66 b) $1.\overline{3}$ c) 256.895 d) $73.\overline{25}$

What Do You Think Now?

Revisit What Do You Think? on page 99. How have your answers and explanations changed?

Chapter Review

Frequently Asked Questions

Q: How do you divide a decimal by a decimal?

A1: You can use a number line. For example, to divide 2.5 by 0.5, use a number line from 0 to 2.5. Count how many 0.5s are on the number line. There are five 0.5s, so $2.5 \div 0.5 = 5$.

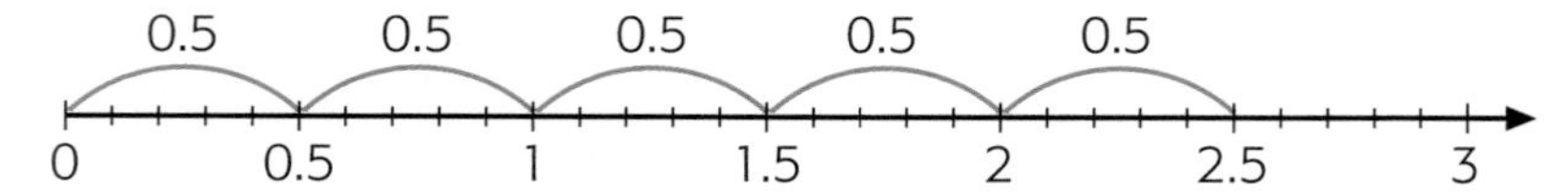

A2: You can use 10×10 grids. For example, to divide 2.5 by 0.4, colour three 10×10 grids to model 2.5. There are 6 sections that represent 0.4, and there are 10 squares left over. Since 10 squares are another fourth of a group, they represent 0.25. So $2.5 \div 0.4 = 6.25$.

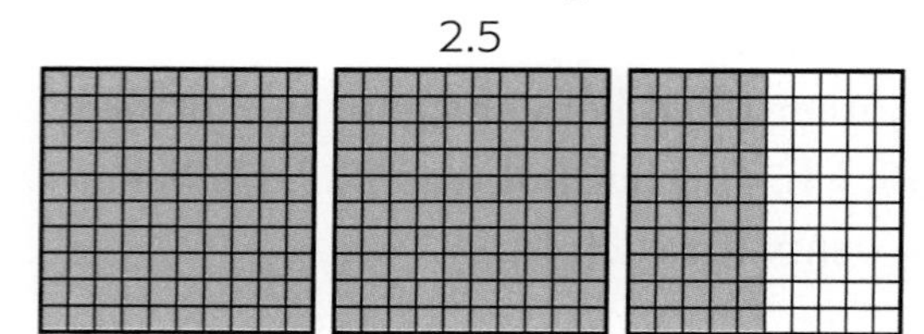

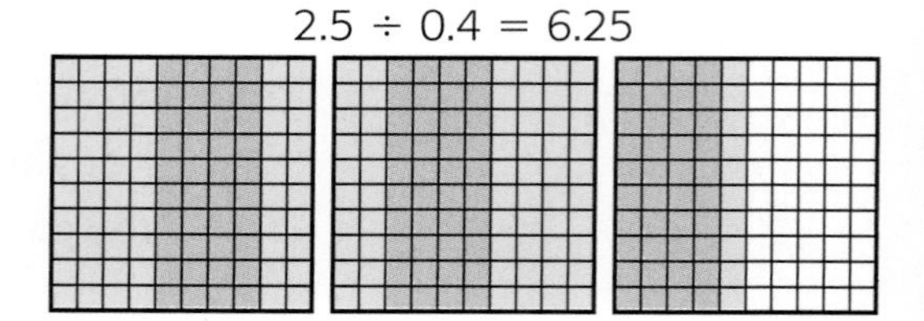

Q: How can you write a fraction as a decimal?

A: You can divide the numerator by the denominator. For example, the decimal equivalent of $\frac{1}{8}$ is 0.125.

1 [÷] 8 [=] 0.125

Q: How can you write a decimal as a fraction?

A: If the decimal terminates, use the decimal as the numerator and a number such as 10, 100, or 1000 as the denominator. For example, the fraction equivalent of 0.42 is $\frac{42}{100}$. If the decimal repeats, use the repeating part as the numerator and a number such as 9, 99, or 999 as the denominator. For example, the fraction equivalent of $0.\overline{42}$ is $\frac{42}{99}$.

Practice

Lesson 3.2

1. Calculate.

a) $3.5 + 370.6$ **b)** $642.13 + 291.89$

2. Six students are holding hands to make the longest line they can. Their arm spans are 1.61 m, 1.66 m, 1.63 m, 1.72 m, 1.78 m, and 1.75 m. How long is their line?

3. Estimate, and then subtract.

a) $39.8 - 12.6$ **b)** $26.32 - 19.56$

4. Calculate.

a) $57.68 - 39.39$ **b)** $46.231 - 16.332$

5. An elevator can hold 650.0 kg. Three people moving a piano have masses of 80.5 kg, 72.8 kg, and 89.9 kg. The piano has a mass of 352.5 kg. Will the elevator hold the people and the piano?

Lesson 3.3

6. Calculate each product. Explain which strategy you used.

a) 9×0.8 **b)** 215×0.6 **c)** 57×0.4 **d)** 0.6×0.9

7. Mariette's table is 0.8 m long and 0.4 m wide. Julie's table is 0.9 m long and 0.3 m wide.

a) Estimate whose table has a bigger area. Explain your reasoning.

b) Calculate the answer, and compare it with your estimate.

8. You want to multiply two decimals that are both less than 1. What do you know about the answer?

Lesson 3.4

9. A single bus fare costs $2.35. A monthly pass costs $45.75.

a) Céline estimates that she will ride the bus 25 times this month. Should she buy a monthly pass? Explain.

b) Kamal estimates that he will ride the bus 18 times this month. Should he buy a monthly pass? Explain.

10. Karen mixed together three 1.36 L cartons of orange juice, two 0.59 L bottles of ginger ale, and 2.52 L of fruit juice. How much punch did Karen make?

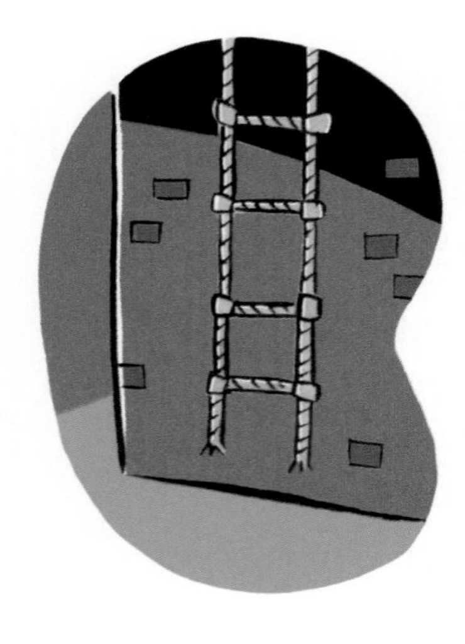

Lesson 3.6

11. The rungs of a rope ladder are 0.3 m apart. Rapunzel is climbing down the ladder from a window that is 3.69 m above ground. How many rungs will Rapunzel climb down?

12. You have a string that is 25.50 m long. You need to cut the string into 0.25 m pieces. Estimate how many pieces you can cut. How did you estimate?

Lesson 3.7

13. Predict the order of the four quotients from least to greatest. Calculate to check your prediction.

a) $36.9 \div 3$
b) $121.5 \div 12.1$
c) $0.6 \div 0.2$
d) $9.2 \div 3.1$

14. A stack of 50 sheets of paper is 0.85 cm high. How many sheets of paper are in a stack that is 48.45 cm high?

15. Estimate $1035.75 \div 24.5$. Check your estimate.

Lesson 3.8

16. Estimate, and then calculate.

a) $(2.6 \times 6) + 25 - (3.2 \times 2.1)$
b) $(6.9 \div 3) + (4.6 \times 0.23)$

Lesson 3.9

17. Write a fraction, in lowest terms, for each decimal.

a) 0.8 **b)** 0.735 **c)** 0.92 **d)** 0.250

18. Does the decimal equivalent of each fraction terminate or repeat?

a) $\frac{11}{25}$ **b)** $\frac{5}{6}$ **c)** $\frac{13}{15}$ **d)** $\frac{3}{8}$

19. Write each fraction in the previous question as a decimal.

20. Order the following numbers from least to greatest:
$0.25, 0.2555 \ldots, 0.252\,525 \ldots, \frac{2}{9}, \frac{13}{15}$.

Lesson 3.10

21. Write the fraction equivalent of each decimal in lowest terms.

a) 0.63
b) $0.\overline{63}$

22. Create a problem in which you multiply and divide decimals. Explain your solution.

Chapter Task

Task | *Checklist*

✔ Did you record the real prices from stores or flyers?

✔ Did you show all your calculations?

✔ Did you explain your thinking?

Planning a Party

You are organizing a party for a sports team. There are 10 players and 2 coaches. Each player has contributed $15.75. You have set aside money to buy each coach a $15 gift certificate from a sports store. You also need to buy

- food for the main course
- drinks
- desserts
- a souvenir for each player

What food and souvenirs will you buy?

A. Determine the total amount of money that you have to spend.

B. Check stores or advertising flyers for prices.

C. Make three different menus for the main course. You need to have enough food to serve four people with each menu. Determine how much money you can spend on the main course, drinks, and dessert, and still have money for souvenirs.

D. Prepare a report. Include the following information:
- the food, drinks, and desserts you will buy; the cost of each food item or drink; and the total cost
- the souvenirs you will buy, the cost of each souvenir, and the total cost

Chapters 1–3

Cumulative **Review**

Note: Select ALL the correct answers to each question.

1. Which number is divisible by 10, 5, and 2?

A. 1168 **B.** 2035 **C.** 21 890 **D.** 35 572

2. The number 637▒16 is divisible by 4 and 8. What is ▒?

A. 2 **B.** 3 **C.** 5 **D.** 8

3. Which number is not a factor of 123 456?

A. 2 **B.** 3 **C.** 6 **D.** 9

4. Which number is a factor of 1235?

A. 2 **B.** 5 **C.** 4 **D.** 3

5. Which expression has a value that is between 0.5 and 1.5?

A. $\frac{1}{4} + \frac{1}{5}$ **B.** $\frac{8}{3} + \frac{1}{9}$ **C.** $1\frac{5}{7} - \frac{5}{7}$ **D.** $4\frac{3}{4} - 2\frac{7}{8}$

6. Which pairs of fractions can be renamed as twelfths?

A. $\frac{1}{2}, \frac{5}{6}$ **B.** $\frac{1}{3}, \frac{3}{4}$ **C.** $\frac{3}{7}, \frac{4}{5}$ **D.** $\frac{6}{7}, \frac{2}{3}$

7. Which expressions have a value that is a whole number?

A. $2\frac{1}{3} + 4\frac{4}{6}$ **B.** $4\frac{1}{5} - 1\frac{6}{5}$ **C.** $6\frac{2}{7} - 3\frac{4}{7}$ **D.** $5\frac{1}{3} + 3\frac{8}{9}$

8. Which equation is represented on the following number line?

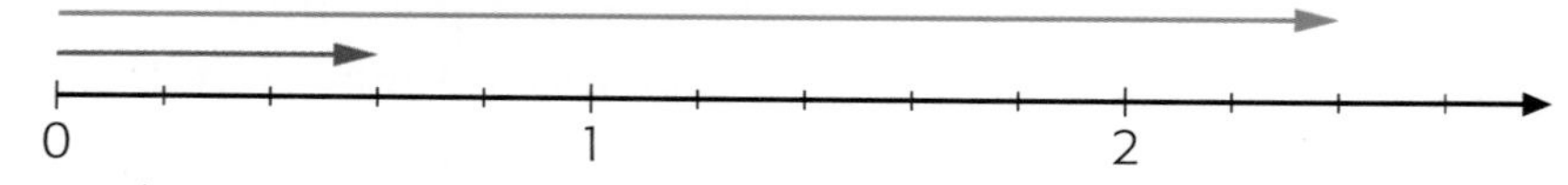

A. $2\frac{2}{5} - \frac{3}{5} = 1\frac{4}{5}$ **C.** $\frac{4}{5} + 1\frac{3}{5} = 2\frac{2}{5}$

B. $2\frac{2}{5} - 1\frac{3}{5} = \frac{4}{5}$ **D.** $2\frac{2}{5} + \frac{3}{5} = 3$

9. Which expressions have the same value as 0.5×750?

A. $750 \div 2$ **B.** 5×750 **C.** 5×75 **D.** 0.05×75

10. Which expressions have the same value as 12.8×48?

A. 128×4.8 **C.** $2 \times 6.4 \times 4 \times 12$

B. 64×9.6 **D.** 25.6×24

11. Jake takes 0.8 mL of medicine each day. The bottle contains 16 mL of medicine. In how many days will he finish his medicine?

A. 2 **B.** 20 **C.** 8 **D.** 10

12. How much of 124.345 is 12.4345?

A. one tenth **C.** one thousandth

B. one hundredth **D.** one ten-thousandth

13. Estimate to determine which value is the product of 0.7×8.987.

A. 62.909 **C.** 0.629 09

B. 6.2909 **D.** 629.09

14. Which value is the best estimate for $12.078 \div 0.498\ 01$?

A. 24 **B.** 240 **C.** 2400 **D.** 24 000

15. Which expression has a product that is greater than 56.8?

A. 1.089×56.8 **B.** $0.000\ 123 \times 56.8$

16. Which expressions have a quotient of 12.3?

A. $369 \div 30$ **B.** $369 \div 3$ **C.** $36.9 \div 3$ **D.** $3.69 \div 0.3$

17. What is the value of ■ in $11.9 - 3 \times 6.4 + 79.2 =$ ■?

A. 136.16 **B.** 761.84 **C.** 71.9 **D.** 966.304

18. Which decimal represents the same amount as $\frac{1}{8}$?

A. 1.25 **B.** 0.125 **C.** 0.0125 **D.** 0.1025

19. Which fraction represents the same amount as 0.6?

A. $\frac{6}{100}$ **B.** $\frac{3}{5}$ **C.** $\frac{6}{1000}$ **D.** $\frac{30}{60}$

20. Which fraction is equivalent to a repeating decimal?

A. $\frac{1}{84}$ **B.** $\frac{1}{20}$ **C.** $\frac{1}{50}$ **D.** $\frac{1}{500}$

Chapter 4

Percent

GOAL

You will be able to

- express percents as fractions and decimals
- solve percent problems by either estimating or calculating
- communicate effectively about percent problems

This is a photo of Yellowknife from the air. About how much of the city's area is used for roads and buildings? Use a percent.

Getting Started

YOU WILL NEED
- centimetre grid paper
- a calculator

Parts of a Whole

Some Canadian farmers build mazes in their cornfields to attract tourists. The following grid shows a plan for a simple maze in a square cornfield. The white squares are the paths.

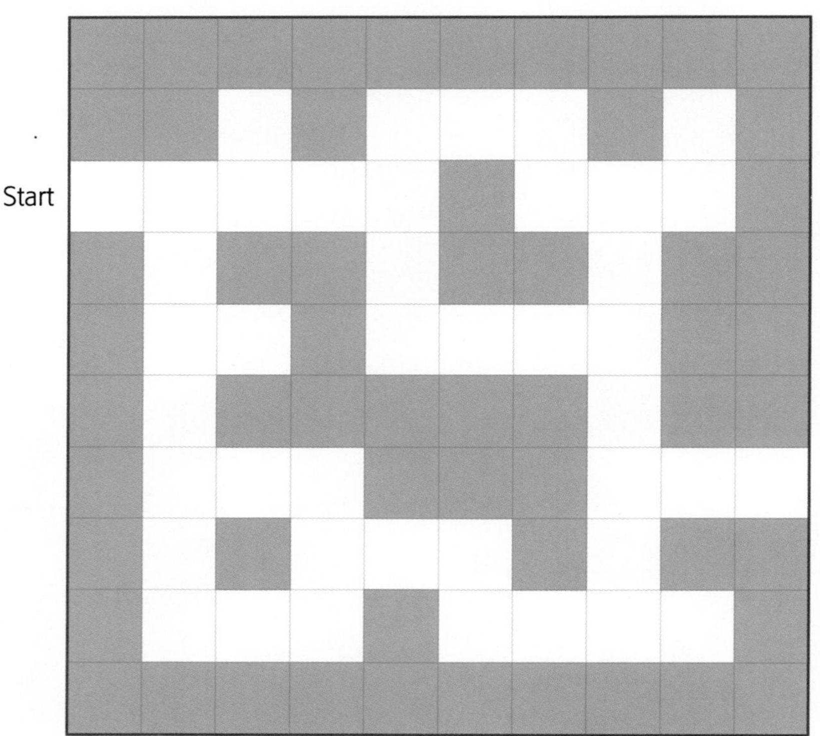

How can you describe paths in the maze using fractions, decimals, and percents?

A. What fraction of the square cornfield is used for the paths in the maze? Write an **equivalent** decimal.

B. What fraction of the cornfield is used for the corn? Write an equivalent decimal.

percent

a part to whole **ratio** that compares a number or an amount to 100; for example, $25\% = 25:100 = \frac{25}{100}$

ratio

a comparison of two quantities with the same units; for example, if you make juice using 1 can of concentrate and 3 cans of water, the ratio of concentrate to juice is 1:4, or 1 to 4

C. What **percent** of the cornfield is used for the paths?

D. What percent of the cornfield is used for the corn?

E. Copy the maze onto grid paper, and trace a path from Start to Finish.

F. Count the squares on your path. Express the area of your path as part of the total area of the cornfield using fractions, decimals, and percents.

G. Explain why the areas of the paths in the maze are easily expressed as fractions, decimals, and percents of the cornfield's total area.

What Do You Think?

Decide whether you agree or disagree with each statement. Be ready to explain your decision.

1. If you get a score of 72% on a test, you must have had 72 questions right.
2. Your legs make up about 40% of your height.
3. 10% of an amount of money is not very much.
4. You can compare fractions, decimals, and percents on a number line.

4.1 Percents as Fractions and Decimals

YOU WILL NEED
- grid paper
- a calculator

GOAL

Solve percent problems using equivalent fractions or decimals.

LEARN ABOUT the Math

48% of Nestor's class stay for lunch. Nestor wants to represent this percent on a 5×5 grid. He knows that he can easily show 48% on a 10×10 grid.

How many squares of the 5×5 grid should Nestor colour?

A. Write 48% as a fraction of 100 and as a decimal.

B. How could you rename your fraction in part A as an equivalent fraction to help you solve the problem?

C. How many of the 25 squares on Nestor's grid represent 48%?

Reflecting

D. How did renaming the percent help you solve the problem?

E. Why is it always easy to write a percent as a decimal?

WORK WITH the Math

Example 1 | Writing a percent as a fraction and a decimal

In Ashley's class, 75% of the students ride the bus to school. Write the number of students who ride the bus as a fraction in lowest terms and as a decimal.

Ashley's Solution

$75\% = \frac{75}{100}$

75% means 75 parts out of 100.

$\frac{75}{100} \underset{\div 25}{\overset{\div 25}{=}} \frac{3}{4}$

To rename $\frac{75}{100}$ as a fraction in lowest terms, I divided the numerator and the denominator by the same number. I know that $\frac{3}{4}$ is in lowest terms because 3 and 4 have no common factors.

$75\% = 0.75$

I can rename $\frac{75}{100}$ as 0.75.

Example 2 | Expressing a fraction as a percent

According to a school newspaper, $\frac{2}{5}$ of the 750 students in the school signed a petition for less homework. What percent of students signed the petition?

Pavlo's Solution

$\frac{2}{5} = \frac{4}{10}$

$\frac{4}{10} = \frac{40}{100}$

To write $\frac{2}{5}$ as a percent, I needed to rename $\frac{2}{5}$ as an equivalent fraction with a denominator of 100.

40% of students signed the petition.

I can rename $\frac{40}{100}$ as 40%.

$\frac{2}{5} < \frac{1}{2}$, so 40% seems reasonable.

I knew my answer must be less than 50%.

A Checking

1. Rename each percent as a fraction.

a) $24\% = \frac{\square}{50}$

b) $40\% = \frac{\square}{10}$

c) $50\% = \frac{\square}{20}$

d) $75\% = \frac{\square}{20}$

2. In Guilia's class, 36% of the students speak more than one language. Write the number of students who speak more than one language as a fraction in lowest terms.

B Practising

3. Rename each decimal as a fraction.

a) $0.10 = \frac{\square}{10}$

b) $0.34 = \frac{\square}{50}$

c) $0.33 = \frac{\square}{100}$

d) $0.2 = \frac{\square}{5}$

4. In Eric's class, 35% of the students have blond hair. Write the number of students with blond hair as a fraction in lowest terms.

5. Write each percent as a fraction in lowest terms.

a) 22% **b)** 5% **c)** 30% **d)** 72%

6. Write each percent as a decimal.

a) 3% **b)** 94% **c)** 100% **d)** 40%

7. Complete this table.

Percent	Decimal	Fraction in lowest terms
60%		
	0.09	
		$\frac{3}{100}$
44%		
		$\frac{6}{25}$
	0.5	
		$\frac{3}{3}$
12%		

8. Match each percent to the figure that represents it.

a) 50% **b)** 75% **c)** 25% **d)** 40%

A. **B.**  **C.** 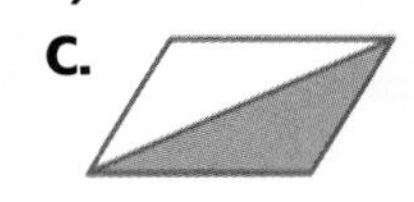 **D.** 

9. Claudia's new coat is made of 60% wool, 30% polyester, and 10% nylon. Write each percent as a fraction in lowest terms.

10. Complete each statement using <, >, or =. Explain your answers.

a) 0.3 ■ 30%

b) 0.45 ■ $\frac{7}{45}$

c) $\frac{3}{5}$ ■ 40%

d) 20% ■ $\frac{4}{25}$

e) $\frac{2}{8}$ ■ 25%

f) 42% ■ 4.2

11. What fraction with a numerator of 1 or 2 could you use to estimate each percent? Explain.

a) 30% **b)** 15% **c)** 70% **d)** 9%

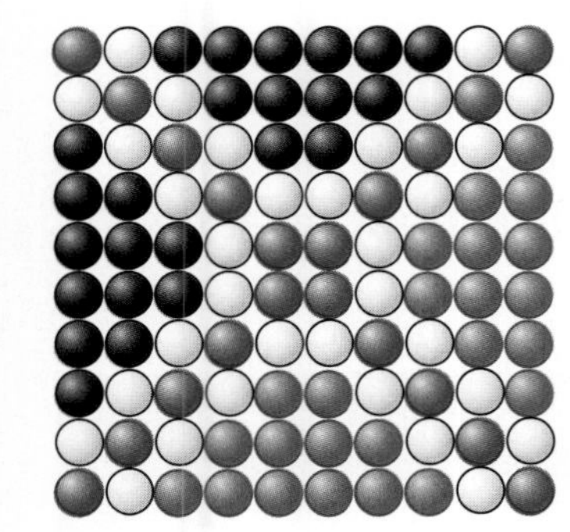

12. a) Describe each colour of beads as a percent of the entire design.

b) Write each percent as a fraction in lowest terms.

13. The air you breathe is 20 parts oxygen and 80 parts other gases.

a) What percent of the air is oxygen? What percent of the air is made up of other gases?

b) Write each percent as a fraction in lowest terms.

14. At a provincial campground, 25% of the sites are for tent camping, 60% are for RVs, and the rest are for groups.

a) What percent of the sites are for groups?

b) The campground has 152 sites. How many sites are for tent camping?

15. How do you know, without calculating, that the percent for $\frac{7}{25}$ is less than the percent for $\frac{7}{20}$?

4.2 Investigating Percents

YOU WILL NEED
- Nutrition Facts labels from snack foods
- a calculator

GOAL

Explore how percents can be used.

EXPLORE the Math

Nutrition Facts **Valeur nutritive** Per 1 cup (50 g) / pour 1 tasse (50 g)	
Amount Teneur	% Daily Value % valeur quotidienne
Calories / Calories 190	
Fat / Lipides 0 g	0 %
Saturated / saturés 0 g + Trans / trans 0 g	0 %
Cholesterol / Cholestérol 0 mg	
Sodium / Sodium 290 mg	12 %
Carbohydrate / Glucides 44 g	15 %
Fibre / Fibres 0 g	0 %
Sugars / Sucres 2 g	
Protein / Protéines 3 g	
Vitamin A / Vitamine A	0 %
Vitamin C / Vitamine C	0 %
Calcium / Calcium	0 %
Iron / Fer	2 %

In 2001, Health Canada recommended that food packages should have a Nutrition Facts label. This label should include the size of one serving, the amounts of the nutritional components (such as calories, fats, carbohydrates, sodium, and some vitamins), and the percent of the recommended daily intake for each component.

Find a Nutrition Facts label from a snack food. Share the label with a group of classmates.

According to the Nutrition Facts labels that your group found, which is the best snack?

4.3 Estimating Percents

GOAL

Develop and apply estimation strategies for percents.

LEARN ABOUT the Math

To prepare for the upcoming baseball season, Nick goes shopping for a new baseball glove and helmet. A sporting goods store is advertising a sale on baseball equipment.

About how much will the baseball equipment cost?

Example 1 | Estimating percent using fractions

A $40 baseball glove is 35% off. About how much does it cost, without tax?

Nick's Solution

The cost is the original price minus the amount of the discount.

I didn't calculate an exact amount, because I only needed to know about how much the glove costs.

$35\% = \frac{35}{100}$

I wanted to estimate 35% with an easy fraction.

$\frac{35}{100}$ is about $\frac{1}{3}$.

$100 \div 35$ is close to 3, so I estimated with $\frac{1}{3}$.

$40 - 13 = 27$

The glove costs about $27.

I estimated by subtracting $\frac{1}{3}$ of 39 from 40.
I used 39 instead of 40 because 39 is a multiple of 3.

Example 2 | Estimating percent using decimals

After a discount, a batting helmet sells for \$18.84, plus 5% tax. Is \$20 enough to buy the helmet?

Jessica's Solution

The difference between \$18.84 and \$20.00 is about \$1.15. If the tax is less than \$1.15, then the purchase price is less than \$20.	I estimated because I just needed to know whether \$20 is enough, not the exact purchase price. I used easy numbers to estimate the tax.
10% of \$18.84 = \$1.88	10% is a good benchmark because it's easy to calculate. To calculate 10%, I moved the digits one place to the right.
Half of \$1.88 is less than \$1, so 5% of \$18.84 is less than \$1. \$1 is less than \$1.15, so \$20 is enough to buy the helmet.	5% is half of 10%.

Gail's Solution

\$18.84 is about \$19.00.	I rounded the cost of the helmet up to the nearest dollar.
1% = 0.01	1% is a good benchmark because it's easy to calculate, and 5% is 5 × 1%.
0.01 x 19.00 = 0.19	To determine 1% of \$19.00, I multiplied by 0.01.
19 x 5 = 20 x 5 – 5, which is 95. So, 0.19 x 5 is 0.95.	Then I multiplied by 5.
19.00 + 0.95 = 19.95 \$20 is enough to buy the helmet.	I added the cost and the tax to get the purchase price.

Reflecting

A. Why did Nick try to use a fraction with a numerator of 1 to solve the problem?

B. Why were Jessica's and Gail's approaches to solving the problem useful?

WORK WITH the Math

Example 3 | Estimating a percent using a number line

In last year's softball games, Ashley had 34 hits in 80 times at bat. About what percent of Ashley's times at bat did she get a hit?

Solution

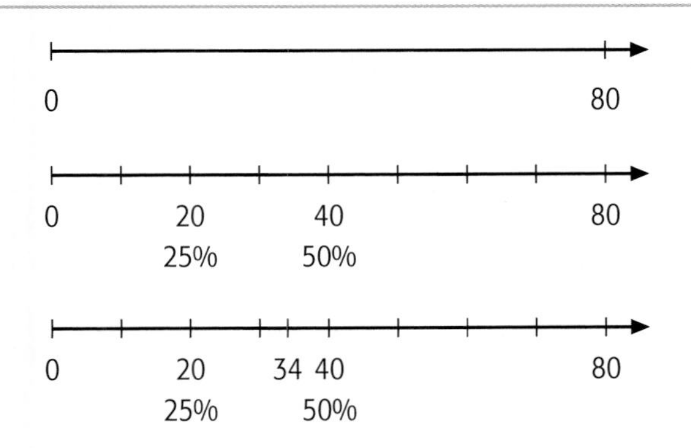

Use a number line to estimate $\frac{34}{80}$ as a percent.

Choose useful benchmarks, such as 20 and 40.

34 is about $\frac{3}{4}$ of the way from 20 to 40.

$50 - 25 = 25$

$\frac{1}{4}$ of 25 is about 6, so

$\frac{3}{4}$ of 25 is about $3 \times 6 = 18$

$25\% + 18\% = 43\%$

Ashley had a hit in about 43% of her times at bat.

The equivalent percent should also be about $\frac{3}{4}$ of the way from 25% to 50%.

Communication | *Tip*

Sometimes writing out what the numerator and the denominator represent in a fraction can be helpful. For example, for 34 hits in 80 times at bat, write $\frac{\text{number of hits}}{\text{number of times at bat}} = \frac{34}{80}$.

A Checking

1. What benchmark would you use to estimate what percent 8 out of 18 is?

2. a) Estimate 24% of 42. **b)** Estimate 65% of 29.

B Practising

3. Estimate what percent 9 is of 38. Explain your answer.

4. Estimate each percent. Explain what benchmark you used to make your estimate.

a) 9% of 27
b) 32% of 62
c) 76% of 25
d) 89% of 48

5. Are your estimates in the previous question greater or less than the actual answers? Explain.

6. Estimate what percent each fraction is. Explain what benchmark you used to make your estimates.

a) $\frac{12}{25}$ **b)** $\frac{22}{80}$ **c)** $\frac{67}{300}$ **d)** $\frac{31}{148}$

7. Are your estimates in the previous question greater or less than the actual answers? Explain.

8. Some of the students in Alan's school want to have a winter carnival on a school day. The principal will allow them to have the carnival if 90% of the students in the school sign up. So far, 448 of the 550 students in the school have signed up. Estimate to determine whether enough students have signed up. Explain what you did.

9. During the first hour of a powwow, 47 people arrived. The other 85% arrived later in the day. About how many people attended the powwow?

10. You need 60% on your test to get a higher mark in a subject. You got 19 out of 26 marks. Why can you estimate to decide if you have the 60% you need?

11. a) Name a situation in which you might estimate a percent.
b) When would you need to calculate a percent exactly?

4.4 Using Percents to Make Comparisons

Compare fractions and ratios using percents.

LEARN ABOUT the Math

Pavlo wrote a science test and a social studies test this week. He scored 21 out of 30 on the science test and 18 out of 25 on the social studies test. He is trying to determine which test he did better on.

On which test did Pavlo score a higher mark?

A. Write fractions that describe Pavlo's marks on the tests.

B. Can you tell from the fractions which is the higher mark? Explain your answer.

C. Rewrite the fractions as equivalent fractions with the same denominator.

D. Write each test mark as a percent.

E. On which test did Pavlo score a higher mark?

Reflecting

F. Why were the fractions in part C easier to compare than the fractions in part B?

G. Why is writing two fractions as percents like writing them as equivalent fractions?

WORK WITH the Math

Example 1 | Comparing different-sized groups

One year in Vancouver, 68% of the days in January and 68% of the days in February had some precipitation. Did one month have more days with some precipitation? (This was a non-leap year.)

Jessica's Solution

There are 31 days in January. In a non-leap year, there are 28 days in February. I had to compare 68% of 31 and 68% of 28. 68% of a greater amount should be more. If the numbers are too close, however, there may be no difference.

68% of 31 = 0.68 x 31 = 21.08
That's 21 days.
68% of 28 = 0.68 x 28 = 19.04
That's 19 days.

31 and 28 were far enough apart for 68% of 31 and 68% of 28 to be different whole numbers.

68% of 31 is greater than 68% of 28. January had more days with some precipitation.

Example 2 | Comparing ratios

On the first day of the Heritage Fair, the ratio of children to adults was 2:5. On the second day, the ratio was 3:7. On which day did a greater percent of children attend the fair?

Nestor's Solution

The ratio 2:5 means that for every 7 people, 2 were children and 5 were adults. The ratio 3:7 means that for every 10 people, 3 were children and 7 were adults.

On the first day, $\frac{2}{7}$ of the people were children.
On the second day, $\frac{3}{10}$ of the people were children. I knew that $\frac{3}{10}$ is 30%.

I rewrote $\frac{2}{7}$ as a percent using my calculator.

2 [÷] 7 [=] 0.28571

$\frac{2}{7}$ is about 29%.

A greater percent of children attended the Heritage Fair on the second day.

A Checking

1. Jerry's lacrosse team won 10 of 25 games. Joel's basketball team won 18 of 45 games.
   a) What percent of the games did each team win?
   b) Who had the better record for wins?

2. Caroline is doing a traffic survey. On the first day, the ratio of cars with passengers to cars with only a driver was 13:7. On the second day, the ratio was 8:5. On which day was the percent of cars with passengers greater? How do you know?

B Practising

3. Tom mixes a punch with 4 parts ginger ale to 6 parts fruit juice. Lina mixes a punch with 3 parts ginger ale to 5 parts fruit juice. Whose punch has a greater percent of ginger ale?

4. On Monday at the Pacific National Exhibition, there were 4 children for every 3 adults. On Tuesday, there were 6 children for every 4 adults. On which day did a greater percent of children attend?

5. Order the fractions $\frac{23}{25}$, $\frac{28}{30}$, $\frac{47}{50}$, and $\frac{37}{40}$ from greatest to least.

6. After taxes, Tara paid \$27 for a \$25 purchase, and Jolene paid \$32.10 for a \$30 purchase.
   a) How much did each girl pay in taxes?
   b) What fraction of each original price were the taxes?
   c) Who paid the higher percent of taxes?

7. According to a weather forecast, there is a 30% chance of rain. Explain what you think this means.

8. Why is 100% of a week not as long as 10% of a year?

9. Sandeep deposited \$500 in a bank account. After one year, the amount increased to \$525. Sunil deposited \$400 in a bank account. After one year, the amount increased to \$420. Who had the better interest rate? Explain.

10. Describe two different ways to compare $\frac{3}{5}$ and $\frac{4}{6}$. One way must involve percents.

Chapter 4

Mid-Chapter Review

Frequently Asked Questions

Q: How are percents, fractions, and decimals related?

A: They are all ways to describe ratios or parts of amounts. If you know one form (percent, fraction, or decimal), you can determine the other two equivalent forms.

For example, 80% means 80 out of 100 or $\frac{80}{100}$, which is equivalent to $\frac{4}{5}$. The fraction $\frac{80}{100}$ means 80 hundredths, which is equivalent to 0.80 or 0.8.

Q: How do you estimate a percent?

A: Use benchmarks (numbers that are easy to use) to estimate. For example, 24% of 38 is about 25% of 40. Since 25% of 40 is $\frac{1}{4}$ of 40, 24% of 38 is about 10.

Practice

Lesson 4.1

1. How many cents does each percent of a dollar represent?

a) 1% **b)** 72% **c)** 100% **d)** 40%

2. Complete each statement using $<$, $>$, or $=$.

a) 15% ■ 0.2

b) $\frac{1}{4}$ ■ 25%

c) 0.8 ■ 75%

d) 0.5 ■ 5%

3. There are 16 children and 24 adults at an art show.

a) What percent of the people are children?

b) What percent of the people are adults?

Lesson 4.3

4. Estimate each percent. Show your work.

a) 42 out of 52

b) $\frac{18}{47}$

c) $19.99 compared to $79.97

d) 29 seconds out of 1 minute

5. Is each statement reasonable or unreasonable? Explain how you know.

a) 12% of 42 is about 4.

b) 35% of 150 is about 50.

c) 72% of 60 is about 58.

d) 45% of 180 is about 90.

6. Which benchmarks would you use to estimate each amount? Estimate each amount using these benchmarks.

a) a 15% tip on a restaurant bill of $39.45

b) 6% tax on an item costing $41.95

7. Bones account for about 20% of a person's total mass. Estimate the mass of the bones in a 62 kg person.

Lesson 4.4

8. Barry got 17 out of 20 on a science test and 39 out of 50 on a math test. On which test did he do better? Explain.

9. Tracy and Tristan both earn a percent of any sales they make at a furniture store. Last month, Tracy earned $750 on sales of $5000, and Tristan earned $825 on sales of $6875. Who earns the greater percent? Show how you know.

10. Explain which sale offers the greatest discount.

4.5 Calculating with Percents

YOU WILL NEED

- a calculator

Solve problems that involve percents using equivalent ratios.

LEARN ABOUT the Math

Nick and his family went out to dinner to celebrate his graduation. Their bill came to $53.00. The family usually leaves a 15% tip for the server.

How much tip should Nick's family leave for the server?

Example 1 | Calculating the percent of a total

Calculate the tip that Nick's family should leave.

Nick's Solution

proportion

a number sentence that shows two equivalent ratios or fractions; for example, $\frac{1}{4} = \frac{5}{20}$

I rounded $53 to $50.
I used the proportion $\frac{15}{100} = \frac{■}{50}$ to estimate the tip.

We don't need an exact amount. I needed the number that is 15% of 50. I wrote this number as ■. I knew that $\frac{■}{50}$ is equivalent to $\frac{15}{100}$, because they are both 15%.

$$\frac{15}{100} = \frac{7.5}{50} \quad (\div 2)$$

Since I divided 100 by 2 to get 50, I had to divide 15 by 2 to get an equivalent fraction.

We should leave about $7.50 for the tip.

Gail's Solution

$50 \div 10 = 5$
$5 \div 2 = 2.5$
$5 + 2.5 = 7.5$
15% of $50 is $7.50

I estimated $53 as $50. I calculated 10% of 50 by dividing by 10.
I calculated 5% as half of 10%.
I added 10% and 5% to get 15%.

Nick's family should leave $8 for the tip.

I added a little bit extra because $53 is greater than $50.

Reflecting

A. Why was it appropriate to estimate 53 with 50?

B. Why is a 15% tip easier to calculate than a 13% tip?

WORK WITH the Math

Example 2 | Calculating a percent

A group of 20 Grade 7 students were surveyed about their favourite type of music. This table shows the results of the survey. What percent of the students did not choose rap?

Type of music	Number of students
country	1
rock	4
hip-hop	6
rap	9

Solution A: Using a grid

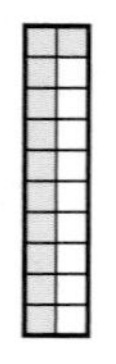

Draw a grid of 20 squares, since 20 students were surveyed. Make the grid 2 squares wide by 10 squares high. Shade 11 squares for students who chose country, rock, or hip-hop. There are 9 unshaded squares for students who chose rap.

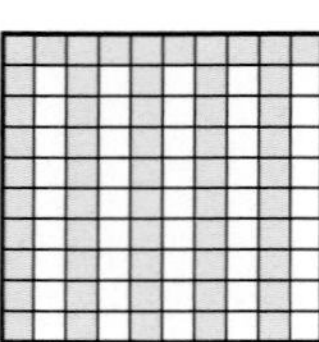

Copy the grid four more times to make 100 squares. Each group of 20 has 11 shaded squares. Multiply 11 by 5 to get the number of shaded squares in the 100 grid.

$5 \times 11 = 55$

$\frac{55}{100} = 55\%$, so 55% of the students did not choose rap.

Solution B: Using a proportion

$\frac{\text{number who did not choose rap}}{\text{number of students}} = \frac{11}{20}$

11 students did not choose rap. Write the ratio as a fraction.

$\frac{11}{20} = \frac{■}{100}$

Write a proportion. Since you're calculating a percent, put the missing term over 100.

$\frac{11}{20} \overset{\times 5}{=} \frac{■}{100}$ (×5 applied to numerator and denominator)

$20 \times 5 = 100$, so $11 \times 5 = ■$.

$\frac{11}{20} = \frac{55}{100}$

$11 \times 5 = 55$

55% of the students did not choose rap.

Example 3 | Calculating an amount from a percent

Suppose that Nick's family had spent $80 for his graduation dinner. How much would a 15% tip be?

Solution

$\frac{15}{100} = \frac{\text{tip}}{80}$

15% means "15 out of 100," so the tip must be the same portion of 80.

$\frac{15}{100} \overset{\div 5}{=} \frac{3}{20}$

First rewrite $\frac{15}{100}$ as an equivalent fraction in lower terms.

$\frac{3}{20} = \frac{\text{tip}}{80}$

Then rewrite $\frac{3}{20}$ as an equivalent fraction with a denominator of 80.

$\frac{3}{20} \overset{\times 4}{=} \frac{12}{80}$

A 15% tip for an $80 dinner is $12.

Example 4 | Calculating a number from a percent

There are 10 boys in Jessica's music class. According to the teacher, 40% of the students in the class are boys. How many students are in the class?

Solution

$\frac{40}{100} = \frac{\text{10 boys}}{\text{total number of students}}$

40% means 40 boys out of 100. Write the ratio as a fraction.
Write a proportion. The missing term in the proportion is the total number of students.

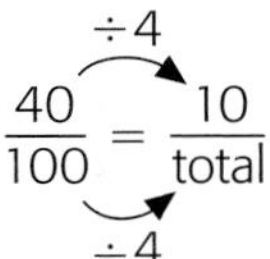

$\frac{40}{100} \overset{\div 4}{=} \frac{10}{\text{total}}$

40 ÷ 4 equals 10, so the total number of students must be 100 ÷ 4.

total = 100 ÷ 4 = 25
There are 25 students in the music class.

Divide.

A Checking

1. Calculate 15% of 60 using each method.

a) Use mental math:
- Think of 10% of 60.
- Take half of your number above.
- Add the two numbers.

b) Use a proportion:
- Rewrite $\frac{15}{100}$ in lowest terms.
- Multiply to rename this fraction as an amount out of 60.

2. Determine each missing number.

a) 20% of ■ = 45

b) 12% of ■ = 54

3. Estimate the 15% tip for each dinner bill.

a) \$26.50

b) \$13.22

B Practising

4. Calculate.

a) 50% of 20

b) 75% of 24

c) 20% of 45

d) 12% of 50

e) 15% of 200

f) 44% of 250

5. Calculate.

a) 50% of ■ = 15

b) 25% of ■ = 22

c) 10% of ■ = 7

d) 75% of ■ = 12

e) 15% of ■ = 24

f) 44% of ■ = 55

6. Out of 600 computers produced in a factory, 30 failed to pass inspection due to bad disk drives. What percent failed to pass inspection?

7. There are 12 girls with blond hair in Katya's gymnastics class. This is 25% of the entire class. Using mental math, calculate the total number of students in the class.

8. About 14% of Canadians who are at least 100 years old live in British Columbia. On the 2001 census, 531 people in British Columbia said they were at least 100 years old. About how many Canadians were at least 100 years old in 2001?

9. A dealer paid $6000 for a used car. The dealer wants to make a profit that is 25% of the price he paid for the car.

a) What profit does the dealer want to make?

b) For how much should the dealer sell the car?

10. If Sarah's mother really likes the service in a restaurant, she leaves a 20% tip. The family's last bill was $110, and Sarah's mother left $22 for the tip. Did she really like the service? Explain.

11. There are four common blood types: O, A, B, and AB. The diagram below shows the percent of people with each blood type in a specific group. In a group of 2500 people, how many would you expect to have each blood type?

O: 45%
A: 41%
B: 10%
AB: 4%

12. A new process in a factory has increased production by 12%. Workers are now producing 30 more skateboards each day. How many skateboards did they produce each day before the new process was introduced?

13. Explain how you could use a proportion to express $\frac{165}{250}$ as a percent.

4.6 Solving Problems that Involve Decimals

YOU WILL NEED
- a calculator

Solve problems that involve percents and decimals.

LEARN ABOUT the Math

In the student council election, Gail received 168 out of 240 votes.

What percent of the votes did Gail receive?

A. Write the ratio of votes Gail received to total votes as a fraction.

B. Write a proportion you could solve to determine a fraction with a denominator of 100 that is equivalent to your fraction in part A.

C. What percent of the votes did Gail receive?

Reflecting

D. Why was it helpful to use an equivalent fraction with a denominator of 100 to calculate the percent?

E. Why would the problem have been harder to solve for an exact percent if Gail had received 170 out of 240 votes?

WORK WITH the Math

Example 1 | Calculating a percent

In the student council election, Pavlo received 72 out of 120 votes. Determine the percent of the votes he received.

Pavlo's Solution

$\frac{\text{votes for Pavlo}}{\text{total votes}} = \frac{72}{120}$

I wrote the first ratio, which is the number of votes I received compared to the total number of votes.

$\frac{72}{120} = \frac{■}{100}$

I used ■ to represent the number of votes I received out of every 100 votes.

$120 \div 100 = 1.2$

I divided 120 by 100 to determine the number I should divide 72 by.

$\frac{72}{100} = \frac{■}{100}$ (÷1.2 on numerator and denominator)

I divided 72 by 1.2 to get the percent.

72 [÷] 1.2 [=] 60.

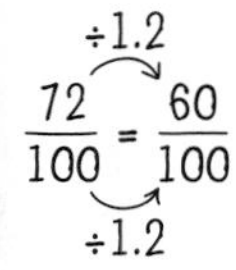

$\frac{72}{100} = \frac{60}{100}$ (÷1.2 on numerator and denominator)

When I divided the numerator and the denominator by 1.2, I got an equivalent fraction with a denominator of 100.

$\frac{60}{100} = 60\%$

I received 60% of the votes.

I wrote the fraction as a percent.

Example 2 | Comparing amounts

In 1989, close to 42 million litres of oil were spilled in Prince William Sound, Alaska. Cleanup crews were able to recover 14% of the spilled oil.
In 2005, about 32 million litres of oil were spilled because of Hurricane Katrina. Cleanup crews recovered about 22.4 million litres of this oil.
Compare the amounts of oil recovered after the two disasters.

Nestor's Solution

I used percents to compare the oil recovered after the two disasters.

$$\frac{22.4}{32} = \frac{\blacksquare}{100} \quad (\times ?)$$

I knew the percent of oil recovered in Prince William Sound. I needed to calculate the percent recovered after Hurricane Katrina.
I had to determine what percent 22.4 is of 32, so I wrote a proportion.
I needed a number that I could multiply 32 by to get 100.

$32 \times \blacksquare = 100$,
so $100 \div 32 = \blacksquare$.

I couldn't solve this, but I was able to write the multiplication as a division.

100 [÷] 32 [=]

I used my calculator.

$$\frac{22.4}{32} = \frac{70}{100} \quad (\times 3.125)$$

When I multiplied the numerator and the denominator by 3.125, I got an equivalent fraction with a denominator of 100.

$$\frac{70}{100} = 70\%$$

70% of the oil was recovered after Hurricane Katrina. This is five times greater than the percent of oil recovered in Prince William Sound.

I wrote this fraction as a percent.

Pavlo's Solution

I compared the quantities of oil recovered after the two disasters.

0.14 [×] 32 [=] 4.48

I knew that 14% of the oil was recovered in Prince William Sound. I calculated what 14% of the Hurricane Katrina spill would be. The decimal equivalent of 14% is 0.14, so I calculated 14% of 32 by multiplying 0.14 × 32 on my calculator.

22.4 [÷] 4.48 [=] 5.00

I compared the amount actually recovered to the amount I calculated.

Five times the percent of oil was recovered after Hurricane Katrina as after the Prince William Sound spill.

A Checking

1. Calculate each percent.

a) 7% of $49.98

b) 10% of $27.99

c) 9% of $69.86

d) 8% of 3000

B Practising

2. Calculate 6% of each price.

a)

b)

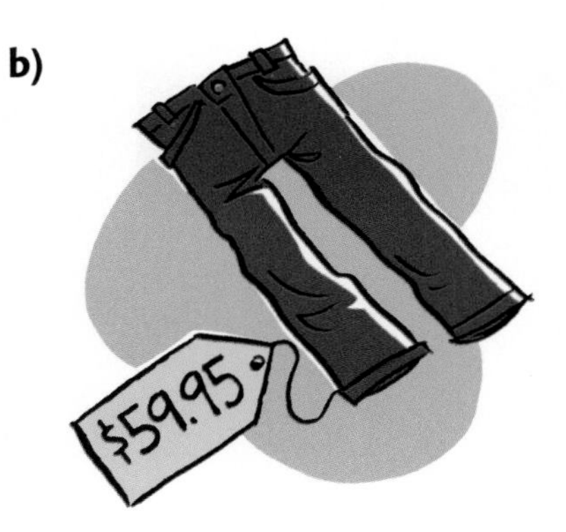

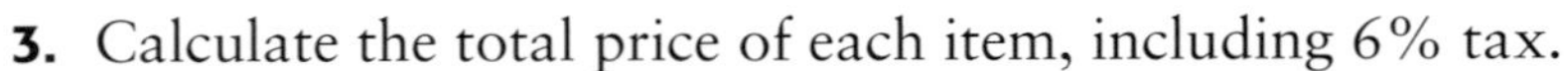

3. Calculate the total price of each item, including 6% tax.

Province	PST
BC	7%
AB	0%
SK	5%
MB	7%

4. A tractor costs $39 500. How much would a farmer in Manitoba pay for the tractor after GST and PST?

5. Richard works at a clothing store. He is paid $150 a week, plus 9% of the value of his sales for the week. Last week, his sales totalled $457.85. Calculate his total earnings for the week.

6. Marie received a 4% raise to her $275 per week salary. She also earned 3% of the value of her sales, which were $1500 that week. How much money did she earn that week?

7. Jorge earned $30 when he collected $375 for newspaper subscriptions. What percent of the total did he earn?

8. A store is offering a 10% early-bird discount on a watch that regularly costs $24.00.

a) What is the sale price of the watch?

b) Calculate the total cost of the watch in British Columbia.

9. Choose a page of advertisements in a newspaper.

a) Calculate the total cost of any two items on the page at 6%, 7%, and 8% sales tax.

b) Why is the difference between taxes at 6% and 7% greater for items that cost more?

10. Give an example that shows how writing a proportion can help you solve a problem that involves percents.

CURIOUS MATH

Elastic Percents

YOU WILL NEED
- a metre stick
- a piece of elastic that stretches to 100 cm

You don't need a calculator to calculate percents if you have a piece of elastic.

Stretch the elastic along the metre stick. Make a mark every 1 cm along the elastic so that each mark represents 1%. Label each 5 cm.

1. To determine 60% of 75, place the 0% mark on the elastic at the 0 cm mark on the metre stick. Stretch the other end of the elastic until it reaches 75 cm. What number on the metre stick aligns with the 60% mark on the elastic?

2. Determine each amount with your percent elastic.

a) 25% of 84 **c)** 80% of 115
b) 35% of 60 **d)** 50% of 72

3. Estimate each amount with your percent elastic.

a) 18% of 55 **c)** 70% of 69
b) 48% of 120 **d)** 12% of 65

4. Why does your percent elastic work?

4.7 Solve Problems Using Logical Reasoning

GOAL

Solve problems that involve percents using logical reasoning.

LEARN ABOUT the Math

On a school ski trip, 10 students sign up for snowboarding. This is 40% of the students going on the trip.

How many students are going on the school ski trip?

Example 1 | Using logical reasoning

Determine the number of students going on the trip.

Nick's Solution

Percent of group not snowboarding = 100% − 40% = 60% Number of students not snowboarding = 60% of group	I knew that 40% of the group is snowboarding, so 60% of the group is not snowboarding.
= 40% of group + 20% of group = 10 + 5 = 15	40% of the group is equivalent to 10 students. Since 20% is half of 40%, 20% of the group is half of 10, which is 5.
Total number of students = 10 + 15 = 25 There are 25 students going on the school ski trip.	15 students in the group are not snowboarding.

Reflecting

A. Why did Nick use 40% + 20% to calculate 60%?

B. Could Nick have solved this problem without determining the number of students who are not snowboarding?

***WORK WITH** the Math*

Example 2 | Using logical reasoning and proportions

The African bush elephant weighs 6 t. This is about 4% of the mass of a blue whale. What is the mass of a blue whale?

Solution A: Comparing equivalent fractions

4% = 6 t	6 t of the blue whale's mass is equivalent to 4%.
25 × 4% = 25 × 6 t 100% = 150 t	100% is 25 times as much as 4%, so the missing amount must be 25 times as big as 6. Multiply both sides of the equation by 25.

The mass of a blue whale is 150 t.

Solution B: Comparing numerators of equivalent fractions

4% = 6 t	6 t of the blue whale's mass is equivalent to 4%.
8% = 12 t 2% = 3 t 10% = 8% + 2% = 12 t + 3 t = 15 t	8% is twice as much as 4%. 2% is half as much as 4%.
100% = 10 × 15 t = 150 t	10% × 10 = 100%

The mass of a blue whale is 150 t.

Example 3 | Comparing percents

About 17% of the students in Ms. Gregg's Grade 7 class wear glasses. About 19% of the students in Mr. Singh's Grade 7 class wear glasses. Can you tell which class has more students who wear glasses?

Solution

Since you don't know how many students are in each class, you can't tell which class has more students who wear glasses.

A Checking

1. On a class field trip, 15 students have sandwiches for lunch. This is 60% of the students on the trip. How many students went on the trip?

B Practising

2. How much would you save if there is a 20% discount on a bike that sells for $259.99?

3. In Canada, about 10% of the people are left-handed. In Fiji, about 40% of the people are left-handed.

a) In a group of 30 Canadians, how many would you expect to be left-handed?

b) In a group of 30 Fijians, how many would you expect to be left-handed?

4. A cheetah can run as fast as 112 kilometres each hour. A leatherback turtle can swim at about 30% of this speed. How fast can the turtle swim?

5. For every nine students in a school, two signed up for intramural sports. That was 208 students. One third of the students in the school are in Grade 7. How many students are not in Grade 7?

6. Estimate which is the better deal on a computer. Explain your reasoning.

7. When water freezes, its volume increases by about 10%.

a) What is the increase in volume if 150 L of water freezes?

b) What is the new volume?

c) What is the new volume when 22.5 L of water freezes?

Reading Strategy

What information in this lesson can help you solve the problem?

What information in other parts of the book can help you?

What do you know that will help you?

8. The lifespan of a black bear is about 40 years. The lifespan of a wolf is about 45% of the lifespan of a black bear. What is the lifespan of a wolf?

9. A set of number patterns is formed by starting with a number and then doubling it to get the next number. However, if the next number is greater than 20, subtract 15.

For example, the pattern could be 3, 6, 12, 9, ...

(since $2 \times 12 = 24$, and then $24 - 15 = 9$).

a) What would the next number be in the pattern that starts with 3?

b) If the 4th number in a pattern is 11, what could the start number be?

10. Hippopotamuses spend much of their time in water. You can hold your breath about 40% as long as a hippopotamus.

a) How long can you hold your breath?

b) How long do you think a hippopotamus can hold its breath?

11. A pair of jeans usually costs $80.00. The jeans are on sale at Jane's Jean Shop for 50% off. Denim Discounters offers the same jeans at 30% off, with a further 20% off the discounted price. Are the jeans the same price at both stores? Justify your answer.

12. Budget cuts caused the wages of employees at a shirt factory to be reduced by 5%. Profits at the end of the year were better than expected, so employees were given a 5% raise on their current wages. Are the employees' wages back to what they were before the salary cut? Justify your answer.

13. In a survey of 100 students who brought lunches,

- 38 students brought fruit
- 82 students brought a sandwich
- 34 students brought both fruit and a sandwich

a) How many students brought neither fruit nor a sandwich?

b) Explain your strategy for solving the problem in part (a).

MATH GAME

Recycling Bin Basketball

Tape a line on the floor, 3 m from your basket. Create a table like the one shown to record your team's results.

Number of players: 4 per team

YOU WILL NEED
- a spongy ball or a crumpled piece of paper
- a recycling bin or another suitable "basket"
- a metre stick
- tape
- a calculator

How to Play

1. Each player on your team takes as many shots as she or he wants, up to a maximum of 10. Record each player's "Shots in basket" and "Shots taken" as a ratio in a table.
2. Calculate the "Percent in basket" for each player on your team. Round the percent to the nearest whole number, and record it in your table.
3. Calculate your team's "Percent in basket" for the total shots taken. Round to the nearest whole number, if necessary.
4. Compare your team's results with the results for the other teams in your class. The team with the highest "Percent in basket" wins.

Nick's Turn

I missed my first shot, but got 3 of the next 4 shots in the basket. I'll stop after 5 shots. Our team scored 12 out of 25 shots. That's 48% in the basket.

Player	Ratio of $\frac{\text{shots in basket}}{\text{shots taken}}$	Percent in basket
Gail	$\frac{4}{10}$	40%
Nestor	$\frac{2}{7}$	29%
Jessica	$\frac{3}{3}$	100%
Nick	$\frac{3}{5}$	60%
Total	$\frac{12}{25}$	48%

Chapter Self-Test

Percent	82%		
Fraction in lowest terms		$\frac{7}{20}$	
Decimal			0.07

1. Complete the table at the left.

2. Calculate.

a) 1% of 600
3% of 600

b) 10% of 40
90% of 40

3. Complete each statement.

a) 40% of 35 is ■.

b) ■% of 30 is 21.

c) 60% of ■ is 39.

d) 4.2 is ■% of 21.

4. A baseball stadium is 65% full. The capacity of the stadium is 1800. About how many people are in the stadium?

5. Akeem bought a video game for $38. He sold it a few days later for 40% less than he paid. How much did he sell the video game for?

6. Why is calculating 10% of an amount easier than calculating 17% of the amount?

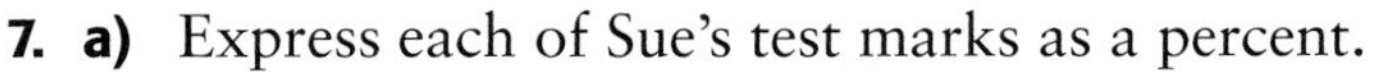

7. a) Express each of Sue's test marks as a percent.

b) Order her tests from lowest mark to highest mark.

8. Calculate 6% tax on each item.

a)

b)

What Do You Think Now?

Revisit What Do You Think? on page 153. How have your answers and explanations changed?

Chapter Review

Frequently Asked Questions

Q: How do you solve a percent problem using a proportion?

A: Write a proportion in which one of the fractions or ratios is out of 100. For example, suppose that a hockey team won 18 out of 40 games. To determine what percent of the games the team won, write $\frac{18}{40}$ in a proportion.

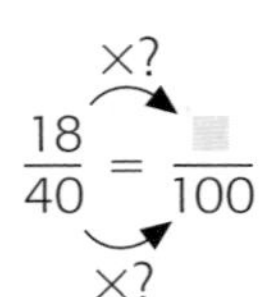

Figure out what number you need to multiply 40 by to get 100.
Using division, $100 \div 40 = 2.5$.

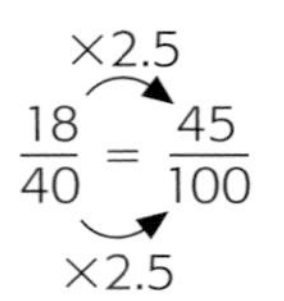

Multiply the numerator and the denominator by 2.5.
$\frac{18}{40}$ is equivalent to 45%.
They have won 45% of the games.

Q: How do you solve a percent problem using decimals?

A: Rename the percent as an equivalent decimal. Then multiply the decimal by the given amount. For example, suppose that you want to determine 27% of 45.

Rename 27% as 0.27, and multiply 0.27 by 45.

$0.27 \times 45 = 12.15$

So, 27% of 45 is 12.15.

Q: How can you solve a percent problem using logical reasoning?

A: Use information you already know to make your calculations easier. For example, if you know that 30% is 20 items, then you can figure out 45%, which is 30% + 15%. Because 15% is half of 30%, and 10 is half of 20, 45% is 20 + 10 items. So, 45% is 30 items.

Reading Strategy

Draw a three-column chart. Use these headings: New Words and Definitions, Key Points, and Pictures. Use your chart to record information from the Frequently Asked Questions.

Practice

Lesson 4.1

1. Rename each percent as a fraction.

a) $55\% = \frac{■}{20}$ **c)** $66\% = \frac{■}{50}$

b) $26\% = \frac{■}{50}$ **d)** $5\% = \frac{■}{40}$

2. Complete the table.

Percent	Decimal	Fraction (lowest terms)
70%		
	0.08	
		$\frac{3}{4}$
	0.15	
		$\frac{1}{4}$
55%		

3. Write each fraction as a percent.

a) $\frac{1}{5}$ **b)** $\frac{3}{4}$ **c)** $\frac{9}{10}$ **d)** $\frac{3}{12}$

4. In John's school, 20% of the students have no brothers or sisters, and 32% have one sibling.

a) What percent of the students have more than one sibling?

b) There are 355 students in the school. How many have no siblings?

Lesson 4.3

5. Estimate.

a) 81% of 70 **c)** 42% of 498

b) 96% of 202 **d)** 28% of 11

6. What benchmarks did you use for your estimates in the previous question?

7. In 2001, Statistics Canada found that 8% of Canada's population had asthma. When Marla surveyed her school, she found that 32 of the 301 students had asthma. Estimate if this number is greater or less than might be expected.

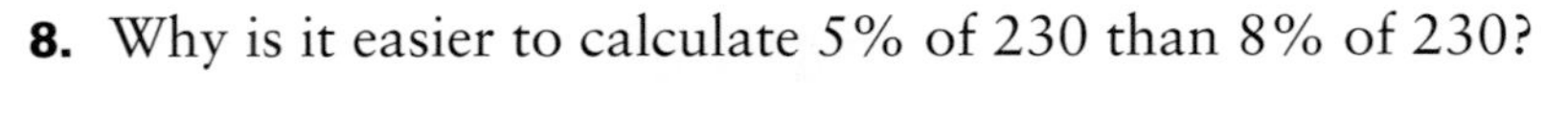

8. Why is it easier to calculate 5% of 230 than 8% of 230?

Lesson 4.4

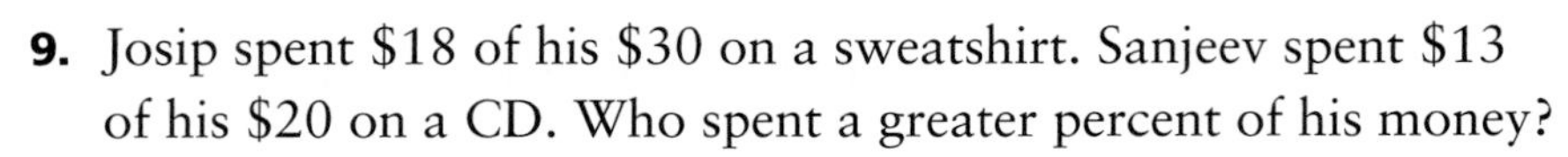

9. Josip spent $18 of his $30 on a sweatshirt. Sanjeev spent $13 of his $20 on a CD. Who spent a greater percent of his money?

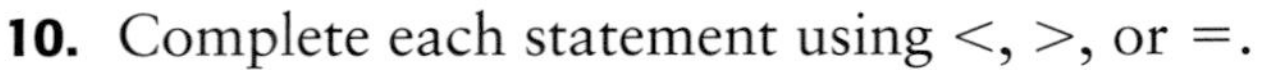

10. Complete each statement using $<$, $>$, or $=$.

a) $\frac{9}{50} \square \frac{7}{40}$ **b)** $\frac{18}{60} \square \frac{21}{75}$

Lesson 4.5

11. 14% of a restaurant's income is from dim sum on Saturdays. Last week, the restaurant made $4100. How much money came from dim sum on Saturday?

12. Determine each missing number.

a) 25% of 84 = $\square$ **b)** 10% of $\square$ = 5

13. A movie theatre has sold 75% of its seats for the 7:00 p.m. show. The theatre has 440 seats. How many tickets have been sold?

14. Renato sold a dining-room set for $144, which was 12% of its value when new. How much did the dining-room set originally cost?

Lesson 4.6

15. Calculate.

a) 79% of 20
b) 40% of 182.8
c) $456 plus 15% tax
d) $49.98 plus 6% tax

16. Dmitri scored 112 out of a possible 140 points in a video game. What is his percent score?

Lesson 4.7

17. **a)** Describe a quick way to determine 25% of 284.
b) Determine 75% of 284 using your answer to part (a). Explain.

18. The mass of a sperm whale is 42 t. This is about 70% of the mass of a fin whale. What is the mass of a fin whale?

19. Mark calculated 34% of 55. Explain each step of Mark's thinking.

10% is 5.5. 30% is 16.5. 2% is 1.1. 4% is 2.2. 34% is 18.7.

Chapter Task

Task | Checklist

- ✔ Did you measure and record all the required data?
- ✔ Did you show all your calculations?
- ✔ Did you explain your thinking?
- ✔ Did you include enough detail in your report?
- ✔ Did you discuss the reasons for the conclusion you made?

Ball Bounce-ability

Have you ever dropped a ball to see how high it would bounce? Do different types of balls bounce better than others?

How can you determine which type of ball bounces the best?

A. With a partner, choose three different types of balls. Each ball should be a different size and material. For example, a basketball, golf ball, tennis ball, and soccer ball are different sizes and made from different materials.

B. Create a table to record the type of ball, the drop height, the bounce height, the ratio of $\frac{\text{bounce height}}{\text{drop height}}$, and the percent.

C. Select a ball. Measure and record the height that the ball is dropped from and the distance that the ball bounces up from the floor on the first bounce.

D. Repeat part C for the other two balls.

E. Determine the ratio of $\frac{\text{bounce height}}{\text{drop height}}$ for each ball. Express this ratio as a percent.

F. Discuss the results of your experiment in a report, and rank the bounce-ability of each ball.

Chapter 5

Measurement

GOAL

You will be able to

- develop and apply a formula for the area of a parallelogram
- develop and apply a formula for the area of a triangle
- construct a circle with a given radius or diameter
- develop and apply formulas for the circumference and area of a circle

This window is about 50 cm wide. How can you estimate its area?

Chapter 5

Getting Started

YOU WILL NEED
- a calculator

Creating Geometric Art

Argentinian artist Jesus Soto creates art using geometric shapes and fabrics. Nolan and Fiona were inspired by his work, and they decided to create their own art using coloured fabrics. First, they sketched a design.

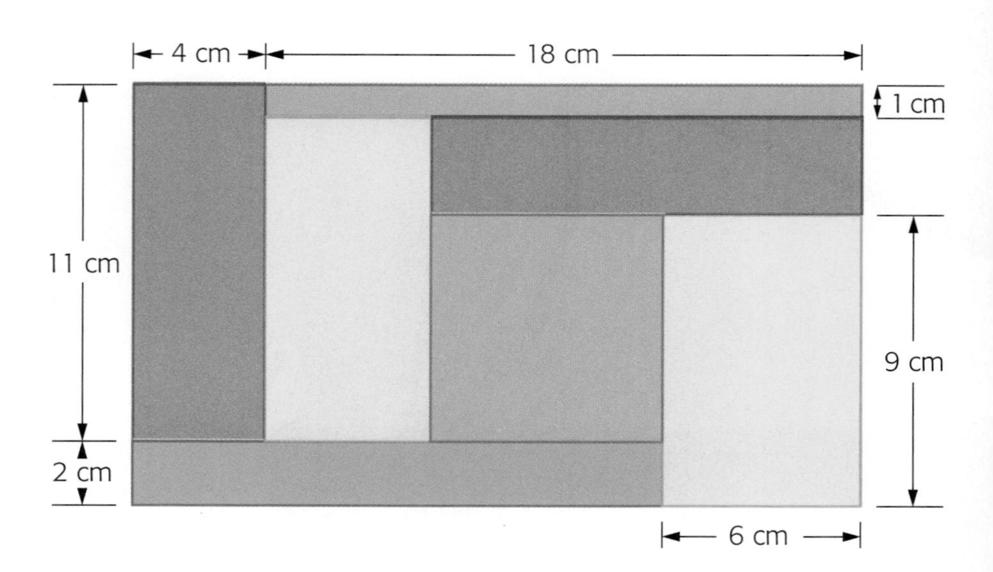

How much of each coloured fabric will they need?

A. Use the given dimensions to determine the missing dimensions.

B. What is the area of the entire design, in centimetres?

C. What is the total area of the yellow fabric in the design?

D. What percent of the design is green?

E. What is the ratio of each coloured fabric to the total area of the design?

What Do You Think?

Decide whether you agree or disagree with each statement.
Be ready to explain your decision.

1. A parallelogram and a rectangle that have the same side lengths also have the same area.

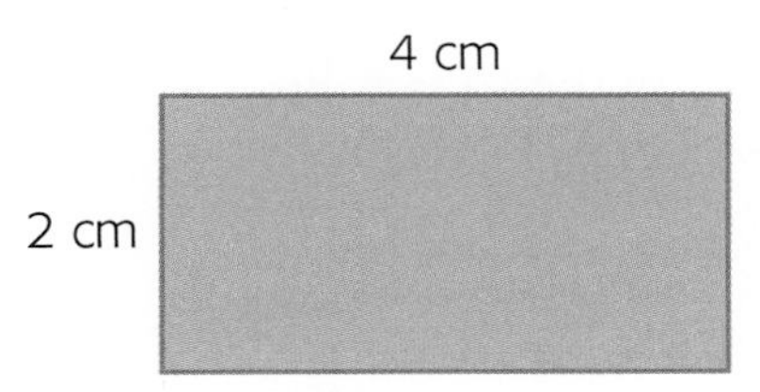

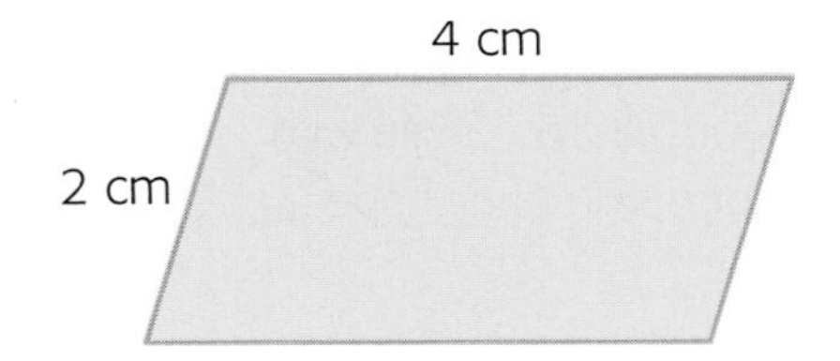

2. The distance around a circle is about twice as great as the width of the circle.

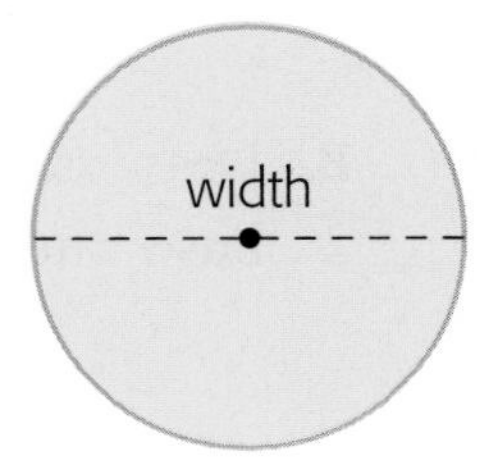

3. A triangle can be $\frac{1}{4}$ of, $\frac{1}{3}$ of, or $\frac{1}{2}$ of a parallelogram.

4. A circle and a square cannot have the same perimeter.

5.1 The Area of a Parallelogram

YOU WILL NEED
- a calculator
- pencil crayons
- 1 cm square dot paper
- a ruler
- scissors

GOAL

Develop and apply the formula for the area of a parallelogram.

LEARN ABOUT the Math

Matthew wrapped the lids of two gift boxes. One lid was a non-square rhombus, with each side measuring 15 cm. The other lid was a square, with each side measuring 15 cm. Matthew used different amounts of wrapping paper for each lid.

Which shape needed more wrapping paper?

A. Draw the square lid. How do you calculate its area?

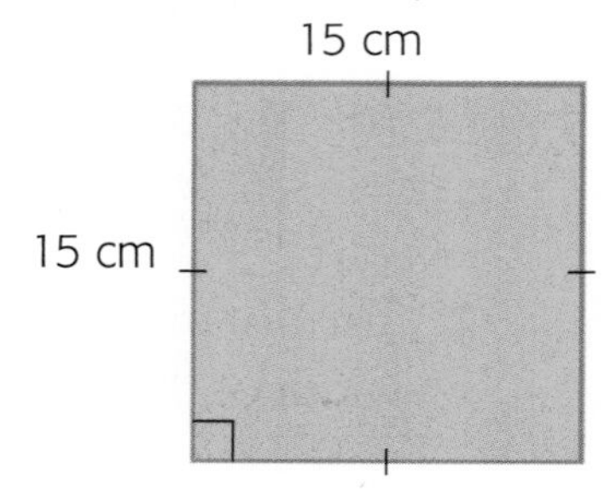

B. Draw the rhombus-shaped lid. Draw its **height**. Measure its **base** and height.

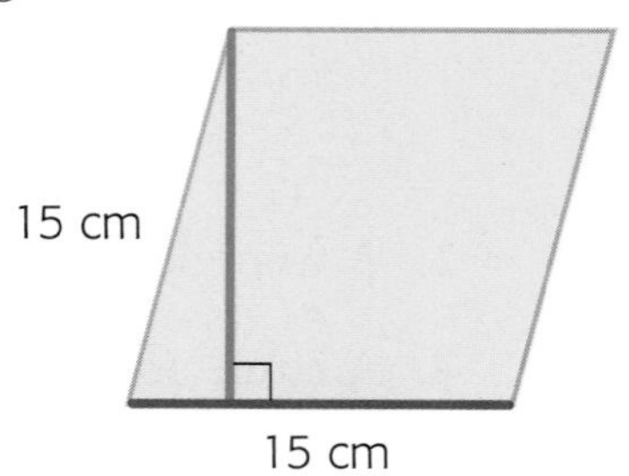

height

a line segment drawn to form a right angle with one side of a shape

base

the side of a shape that is measured to calculate the area or perimeter of the shape; any side of a shape can be the base of the shape

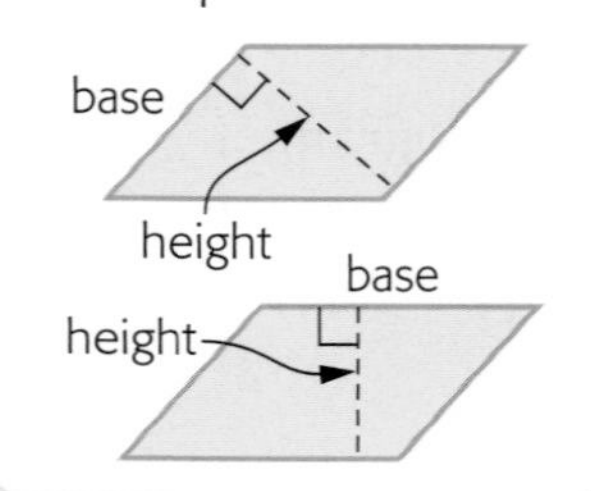

C. Cut the rhombus along its height, and move the triangular piece as shown. What do you notice about the new shape? How could you calculate its area?

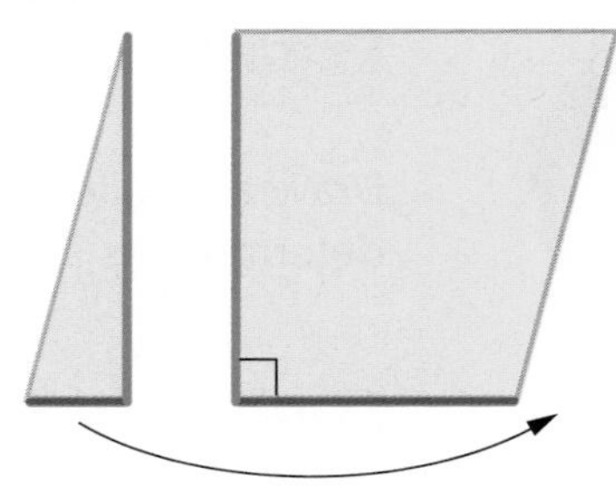

D. What is the area of the rhombus?

E. Which shape needed more wrapping paper? How do you know?

Communication | *Tip*

- The little square in the diagram above means that the two sides form a right angle (90°).
- Units of area usually have a small raised 2 written after them, as follows: 12 m^2. This indicates that the product of two dimensions, length and width or base and height, is involved in the measurement.

Reflecting

F. Can you cut any parallelogram and rearrange the pieces as in part C? Use some examples.

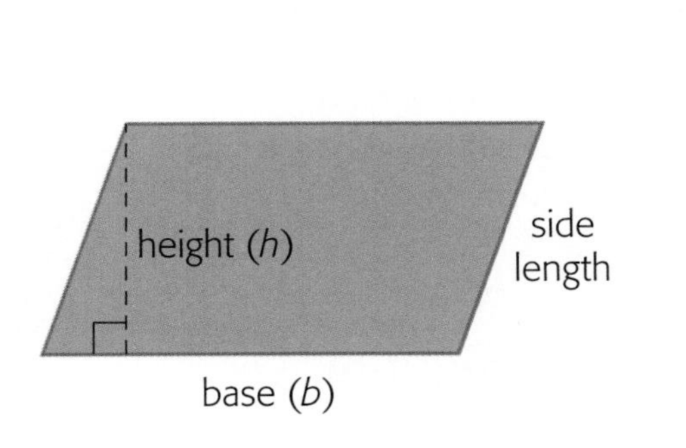

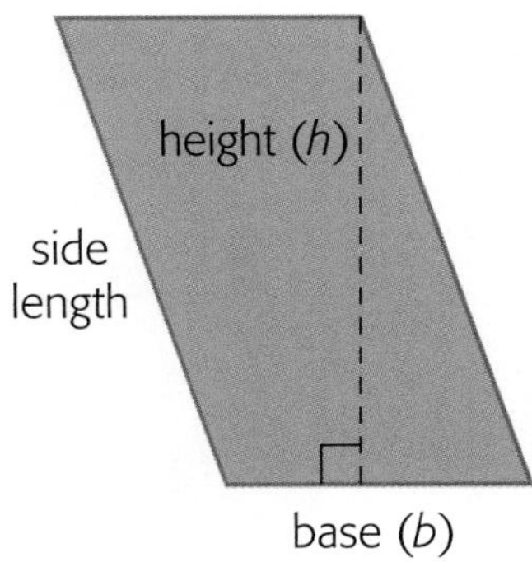

G. What is the **formula** for the area of a parallelogram with base *b* and height *h*? Explain.

formula

a rule represented by symbols, numbers, or letters, often in the form of an equation; for example, Area of a rectangle = length × width, or $A = l \times w$

WORK WITH the Math

Example 1 | Drawing and measuring a parallelogram

Draw a parallelogram. Measure its base and height, and then determine its area.

Matthew's Solution

I drew a rectangle. A rectangle is one kind of parallelogram, and the height of a rectangle is easy to measure.

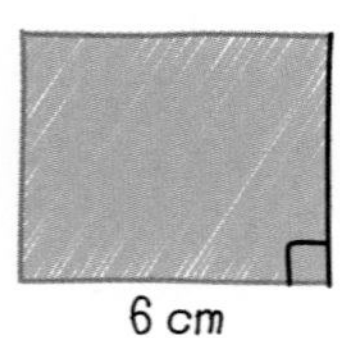

I measured the base and the height. The base is 6 cm, and the height is 5 cm.

$A = b \times h$
$= 6 \text{ cm} \times 5 \text{ cm}$
$= 30 \text{ cm}^2$
The area is 30 cm^2.

The area is the product of the base and the height. The area of my parallelogram is 30 cm^2.

Example 2 | Calculating the area of a parallelogram

Calculate the area of parallelogram *WXYZ*.

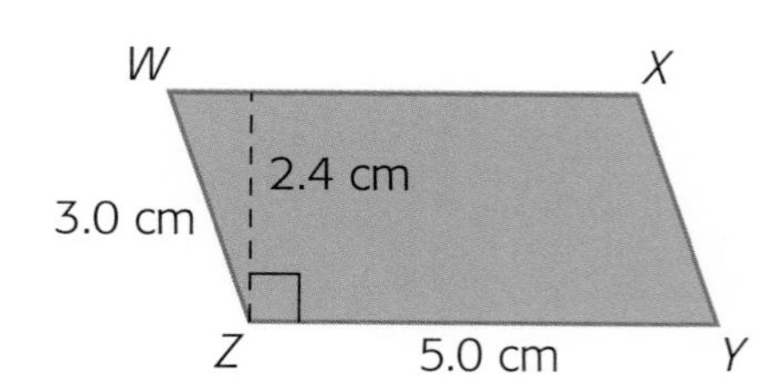

Julie's Solution

$A = b \times h$
$= 5.0 \text{ cm} \times 2.4 \text{ cm}$
$= 12.0 \text{ cm}^2$
The area of WXYZ is 12 cm^2.

The area of a parallelogram is base × height. I decided to use *ZY* as the base. This meant that I had to use 5.0 cm for the base and 2.4 cm for the height.

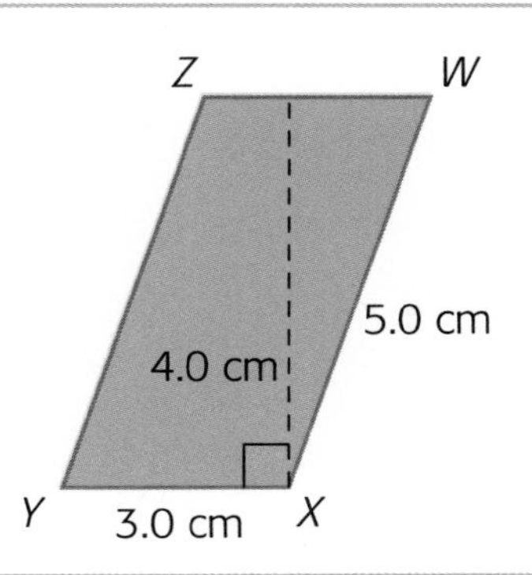

Max's Solution

A = b x h
= 3.0 cm x 4.0 cm
= 12.0 cm^2
The area of WXYZ is 12 cm^2.

I decided to use *YX* as the base. This meant that I had to use 3.0 cm for the base and 4.0 cm for the height.

A Checking

1. Complete the table for the parallelograms shown.

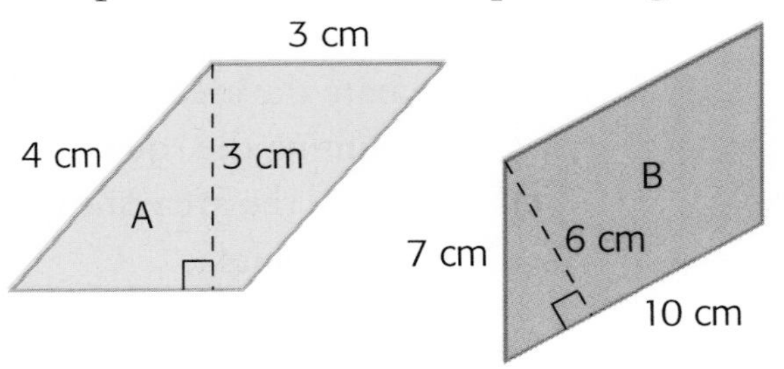

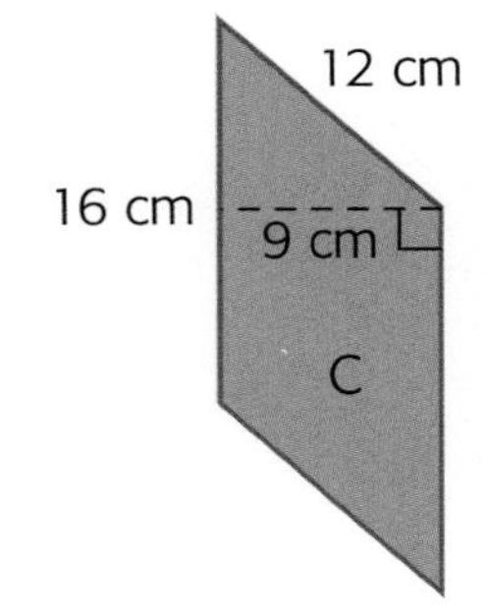

Parallelogram	Base (cm)	Height (cm)
A		
B		
C		

2. Calculate the area of parallelogram *WXYZ* using two different bases. Show your work.

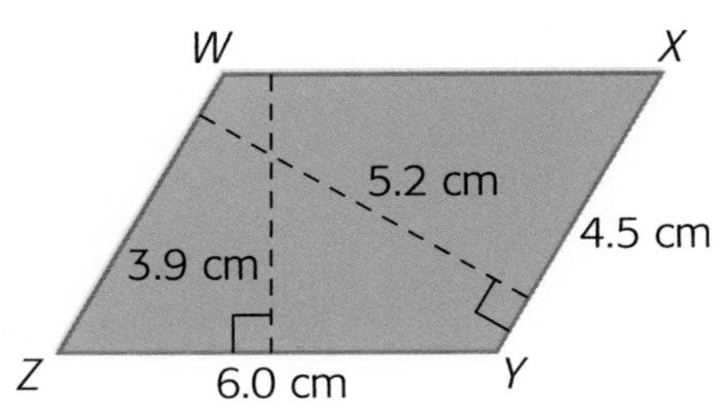

B Practising

3. Why do all these geoboard shapes have the same area?

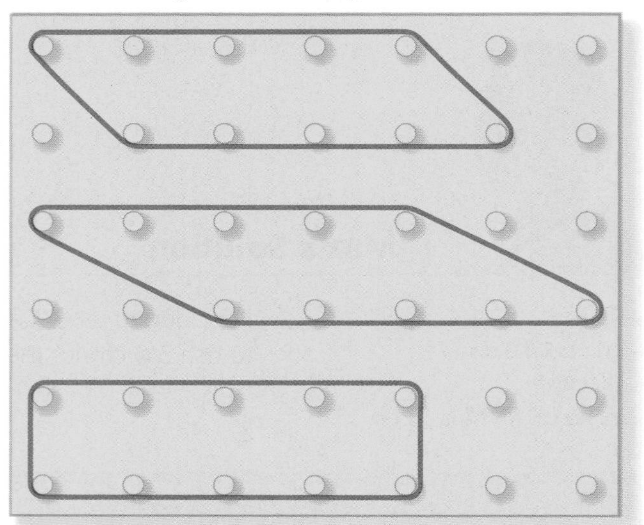

4. Create three parallelograms on a geoboard or dot paper.

a) Show the height of each parallelogram. Record your results in a table.

b) Estimate the area of each parallelogram, in square units, by counting the squares.

c) Calculate the area of each parallelogram, in square units, using a formula.

5. Calculate the area of each parallelogram to two decimal places.

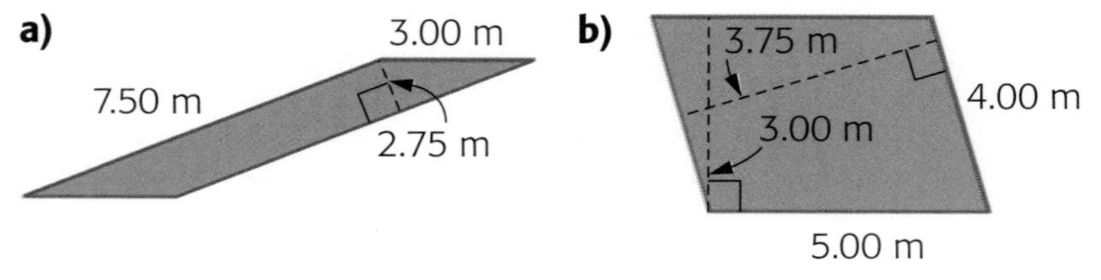

6. a) Draw each parallelogram on 1 cm square dot paper. Then label a base and the corresponding height.

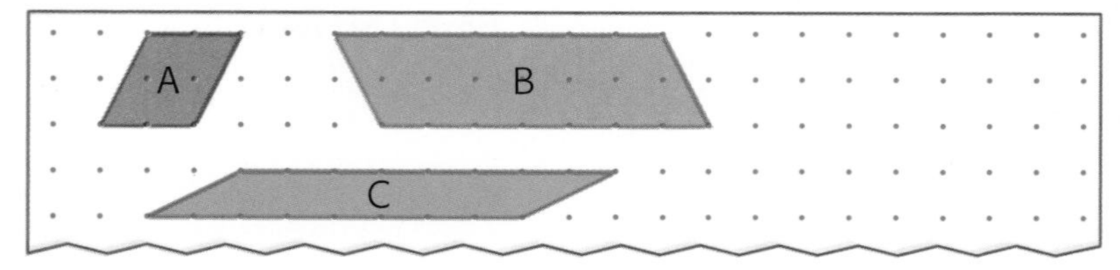

b) Calculate the area of each parallelogram.

7. Complete the table.

	Base	Height	Area of parallelogram
a)	4 m	■ m	28 m^2
b)	20 cm	11 cm	■ cm^2
c)	■ cm	9 cm	63 cm^2
d)	1.7 m	2.6 m	■ m^2
e)	0.6 m	■ m	4.2 m^2
f)	27.5 cm	32.6 cm	■ cm^2

8. Draw three different parallelograms, each with an area of 36 cm^2.

Reading Strategy

Use what you already know about calculating the area of a rectangle to help you solve this problem.

9. Draw a parallelogram, and label it A. Now draw two more parallelograms, as described below.

a) a parallelogram with half the area of A

b) a parallelogram with twice the area of A

10. Draw a parallelogram in which both the base and the height are sides. Explain your thinking.

11. Thrillville Amusement Park needs a parking lot. The parking spaces will be angled in a row. The owners of the park expect that most vehicles will be less than 5.0 m long and 2.8 m wide, with both doors open. The cost to pave is $1.25 for each square metre.

a) Sketch the parking lot.

b) Complete the following table. Show your calculations.

Number of parking spaces	Area (m^2)	Total cost ($)
1		
5		
10		
15		

12. Why do you not usually multiply the side lengths of a parallelogram to calculate its area?

5.2 The Area of a Triangle

YOU WILL NEED
- graph paper

Develop and apply the formula for the area of a triangle.

LEARN ABOUT the Math

Yan designed three class flags. The class decided to choose the biggest flag.

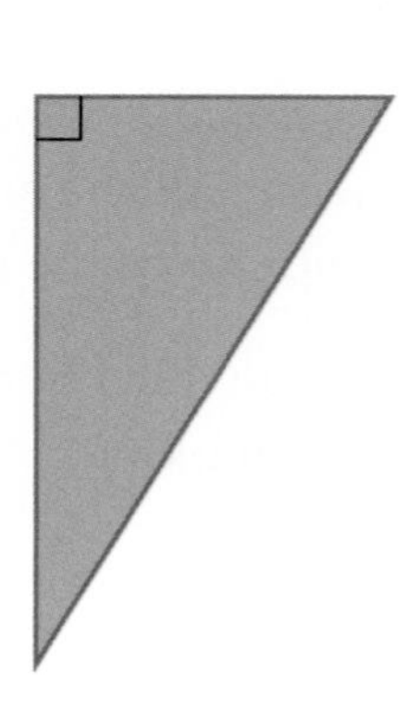

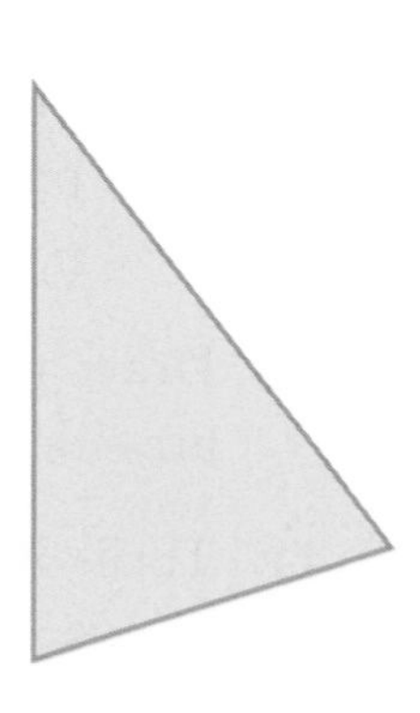

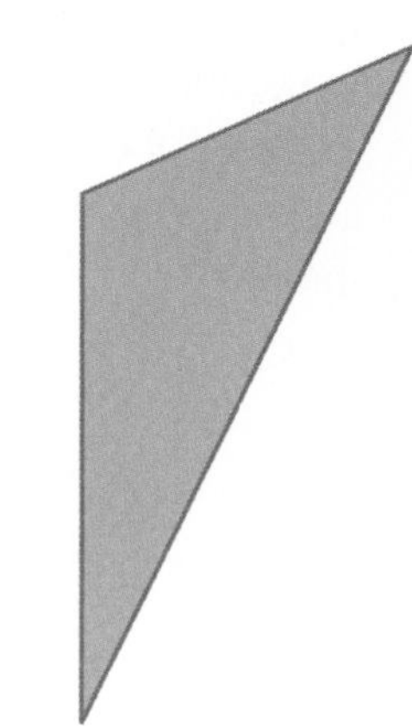

Which flag is the biggest?

Example 1 | Calculating the area of a right triangle

Calculate the area of the green flag.

Yan's Solution

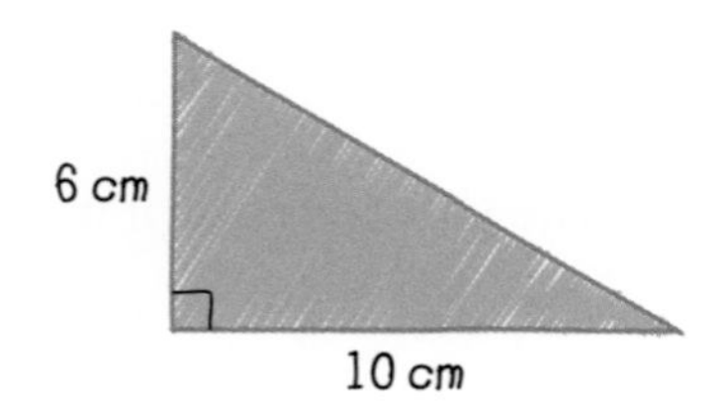

I measured the triangle. It's a right triangle.
It has a base of 10 cm and a height of 6 cm.

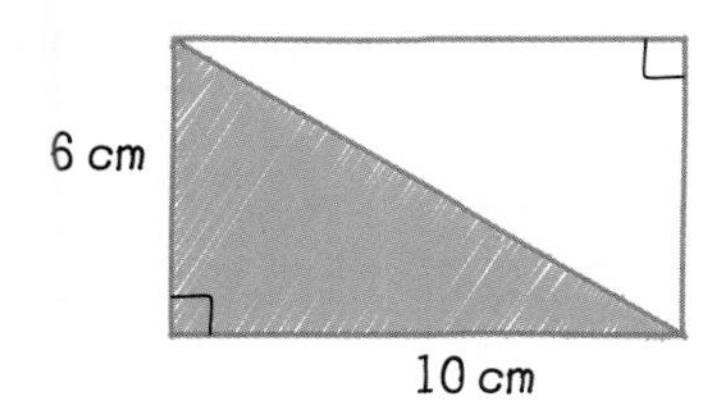

The triangle has a right angle, so I made a rectangle that includes it. The flag is half of the rectangle. The rectangle has the same base and height that the triangle does.

Area = (6 cm x 10 cm) ÷ 2
= 30 cm^2
The area of the green flag is 30 cm^2.

The area of the rectangle is 6 cm × 10 cm.
The area of the triangle is half of this.

Example 2 | Calculating the area of an acute triangle

Calculate the area of the yellow flag.

Liam's Solution

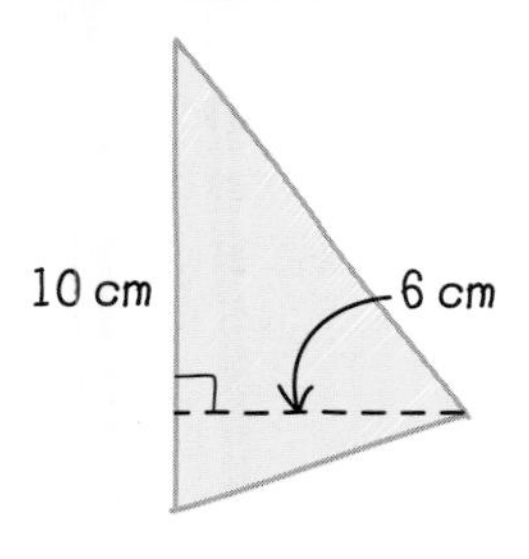

I measured the triangle. It's an acute triangle.
It has a base of 10 cm and a height of 6 cm.

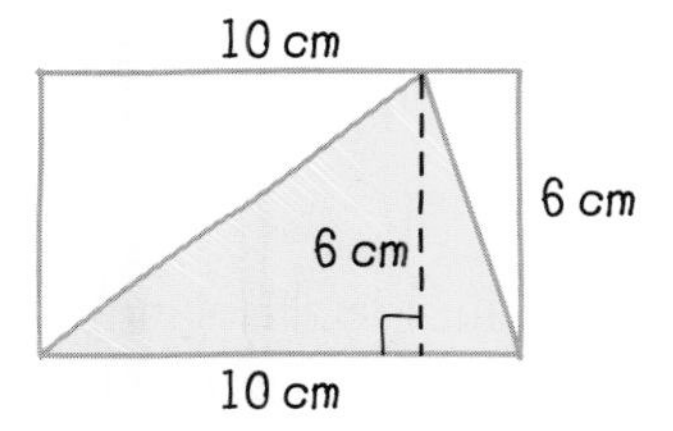

I imagined the triangle as part of a rectangle with the same base and same height as the triangle.

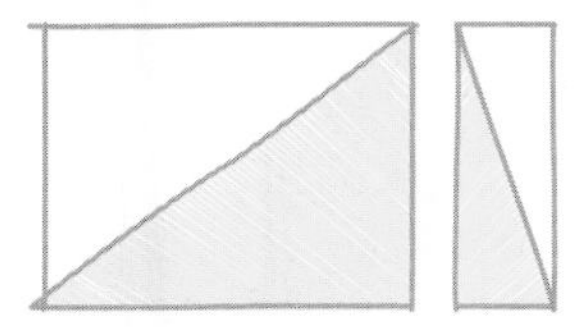

I imagined the rectangle being split into two rectangles along the triangle's height.
I noticed that each part of the yellow triangle is half the area of each of the two new rectangles.

Area = (6 cm x 10 cm) ÷ 2
= 30 cm^2
The area of the yellow flag is 30 cm^2.

This meant that the area of the triangle must have been half the total area of the rectangle with the same base and same height.

Example 3 | Calculating the area of an obtuse triangle

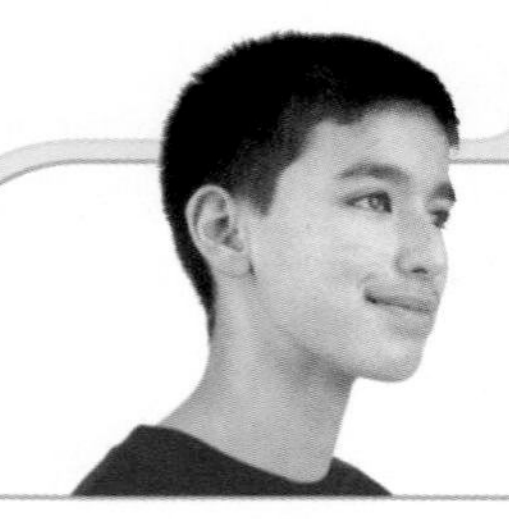

Calculate the area of the blue flag.

Nolan's Solution

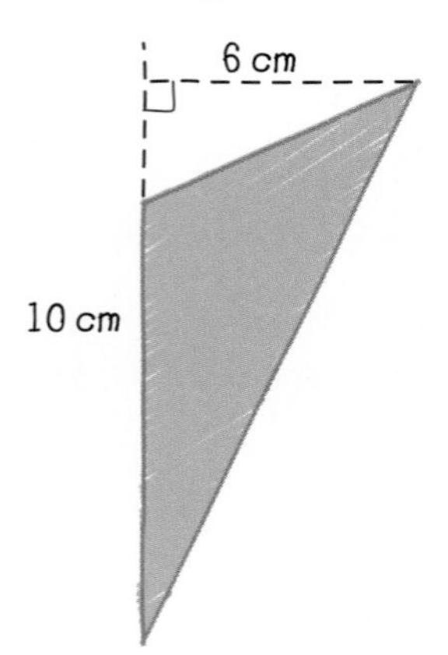

I measured the triangle. It's an obtuse triangle. It has a base of 10 cm. The height of the triangle is 6 cm. I measured it outside the triangle.

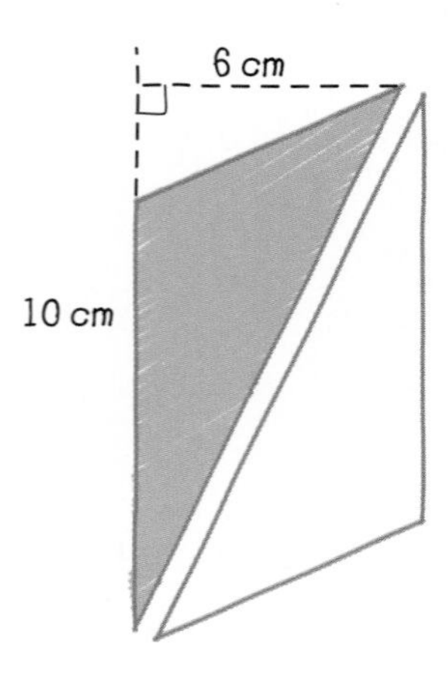

It was hard to imagine the triangle as half of a rectangle. It was easier to imagine another identical triangle, arranged to form a parallelogram. This parallelogram has the same base and same height as the triangle.

Area = (6 cm x 10 cm) ÷ 2
= 30 cm^2

The area of the blue flag is 30 cm^2.

All the flags have the same area, so the class can pick any one of them.

I thought about rearranging this parallelogram into a rectangle, but I knew that the area of a parallelogram is base × height. I multiplied 6 × 10, and then divided by 2. I didn't need to do the rearranging.

Reflecting

A. Can every triangle be shown as half of a parallelogram?

B. What is the formula for the area of a triangle?

***WORK WITH** the Math*

Example 4 | Choosing dimensions to calculate area

Fiona designed this flag. Is her flag bigger or smaller than Yan's flags?

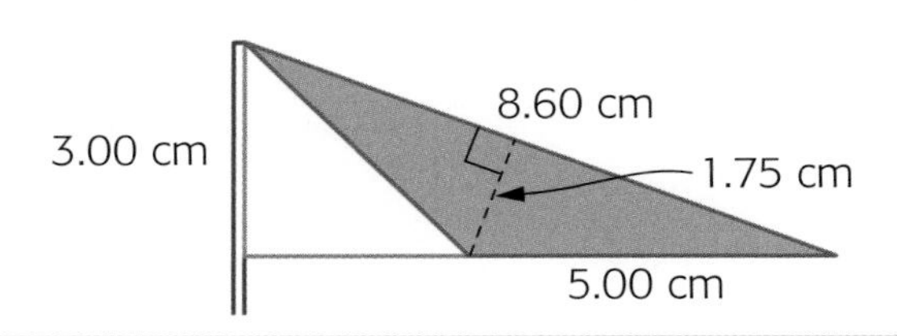

Solution

$A = (5.00 \text{ cm} \times 3.00 \text{ cm}) \div 2$
$= 7.50 \text{ cm}^2$

Use the 5.00 cm side as the base and 3.00 cm as the height.

$A = (8.60 \text{ cm} \times 1.75 \text{ cm}) \div 2$
$= 7.53 \text{ cm}^2$

Or, use the 8.60 cm side as the base and 1.75 cm as the height.
The second answer is a little different from the first answer, probably because Fiona didn't measure as carefully as she should have. It's very close, though.

The area of Fiona's flag is about 7.5 cm^2.
This is a lot less than the area of Yan's flags.

Example 5 | Calculating area on a geoboard

Michael created a triangle on a geoboard. What is the area of the triangle?

Solution

$A = (b \times h) \div 2$
$= (6 \times 9) \div 2$
$= 54 \div 2$
$= 27$ square units

The triangle is obtuse. Its base is from 1 to 7, or 6 units. Its height is from 1 to 10, or 9 units. Its area is the base multiplied by the height, divided by 2.

A Checking

1. Calculate the area of each triangle.

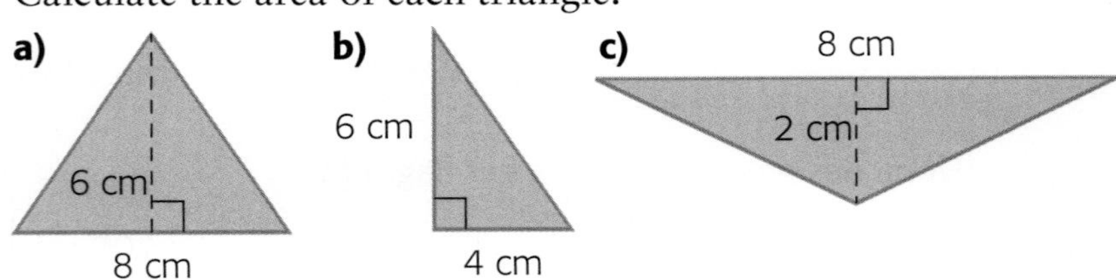

2. Complete the table.

	Base	Height	Area of triangle
a)	4 cm	9 cm	■ cm^2
b)	12 cm	45 cm	■ cm^2
c)	3.5 m	3.0 m	■ m^2
d)	6.0 m	7.5 m	■ m^2

A Practising

3. Draw each triangle on centimetre grid paper and estimate its area. Based on your estimates, predict whether any of the triangles have the same area. Check by measuring and by calculating.

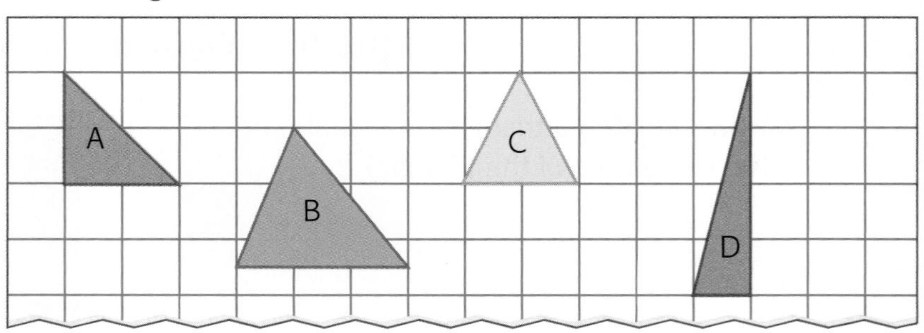

4. Calculate the area of each purple triangle.

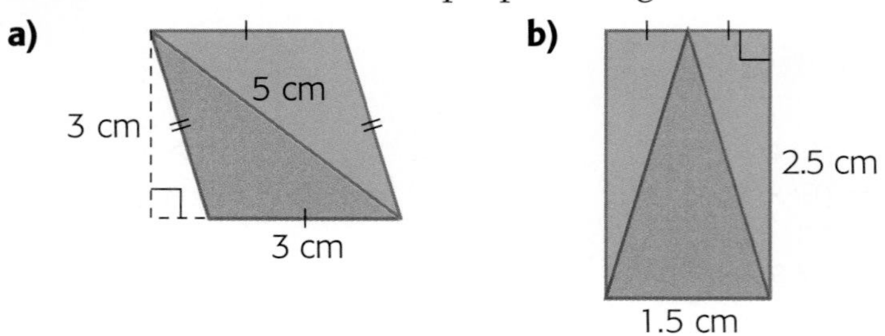

5. Complete the table.

	Base	Height	Area of triangle
a)	6 cm	■ cm	72 cm^2
b)	■ m	6.0 m	10.2 m^2
c)	40 mm	9 cm	■ cm^2
d)	250 mm	■ cm	625 cm^2

6. Measure a base and a height for each triangle. Then calculate the area of each triangle.

a)

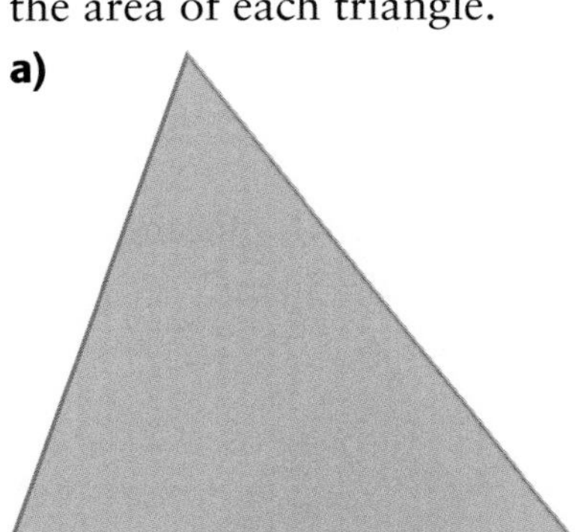

b)

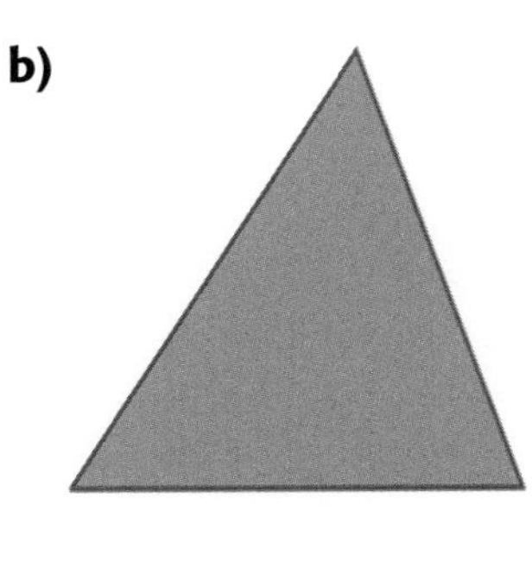

5 m

4 m

7. Calculate the area of the green triangle at the left.

8. Calculate the area of each shape. Use a ruler to measure the sides.

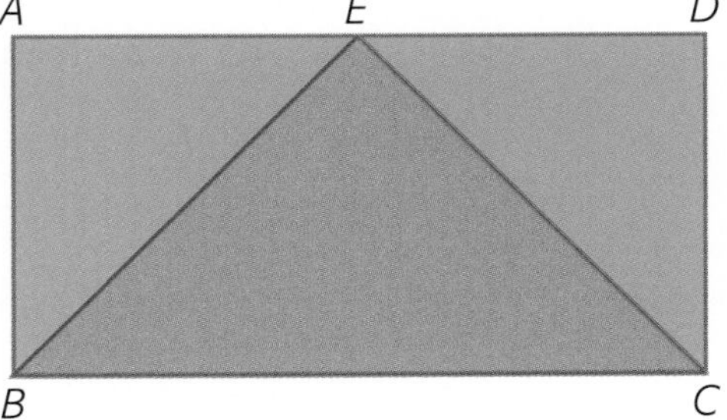

a) $\triangle BEC$

b) $\triangle EDC$

c) $\triangle ABE$

d) rectangle $ABCD$

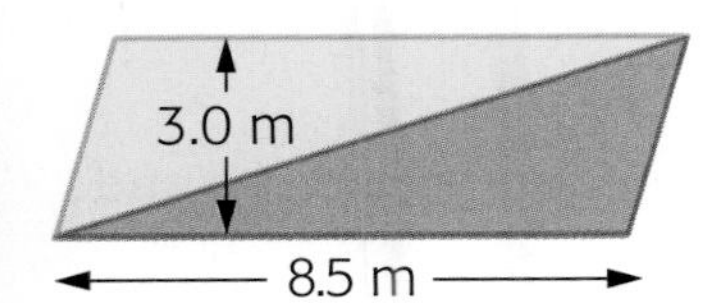

9. a) Calculate the area of the yellow fabric in the flag at the left.

b) The price of the yellow fabric is $8.40/m^2. Calculate the cost of the yellow fabric for one flag.

c) Calculate the area of the yellow fabric needed for 10 flags.

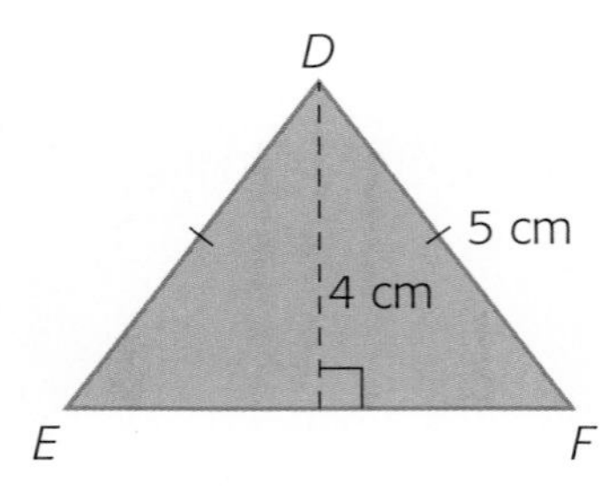

10. The perimeter of $\triangle DEF$ is 16 cm.

a) How long is EF?

b) Calculate the area of $\triangle DEF$.

11. The perimeter of $\triangle ABC$ is 58 cm. Calculate the area of $\triangle ABC$.

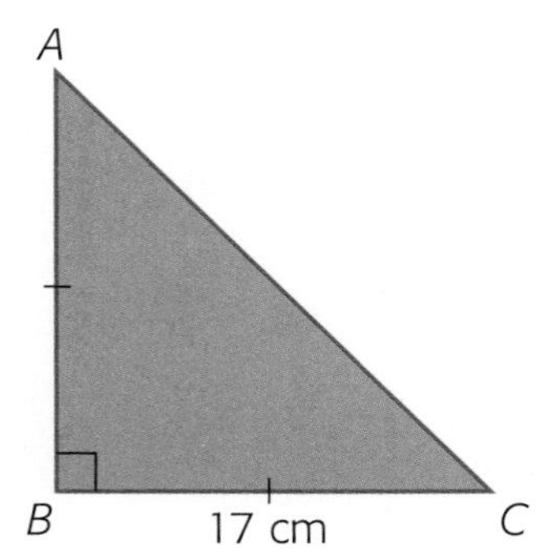

12. Determine each missing value.

a) $A = 283.5 \text{ cm}^2$

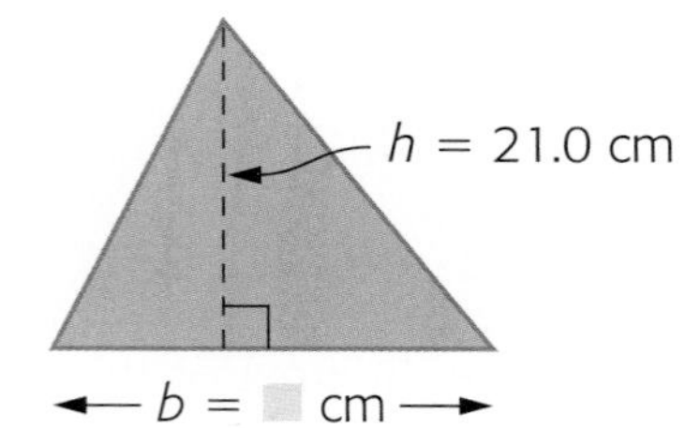

b) $A = 1.6 \text{ mm}^2$

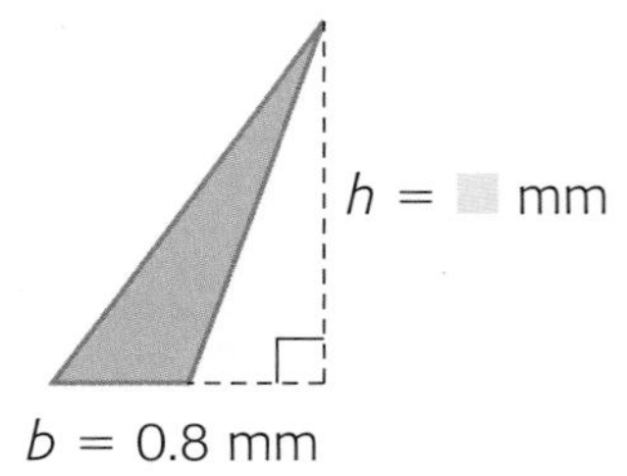

13. Design a kite by combining four triangles. Calculate the area of each triangle and the total area of the kite.

14. A triangle with an area of 8 cm^2 is twice as long and twice as high as another triangle. What is the area of the other triangle?

15. Can a triangle and a parallelogram have the same area? Explain.

16. Triangle A has two sides that measure 4 cm and one side that measures 5 cm. Triangle B has a base of 4 cm and a height of 5 cm. Which triangle has the greater area?

17. $\triangle ABC$ has three different pairs of bases and heights, as shown at the left.

a) Does every triangle have three different pairs of bases and heights? Explain.

b) When you use a formula to calculate the area of a triangle, does it matter which base-height pair you use? Explain.

A height B C base
A base B C height
A base B C height

5.3 Exploring Circumference and Diameter

YOU WILL NEED

- wheels
- a measuring tape or a metre stick

GOAL

Investigate the relationship between the diameter and circumference of a circle.

circumference

the boundary of a circle; the length of this boundary

diameter

a line segment that joins two points on the circumference of a circle and passes through the centre; the length of this line segment; the diameter is the longest line segment that can be drawn inside a circle

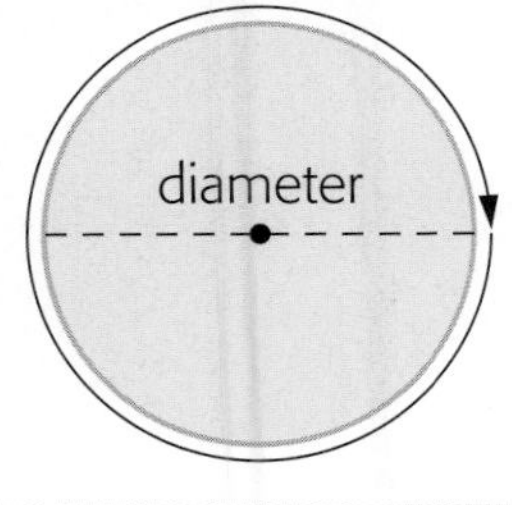

EXPLORE the Math

Matthew is building a trundle wheel for his school. A trundle wheel can be used to measure long distances. Matthew wants his trundle wheel to roll around exactly once every metre, so the wheel must have a **circumference** of 1 m. He wonders what the **diameter** of the wheel should be.

What should be the diameter of Matthew's trundle wheel?

5.4 Calculating Circumference

YOU WILL NEED

- a calculator
- a compass

GOAL

Apply the formula for the circumference of a circle using π.

LEARN ABOUT the Math

Nolan is making dream catchers. He wants to know how to predict the length of the branches he needs for the circle frame.

How can you predict the circumference when you know the diameter?

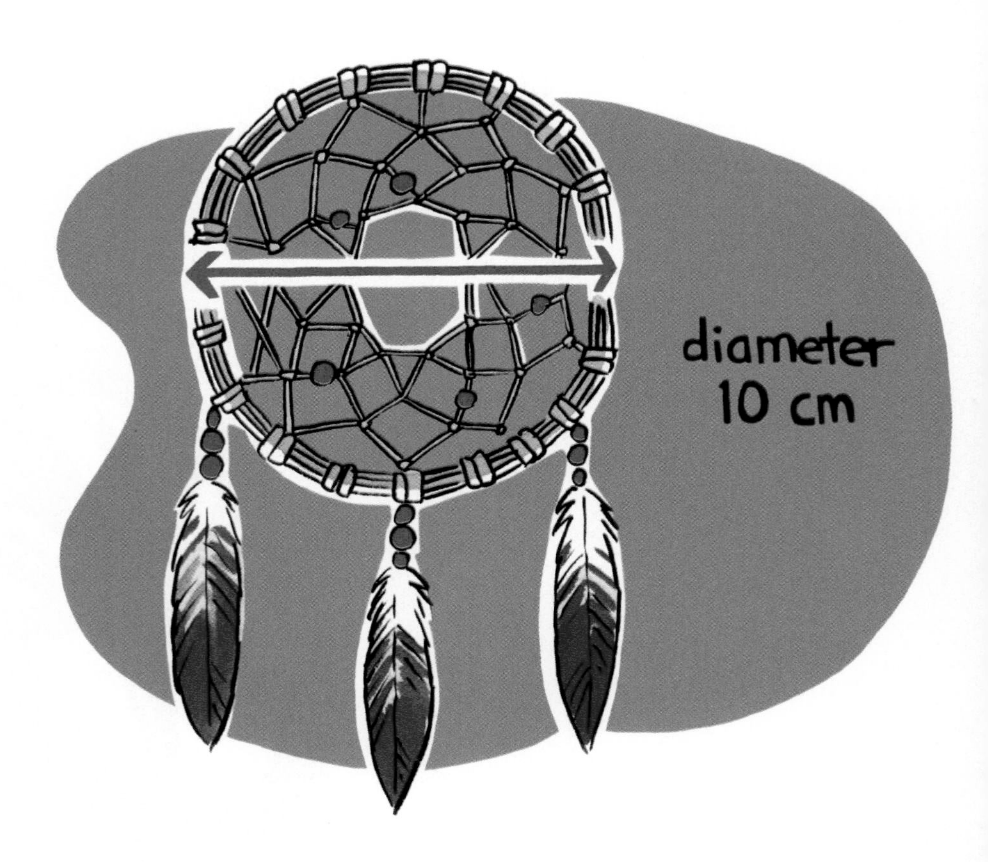

Example 1 | Calculating circumference using diameter

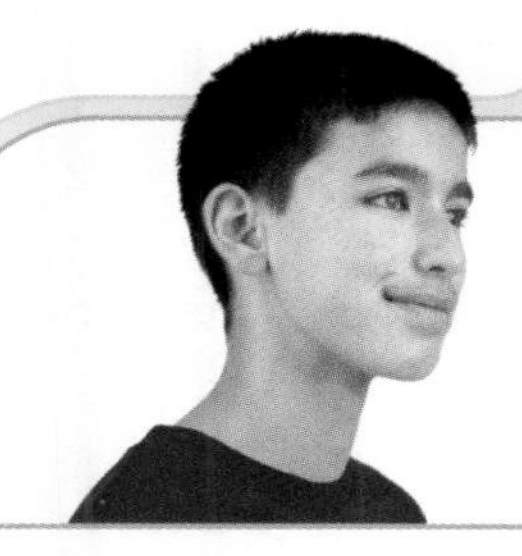

Write a formula that uses the diameter of a circle to calculate its circumference.

Nolan's Solution

Diameter (cm)	Circumference (cm)
5.0	15.7
10.0	31.4
15.0	47.1
20.0	62.8

I modelled dream catchers with circles.
I traced circles that were different sizes and measured the diameters.
Then I measured the circumferences with string and a tape measure.
I recorded the measurements in a table.

$15.7 : 5.0 = 3.14 : 1$
$31.4 : 10.0 = 3.14 : 1$
$47.1 : 15.0 = 3.14 : 1$
$62.8 : 20.0 = 3.14 : 1$

I wrote the measurements as ratios.

I calculated the ratio of the circumference to the diameter for each circle. I noticed they were all equal. My teacher told me that this ratio is called **π.**

Another way to write this is
Circumference : Diameter = $\pi : 1$
Each time,
$C = \pi \times d$

π (pi)
the ratio of the circumference of a circle to its diameter; its value is about 3.14

Communication | *Tip*

When you do calculations that involve measurements, it is important that the result not seem more precise than the measurements, so you should round the results. In this book, round your final result to the same number of decimal places that are in the least precise measurement.

For example, $1.60 \text{ m} \times 1.24 \text{ m} = 1.984$
round to two decimal places $= 1.98 \text{ m}^2$

radius

half of a diameter; the distance from the centre of a circle to a point on the circumference

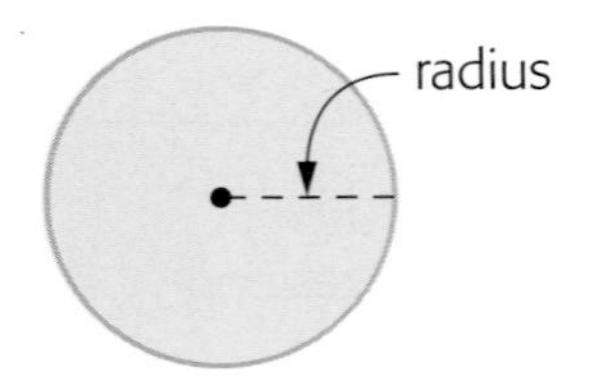

Reflecting

A. How can you estimate the circumference of a circle when you know its **radius** instead of its diameter?

B. How can you estimate the diameter of a circle when you know its circumference?

C. Suppose that you had to determine the circumference of the following circle. Would you use a formula with the diameter, or would you measure the circumference? Explain your choice.

WORK WITH the Math

Example 2 | Determining circumference using a calculator

Determine the circumference of this circle.

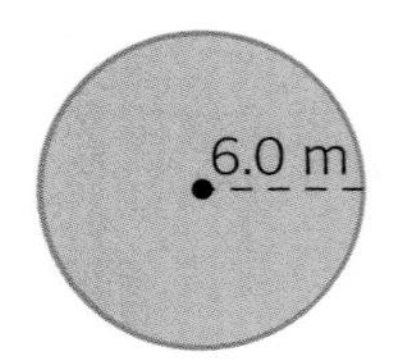

Solution

$C = \pi d$	Use the formula for circumference. The radius of the circle is 6.0 m, so its diameter is 12.0 m.
1 2 . 0 [×] [π] [=] 37.69911184	Multiply the diameter by π. Use the [π] key on your calculator. If you don't have a [π] key, estimate with 3.14.
The circumference is about 37.7 m.	Answer to one decimal place because the radius is given to one decimal place.

Example 3 | Determining diameter

This circle has a circumference of 10.0 cm.
Determine its diameter.

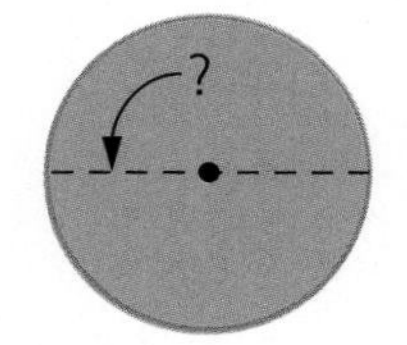

Solution

$C = \pi \times d$ $10.0 \text{ cm} = \pi \times d$	Use the formula. Substitute in the measurement you know.
$d = 10.0 \text{ cm} \div \pi$ $= 3.184 \ldots$	The circumference is equal to $\pi \times d$, so the diameter must be equal to the circumference divided by π. Use a calculator. Use the [π] key or 3.14.
The circumference is about 3.2 cm.	Answer to one decimal place because the circumference is given to one decimal place.

A Checking

1. Determine the circumference of a circle with each diameter.

a) 5 cm **b)** 4.7 cm

2. Determine the diameter and the circumference of a circle with each radius.

a) 10 cm **b)** 8.2 m

B Practising

3. Determine the circumference of a circle with each diameter.

a) 4.5 cm **c)** 6.4 cm **e)** 7 mm
b) 1.7 cm **d)** 36.0 m **f)** 4.0 cm

4. Determine the circumference of a circle with each radius.

a) 7 mm **c)** 6.3 cm **e)** 23.1 m
b) 19.5 cm **d)** 9.0 cm **f)** 0.05 m

5. The diameter of each wheel on Xavier's bicycle is 80 cm. Determine the circumference of each wheel.

6. Measure the diameter of each circle. Then determine the circumference.

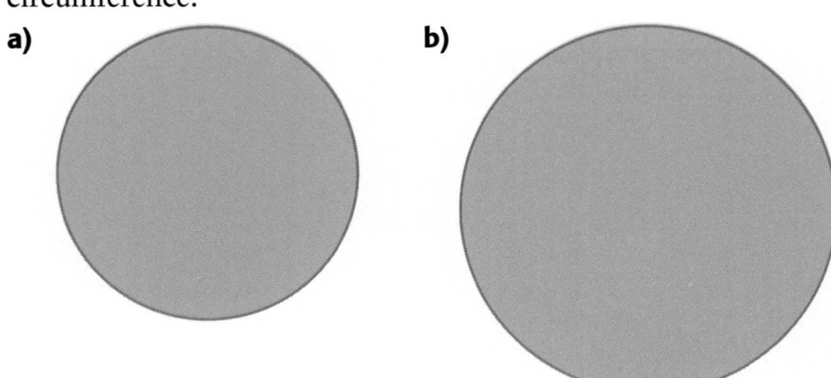

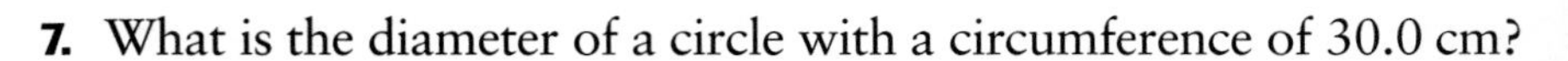

7. What is the diameter of a circle with a circumference of 30.0 cm?

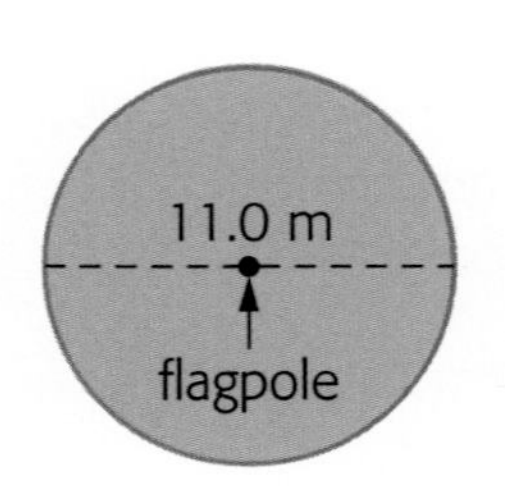

8. At summer camp, Maria uses chalk to draw a meeting circle around a flagpole. The distance from one side of the circle to the other through the flagpole in the centre is 11.0 m. What is the circumference of the chalk circle?

9. Complete the table.

Item	r	d	C
clock	9.0 cm	■	■
watch	■	36 mm	■
round tea bag	1.9 cm	■	■
sewer cover	■	62 cm	■
circle protractor	5.9 cm	■	■
electric fan	■	201 mm	■

10. At a zoo, the giraffes are fenced inside a circular field with a radius of 700 m. How long is the fence?

11. The bicycle at the left is called a penny-farthing. In one model, the diameter of the front wheel is 120.0 cm. In another model, the diameter is 150.0 cm. What is the difference in the circumferences of these front wheels?

12. For hockey practice, Rosa has to skate around a faceoff circle five times. The faceoff circle has a diameter of 9.0 m. About how far does Rosa have to skate?

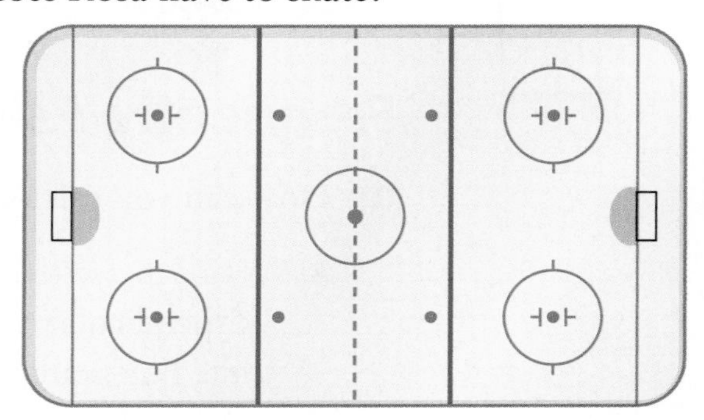

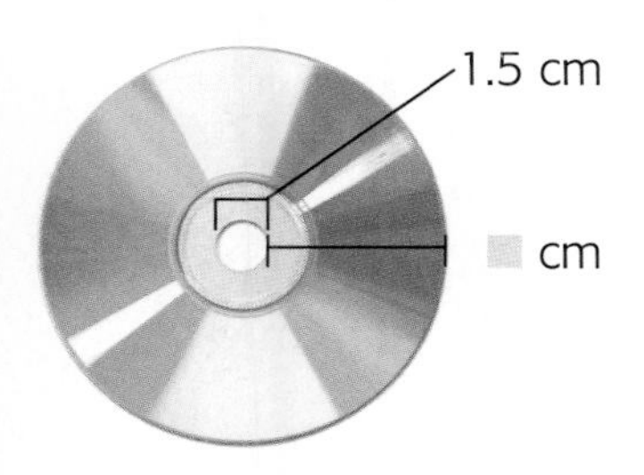

13. The circumference of the CD at the left is 37.7 cm. The diameter of the hole in the centre is 1.5 cm. What is the distance from the outside edge of the CD to the inside edge?

14. One of the largest trees in the world is the giant sequoia. It is more than 90 m tall. The diameter of one giant sequoia is 9.2 m. What is the circumference of its trunk?

15. This racetrack consists of a rectangle and two half circles. What is the length of one lap?

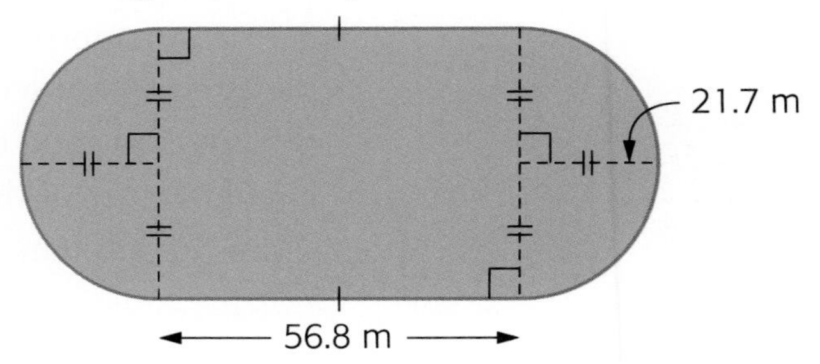

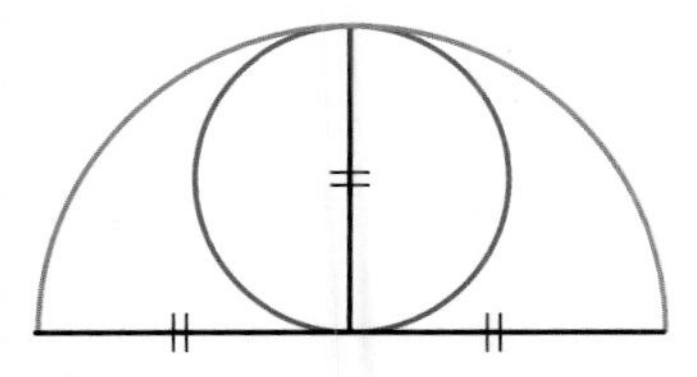

16. The radius of the blue circle at the left is 8 m. Determine the red half-circumference.

17. Brian says that two circles with the same radius can have different circumferences. Do you agree or disagree? Explain.

Mid-Chapter Review

Frequently Asked Questions

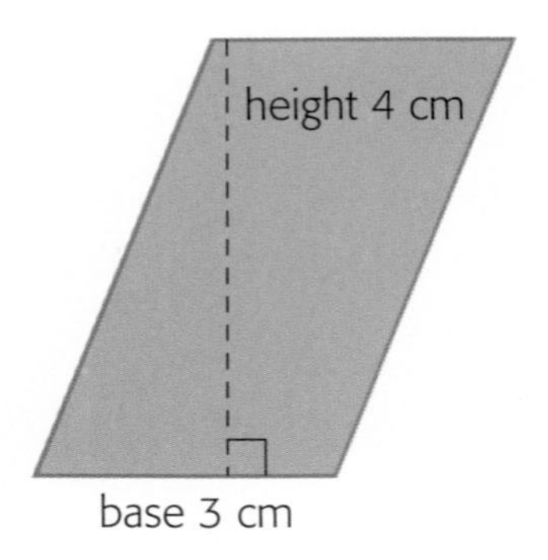

Q: How can you calculate the area of a parallelogram?

A: You can use the formula $A = b \times h$. The height (h) is the perpendicular distance from the base (b) to the opposite side. For example, the area of this parallelogram is $3 \text{ cm} \times 4 \text{ cm} = 12 \text{ cm}^2$.

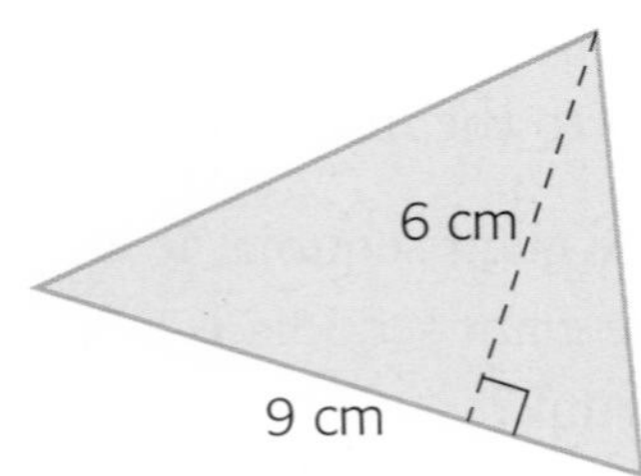

Q: How can you calculate the area of a triangle?

A: You can use the formula $A = (b \times h) \div 2$. For example, the area of this triangle is $(9 \text{ cm} \times 6 \text{ cm}) \div 2 = 27 \text{ cm}^2$.

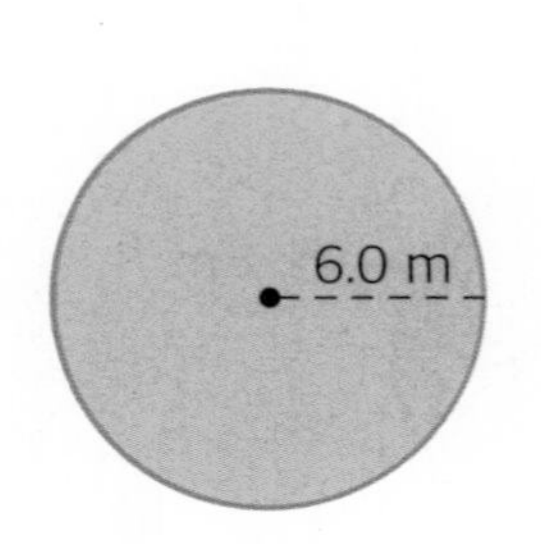

Q: How can you determine the circumference of a circle using the diameter of the circle?

A: You can use the formula $C = \pi \times d$ or $C = 2 \times \pi \times r$, with 3.14 as an approximate value for π. π (pi) is the ratio of the circumference of a circle to its diameter. The value of π is 3.14, expressed to two decimal places. For example, the circumference of the circle at the left is about $2 \times 3.14 \times 6.0 \text{ m} = 37.7 \text{ m}$.

Practice

Lesson 5.1

1. Calculate the area of each parallelogram. Measure, if necessary.

a)

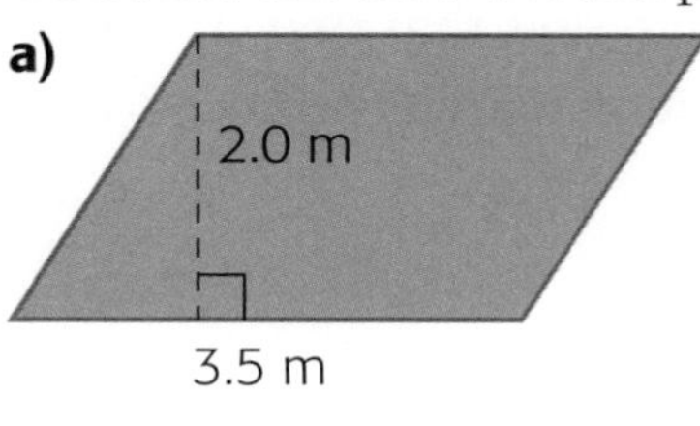

b)

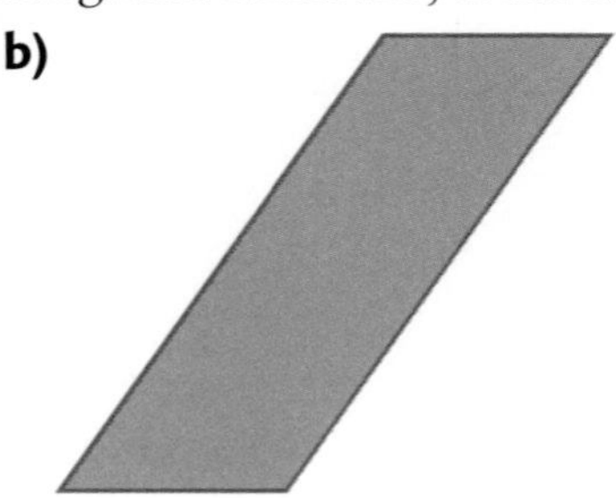

Lesson 5.2

2. Calculate the area of each triangle. Measure, if necessary.

a)

b)

6.96 m

2.5 m

6.5 m

Lesson 5.4

3. Determine the circumference of a circle with each diameter.

a) 26 cm **b)** 10.8 m **c)** 17.2 cm **d)** 3 km

4. What is the circumference of the circle in each sign?

a) 15 cm

c) 20 cm

P

30 M

9 AM-6 PM

MON-FRI

e) 44 cm

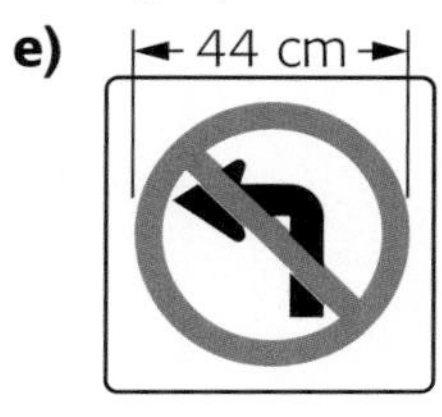

b) 60 cm

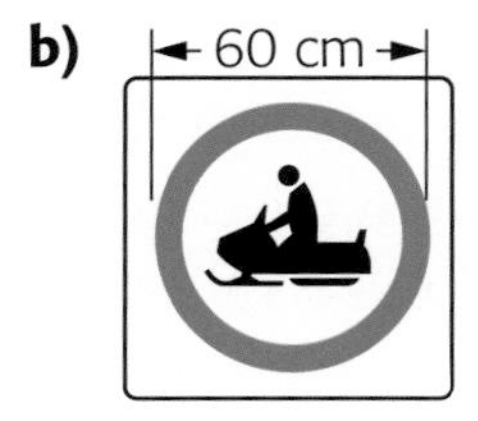

d) 17 cm

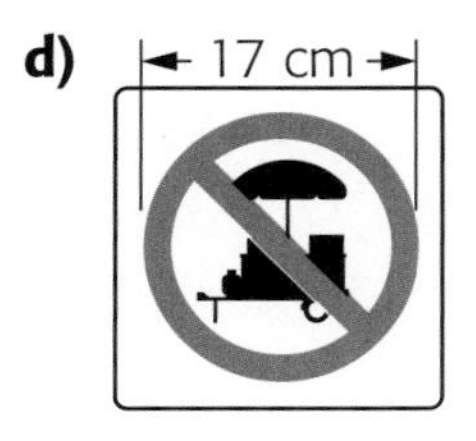

f) 20 cm

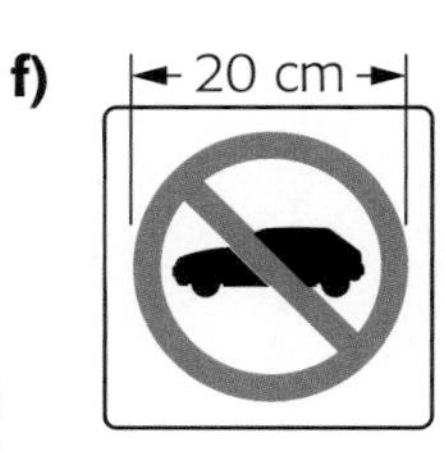

5. Measure the diameter of this circle. Then determine its circumference.

5.5 Estimating the Area of a Circle

YOU WILL NEED

- a compass
- a ruler
- scissors
- centimetre grid paper
- glue or tape
- a CD

GOAL

Estimate the area of a circle.

LEARN ABOUT the Math

Julie's school has made a CD of their concert. The school plans to sell the CDs as a fundraiser. Each student in Julie's class needs to design a CD label, which will be printed on sheets of label paper and then cut out. Julie wants to know the area of one CD label so that she can detemine how many label sheets she needs to buy for the class.

How can you estimate the area of a CD label?

A. Measure the diameter of a CD. Then determine its radius.

B. Make a paper model of the CD. Adjust a compass so that the distance between the compass point and the pencil tip is equal to the radius. Use a ruler to adjust the compass.

C. Put the compass point where you want the centre of the circle to be, and draw the circle.

D. Cut out the circle. You now have a model of the CD.

E. Fold your model into quarters, and then cut out the four equal sections.

F. Form the sections into a shape that almost fills a parallelogram, as shown. Draw the parallelogram.

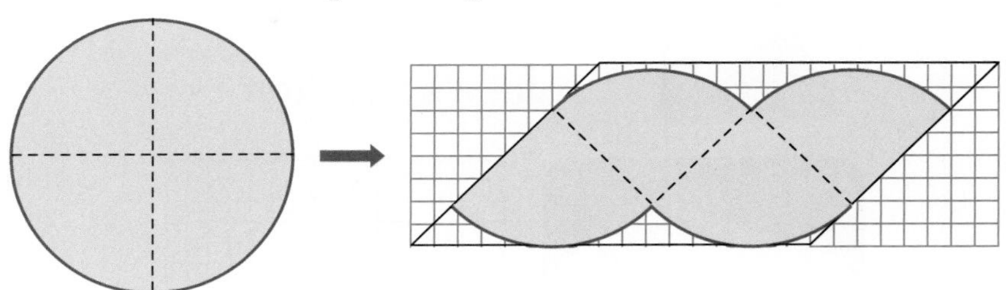

G. Record your data in the following table.

Number of sections	Length of base of parallelogram	Height of parallelogram	Area of parallelogram
4			
8			
16			

H. Make two more models of the CD. Fold one into 8 equal sections and the other into 16 equal sections. Repeat parts F and G for each model.

I. Estimate the area of a CD label using the three values for the area of a parallelogram.

Reflecting

J. In part B, why did you have to adjust your compass to the size of the radius to create the circle?

K. Why is the area of a parallelogram with more sections a better estimate for the area of the circle?

L. What information about the circle do you need in order to calculate the area of the parallelogram that best estimates the area of the circle?

Reading Strategy

Share your answer with a partner. Can your partner add any new ideas or information?

***WORK WITH** the Math*

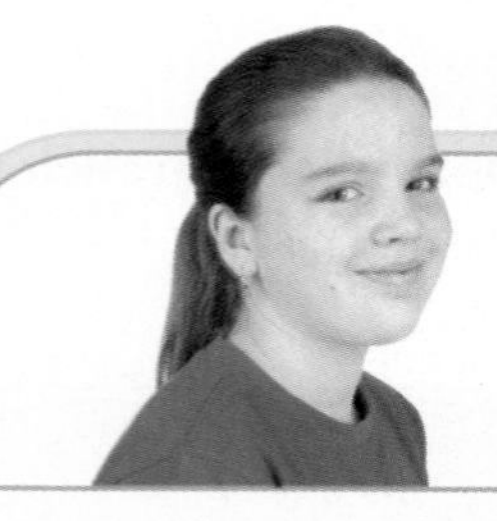

Example 1 | Estimating the area of a circle

Estimate the area of the CD label by counting grid squares.

Julie's Solution

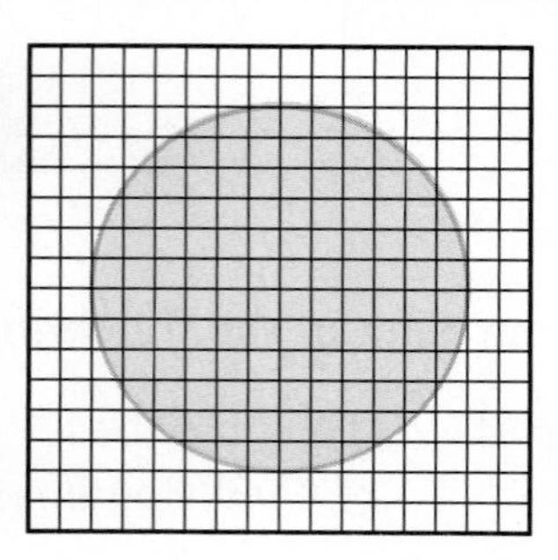

I traced around a CD on centimetre grid paper. I counted the number of whole squares inside the circle. There are 96. Then I mentally combined parts of squares to make whole squares. There are about another 12 squares.

The area is about $96 + 12 = 108\ \text{cm}^2$.

Example 2 | Estimating the area of a circle with squares

Estimate the area of the CD label by enclosing it with squares.

Max's Solution

I traced a model on paper using the CD.

I drew a large square outside the circle and a small square inside the circle.

The area of the large square is $12\ \text{cm} \times 12\ \text{cm} = 144\ \text{cm}^2$.
The area of the small square is $8\ \text{cm} \times 8\ \text{cm} = 64\ \text{cm}^2$.
The area of the CD must be between these areas, or about $104\ \text{cm}^2$.

A Checking

1. Estimate the area of the face of each coin using the method in one of the examples.

B Practising

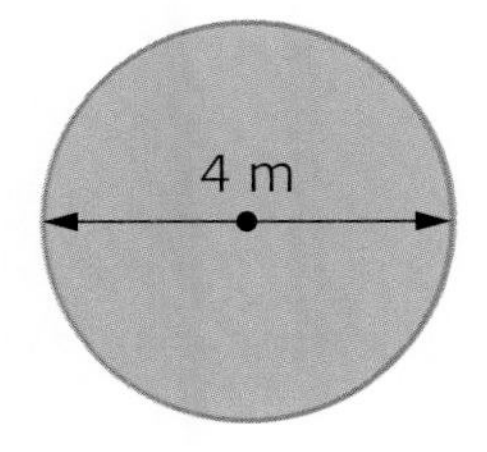

2. The distance across a park fountain is 4 m, as shown at the left. Estimate the area of the cover used during the winter.

3. Katie is building a wall clock in the design and technology club. The minute hand is 15 cm long, and the clock face is flat. About how much glass will she need to cover the clock face?

4. A new circular wading pool at an amusement park is tiled with a design on the bottom. The wading pool is 5 m across. Estimate the area that the tile will need to cover.

5. Estimate the area of each circle.

a) 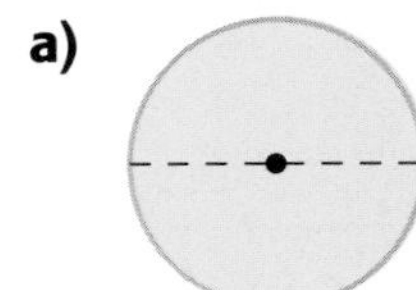

b) 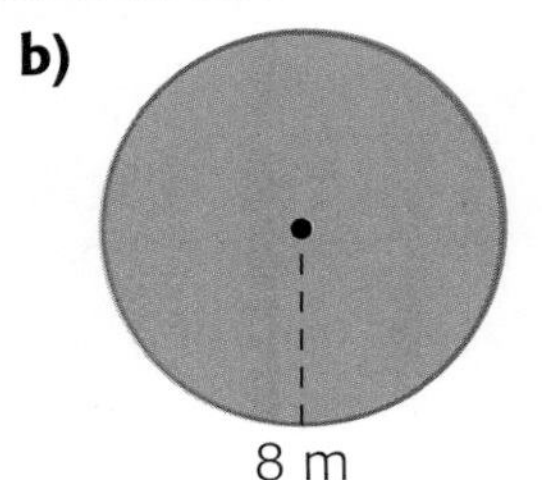

c) 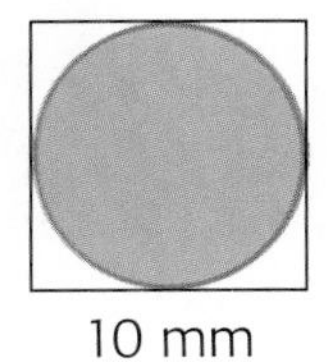

6. About what fraction of the game mat is covered in circles?

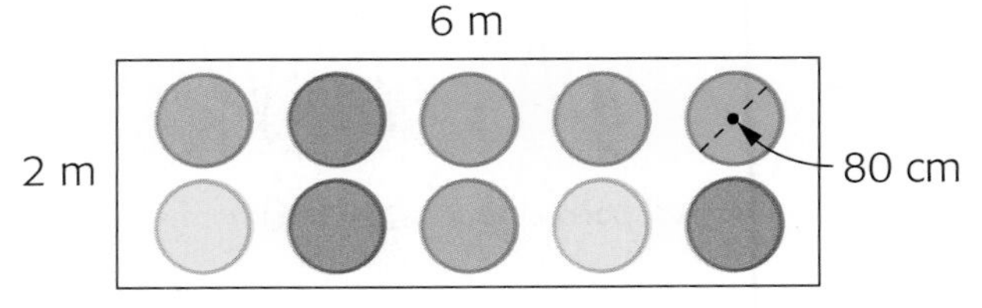

7. One way to estimate the area of a circle is to cut the circle into equal sections and rearrange the sections to form a parallellogram. Another way is to count squares on grid paper. Which way do you think gives the better estimate? Why?

5.6 Calculating the Area of a Circle

YOU WILL NEED
- a calculator
- a compass
- scissors

Develop and apply the formula for the area of a circle.

LEARN ABOUT the Math

Yan is setting up sprinklers to water a field. Each sprinkler sprays water in a circle with a diameter of 8.0 m.

What area of the field does each sprinkler water?

Example 1 | Estimating the area of a circle using a model

I decided a rough estimate is good enough.

Yan's Solution

My circle had a diameter of 8.0 cm. Each 1 cm represents 1 m. I cut my circle into 20 sections and arranged the sections into a parallelogram.

I drew a circle to represent the spray.

radius

height of parallelogram ≐ radius of circle

base of parallelogram ≐ half of circumference

The height of the parallelogram is about 4.0 cm. This is the same as the radius of the circle.
The base of the parallelogram is about 12.0 cm. This is the same as half the circumference of the circle.

$A = b \times h$
$= 12.0 \text{ m} \times 4.0 \text{ m}$
$= 48.0 \text{ m}^2$

The area of the parallelogram is about 48.0 m^2.
Therefore, the area of the circle is also about 48.0 m^2.

I calculated the area of the parallelogram.

Example 2 | Estimating area using a formula

I wanted a more exact value for the area than a rough estimate, so I developed a formula.

Liam's Solution

The formula for the area of a parallelogram is A = b x h.

I used Yan's parallelogram to develop a formula.

Since the base of the parallelogram is half the circumference of the circle, and the height is the radius, I can write the formula as $A = (C \div 2) \times r$.

$C \div 2$ is half the circumference. Half of π x diameter is the same as π x radius. So, I can rewrite the formula for the area of a parallelogram as $A = \pi \times r \times r$.

The height of the parallelogram was about the same as the radius of the circle.
The base of the parallelogram was about half the circumference of the circle.
I didn't want to calculate the circumference if I didn't have to, so I used the idea that the circumference is really $\pi \times$ diameter.
The radius is half the diameter, so the radius is easier to use in my formula.

$$\begin{aligned} A &= \pi \times r \times r \\ &= 3.14 \times 4.0 \text{ m} \times 4.0 \text{ m} \\ &= 3.14 \times 16.0 \text{ m}^2 \\ &= 50.2 \text{ m}^2 \end{aligned}$$

The area watered by each sprinkler is about 50.2 m^2.

I used my formula to calculate the area of the circle.
The diameter of the circle is 8.0 m, so the radius is 4.0 m.
I answered to the same number of decimal places as given in the problem.

Communication | *Tip*

You might see the formula for the area of a circle written as $A = \pi r^2$. The raised 2 after the r means that r is multiplied by itself ($r^2 = r \times r$).

Reflecting

A. What do you need to know about a circle to calculate its area?

B. Suppose that you had to determine the area of the circle at the left. Would you use a formula with the radius, or only measurements? Explain your choice.

***WORK WITH** the Math*

Example 3 | Calculating area using the [π] key

Calculate the area of a circle with a radius of 9.0 cm.

Solution

Use the formula for the area of a circle.

$A = \pi \times r \times r$
$= \pi \times 9.0 \text{ cm} \times 9.0 \text{ cm}$
$= \pi \times 81.0 \text{ cm}^2$
= 254.4690049

Multiply the radius by itself.
Multiply this product by π. Use the [π] key on your calculator.

The area of the circle is 254.5 cm^2.

Answer to one decimal place.

Example 4 | Using an estimate for π

A circular garden stone is needed for the school environment project. The garden stone has a diameter of 5.0 m. What is the area of the garden stone?

Solution

Use the formula for the area of a circle.

$A = \pi \times r \times r$
$= 3.14 \times 2.5 \text{ m} \times 2.5 \text{ m}$
$= 3.14 \times 6.25 \text{ m}^2$
$= 19.625 \text{ m}^2$

The radius of the stone is half the diameter, or 2.5 m.
Multiply the radius by itself.
Use the approximate value for π, which is 3.14.

The area of the garden stone is about 19.6 m^2.

Answer to one decimal place.

A Checking

1. Estimate the area of each object using the formula $A = \pi \times r \times r$.

a)

radius = 10.5 cm

c)

radius = 13 cm

b)

diameter = 14 cm

d)

diameter = 2.8 cm

B Practising

2. Calculate the area of a circle with each measurement.

a) diameter = 7.3 cm

b) radius = 2 cm

c) radius = 2.7 cm

d) diameter = 1.7 cm

7.0 cm

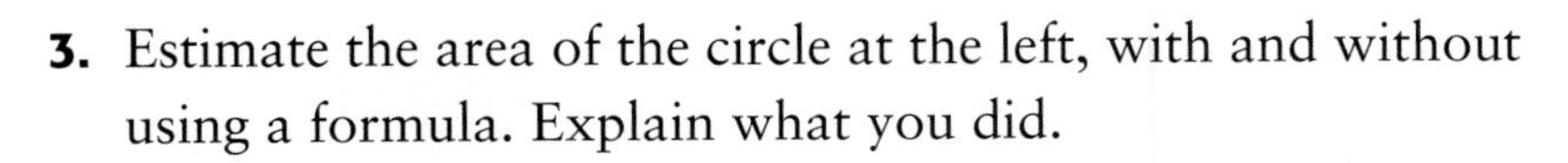

3. Estimate the area of the circle at the left, with and without using a formula. Explain what you did.

4. a) Describe a situation where you would need to know the area of a circle.

b) Describe a situation where you would need to know the circumference of a circle.

5. a) Determine the area of this circle using a formula.

b) Determine the area of each section.

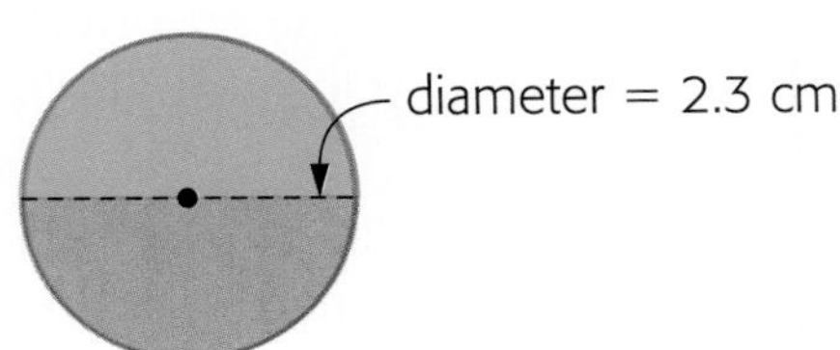

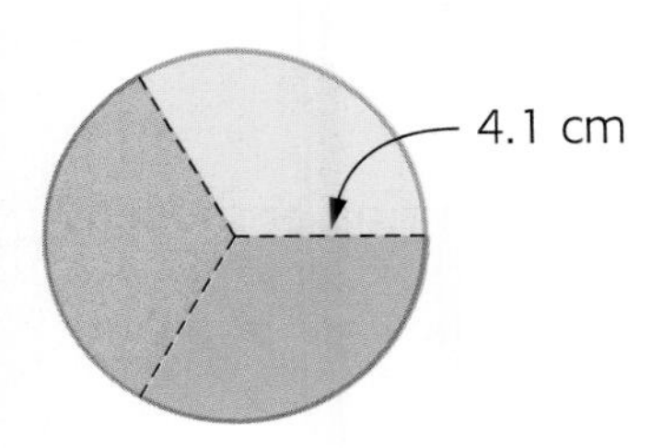

6. a) Determine the area of the circle at the left.

b) The three sections are equal. Determine the area of each section.

7. The radius of a circular pizza is 22.0 cm.
   a) Determine the area of the pizza.
   b) The pizza is cut into four equal pieces. Determine the area of each piece.

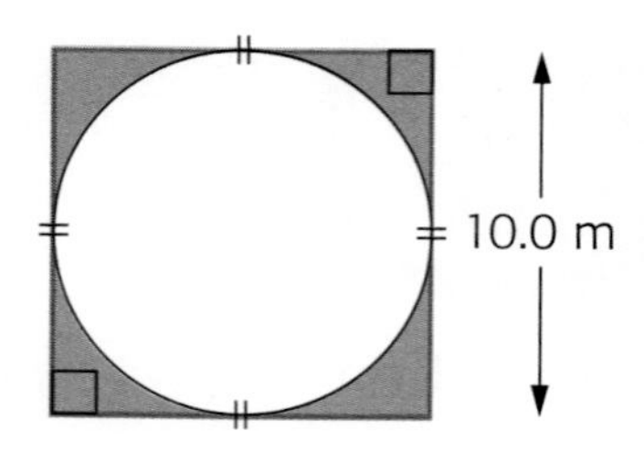

8. a) Determine the area of the square at the left.
   b) Determine the area of the white circle.
   c) Determine the total area of the four red sections.

9. Determine the total area of this figure.

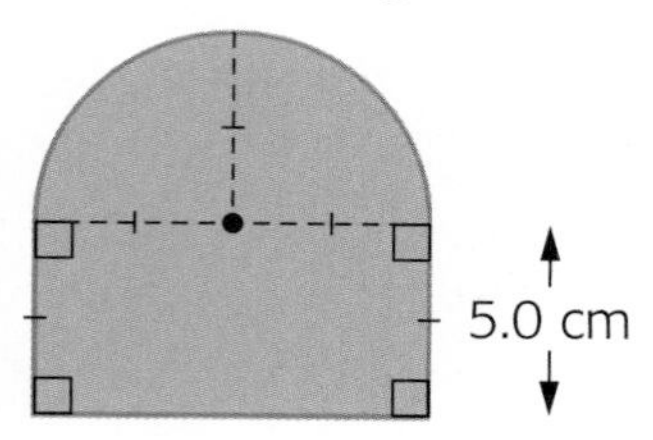

10. Roberto has designed the following park for a new housing development. The park will be a square with a half circle at each end. It will be covered with sod and have a border made of paving stones.

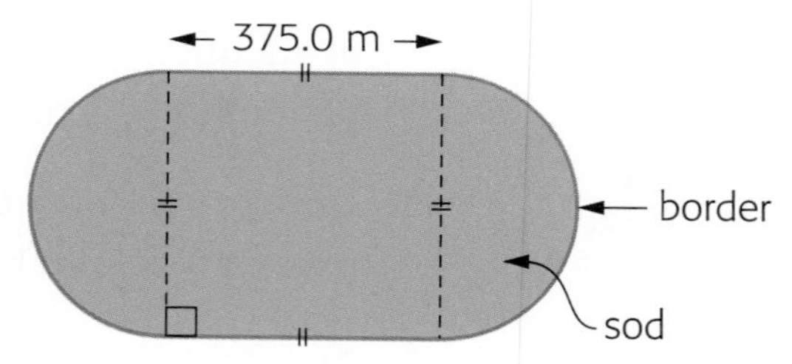

   a) Determine the area of the sod needed to cover the park.
   b) Sod costs $1.25 for each square metre. Determine the cost of the sod needed to cover the park.
   c) Determine the length of the border.
   d) Paving stones cost $2.75 for each square metre. Determine the cost of the border.
   e) Determine the total cost of the sod and the border.

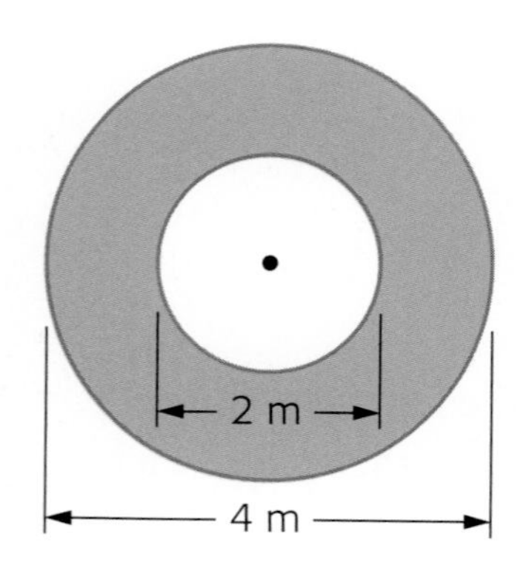

11. Suppose that the radius of a circle doubles. How does the area change?

12. How would you calculate the area of the green ring at the left?

13. Explain the steps you would use to calculate the area of a circle with a circumference of 10.0 cm.

CURIOUS MATH

Pick's Theorem

You can calculate the areas of some shapes on a geoboard by counting squares or using a formula. You can calculate the area of *any* enclosed shape on a geoboard, however, using *Pick's theorem*.

Using Pick's Theorem

Step 1: Count the number of pegs (p) that the elastic band touches.
Step 2: Divide by 2.
Step 3: Add the number of pegs (i) inside the shape.
Step 4: Subtract 1.

For example, $\triangle ABC$ has 6 perimeter pegs and 0 interior pegs.

Area of $\triangle ABC = p \div 2 + i - 1$
$= 6 \div 2 + 0 - 1$
$= 2$ square units

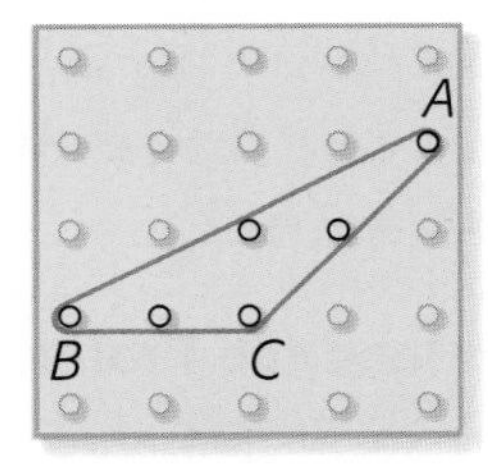

1. Check the area of $\triangle ABC$.

a) Calculate the area of the rectangle around $\triangle ABC$.

b) Calculate the area of each blue triangle.

c) Subtract the total area of the blue triangles from the area of the rectangle. Does your answer agree with the answer using Pick's theorem?

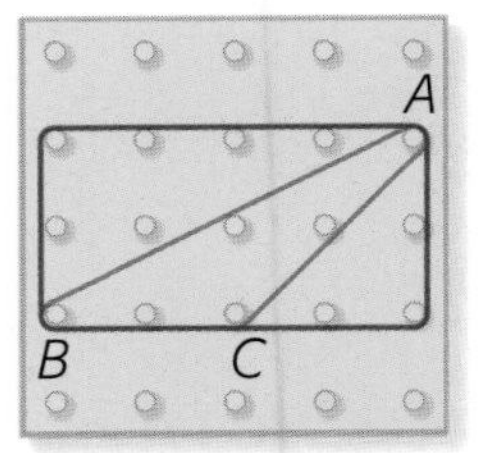

2. Calculate the area of each shape using Pick's theorem. Check by counting squares or using a formula.

a)

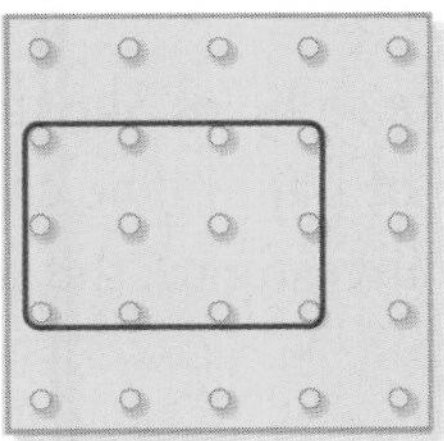

b)

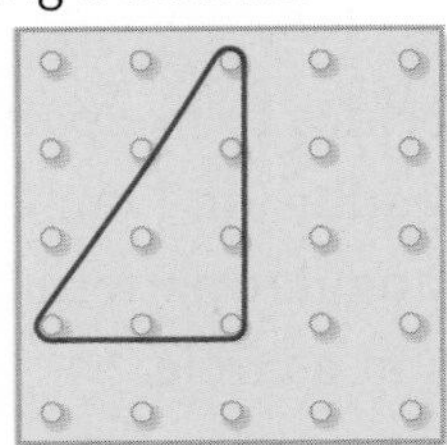

c)

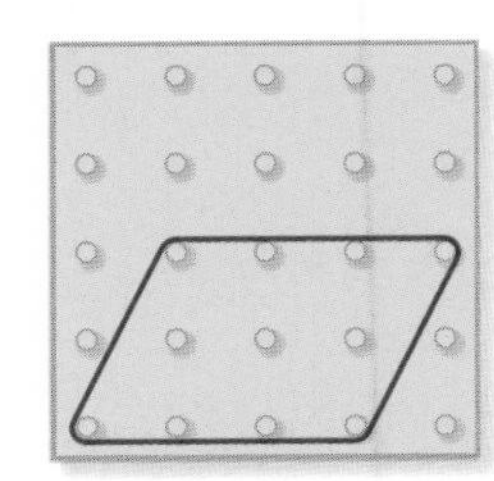

5.7 Solve Problems Using Diagrams

YOU WILL NEED

- pattern blocks
- a ruler
- a calculator
- a compass
- a protractor

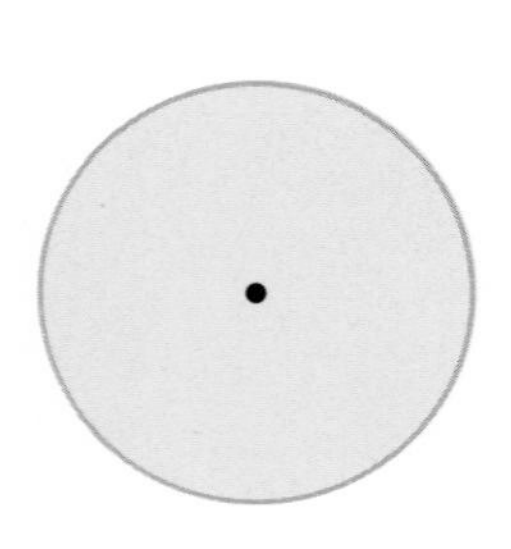

GOAL

Use diagrams to solve problems about the number of degrees in a circle.

LEARN ABOUT the Math

Julie is trying to divide a circle with a marked centre into six equal sections so that she can model the fraction $\frac{5}{6}$.

How can Julie divide the circle using her protractor?

1 Understand the Problem

Julie draws a sketch. She knows that doing this will help her figure out how many degrees she should make the angles at the centre of the circle.

?

2 Make a Plan

Julie decides to use pattern blocks to help. She draws a circle with a radius of 4 cm on a piece of paper. She chooses square and triangular pattern blocks to investigate the number of degrees in a circle.

4 cm

③ Carry Out the Plan

First Julie tries the squares. She puts a vertex of each square on the centre dot of the circle. Only four squares fit.

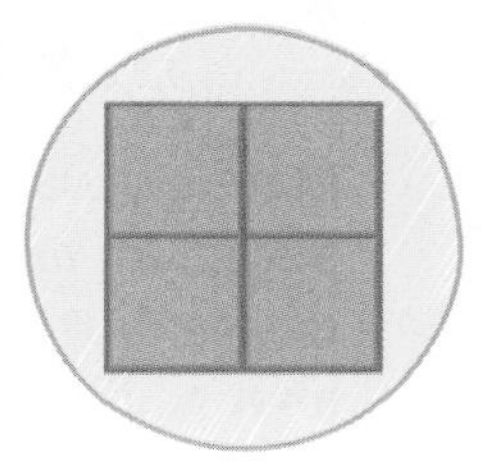

Julie knows that the angle at each vertex of the square is 90°. She realizes that the total of the angles in the centre must be $4 \times 90° = 360°$, but there are only four sections. She needs to divide the circle into six sections.
She decides to try the green triangles. Six green triangles fit.

The triangles are equilateral, so she knows that the angle at each vertex in the centre is 60°. The total of the angles in the centre must be $6 \times 60° = 360°$.

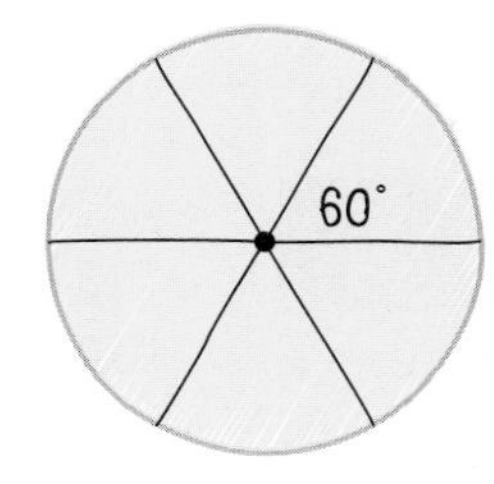

Julie says, "Since the total measure of the angles in the centre of the circle is 360°, each of my sections has to be 60°."

Reflecting

A. How did Julie's diagrams model the angle relationships of the pattern blocks and the circles?

B. How did Julie's original sketch support her method of solving the problem?

WORK WITH the Math

Example | Using diagrams to represent possible solutions

Matthew wants to use 16 square paint-sample cards to create a design for an art project. He wants to use a gold cord to frame the design, but he does not have very much cord. How can Matthew arrange the paint cards so there is the least amount of trim around the design?

Matthew's Solution

1 Understand the Problem

Matthew has to determine the perimeter of some possible designs to figure out if he has enough cord to go around the designs.

2 Make a Plan

Matthew decides to arrange the paint-sample cards in different ways to figure out which design has the least perimeter.

3 Carry Out the Plan

Matthew tries some possible designs.

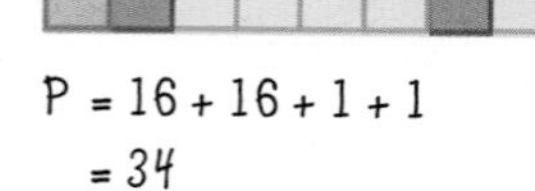

P = 16 + 16 + 1 + 1
= 34

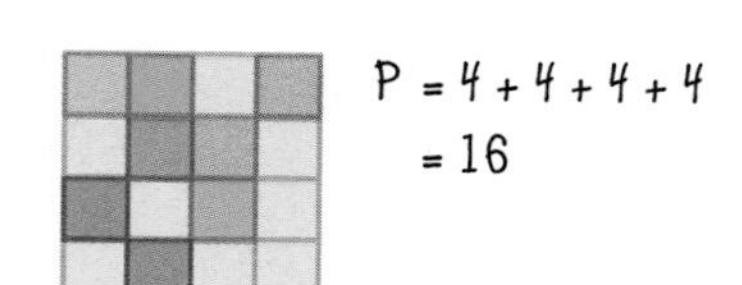

P = 4 + 4 + 4 + 4
= 16

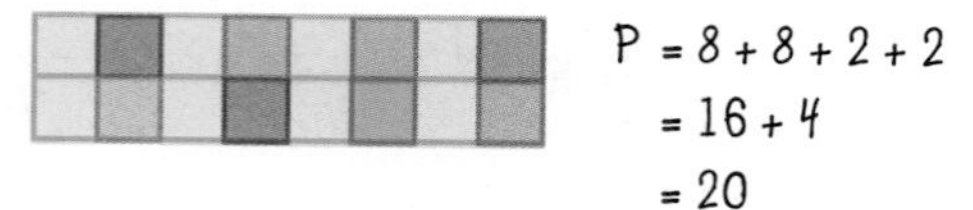

P = 8 + 8 + 2 + 2
= 16 + 4
= 20

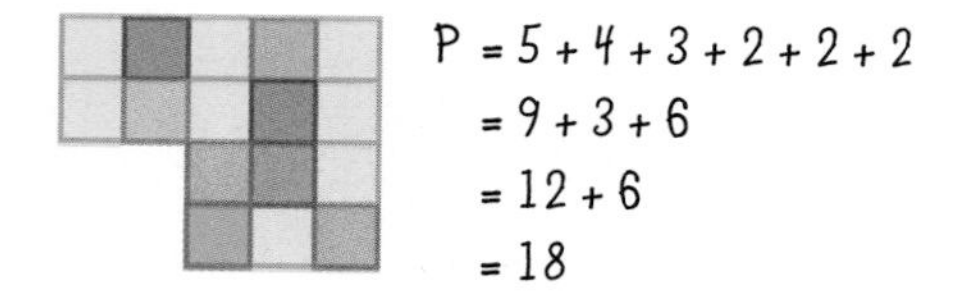

P = 5 + 4 + 3 + 2 + 2 + 2
= 9 + 3 + 6
= 12 + 6
= 18

Of these four designs, the 4 × 4 tile design has the least perimeter because more sides of the cards are inside the design. Matthew decides to use a square shape for his design.

4 Look Back

Matthew knows he did not try every possible design because he noticed that the perimeter increased when the design became longer. He thinks that the square design will always have the least perimeter because more card sides are inside that design.

A Checking

1. Arlene is making a stained-glass window using a rectangle and a half circle, as shown. How much glass will Arlene need?

B Practising

2. A rectangular wading pool at a park measures 6 m by 8 m. Around the pool, there is a tiled border that measures 10 m by 12 m. What is the area of the tiled border around the pool?

3. Julie is estimating the amount of paint she needs for the walls of her 3.4 m by 2.6 m bedroom. Her bedroom is 2.7 m high. One litre of paint covers about 10 m^2. About how much paint does Julie need?

4. Parallelogram A has a base of 10 cm and a height of 50 cm. Parallelogram B is 3 cm higher and has a base that is 5 cm longer. How much greater is the area of parallelogram B?

5. How many different ways can a 360-player marching band be arranged in a rectangle?

6. A tan pattern block has a 30° angle. How many of these blocks can be put together to meet at a point?

7. Sarah cares for 24 cats at the local animal refuge. Six of these cats have short tails, 12 are black, and 15 have long hair. All the cats in the refuge have at least one of these features. One cat is black and has a short tail and long hair. Two cats are black and have short tails, but do not have long hair. Two cats have short tails and long hair, but are not black. How many cats are black and have long hair, but do not have short tails?

MATH GAME

Rolling Circles

In this game, you will estimate the area of a circle, given its radius. Then you will try to form a two-digit number that is close to this area.

Number of players: 2 or more

YOU WILL NEED
- a 10-sided die numbered 0 to 9
- a pair of dice numbered 1 to 6
- a calculator

How to Play

1. Roll the 10-sided die. The number you roll represents the radius of a circle. Estimate the area of the circle.
2. Roll the pair of dice. Use the numbers you roll to form any two-digit number.
3. If the difference between the area of the circle and the two-digit number is 10 or less, score 4 points.
   If the difference is between 10 and 20, score 2 points.
   If the difference is 20 or greater, score 1 point.
4. Take turns. The first player to score 10 points wins.

Nolan's Turn

I rolled a 2 with the 10-sided die.

The area of the circle is $\pi \times 2 \times 2$, which is about $3 \times 2 \times 2$, or 12 square units.

Then I rolled a 3 and a 1 with the regular dice.

I can make 13 or 31. I'll make 13.

$13 - 12 = 1$
$1 < 10$, so I score 4 points.

Chapter Self-Test

1. Calculate the area of each parallelogram.

a)

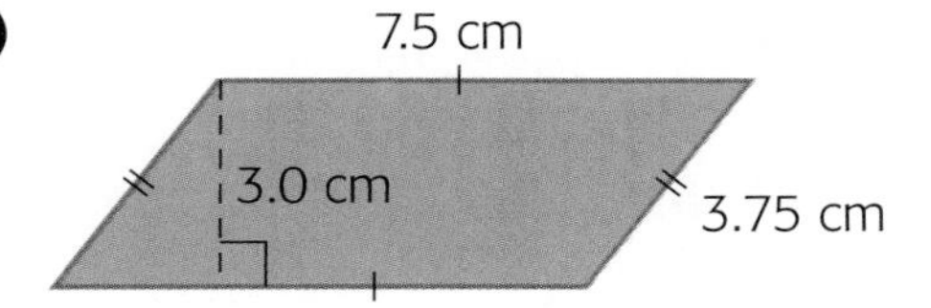

b)

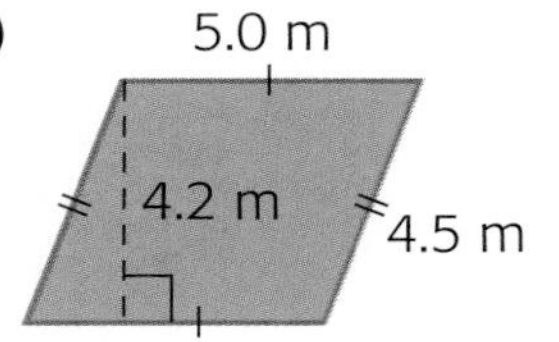

2. Calculate the area of the orange triangle in each parallelogram.

a)

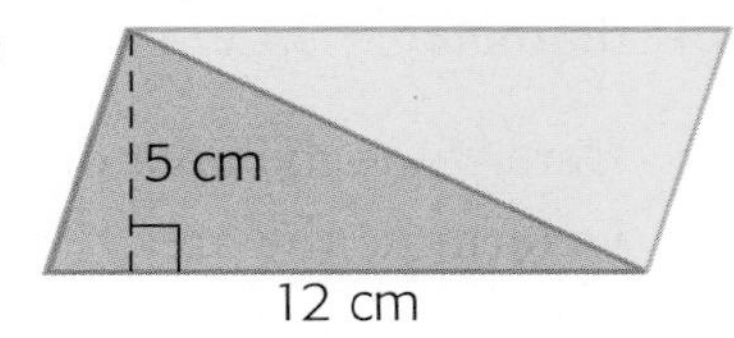

b)

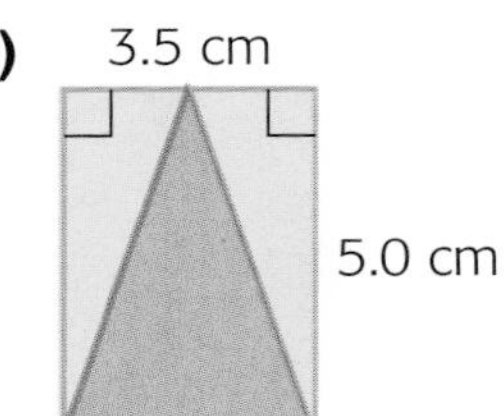

c)

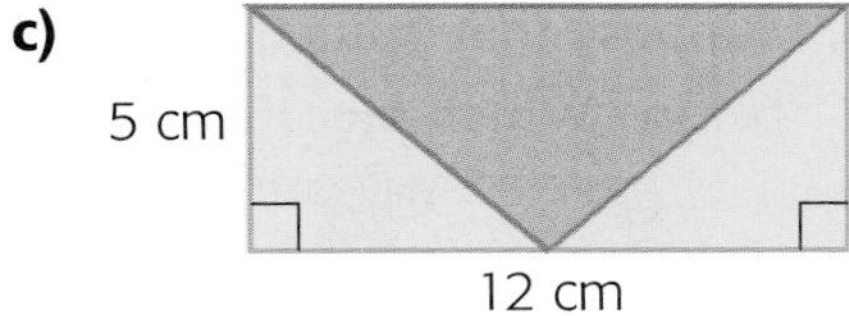

3. Calculate the area of the green shape in each rectangle.

a)

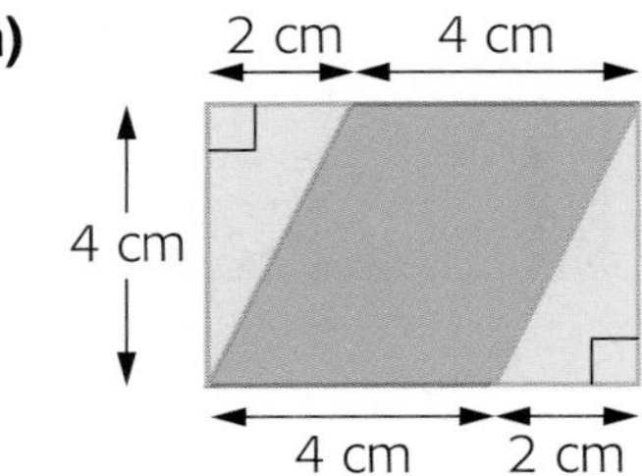

b)

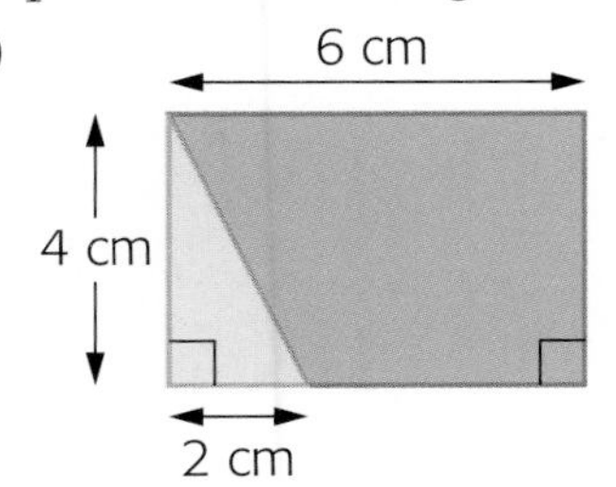

4. State whether each measurement is an area or a circumference.
   a) the amount of sod needed to cover the circular green on a golf course
   b) the amount of material needed to make a pool cover
   c) the length of stone used for the border of a round garden

5. Determine the circumference of a circle with each measurement.
   a) radius = 2.5 km
   b) radius = 26 cm
   c) diameter = 3.0 cm
   d) diameter = 21 cm

6. Calculate the area of a circle with each measurement.
   a) radius = 2 cm
   b) diameter = 11 cm
   c) diameter = 5.7 cm
   d) radius = 6.2 cm

7. a) Determine the area of the square.
   b) Determine the area of the white circle.
   c) Determine the area of the blue sections.

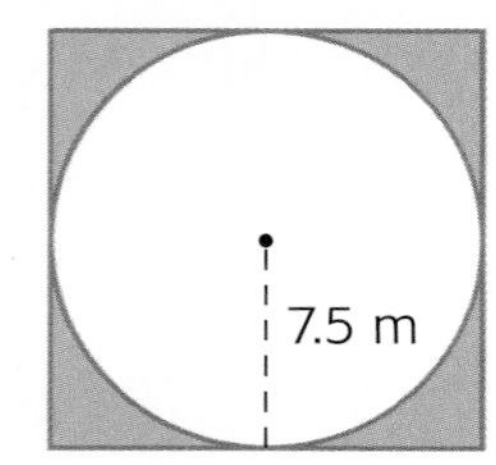

8. Suppose that you cut circles in two pieces of cloth, as shown below. Which piece would have more cloth left?

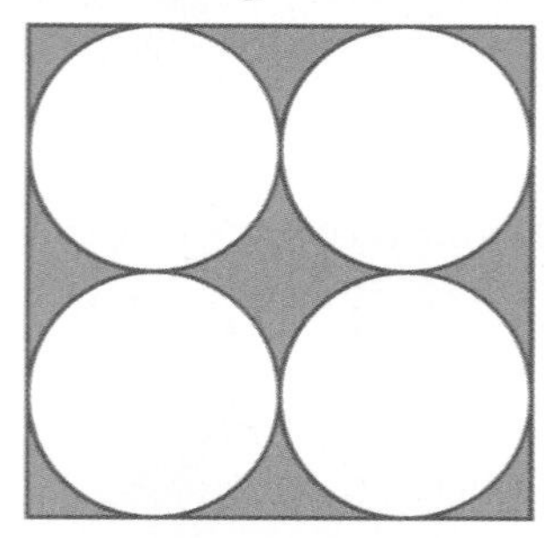

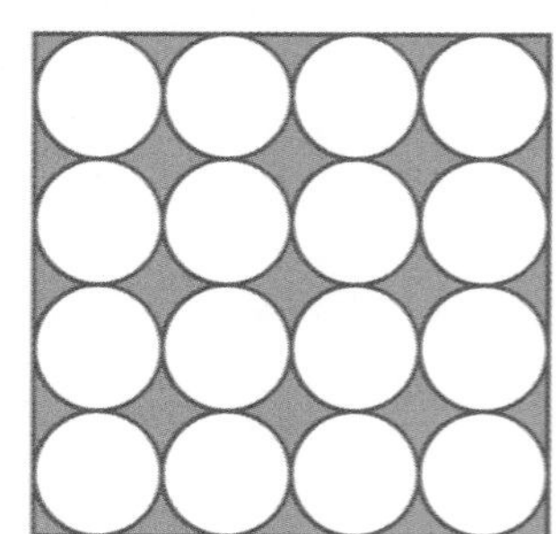

What Do You Think Now?

Revisit What Do You Think? on page 193. How have your answers and explanations changed?

Chapter Review

Frequently Asked Questions

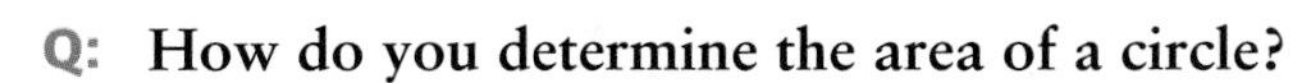

Q: How do you determine the area of a circle?

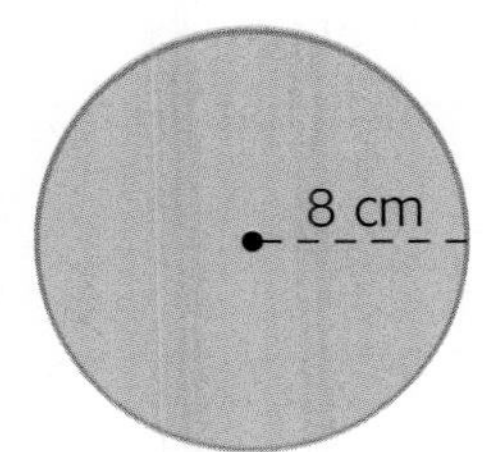

A: You can use the formula $A = \pi \times r \times r$. For example, consider the circle at the left:

$$A = 3.14 \times 8 \text{ cm} \times 8 \text{ cm}$$
$$= 201 \text{ cm}^2$$

The area is about 201 cm^2.

Q. How can you draw a circle when you know its radius or diameter?

A: Adjust a compass so that the distance between the compass point and the pencil tip is equal to the radius. Put the compass point where you want the centre of the circle to be, and draw the circle.

Practice

Lesson 5.1

1. Calculate the area of each parallelogram.

a)

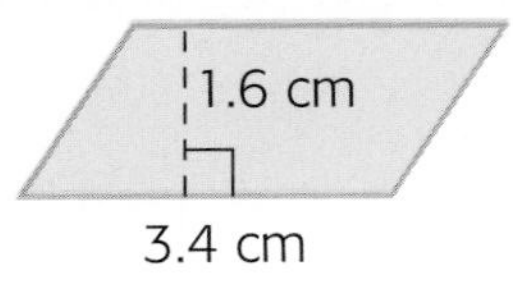

b)

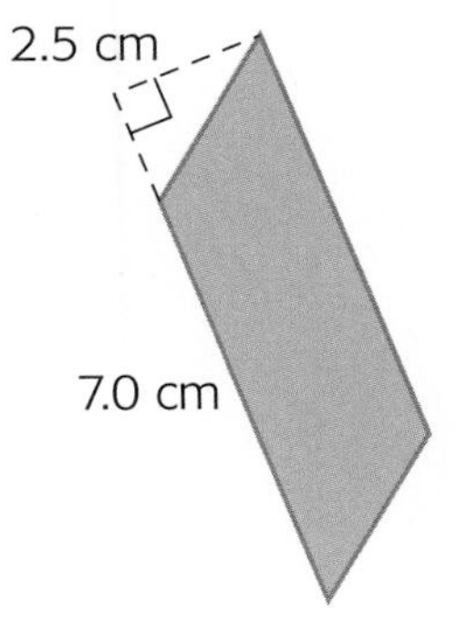

c)

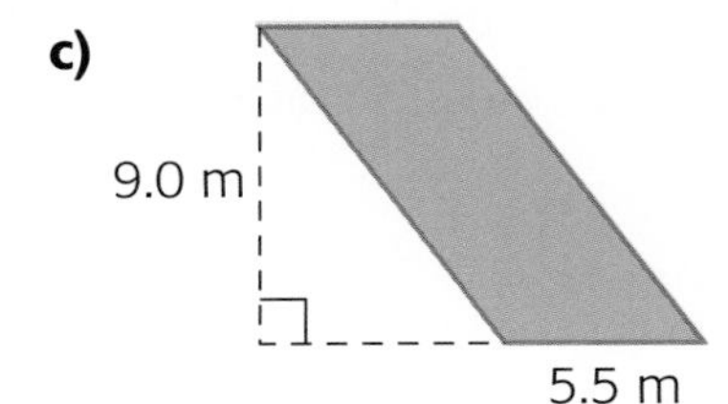

2. Determine the area of this parallelogram.

Lesson 5.2

3. **a)** Draw three different triangles, each with a height of 5 cm.
   b) Calculate the area of each triangle. Explain what you did.

4. Determine the area of this triangle.

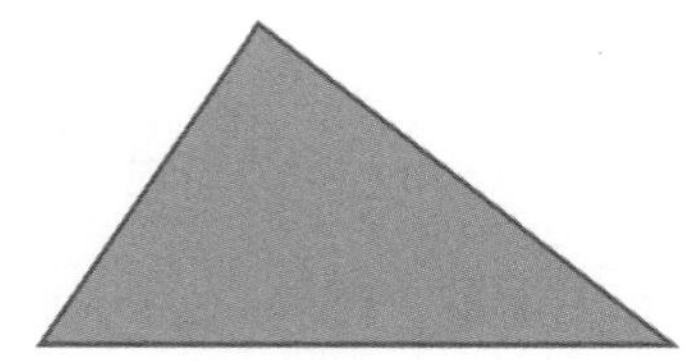

Lesson 5.4

5. Determine the circumference of this circle.

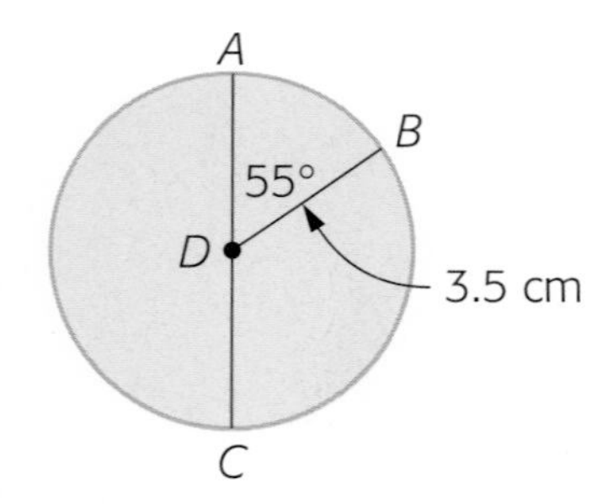

6. Determine the circumference of the circle at the left.

Lesson 5.5

7. Draw the circle in question 6 using a compass.

Lesson 5.6

8. Determine the area of the circle in question 6.

Lesson 5.7

9. **a)** Determine the measure of $\angle ADC$ in the circle in question 6.
   b) Determine the measure of $\angle BDC$ in the circle in question 6.

Chapter Task

Task | *Checklist*

- ✔ Did you include all the required diagrams and sketches?
- ✔ Did you include all the required shapes in your design?
- ✔ Did you prepare a table that accurately lists the measurements required for the design?
- ✔ Did you use correct math language?

Portable Player Design

Portable players have buttons to select, play, rewind, fast forward, and stop music files. Suppose that you were asked to design the face of a portable player to win a prize.

How will you use parallelograms, triangles, and circles in your portable player design?

A. Design a portable player that will be appealing to customers.

B. Your design entry must include

- a diagram of the face of the player—the face must include parallelograms, triangles, and circles, and it must have an area of 60 cm^2 or less
- a circle divided into sections, with the measure of the vertex of each section
- a table that includes the percent of the total area of the face used by each different-shaped button, as well as the length of each button
- a convincing argument explaining why your design should be chosen

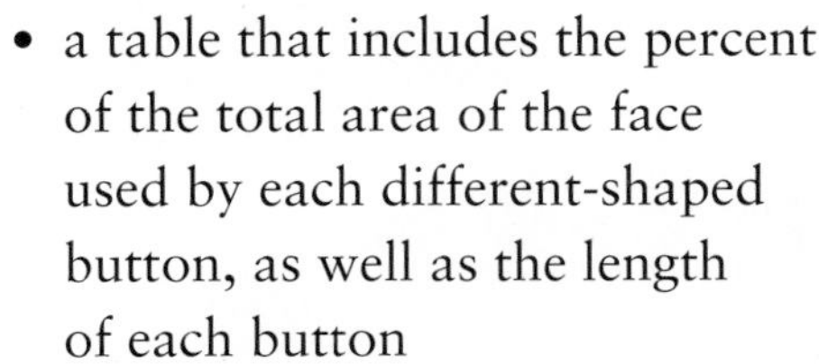

Chapter 6

Addition and Subtraction of Integers

GOAL

You will be able to

- represent addition and subtraction of integers using concrete materials, drawings, and number lines
- record the addition or subtraction of integers symbolically
- solve problems that involve the addition and subtraction of integers

Why should a pilot know how to read and use integers?

Getting Started

Interpreting Data

Five students in Tynessa's class in Lethbridge had birthdays in January. They wondered whose birthday was on the coldest day.

Student	Birthday	Low temperature on birthday (°C)
Aaron	January 1	−7
Kelly	January 6	4
Charles	January 11	−6
Janet	January 17	−3
Fred	January 25	−8

Whose birthday was on the coldest day?

integer

the counting numbers (+1, +2, +3, ...), zero (0), and the opposites of the counting numbers (−1, −2, −3, ...)

A. Mark each daily low temperature on an **integer** number line like the one below.

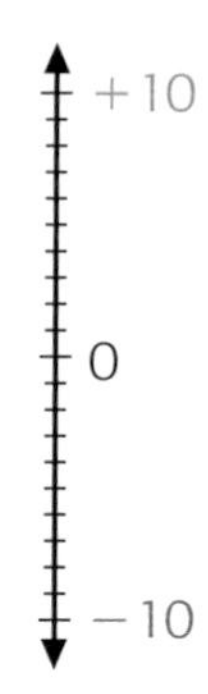

B. Whose birthday was on the warmest day? How do you know?

C. Whose birthday was on the coldest day? How do you know?

What Do You Think?

Decide whether you agree or disagree with each statement. Be ready to explain your decision.

1. When you add two numbers, the sum is always greater than either number.

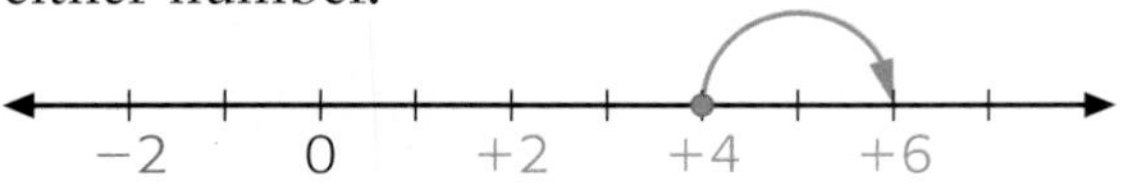

2. It is 40 °C warmer inside than outside.

3. The integer −4 is halfway between −9 and +1.

6.1 An Integer Experiment

YOU WILL NEED
- a coin

Add positive and negative integers.

EXPLORE the Math

Nestor and Gail are playing a game. Nestor tosses a coin 20 times.
For each Head that Nestor tosses, Gail records $+1$.
For each Tail that Nestor tosses, Gail records -1.
Gail adds the positive and negative integers.
If the total is from -2 to $+2$, Nestor wins.
Otherwise, Gail wins.

What outcomes result in a win for Nestor?

CURIOUS MATH

Time Zones

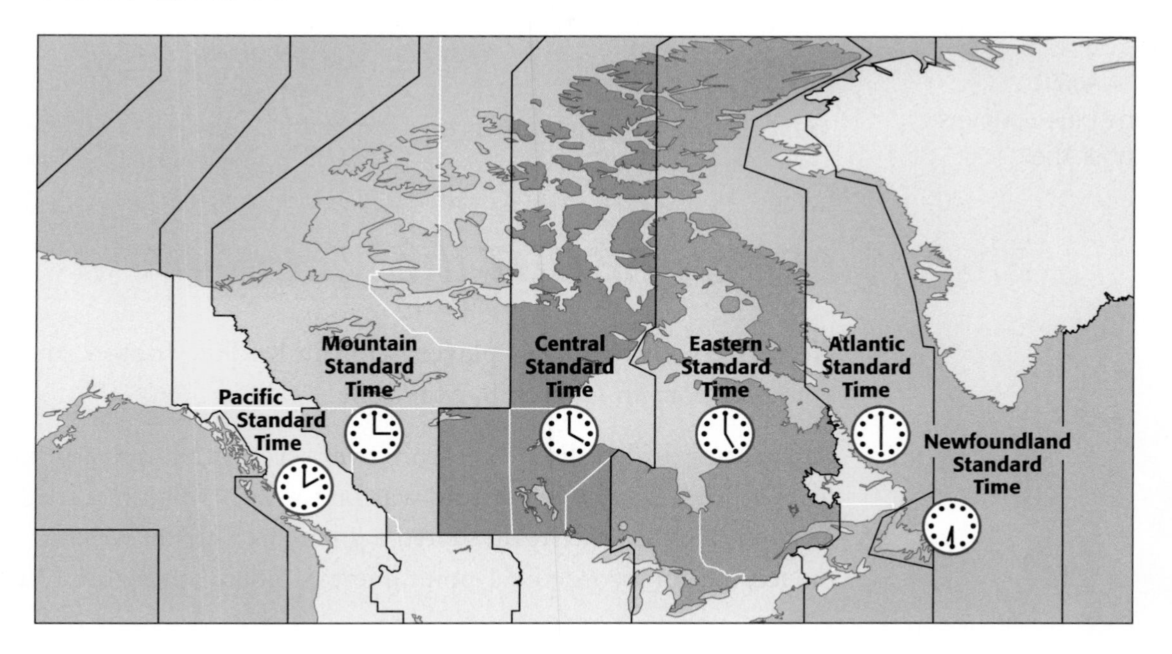

Canada is divided into six time zones. For the five mainland zones, if you travel east, you add $+1$ hour to your watch each time you enter a new time zone. If you travel west, you add -1 hour to your watch each time you go to a new time zone.

1. What is the time in Vancouver when it is noon in Halifax? Explain how you added integers to solve the problem.

2. What is the time in each of the other time zones when it is noon in your time zone? Explain.

3. The clocks show the time in each city when it is 7:00 in Edmonton. How many hours behind or ahead of Edmonton is each city? Explain how you added integers to solve the problem.

4. Survey your classmates. In what other time zones do their relatives or friends live? What is the time in each of those time zones when it is noon in your time zone?

6.2 Adding Integers Using the Zero Principle

YOU WILL NEED
- red and blue counters
- a number line

Use the zero principle to add integers.

LEARN ABOUT the Math

Nolan's favourite hockey player is Jordin Kudluk Tootoo, an Inuit who was born in Churchill, Manitoba.

Nolan recorded Jordin's +/− score over several games. If Jordin's team scored a goal while Jordin was on the ice, Nolan recorded +1 point. If the other team scored a goal while Jordin was on the ice, Nolan recorded −1 point. Here is Nolan's table for 11 goals.

Goal	1	2	3	4	5	6	7	8	9	10	11
Result (+1) or (−1)	−1	−1	+1	+1	+1	−1	+1	−1	+1	−1	+1

How can you calculate Jordin's +/− score?

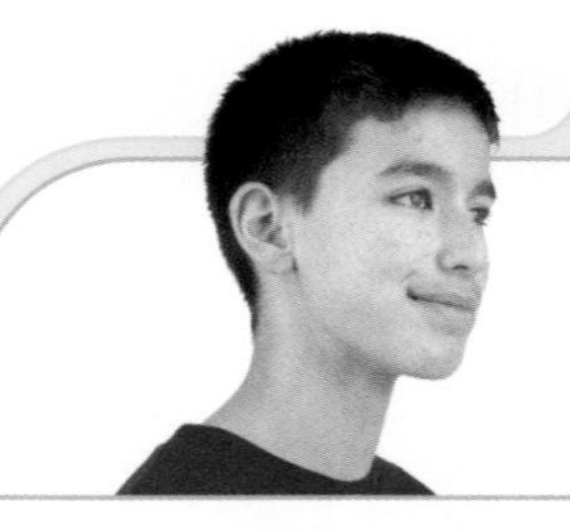

Example 1 | **Using a number line**

Calculate Jordin's +/− score using a number line.

Nolan's Solution

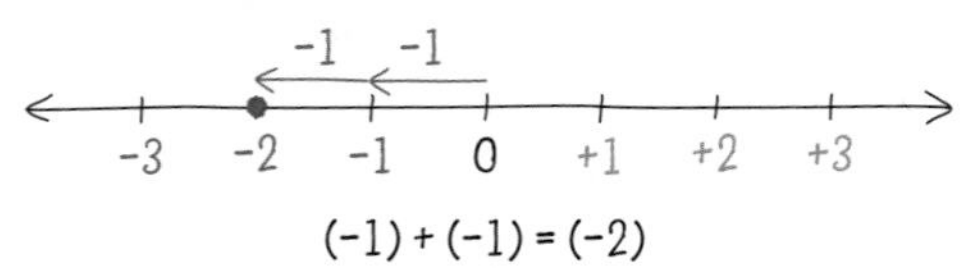

I added the first two integers in my table.
To represent −1, I drew an arrow pointing to the left.

I recorded the result using symbols.

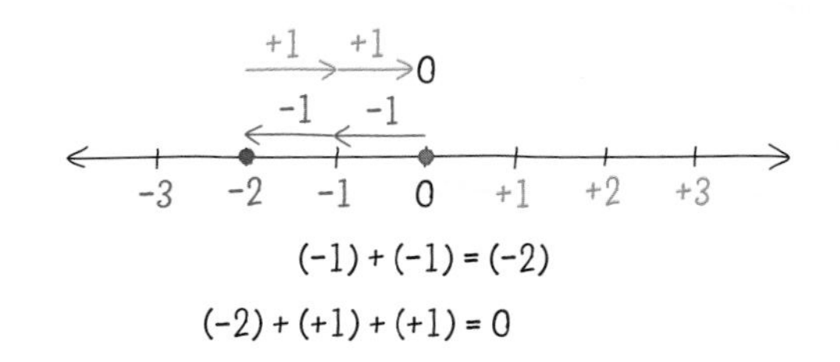

I added the next two integers.
To represent $+1$, I drew an arrow pointing to the right.
This brought me back to 0.

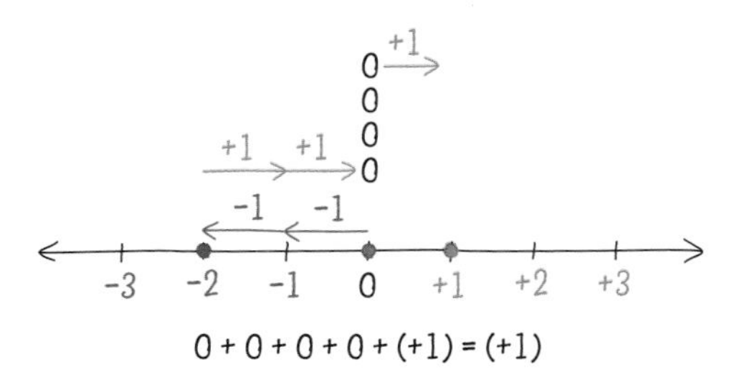

The next two scores were $+1$ and -1. I knew they would bring me back to 0, so I just recorded the 0. There were two more pairs of 0s, which I recorded. Then I added the last integer.

Jordin's +/− score is $+1$.

Example 2 | Modelling a sum with counters

Calculate Jordin's +/− score using counters.

Nayana's Solution

opposite integers

two integers that are the same distance from 0 on a number line; for example, $+2$ and -2 are opposite integers

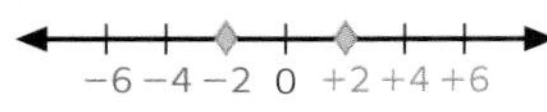

zero principle

the sum of two opposite integers is 0; for example,

(● ●) + (● ●) = 0

$(-2) + (+2) = 0$

I modelled the results. I used blue counters to represent -1s and red counters to represent $+1$s.

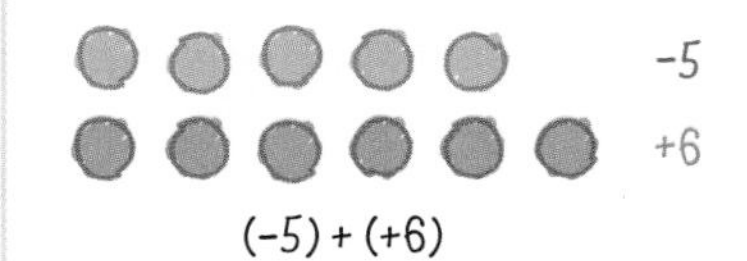

I put the blue counters in one row and the red counters in another row. The total is the sum of the counters.

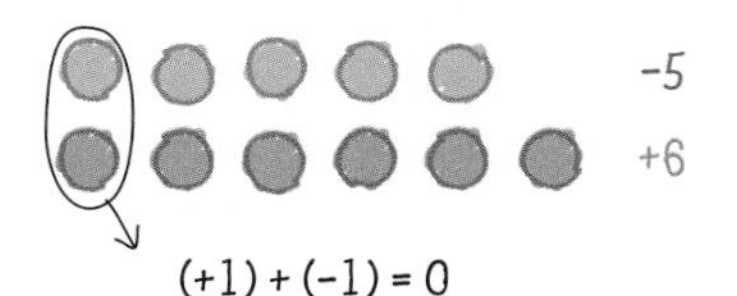

I paired a $+1$ with a -1 because they are **opposite integers.**

By the **zero principle,** the sum of $+1$ and -1 is 0.

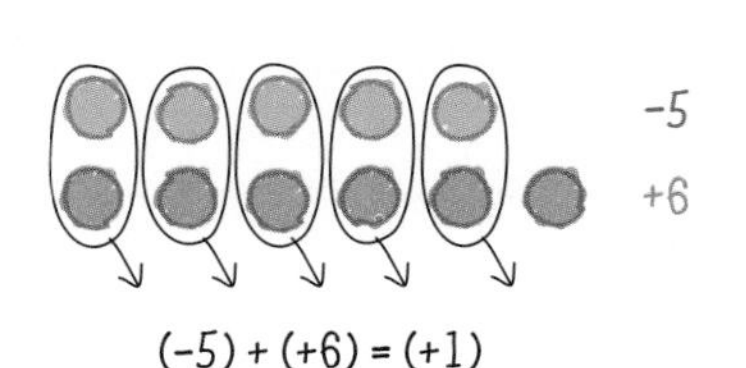

I was able to pair all the counters, except one. One red counter, or $+1$, was left over.

Jordin's +/− score is $+1$.

Communication | *Tip*

When you write the sign of an integer (+, −), use brackets so you do not confuse it with the operation signs (+ for addition or − for subtraction). For example, write the addition of +2 and −5 as (+2) + (−5). This is read as "positive two plus negative five."

Example 3 | Renaming an integer

Calculate Jordin's +/− score by renaming.

Liam's Solution

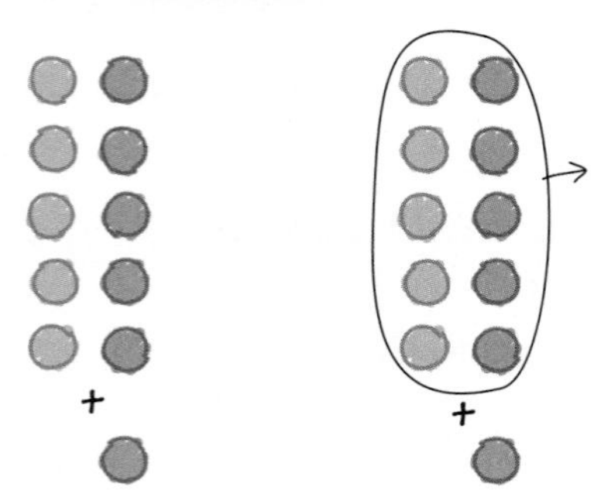

I used counters.
I renamed +6 as (+5) + (+1).

(-5) + (+5) = 0
(-5) + (+6) = (+1)

Since −5 and +5 are opposite integers, their sum is 0.

One red counter is left, so Jordin's +/- score is +1.

Reflecting

A. How are Nayana's solution and Liam's solution alike? How are they different?

B. Nolan added each integer in order. How might he have paired more of the numbers to make the addition easier?

C. How do you think Liam knew that he could rename +6 as (+5) + (+1)?

WORK WITH the Math

Example 4 | Adding integers

Calculate (+4) + (−2).

Solution A

Rename +4 as (+2) + (+2).

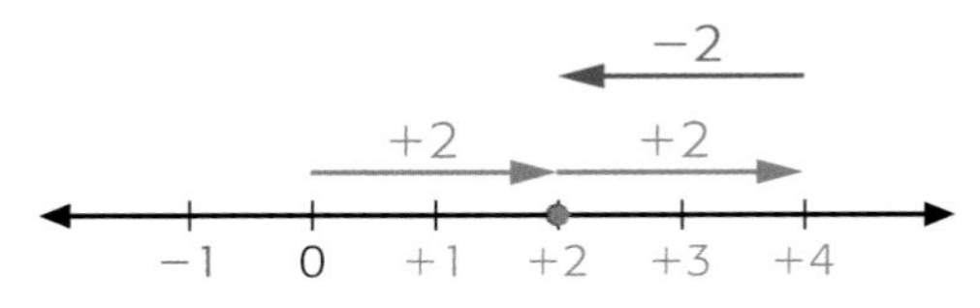

By the zero principle, (+2) + (−2) = 0.

So, (+4) + (−2) = (+2) + (+2) + (−2)
= (+2)

Solution B

Use counters to represent the integers.

Group the counters to make opposite integers.

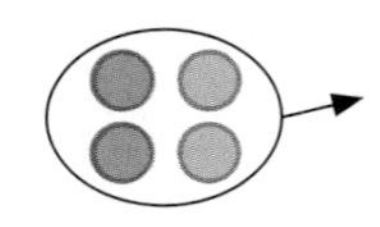

(+4) + (−2) = (+2)

A Checking

1. Add the integers in each expression using counters. Then record the addition using symbols. The first one is done for you.

	Expression	Addition model	Recording
a)	(−3) + (+2)		(−3) + (+2) = (−1)
b)	(−4) + (+6)		
c)	(+5) + (−6)		
d)	(−5) + (+7)		
e)	(+2) + (−8)		
f)	(−1) + (−9)		

2. Calculate.

a) (+3) + (−3) = ■ **b)** (−7) + (+7) = ■

Ⓑ Practising

3. Complete.

a) $(-3) + (-2) = ■$

b) $(+2) + (-2) = ■$

c) $(-4) + (+1) = ■$

d) $(+3) + (-5) = ■$

e) $(-2) + (-1) = ■$

f) $(-6) + (+7) = ■$

4. Hailey's +/− score was +2 in one game and −3 in another game. What was her total +/− score?

5. Explain why $(-25) + (+25) = 0$.

6. Each pattern is based on adding integers. Continue each pattern. Then write a rule for the pattern.

a) 0, −1, −2, −3, −4, ■, ■, ■

b) −3, −2, −1, 0, ■, ■, ■

7. Replace each ■ with +1 or −1 to make each statement true.

a) $(+1) + ■ + ■ = (-1)$

b) $(-1) + ■ + ■ = (+1)$

c) $(+1) + ■ + ■ + ■ + ■ = (-1)$

d) $(+1) + ■ + ■ + ■ + (+1) = (-1)$

8. Complete.

a) $(-3) + (+3) + (+5) = ■$

b) $(+2) + (+1) + ■ = (-1)$

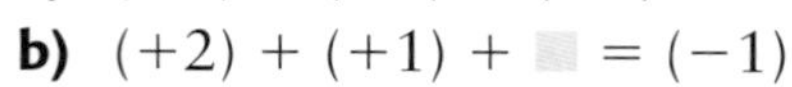

9. Replace the ■ with =, <, or > to make each statement true.

a) $(-1) + (-2)$ ■ (-4)
b) $(+2) + (-5)$ ■ (-3)
c) $(-3) + (+6)$ ■ $(+2)$
d) $(+5) + (-7)$ ■ (-2)
e) $(-2) + (-4)$ ■ (-5)
f) $(-2) + (+1)$ ■ 0

10. Using $+1$ and -1 only, create an addition question that has each sum. Use at least four numbers for each question.

a) $+3$ b) -2 c) 0 d) -1

11. Replace each ■ with an integer to make the equation true. Show three different solutions.

■ + ■ + ■ = (-5)

12. Explain why you cannot complete this equation using only $+1$s or -1s.

$(+1)$ + ■ + ■ + ■ = $(+1)$

+1	−6	−1
−4	−2	0
−3	+2	−5

$(-1) + 0 + (-5) = (-6)$

13. a) In a Magic Square, all rows, columns, and diagonals have the same sum. No number appears more than once. The Magic Square at the left uses integers from -6 to $+2$. Show that the rows, columns, and diagonals all have the same sum. The sum of the third column is shown.

b) Create a Magic Square that uses the integers from -10 to -2.

14. a) Add all the integers from -10 to $+10$. What pattern can you use to calculate the sum?

b) Add all the integers from -50 to $+50$, using the pattern in part (a).

15. Is each statement true or false? Explain your reasoning.

a) The sum of two positive integers is always positive.
b) The sum of two negative integers is always negative.
c) The sum of a negative integer and a positive integer is always positive.

6.3 Adding Integers that Are Far from Zero

YOU WILL NEED

- a number line

GOAL

Add integers using number lines.

LEARN ABOUT the Math

Fiona is doing a project for a science fair. She is recording the rise and fall of the water level in a pond. One day, she had this result.

The next time Fiona measured the water level, it had risen by 40 cm.

What was the new reading on the rod?

A. Why can you solve the problem by calculating $(-35) + (+40)$?

B. Mark -35 on a number line. How can you represent adding $+40$ to -35?

C. Why might you want to first add $+35$ instead of $+40$?

D. Use your number line to calculate $(-35) + (+40)$. What was the new reading on the rod?

Reflecting

E. Another time, Fiona calculated (+40) + (−35). What had happened to the water level in the pond?

F. Look at part A again. How can you tell, without calculating, whether the sum is positive or negative?

G. When is the sum of two integers negative? Use an example to help you explain.

WORK WITH the Math

Example 1 | Adding integers on a number line

Add +35 and −40 on a number line.

Fiona's Solution

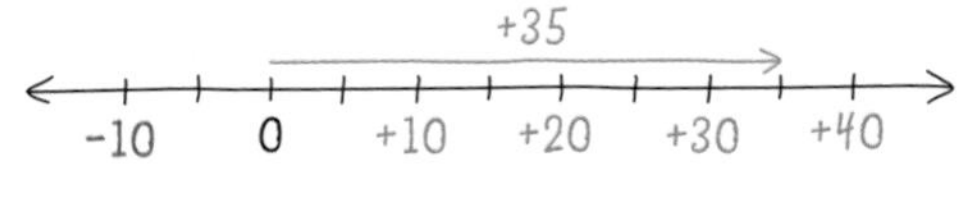

I thought of +35 as an increase from 0 to 35. I represented +35 with a red arrow going to the right.

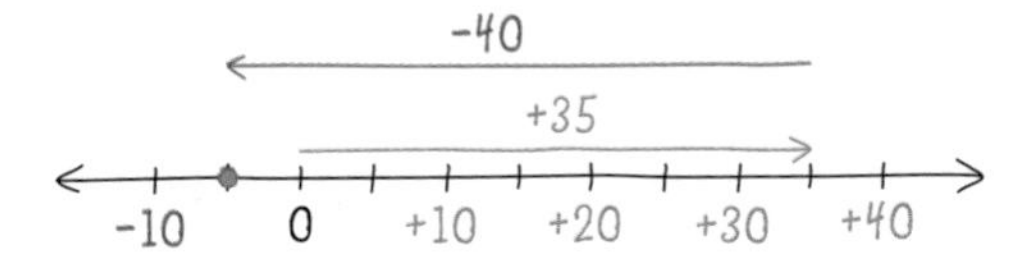

I thought of −40 as a decrease. I represented −40 with a blue arrow starting at the tip of the first arrow and going to the left.

I ended up at −5. This makes sense, since −35 balances the +35 and there is still −5 left.

(+35) + (-40) = (-5)

The sum is −5.

Example 2 | Adding negative numbers on a number line

Add $(-24) + (-39)$ on a number line.

Liam's Solution

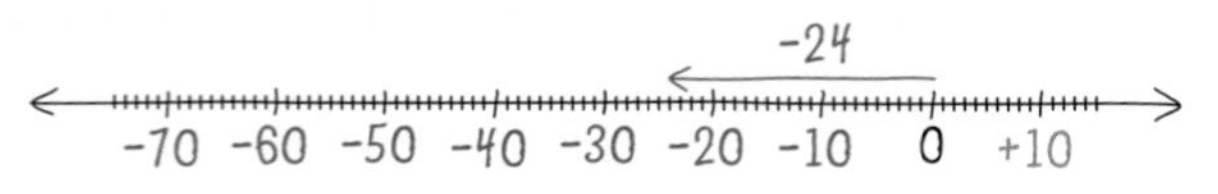

I thought of -24 as a decrease from 0 to -24. I represented -24 with a blue arrow going to the left.

-39 -24
-70 -60 -50 -40 -30 -20 -10 0 +10
-63

I thought of -39 as another decrease. I represented -39 with an arrow starting at the tip of the first arrow and going to the left.

$(-24) + (-39) = (-63)$

The sum is -63.

A Checking

1. Use a number line to model $(-27) + (+34)$.

a) Where does the first arrow start?
b) Where does the first arrow end?
c) Where does the second arrow start?
d) Where does the second arrow end?
e) What is the sum?

2. Predict whether each sum will be positive or negative. Then calculate the sum. Show what you did.

a) $(-50) + (-20)$
b) $(-50) + (+20)$
c) $(-20) + (+50)$
d) $(-20) + (-50)$

B Practising

3. Calculate.

a) $(+5) + (+3)$
b) $(-5) + (-3)$
c) $(-60) + (+20)$
d) $(-10) + (-15)$
e) $(-15) + (+10)$
f) $(+100) + (-80)$

4. How much greater is the second sum than the first sum? Show your work.
   a) $(-25) + (+38)$ and $(-15) + (+38)$
   b) $(+125) + (-52)$ and $(+125) + (-32)$

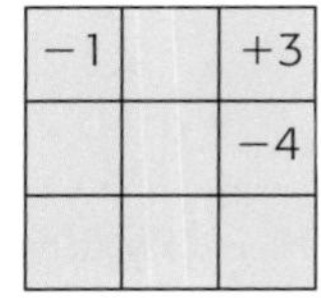

5. In the Magic Square at the left, every row, column, and diagonal adds to 0. Copy and complete this Magic Square.

6. Order the players from highest to lowest +/− score.

Player	Goals for (+)	Goals against (−)
Heidi	110	94
Rana	103	89
Meagan	99	108
Sonya	105	97
Indu	101	102

7. Copy and complete this table.

	Starting temperature (°C)	Temperature change (°C)	Final temperature (°C)
a)	−5	+1	
b)	−10	−6	
c)	0		−8
d)		−5	0
e)	+7		−2
f)		−10	+8

8. Why can you calculate $(-20) + (+8)$ by calculating $20 - 8$ and taking the opposite of your result?

9. Explain why you can calculate $(+20) + (-8)$ by calculating $20 - 8$.

10. How can you calculate $(-20) + (-8)$ without counters or a number line?

6.4 Integer Addition Strategies

YOU WILL NEED
- a number line
- red and blue counters

GOAL

Develop personal addition strategies for integers.

LEARN ABOUT the Math

Fiona is following the launch of a space shuttle on the NASA website. The countdown clock shows the number of hours before launch with negative integers and the number of hours after launch with positive integers.

-31:00:00
HOURS TO LAUNCH
COUNTDOWN

It is now 31 h before launch, or −31. Exactly 12 h ago, the ground crew started an equipment check. In 12 h, the astronauts will begin their final preparations. Fiona wonders what the clock will show 12 h from now, and what it showed 12 h before.

What are the countdown integers?

A. Fiona calculated $(-31) + (+12)$. What problem did she solve?

B. Calculate $(-31) + (+12)$ using counters. Draw pictures and describe each step.

C. Calculate $(-31) + (+12)$ on a number line. Draw pictures and describe each step.

D. Fiona calculated $(-31) + (-12)$. What problem did she solve?

E. Calculate $(-31) + (-12)$ using counters or a number line. Draw pictures and describe each step.

F. What will the integers be in 12 h, and what were they 12 h ago?

Reflecting

G. In part A, how could you tell that the sum would be greater than −31?

H. In part D, how could you tell that the sum would be less than −31?

I. Suppose that you want to add an integer to −31. How can you tell whether the answer will be positive, negative, or zero?

WORK WITH the Math

Example 1 | Adding integers on a number line

Calculate $(+18) + (-23) + (-31) + (+21) + (+13)$.

Fiona's Solution: Adding positives and negatives

-31 -23
+18 +21 +13
-10 0 +10 +20 +30 +40 +50

I grouped the positive integers and the negative integers on a number line.

$(+18) + (+21) + (+13) = (+52)$

$(-23) + (-31) = (-54)$

$(+52) + (-54) = (-2)$

The sum of the positive integers is $+52$.
The sum of the negative integers is -54.
The sum is -2.

Nayana's Solution: Using zero pairs

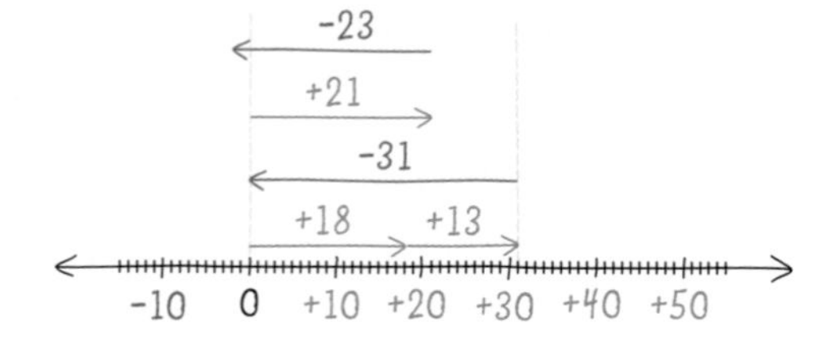

I noticed that $(+18) + (+13) = (+31)$.

$+31$ and -31 are a zero pair, so $+21$ and -23 are left.

I added $(+21) + (-23)$ on a number line.
The sum is -2.

Example 2 | Adding positive and negative integers

Calculate $(+35) + (+11) + (-15) + (-20)$.

Megan's Solution: Using zero pairs

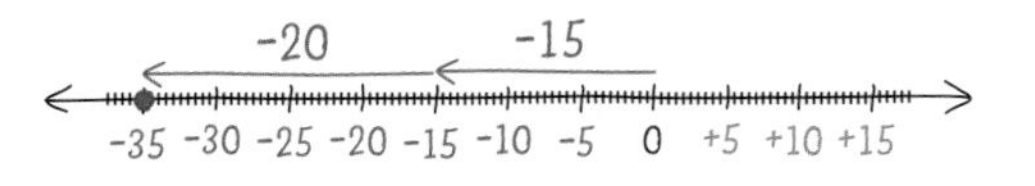

I added -15 and -20 on a number line. The sum is -35.

I added $+35$ to get 0.

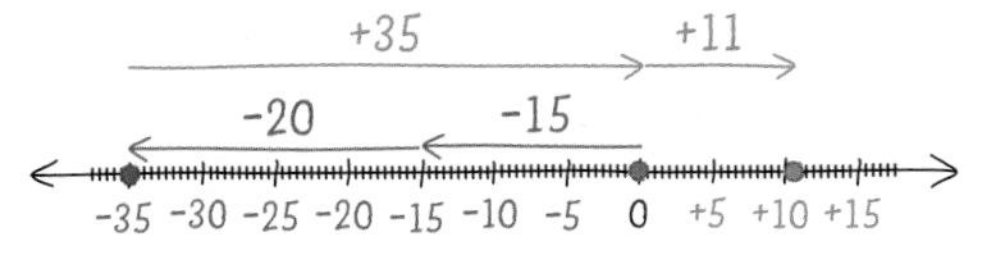

$+11$ is left. I added $+11$ to 0.

The sum is $+11$.

$(-15) + (-20) = (-35)$

$(-35) + (+35) = 0$

$0 + (+11) = (+11)$

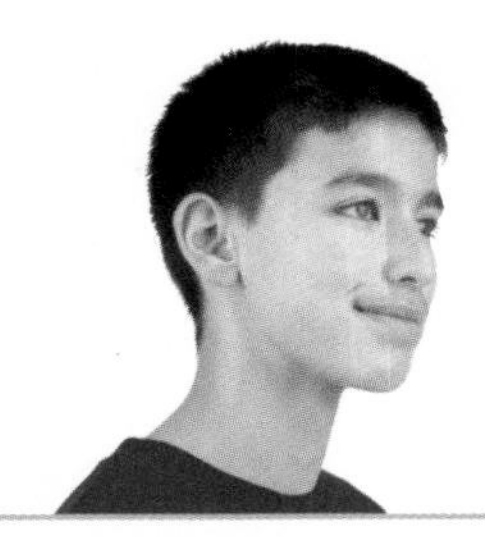

Nolan's Solution: Adding positives, then negatives

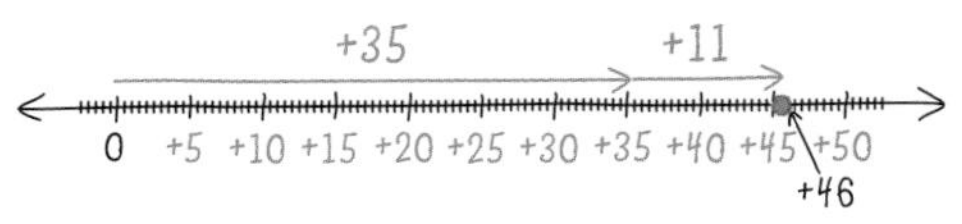

I added the two positive integers.

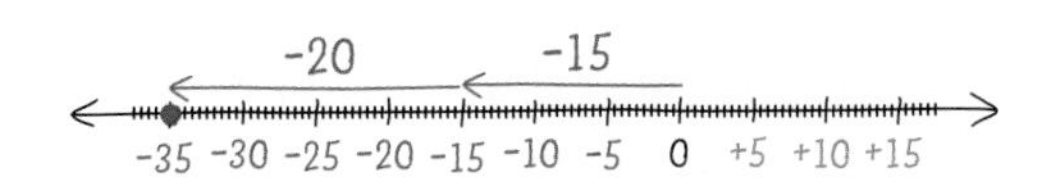

I added the two negative integers.

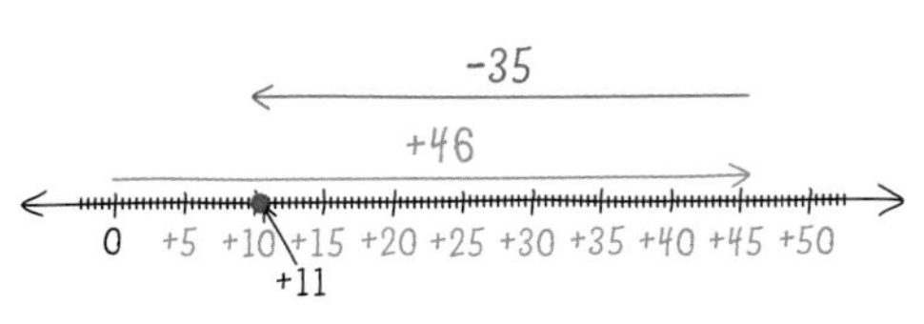

I added $+46$ and -35.

The sum is $+11$.

$(+46) + (-35) = (+11)$

A Checking

1. Calculate.

a) $(-40) + (+55) + (+5) + (-40) + (-10)$

b) $(-13) + (+8) + (-12) + (+10) + (+9)$

B Practising

2. Explain why all of these sums are the same.

A. $(-5) + (-2) + (-3) + (+5)$

B. $(-5) + (+5) + (-2) + (-3)$

C. $(-2) + (-3) + (+5) + (-5)$

D. $(+5) + (-2) + (-3) + (-5)$

3. Troy had a +/− score of +11. The following table shows how his score changed over seven games. What is his score now?

Game	start	1	2	3	4	5	6	7
+/− score		−1	+4	−3	−2	+5	0	+1
Total	+11							

4. Look at the expression $(+4) + (-3) + (+1) + (+6) + (-2)$.

a) Add the integers in order.

b) Group and add the positive integers. Then group and add the negative integers. Add the two sums.

c) Why do you get the same answer in parts (a) and (b)?

5. Calculate.

a) $(-12) + (+2) + (-5)$

b) $(+23) + (-14) + (-7)$

c) $(-18) + (+5) + (+18)$

d) $(-10) + (-15) + (+15) + (+20)$

6. Replace each ■ with a different two-digit integer to make the equation true. Write two solutions.

■ + ■ + ■ + ■ + ■ = (+4)

Reading Strategy

What is the useful information in this problem?
Why is it useful?

7. The depth of a submarine is shown at 10:00. How deep was it at 15:00?

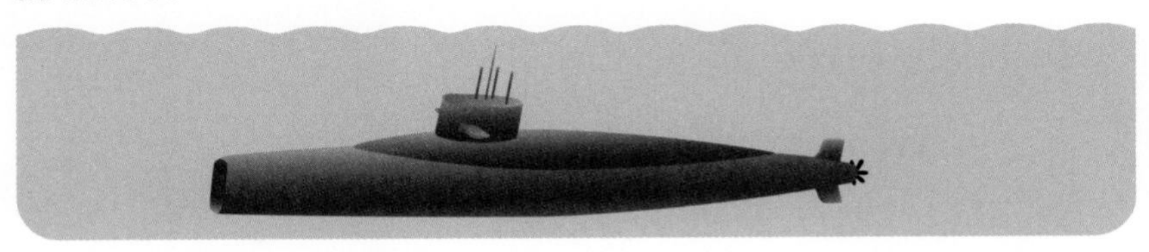

Time	10:00	11:00	12:00	13:00	14:00	15:00
Change in depth (m)		−53	−31	+18	−64	+85
Depth (m)	−300					

8. a) Copy the diagram shown below. Start with +5 in the top circle. Fill in the other circles by following the arrows and adding the indicated integers.

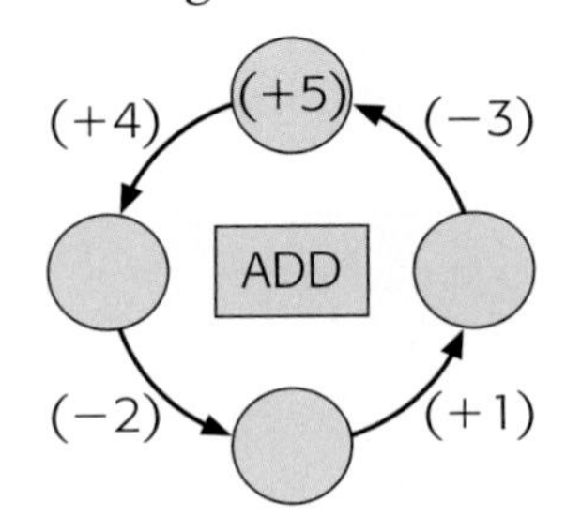

b) Why is the final sum +5 after you finish the last addition?

c) Why is the final sum +5 if you add in both a clockwise direction and a counterclockwise direction?

d) Copy the diagram again. Replace the numbers on the arrows with four different two-digit integers, so that you still end up with a sum of +5.

9. Describe two ways to add these integers. State which way you prefer and explain why.
$(+22) + (-4) + (+12) + (-10) + (+8) + (-6)$

Chapter 6

Mid-Chapter **Review**

Frequently Asked Questions

Q: What is the zero principle?

A: The zero principle means that the sum of two opposite integers is 0. For example, $(+3) + (-3) = 0$.

Q: How do you add integers, such as $(-5) + (+3)$?

A1: You can use counters. You can pair red and blue counters and use the zero principle. Each pair of red $(+1)$ and blue (-1) counters has a sum of 0. Then remove the zero pairs. The counters that remain give the sum. This model shows that $(-5) + (+3) = (-2)$.

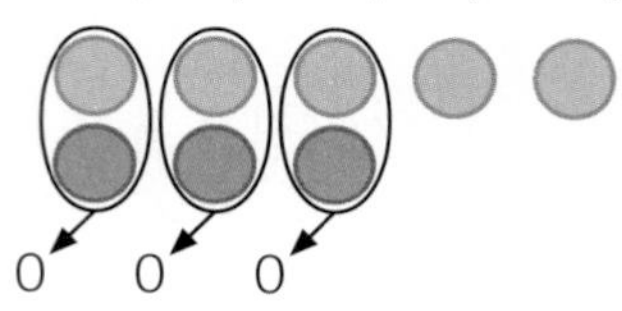

$(+1) + (-1) = 0$

A2: You can use a number line. Represent the first integer with an arrow that starts at 0. Represent the second integer with an arrow that starts at the end of the first arrow. An arrow points to the left if it represents a negative integer and to the right if it represents a positive integer. The sum is the end point of the second arrow. This model shows that $(-5) + (+3) = (-2)$.

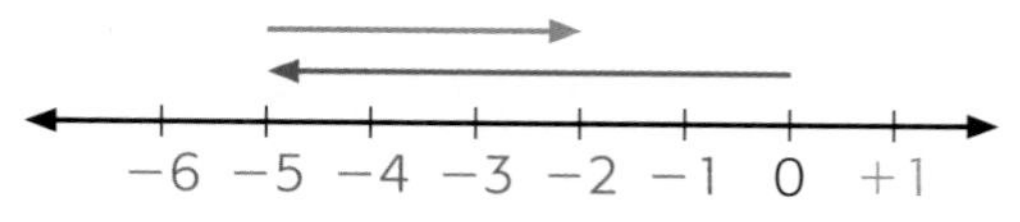

Q: How do you add more than two integers, such as $(-38) + (+17) + (-3) + (-14) + (+5)$?

A1: You can add the positive and negative integers separately, and then calculate the total sum. For example,

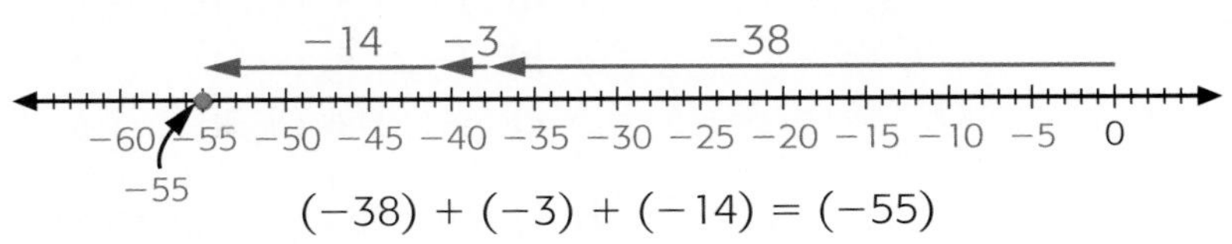

$(-38) + (-3) + (-14) = (-55)$

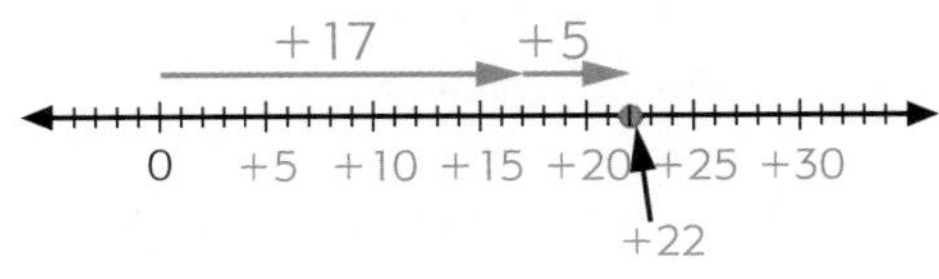

$(+17) + (+5) = (+22)$

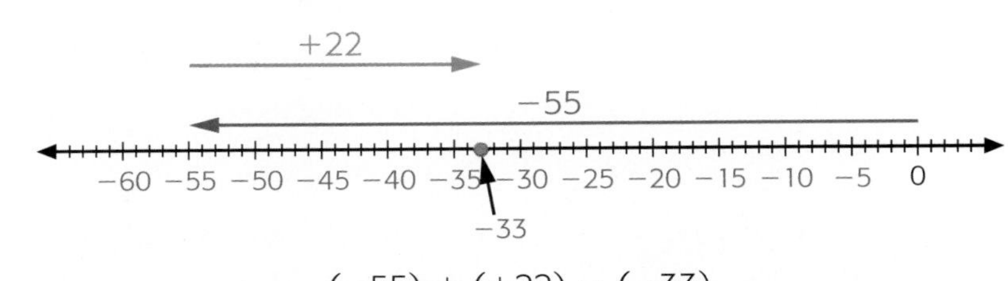

$(-55) + (+22) = (-33)$

A2: You can look for zero pairs and remove them. Then you add the remaining integers on a number line or with counters. For example, in $(-38) + (+17) + (-3) + (-14) + (+5)$, notice that $(+17)$ makes a zero pair with $(-3) + (-14)$.

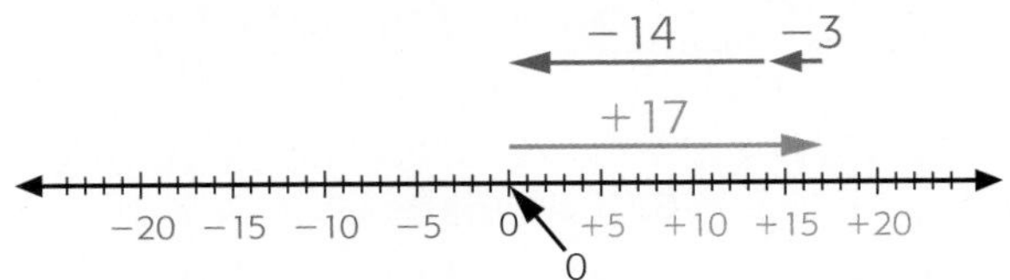

This leaves $(-38) + (+5)$, so the sum is -33.

+5
−38
−60 −55 −50 −45 −40 −35 −30 −25 −20 −15 −10 −5 0
−33

$(-38) + (+5) = (-33)$

Practice

Lesson 6.2

1. Draw a picture to represent each sum.

a) $(+5) + (-2)$
b) $(-2) + (-5)$
c) $(-4) + (+5)$
d) $(+3) + (-4)$
e) $(-2) + (+7)$
f) $(-1) + (-3) + (+4)$

2. Complete each equation.

a) $(-8) + ■ = (-5)$
b) $(+2) + ■ = 0$
c) $(-5) + ■ + (+7) = (+12)$
d) $(+6) + ■ + (-4) = (+10)$

3. Think about adding two integers.

a) What must be true about the integers for the sum to be positive?

b) What must be true about the integers for the sum to be negative?

Lesson 6.3

4. Anthony hiked uphill from a valley that was 45 m below sea level. After an hour, he was 100 m higher than where he started. Using integers, determine how high he was above sea level. Show what you did.

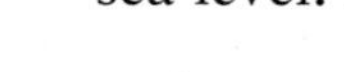

5. Calculate.

a) $(+30) + (-20)$
b) $(-150) + (+50)$
c) $(-110) + (-20)$
d) $(+20) + (-40)$

Lesson 6.4

6. Calculate.

a) $(+11) + (-26) + (-15)$
b) $(-33) + (-20) + (+12)$
c) $(-50) + (+23) + (-17)$
d) $(-40) + (+20) + (-14)$

7. Calculate.

$(+34) + (+17) + (-20) + (-15) + (-2) + (+18)$

8. Gillian walks up and down a staircase. She starts on the fifth step and walks as follows:

- up 2 steps
- down 3 steps
- up 4 steps
- down 5 steps

On what step does she finish?

6.5 Subtracting Integers Using Counters

YOU WILL NEED
- red and blue counters

GOAL

Develop a counter model for subtracting integers.

LEARN ABOUT the Math

Ashley, Nick, and Gail have electronic gift cards to buy items online. They can add money to their cards when the balance is low or negative. Money is subtracted from their cards when they buy an item.

How can you subtract integers using counters?

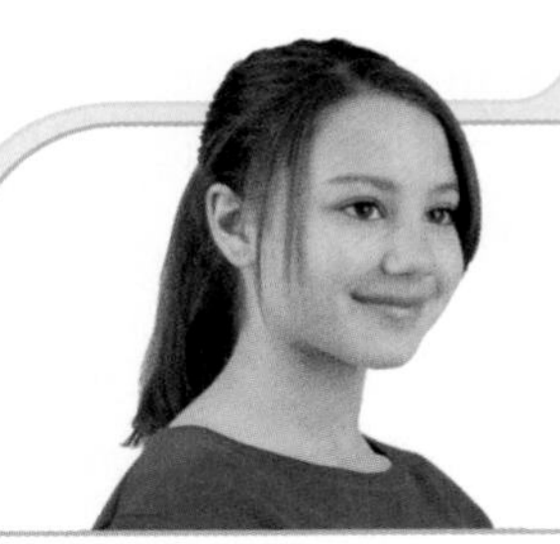

Example 1 | Subtracting a positive integer

Ashley's card had a balance of −$10. Then she spent $5. What is the balance now?

Ashley's Solution

-10

I had to calculate $(-10) - (+5)$.
I used blue counters to represent -10.

-10 -5 +5
-10 + 0 = -10

I know that $-10 + 0$ is still -10.
I wanted to subtract $+5$, so I needed five red counters. I used the zero principle to get more blue and red counters.

-10 -5

I subtracted 5 red counters, or $+5$.

-15
(-10) - (+5) = (-15)

The balance on my card is now −$15. It makes sense that the balance is less than −$10, because now I should owe more.

Example 2 | Subtracting a negative integer

Nick ordered a book worth \$8. The balance on his card became −\$10. Then Nick decided to cancel the order. What is the balance now?

Nick's Solution

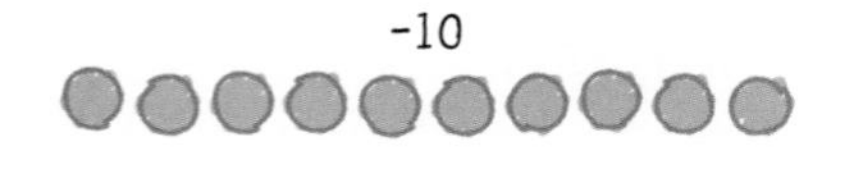

When I cancelled the order, I had to subtract −\$8 from my balance of −\$10 to get my new balance.
I calculated $(-10) - (-8)$.
I used blue counters to represent −10.

I had enough blue counters to subtract −8.

-2

$(-10) - (-8) = (-2)$

My balance is now −\$2. It makes sense that the answer is more than −\$10, because now I should owe less.

Example 3 | Subtracting integers by adding

Calculate $+5 - (-3)$.

Gail's Solution

You can subtract whole numbers by adding on to the second number.
$5 - 3 = ■$ means "What number can you add to 3 to get 5?"
So I can rewrite the equation as $3 + ■ = 5$.
Subtracting with integers is the same. $(+5) - (-3) = ■$ means "What number can you add to −3 to get +5?"
I can rewrite the equation as $(-3) + ■ = (+5)$.

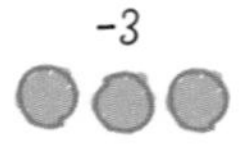

I used 3 blue counters to represent −3.

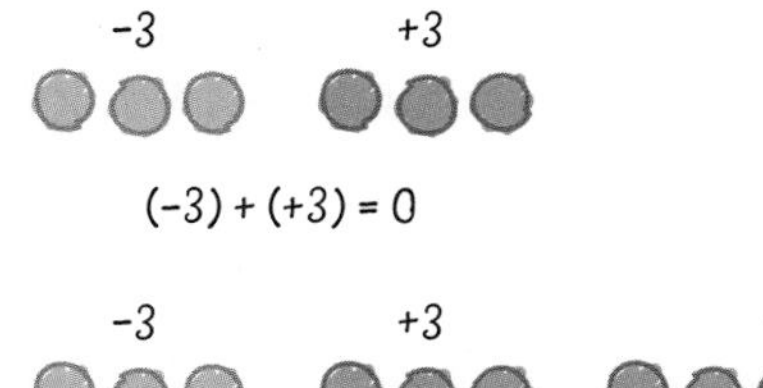

$(+5) - (-3) = (+8)$

I had to get a result of +5, or 5 red counters, so I added red counters.
First I added 3 red counters, or +3, to get 0.

I added another 5 red counters to get +5.
I added 8 red counters in all, or +8, to −3.
The answer is +8.

Reflecting

A. How could Ashley and Nick add to check the new balances they calculated?

B. Suppose that you subtract −3 from an integer. Will the difference be less than or greater than the integer? Use an example to help you explain.

C. How is subtracting −5 from an integer like adding +5 to the same integer? Use an example to help you explain.

WORK WITH the Math

Example 4 | Subtracting integers with the same sign

Calculate (−2) − (−5) using counters.

Solution

Start with 2 blue counters.

Add 0 by adding 3 blue and 3 red counters.

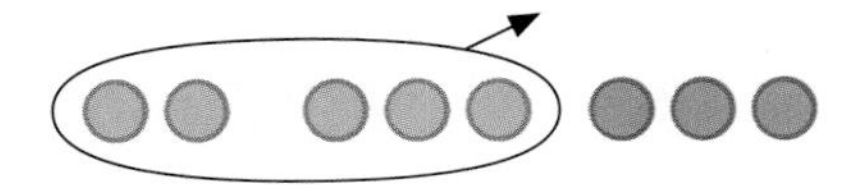

Subtract 5 blue counters.

Three red counters are left.

$(-2) - (-5) = (+3)$

A Checking

1. Calculate using counters. For which calculations did you need to add red and blue counters that equalled 0?

a) $(-4) - (+2)$

b) $(+3) - (+2)$

c) $(+3) - (-2)$

d) $(-3) - (-2)$

B Practising

2. a) Calculate $(-4) - (-1)$ using counters.

b) Why didn't you need to add red and blue counters that equalled 0?

3. a) Calculate $(-1) - (-4)$ using counters.

b) Why did you need to add red and blue counters that equalled 0?

4. Rosa solved a subtraction problem as shown. What problem did she solve?

Step 1

Step 2

Step 3

Step 4

5. Are $(+6) - (-4)$ and $(-4) - (+6)$ equal? Use counters to help you explain.

6. Which expressions have the same result? Use counters to help you explain.

A. $(+3) - (+4)$

B. $(-4) - (-3)$

C. $(+9) - (+5)$

D. $(-4) - (-9)$

E. $(-4) - (+3)$

F. $(+4) - (-3)$

7. Complete each pattern. What does the pattern show about subtracting integers?

a) $(+5) - (+4) = (+1)$
$(+5) - (+3) = ■$
$(+5) - (+2) = ■$
$(+5) - (+1) = ■$

b) $(-5) - (+4) = (-9)$
$(-5) - (+3) = ■$
$(-5) - (+2) = ■$
$(-5) - (+1) = ■$

8. Subtract the second integer from the first integer. Model the subtraction with counters and record the result. The first one is done for you.

	First integer	Second integer	Model
a)	−1	−3	(−1) (−2) + (+2) = 0 (−1) − (−3) = (+2)
b)	−4	+5	
c)	+6	−10	
d)	0	−10	
e)	+7	+10	
f)	−1	−8	

9. The following table shows the balances on some electronic gift cards. Copy and complete the table.

	Person	Day 1 balance ($)	Day 2 balance ($)	Change in the balance ($)
a)	Ming	−5	−1	
b)	Kaitlyn	+5	+10	
c)	Omar	−10	+6	
d)	Anthony	−10		−8
e)	Braydon		−5	+10
f)	Tynessa		+7	+2

10. Calculate.

a) $(+4) + (+2) - (+3)$

b) $(-4) + (-3) - (-2)$

c) $(+3) - (-8) + (-10)$

d) $(-2) - (-6) + (+3)$

11. Is each statement true or false? Explain your thinking using examples.

a) When you subtract a negative integer from another negative integer, the result is always negative.

b) When you subtract a positive integer from another positive integer, the result is always positive.

c) When you subtract a negative integer from a positive integer, the result is always positive.

d) When you subtract a positive integer from a negative integer, the result is always positive.

e) When you subtract one integer from another integer, the result always has the same sign as the greater integer.

12. The opposite of $+3$ is -3.

a) How do you know that $(-2) - (+3) = (-2) + (-3)$?

b) Is subtracting an integer always the same as adding its opposite? Use counters to explain your answer.

MATH GAME

Integro

If you are using a standard deck of cards, aces count as 1, numbered cards count as their face values, and jokers count as 0. Red cards are positive, and black cards are negative.

Number of players: 2 or 4

YOU WILL NEED

- integer cards numbered -10 to $+10$ (two of each) OR a standard deck of cards, including two jokers, with face cards removed

How to Play

1. If there are four players, remove the jokers. Shuffle the cards. Deal the cards equally to all the players.
2. In a round, each player places one card face up on the table.
3. The first player to call out the sum of the cards wins all the cards in the turn. These cards go into the player's bank pile.
4. If there is a tie, the tied players play additional rounds until one of them wins.
5. When a player runs out of cards, the player shuffles his or her bank pile and continues playing. If the player's bank is empty, the player is out of the game.
6. The game ends when one player has won all the cards.

6.6 Subtracting Integers Using Number Lines

YOU WILL NEED

- a number line

GOAL

Calculate the difference between integers using a number line.

LEARN ABOUT *the Math*

Matthew, Julie, and Sarah researched the record extreme temperatures of the capital cities in western and northern Canada.

Capital city	Lowest recorded temperature (°C)	Highest recorded temperature (°C)	Difference (°C)
Winnipeg	−45	+41	
Iqaluit	−46	+25	
Yellowknife	−51	+33	
Whitehorse	−52	+34	
Regina	−50	+43	
Edmonton	−48	+35	
Victoria	−16	+36	

They wanted to know how much higher the highest temperature was than the lowest temperature for each city.

What is the difference between the highest temperature and the lowest temperature for each city?

A. Suppose that the lowest Winnipeg temperature was +2. How would you express the temperature difference on a number line?

B. Express the difference between Winnipeg's actual temperatures as a subtraction.

C. Calculate the difference between Winnipeg's temperatures on a number line.

D. Calculate the difference between the highest and lowest temperatures for each of the other cities on a number line. Record your subtraction for each difference.

Reflecting

E. What temperature problem would you be solving if you calculated $(-45) - (+41)$? Use a number line to help you explain.

F. How can you tell, without calculating, that the answer for part C is a positive integer?

G. Suppose that you use a number line to calculate $(+35) - (-40)$. How does jumping from -40 to 0 help you calculate this difference?

WORK WITH the Math

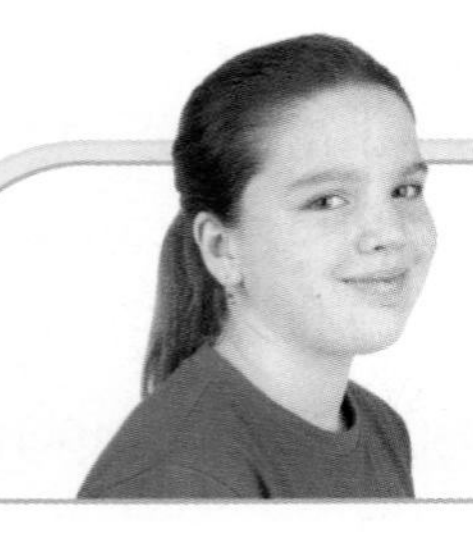

Example 1 | Subtracting integers on a number line

Calculate $(-15) - (-20)$ on a number line.

Julie's Solution

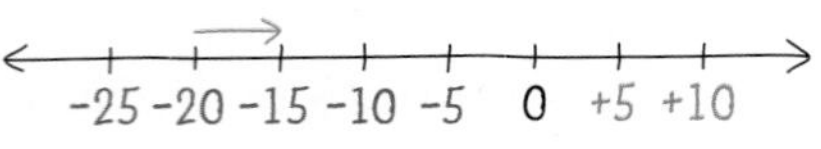

I wanted to calculate the difference between -20 and -15.

I started at -20 and went to -15.

The arrow is 5 units long.

The arrow points to the right, so I recorded the difference as a positive integer.

$(-15) - (-20) = (+5)$

The difference is $+5$.
This makes sense, because $(-20) + (+5) = (-15)$.

Example 2 | Subtracting integers on a number line

Calculate $(-20) - (+15)$ on a number line.

Matthew's Solution

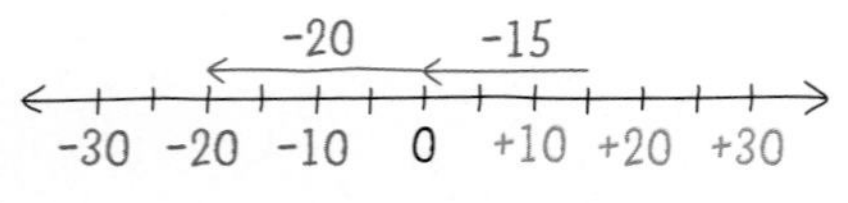

I wanted to calculate the difference between $+15$ and -20.
I started at $+15$.
It was 15 units from $+15$ to 0
and 20 more units to -20.

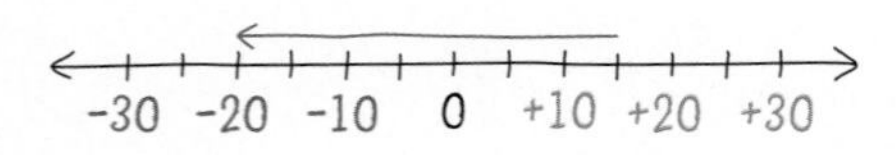

The arrow is 35 units long.

The arrow points to the left, so I recorded the difference as a negative integer.

$(-20) - (+15) = (-35)$

The difference is -35.
This makes sense, because $(+15) + (-35) = (-20)$.

Example 3 | Subtracting integers on a number line

Calculate $(+15) - (-20)$ on a number line.

Sarah's Solution

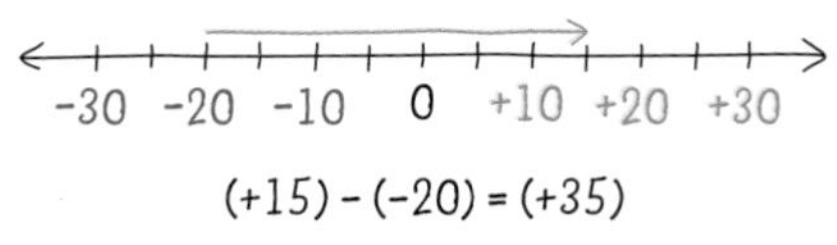

I wanted to calculate the difference between -20 and $+15$.

I started at -20 and went to $+15$. It was 20 units from -20 to 0, and 15 more units to $+15$. The arrow is 35 units long. The arrow points to the right, so I recorded the difference as a positive integer.

The difference is $+35$.
This makes sense, because $(-20) + (+35) = (+15)$.

A Checking

1. a) Calculate $(-35) - (+40)$ on a number line.

b) What is the starting point of the arrow?

c) What is the end point of the arrow?

2. Calculate.

a) $(-12) - (-20)$ **b)** $(+31) - (+32)$

B Practising

3. a) Calculate $(+36) - (-34) = \blacksquare$ and $(-34) - (+36) = \blacktriangle$ on a number line.

b) Explain why $\blacksquare$ and $\blacktriangle$ are opposite integers.

4. Calculate.

a) $(-20) - (-40)$ **d)** $(+35) - (+32)$

b) $(+30) - (+70)$ **e)** $(+10) - (-10)$

c) $(-23) - (-21)$ **f)** $(-20) - (-20)$

5. Record the subtraction that each model represents.

a) 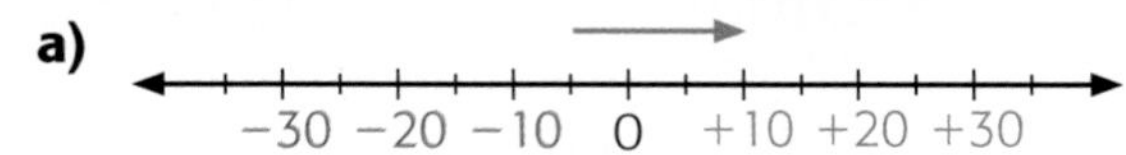

b) −30 −20 −10 0 +10 +20 +30

c) −50 −40 −30 −20 −10 0 +10

d) −100 −80 −60 −40 −20 0 +20 +40

6. The difference between two integers is -5. What does this tell you about the positions of the integers on a number line?

7. Determine the unknown value.

a) $\blacksquare - (-4) = -30$

b) $(-12) - \blacksquare = -19$

c) $\blacksquare - (+7) = -32$

d) $(+8) - \blacksquare = -15$

8. The following table shows the changing balances in some bank accounts. Copy and complete the table.

	Starting balance ($)	Final balance ($)	Model	Change in value ($)
a)	−300	−350	−400 −350 −300 −250	(−350) − (−300) = (−50)
b)	+200	−150		
c)	+150	+20		
d)	−595	+105		
e)	−1005	−950		
f)	+537	−111		

9. Which of these expressions has the greatest result?

A. $(+40) + (+20) - (+30)$

B. $(+37) - (-85) + (-10)$

C. $(-100) - (-510) + (-520)$

D. $(+25) + (-40) - (-135)$

10. a) Explain why $(+15) - (-9) = (+15) + (+9)$.

b) Can you always add the opposite to subtract an integer? Use an example to help you explain.

6.7 Solve Problems by Working Backward

YOU WILL NEED
- a number line
- red and blue counters

Solve problems using the strategy of working backward.

LEARN ABOUT the Math

Nayana showed a number trick to Nestor.
She told him to follow these steps:

1. Think of a number.	→	**2.** Add +1.	→	**3.** Subtract −3.	→	**4.** Add −5.	→	**5.** Name the result.

Nestor said that his result was −2.
Nayana said, "I think your starting number was −1."

How did Nayana know Nestor's starting number?

1 Understand the Problem

Nestor wants to know how Nayana determined his number from his result.

2 Make a Plan

Nestor realizes that he needs to start with the result and work backward through the steps to figure out the original number.

3 Carry Out the Plan

Nestor completes the original steps in order.
Then he works backward from the result.

Original Steps

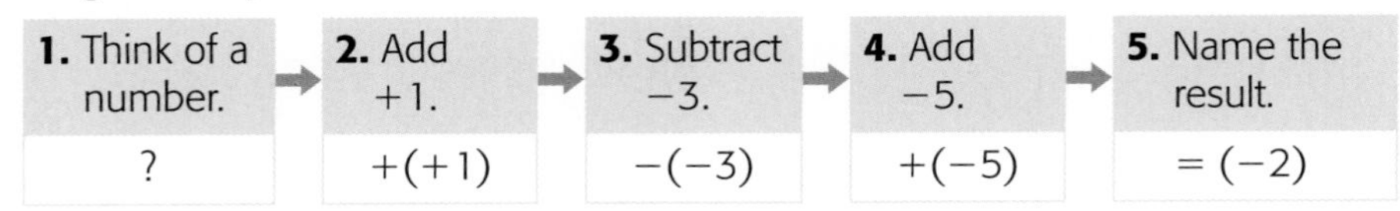

1. Think of a number.	**2.** Add +1.	**3.** Subtract −3.	**4.** Add −5.	**5.** Name the result.
?	+(+1)	−(−3)	+(−5)	= (−2)

Working Backward

5. The result is −2.	→	**4.** Subtract −5.	→	**3.** Add −3.	→	**2.** Subtract +1.	→	**1.** The number I thought of is −1.
(-2)		$-(-5)$		$+(-3)$		$-(+1)$		$= (-1)$

It works!

Reflecting

A. How does working backward help Nestor solve Nayana's number trick?

***WORK WITH** the Math*

Example | Working backward

Bill played three rounds in a golf tournament. His second-round score was 6 lower than his first-round score. His third-round score was 2 higher than his second-round score. His score for the third round was −3. What was his first-round score?

Nayana's Solution

1 Understand the Problem

I need to determine the first-round score. I already have the score for the third round. I also know how he did in the second round.

2 Make a Plan

I will draw boxes to show each step. Then I will work backward.

3 Carry Out the Plan

Each box represents one step.

First-round score → Add −6. → Second-round score → Add +2. → Third-round score is −3.

I can work backward from the result.

Third-round score is −3. → Subtract +2. → Second-round score → Subtract −6. → First-round score

$(-3) - (+2) = (-5)$
His second-round score was −5.

$(-5) - (-6) = (+1)$
His first round score was +1.

A Checking

1. Try Nayana's trick using another number. Is there a quick way to figure out the original number? If so, explain how it works.

2. John did this number trick.
   - Think of a number.
   - Add +2.
   - Subtract −1.
   - Add −2.
   - The result is +4.

   What was the original number? State the steps, in order, that you used.

B Practising

3. Jane did this calculation.
   - Add −12.
   - Subtract −9.
   - Add +8.
   - Subtract −2.
   - The result is +5.

   What was the original number? State the steps, in order, that you used.

4. Make up a number trick that gives you the original number as the result. Your trick must have at least four steps. The last step must be subtract +3.

5. Lloyd is lifting weights over a nine-week training period. Every week, he lifts 2 kg more than he lifted the previous week. During the ninth week, he lifts 80 kg. How much was he lifting during his first week?

6. During a clothing sale, the price goes down by half each day an item is not sold. If an item costs $2.50 after eight days, what was the original price?

7. Ramona takes a shape and cuts away half of it five times. The triangle at the left is what remains. Draw the original shape.

8. Make up a problem you can solve by working backward. Show how to solve it.

Chapter Self-Test

1. Calculate.

a) 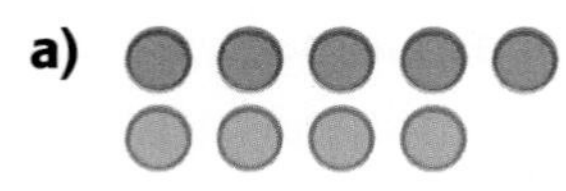

b) 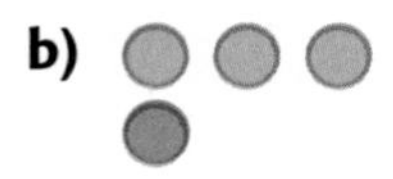

c) 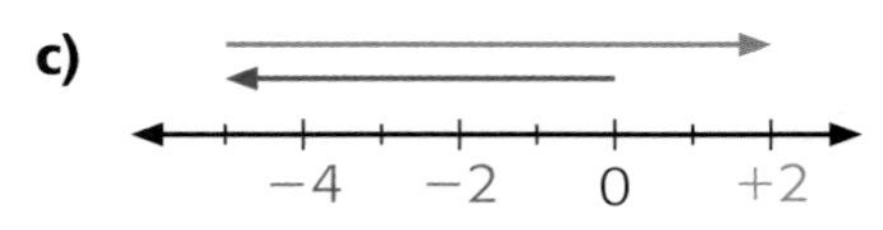

d) 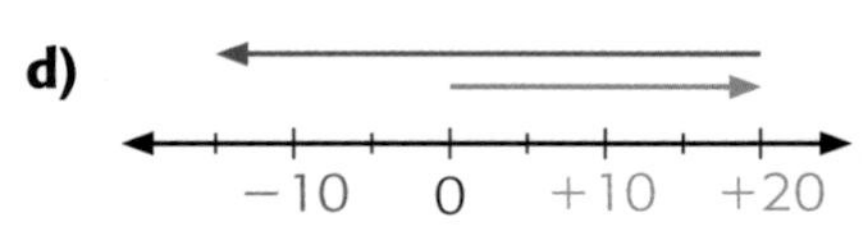

2. Calculate. Then explain what you did in each calculation.

a) $(-2) + (+3)$ **b)** $(+3) + (-2)$ **c)** $(-3) - (+4)$

3. Write the subtraction that each model represents.

a)

−5

−2 0 +2

b) 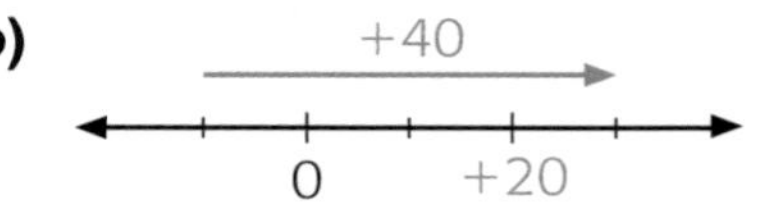

4. Calculate.

a) $(+5) + (-8)$

b) $(-10) + (-3)$

c) $(-7) - (+2)$

d) $(-8) - (-4)$

5. On Monday morning, Sam had $50 in his wallet. The following table shows how this amount changed over the week. How much did Sam put into, or take out of, his wallet on Friday afternoon?

Day	start	Mon.	Tues.	Wed.	Thu.	Fri.
Gain/loss ($)		+30	−19	−25	+51	
Total ($)	50					20

6. a) How could you predict that $(-4) + (+12)$ is positive and 8 units to the right of 0?

b) How could you predict that $(-15) - (+23)$ is negative and 38 units to the left of 0?

What Do You Think Now?

Revisit What Do You Think? on page 239. How have your answers and explanations changed?

Chapter Review

Frequently Asked Questions

Q: How do you subtract integers, such as $(-2) - (-6)$?

A1: You can use counters. If necessary, you can use the zero principle to add red and blue counters that equal 0. Then you remove the counters you need to. The remaining counters represent the answer. This model shows that $(-2) - (-6) = (+4)$.

(-2)

$(-4) + (+4) = 0$

$(-2) - (-6) = (+4)$

A2: You can use a number line. Determine the difference between the second number and the first number. If the arrow from the second number points to the left, the answer is negative. If the arrow points to the right, the answer is positive. This model shows that $(-2) - (-6) = (+4)$.

+4

−10 −9 −8 −7 −6 −5 −4 −3 −2 −1 0

A3: You can add the opposite. This model shows that $(-2) - (-6)$ has the same value as $(-2) + (+6)$, which is $+4$.

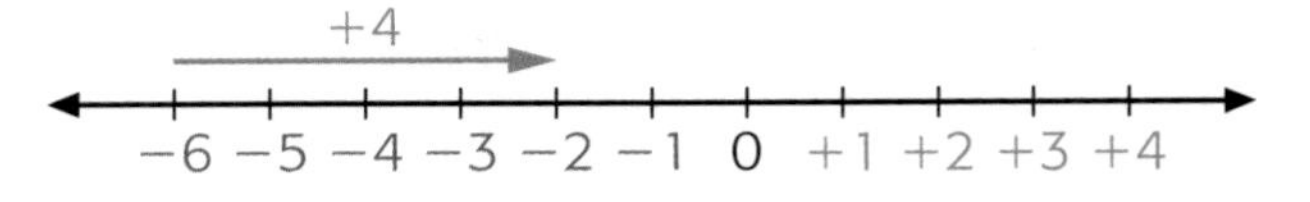

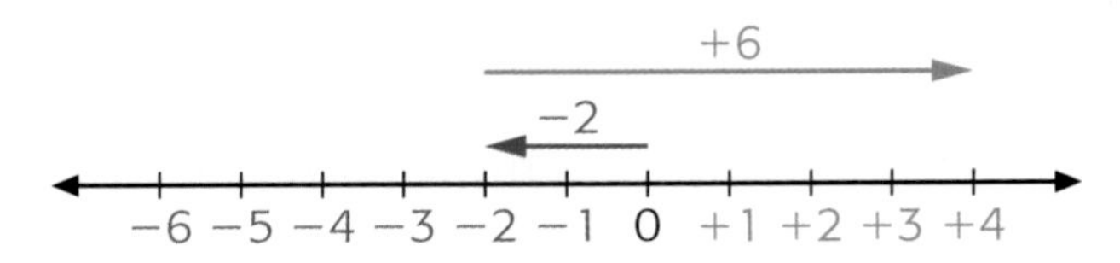

Practice

Lesson 6.2

1. Write three different addition questions that have a result of -2.

Lesson 6.4

2. On Monday morning, Polly had \$30 in her wallet. How much did Polly put into, or take out of, her wallet on Friday?

Day	start	Mon.	Tues.	Wed.	Thu.	Fri.
Gain/loss (\$)		+4	+5	−2	−10	
Total (\$)	30					17

3. Calculate.

a) $(-12) + (-6) + (-18)$ **b)** $(-37) + (-20) + (+12)$

Lesson 6.5

4. ▒ represents an integer. Which is greater, ▒ $- (+1)$ or ▒ $+ (+1)$? Explain your reasoning.

5. Which expression has the greatest result? Which expression has the least result?

A. $(+4) - (+2)$
B. $(-7) - (+4)$
C. $(+6) - (-3)$
D. $(-3) - (-5)$

6. How is subtracting integers like adding integers? How is it different?

Lesson 6.6

7. Calculate.

a) $(+8) + (-3)$ **c)** $(-7) + (+6)$
b) $(-8) - (-3)$ **d)** $(+2) - (+4)$

8. One integer is 5 greater than another integer. Their sum is -13. What are the two integers?

Lesson 6.7

9. The temperature dropped 5 °C from midnight to noon. Then it rose 10 °C from noon to 10:00 p.m. It is now −25 °C. What was the temperature at midnight?

Chapter Task

Task | Checklist

- ✔ Do your clues involve both addition and subtraction of integers?
- ✔ Does at least one of your clues compare integers?
- ✔ Did you include a clue you did not need?
- ✔ Did you check to make sure that your clues give the correct integers?

Mystery Integer

Choose three integers. Make up a set of clues that will allow others to figure out which integers you chose. All of the clues must be necessary.

The clues must
- include both addition and subtraction of integers
- compare integers

For example, suppose that your integers are -8, $+17$, and -33. Here are three possible clues:
- If you subtract one integer from another, the result is $+25$.
- If you add all three integers, the result is less than -20.
- The sum of the least and greatest integers is -16.

What clues can you write to describe your three integers?

A. The three clues above do not give enough information for someone to figure out the integers. What clues can you add to give enough information?

B. Select three integers of your own, and make up some clues.

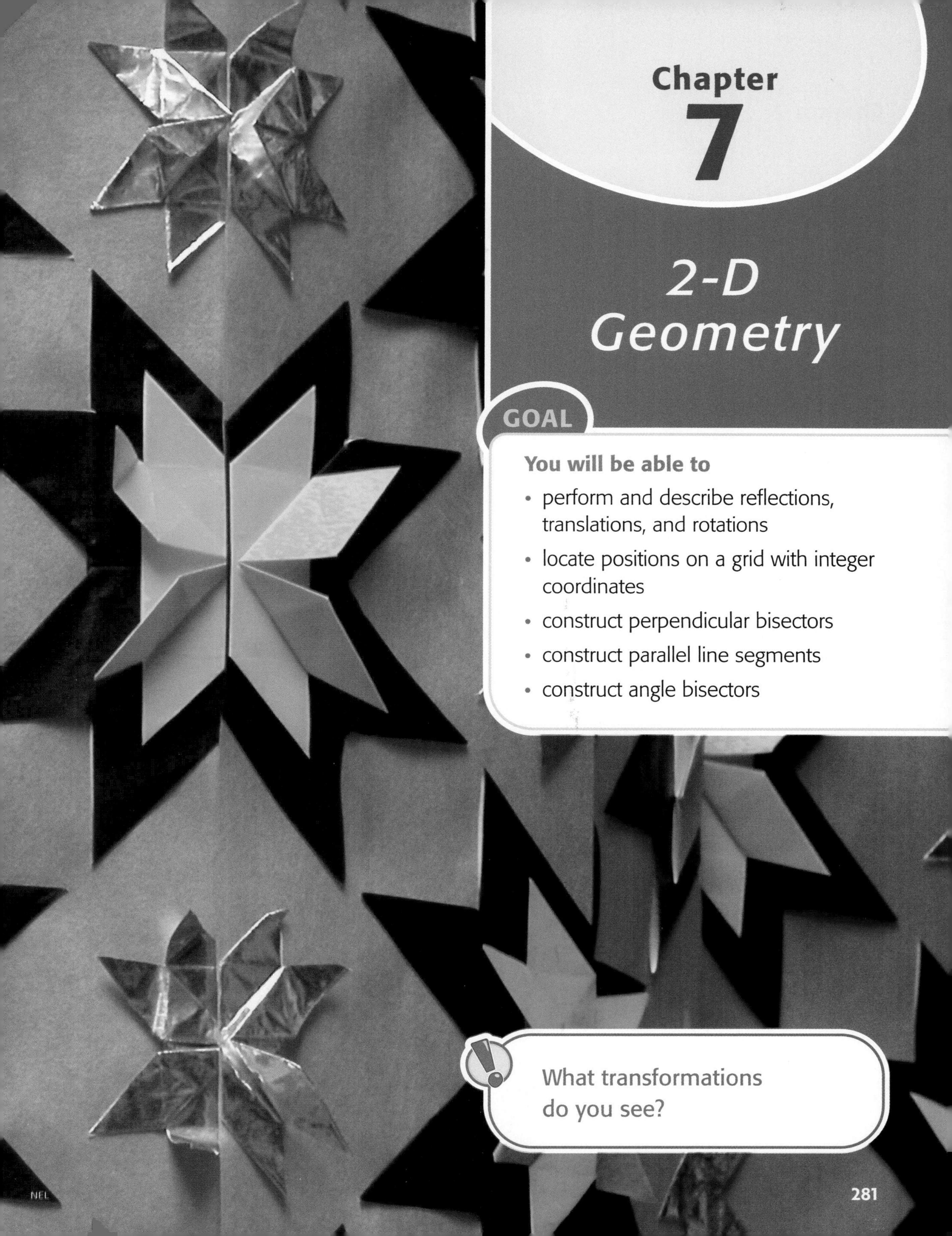

Chapter 7

2-D Geometry

GOAL

You will be able to

- perform and describe reflections, translations, and rotations
- locate positions on a grid with integer coordinates
- construct perpendicular bisectors
- construct parallel line segments
- construct angle bisectors

What transformations do you see?

Getting Started

YOU WILL NEED
- a tangram set
- grid paper

Tangram Challenge

In this game, students create a tangram design. Then they describe their design to a partner, so their partner can re-create it. Nestor decides to use **rotations**, **reflections**, and **translations** to describe his design.

How can Nestor describe his tangram design using transformations?

A. Sketch Nestor's tangram design on grid paper.

B. Label each vertex of all seven pieces with coordinates.

C. Describe the transformations you see using a combination of sketches, math terms, and coordinates.

What Do You Think?

Decide whether you agree or disagree with each statement.
Be ready to explain your decision.

1. Railroad tracks are an example of parallel lines.

2. If two shapes are congruent, a translation can always be used to move one shape onto the other.

3. To get from the red shape to the blue shape, two different transformations are needed.

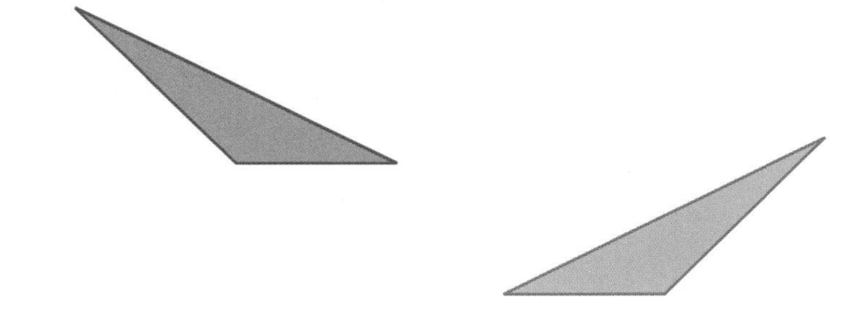

7.1 Translating Points

YOU WILL NEED

- grid paper
- a transparent geoboard and elastic bands
- a ruler

GOAL

Identify the points of a translated figure.

EXPLORE the Math

The students in Nick's class are practising translations with a partner. Nick's partner, Pavlo, has drawn a figure. Nick must translate the figure 3 units left and 4 units down. He wants to write the coordinates of the new vertices.

Communication | *Tip*

Positive numbers are often written without the positive sign (+). For example, +2 can be written as 2.

Vertices of Figure A
(1, 3)
(2, 4)
(2, 5)
(6, 5)
(6, 0)
(4, 2)
(3, 1)

How can Nick write the coordinates of the vertices of the translated figure?

7.2 Comparing Positions on a Grid

YOU WILL NEED
- grid paper
- a ruler

GOAL

Locate positions on a grid with integer coordinates.

LEARN ABOUT the Math

Cartesian coordinate system

a method (named after mathematician René Descartes) for describing a location by identifying the distance from a horizontal number line (the *x*-axis) and a vertical number line (the *y*-axis); the location is represented by an ordered pair of coordinates, (*x*, *y*); the axes intersect at (0, 0), which is called the **origin**

Ashley and Gail are planning a hiking and camping trip. Ashley draws a grid of squares on her copy of the map to help her find different locations. Gail uses a **Cartesian coordinate system** that is divided into four areas called quadrants.

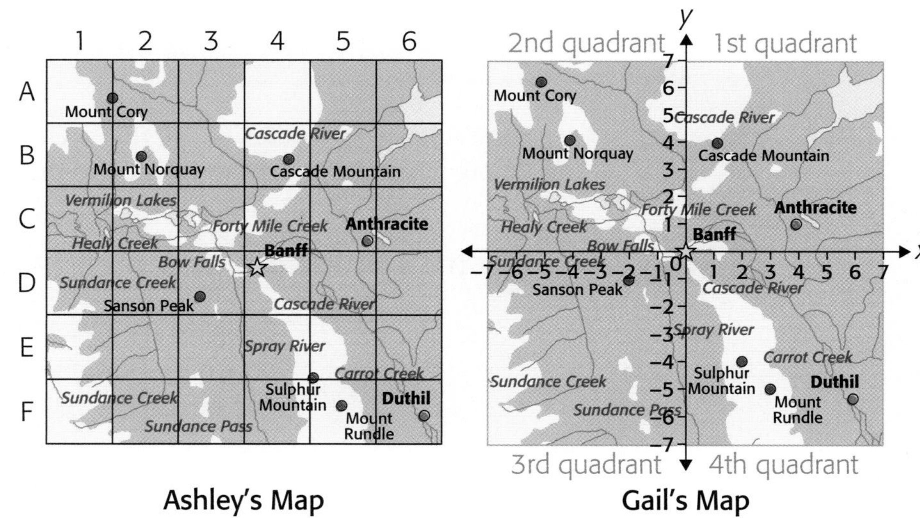

Ashley's Map

Gail's Map

How can Ashley and Gail use their maps to plan their route?

A. Identify the location that is represented by each set of coordinates below using Gail's map.

a) (1, 4) **b)** (−2, −1) **c)** (−4, 4) **d)** (−5, 6)

B. Identify the quadrant for each location in part A.

C. Name the coordinates of each location below using the grid system on Ashley's map and Gail's map.

a) Banff **b)** Mount Rundle **c)** Sulphur Mountain

D. Describe a route that begins at Mount Rundle and includes at least two other mountains, using the grid map and then the Cartesian coordinate map.

Reflecting

E. How can you tell which quadrant a point is in by looking at the signs (positive or negative) of the x- and y-coordinates?

F. Which system is more precise for identifying specific locations—Ashley's or Gail's? Explain your thinking.

WORK WITH the Math

Example 1 | Describing the locations of points

Point A has coordinates $(4, -2)$ on a Cartesian coordinate system. Where is point $B(-3, 3)$ in relation to point A?

Nestor's Solution

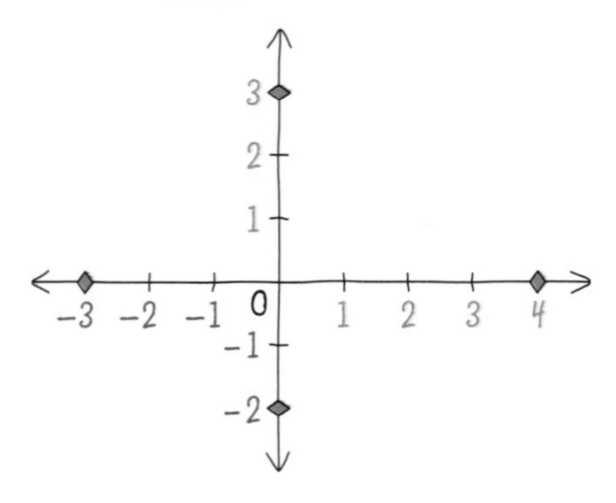

I compared the first coordinates of the two ordered pairs, 4 and -3, using the horizontal number line. Since $-3 < 4$, B is to the left of A.

I compared the second coordinates of the two ordered pairs, -2 and 3, using the vertical number line. Since $3 > -2$, B is above A.

Point B must be above and to the left of point A.

Example 2 | Comparing positions using coordinates

Name the coordinates of two points that match each description.

a) to the left of P
b) to the right of P
c) above P
d) below P

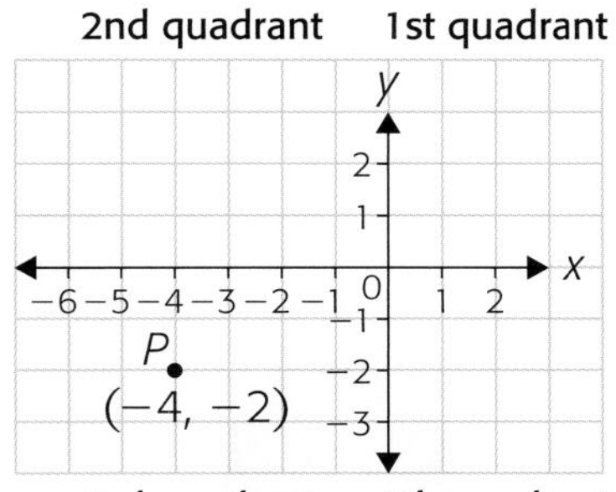

Jessica's Solution

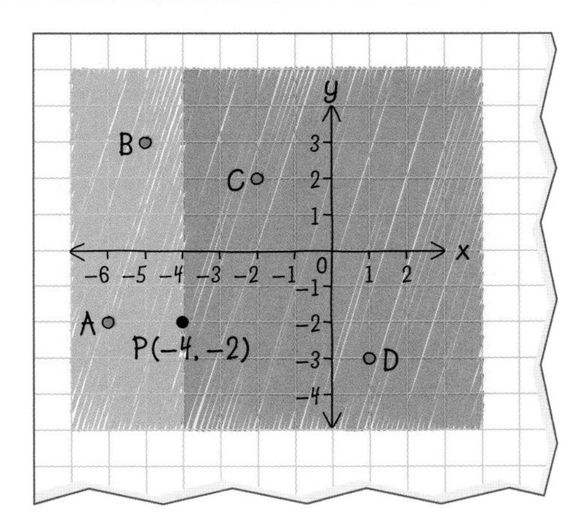

I used number lines to help me locate the points.

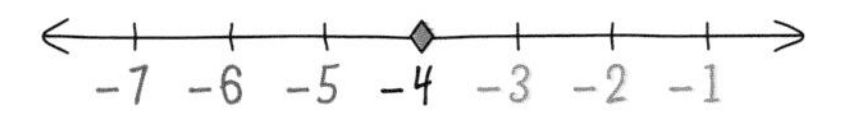

a) "To the left" means "less than." The x-coordinates of the new points must be less than -4. I chose $A(-6, -2)$ and $B(-5, 3)$.

b) If points are to the "right" of P, their x-coordinates must be greater than -4. I chose $C(-2, 2)$ and $D(1, -3)$.

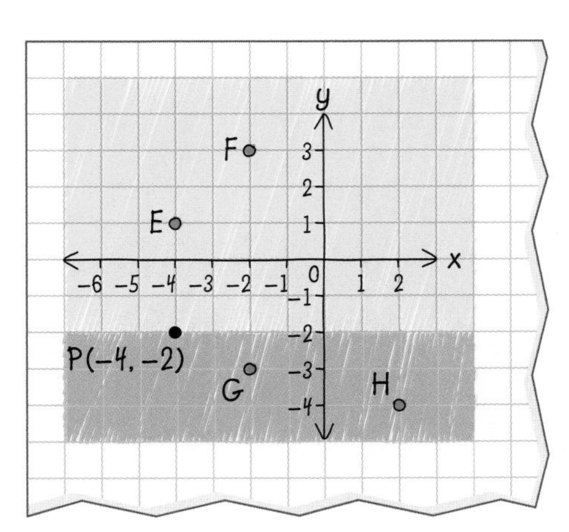

c) If the points are "above" P, their y-coordinates must be greater than -2. I chose $E(-4, 1)$ and $F(-2, 3)$.

d) If the points are "below" P, their y-coordinates must be less than -2. I chose $G(-2, -3)$ and $H(2, -4)$.

Example 3 | Calculating distance using points

Nick plans to walk west and then north to get from the theatre to the mall. How far will he travel in each direction?

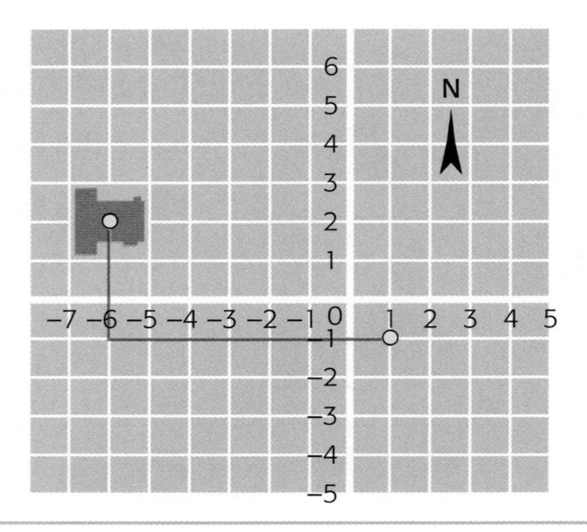

Nick's Solution

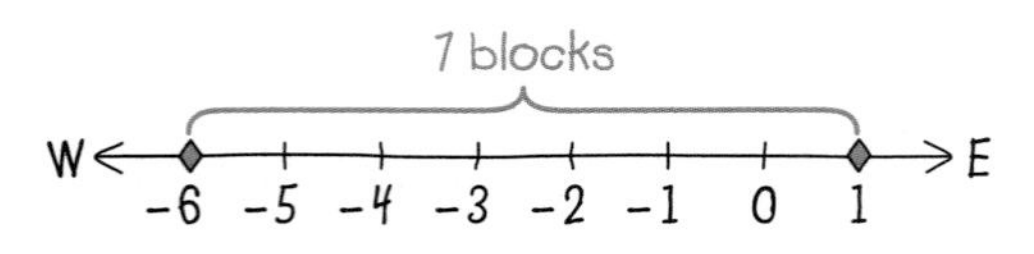

First I used a horizontal number line to compare the *x*-coordinates.

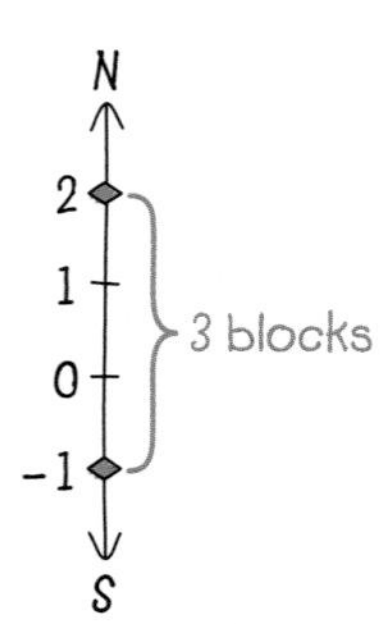

Then I used a vertical number line to compare the *y*-coordinates.

I will travel 7 blocks west and 3 blocks north.

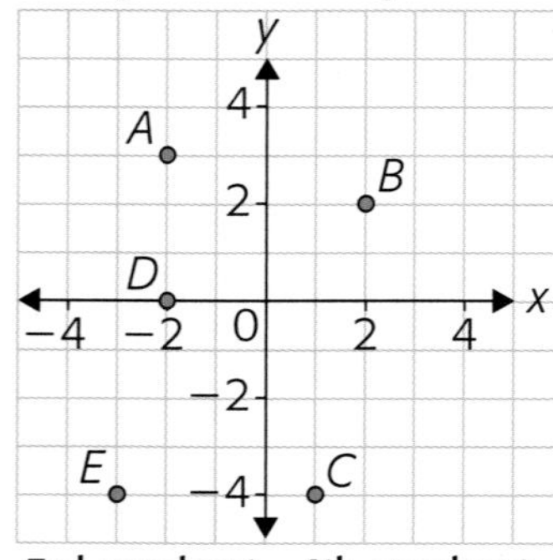

A Checking

1. Name the coordinates of each point shown.
2. Plot the points (2, 3), (−1, 4), (−3, −5), (4, −6), and (0, 0) on a Cartesian coordinate system.
3. Identify the distance between the points.
   - **a)** (−8, 3) and (−5, 3)
   - **b)** (3, 3) and (3, −7)
   - **c)** (5, −4) and (−2, −4)

B Practising

4. Plot each set of points on a Cartesian coordinate system. Connect the points to form a polygon. Name the polygon.

a) $A(0, 5)$, $B(4, 5)$, $C(4, 0)$

b) $D(-3, 1)$, $E(-3, -3)$, $F(-1, -4)$, $G(-1, 0)$

5. Copy and complete each statement. Write "above" or "below" in the green box.

a) $(4, -5)$ is ______ $(-4, -3)$ because ___ $<$ ___.

b) $(-7, -1)$ is ______ $(-4, -3)$ because ___ $>$ ___.

6. Plot the points $(-11, 28)$, $(-18, 15)$, $(-15, -28)$, and $(-29, -15)$.

a) Which point is farthest right? **b)** Which point is lowest?

7. a) List five points that have opposite integers as their x-coordinate and y-coordinate.

b) Plot your points on a Cartesian coordinate system.

c) What pattern do these points form?

d) As the first coordinate of a point increases, what happens to the position of the point?

8. A and Z are two vertices of a right triangle. What are the coordinates of the other vertex? Give two possible answers.

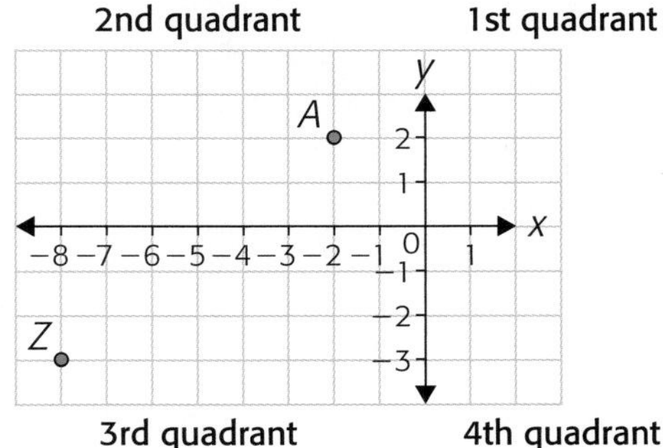

9. Draw a parallelogram that has $(-5, -3)$ as its top right vertex. State the coordinates of the other vertices. Explain how you determined these coordinates.

10. The diagonals of a rectangle intersect at $(0, 0)$. The rectangle is 6 units long and 4 units wide. Determine the coordinates of the vertices of the rectangle.

11. How is the location of $(3, -4)$ different from the location of $(-4, 3)$?

7.3 Translations and Reflections

YOU WILL NEED
- centimetre grid paper
- a ruler

GOAL

Perform and describe translations and reflections of a 2-D shape in all four quadrants of a Cartesian coordinate system.

LEARN ABOUT the Math

Gail's math fair project is about designing logos. Each visitor to her station will follow her directions to transform the red figure into the blue logo.

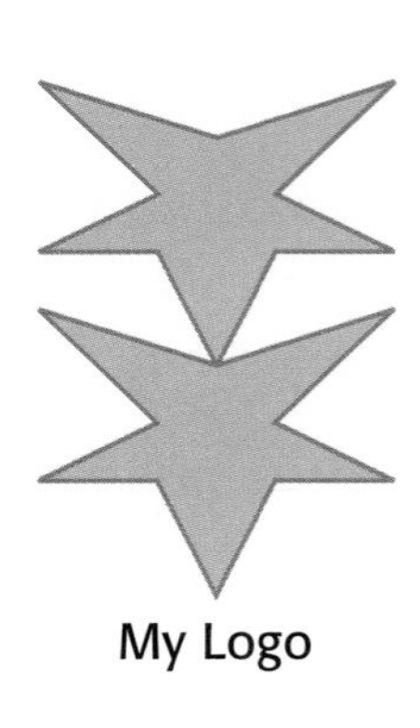
My Logo

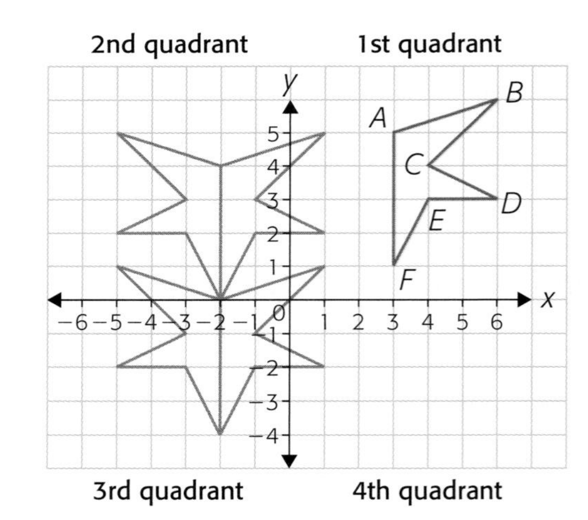

How can Gail describe the transformations she used to create the blue logo?

Communication | *Tip*

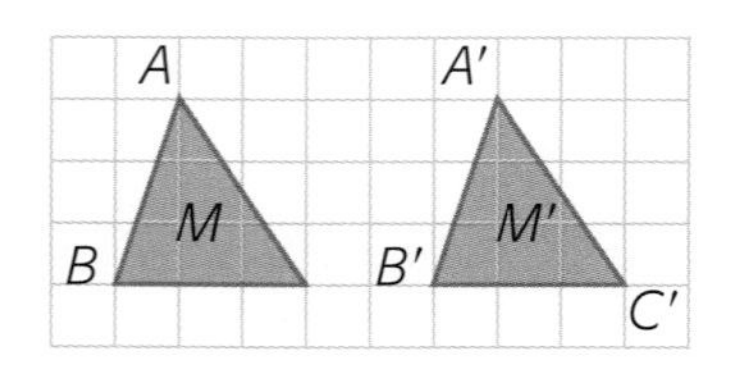

The new shape that is created when a shape is transformed is called the image. The original shape is sometimes called the pre-image. The vertices of the image are often labelled using the same letters as the pre-image, but with primes. For example, the image of M is M'. (M' is read as "M prime.") An arrow is used to show the result of a transformation. For example, $M \rightarrow M'$.

Example 1 | Describing transformation images

Describe the transformations that Gail used to create the blue logo.

Gail's Solution

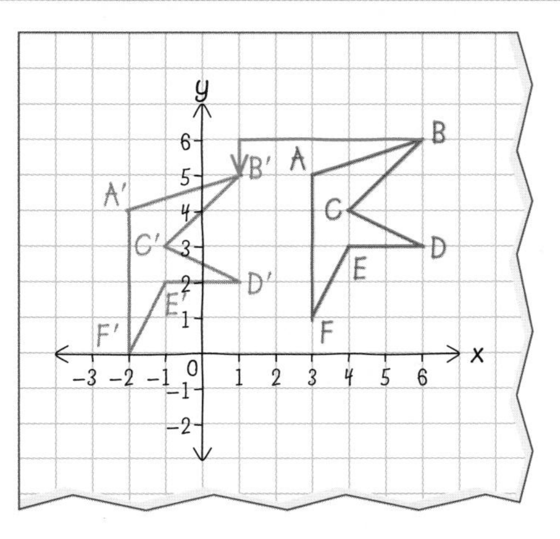

I started with the red figure. The vertices of the red figure are $A(3, 5)$, $B(6, 6)$, $C(4, 4)$, $D(6, 3)$, $E(4, 3)$, and $F(3, 1)$.

First, I used a translation. Each point in the red figure is moved 5 units to the left and 1 unit down. The vertices of the image are $A'(-2, 4)$, $B'(1, 5)$, $C'(-1, 3)$, $D'(1, 2)$, $E'(-1, 2)$, and $F'(-2, 0)$.

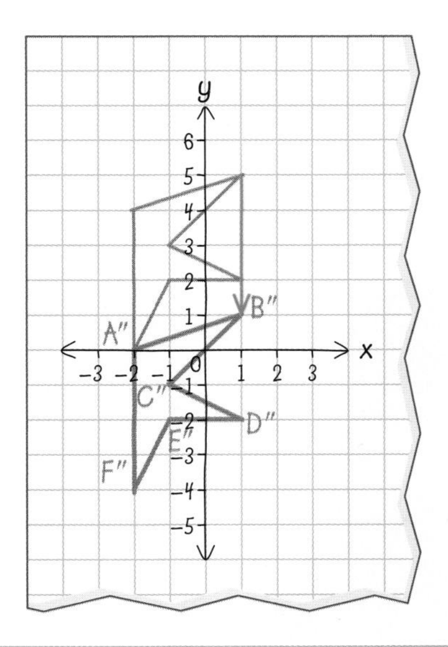

Then I used a second translation. This moved the image 4 units down.

I used letters with two primes to show that I had completed two transformations. The new vertices are $A''(-2, 0)$, $B''(1, 1)$, $C''(-1, -1)$, $D''(1, -2)$, $E''(-1, -2)$, and $F''(-2, -4)$.

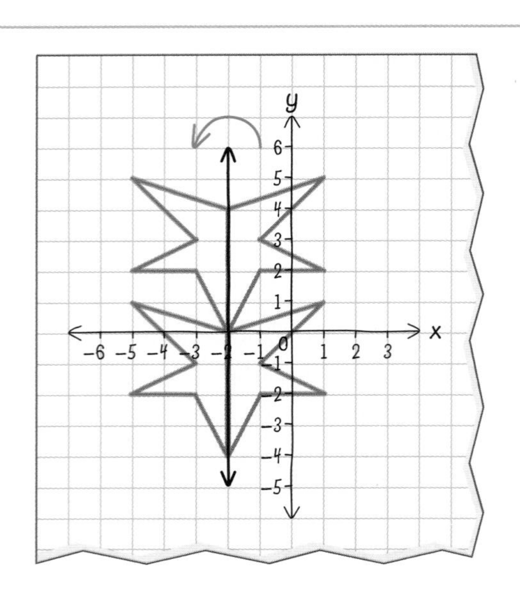

Finally, I reflected $A'B'C'D'E'F'$ and $A''B''C''D''E''F''$ across a vertical reflection line that passes through the point (−2, 0). Each image vertex is the same distance from the reflection line as its pre-image.

Reflecting

A. How did the x-coordinates change in the first translation? How did the y-coordinates change?

B. Which coordinates changed in the second translation? Why?

C. Why did the reflection change the sign (positive or negative) of some of the coordinates, but not all of them?

WORK WITH the Math

Example 2 | Determining reflection image coordinates

Predict the vertices of the image of $\triangle ABC$ after $\triangle ABC$ has been reflected across the y-axis.

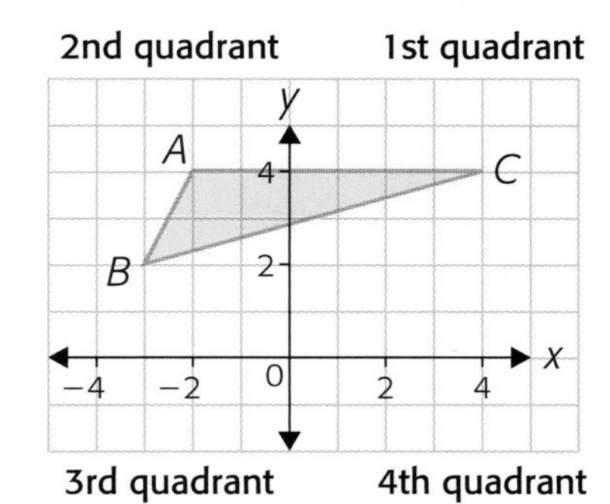

Solution

The y-axis is the reflection line. Count squares to predict the vertices of the image of $\triangle ABC$.

$A(-2, 4) \rightarrow A'(2, 4)$

A is 2 squares to the left of the y-axis. A' will be 2 squares to the right of the y-axis.

$B(-3, 2) \rightarrow B'(3, 2)$

B is 3 squares to the left of the y-axis. B' will be 3 squares to the right of the y-axis.

$C(4, 4) \rightarrow C'(-4, 4)$

C is 4 squares to the right of the y-axis. C' will be 4 squares to the left of the y-axis.

In this reflection, the x-coordinates of the image and pre-image are opposite integers.

A Checking

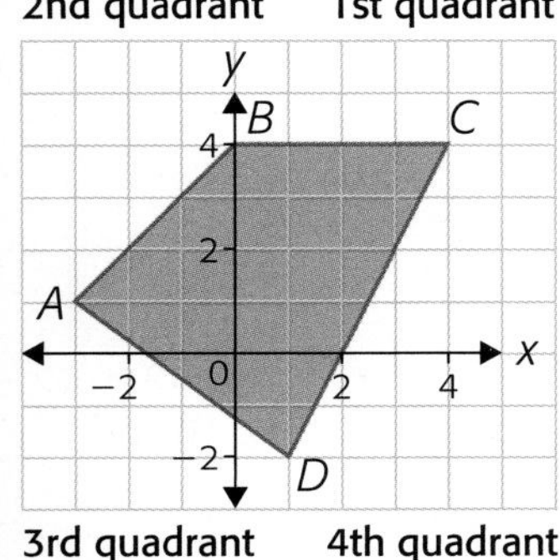

1. a) Draw the image of this shape after a translation 2 units to the left and 1 unit up.
   b) Name the coordinates of the image vertices.

2. $\triangle PQR$ has vertices $P(-6, 2)$, $Q(-4, 0)$, and $R(-2, 5)$. Determine the vertices of its image after a reflection across the y-axis.

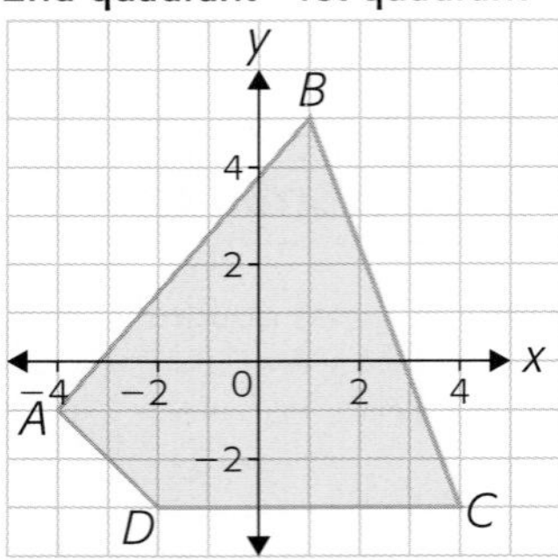

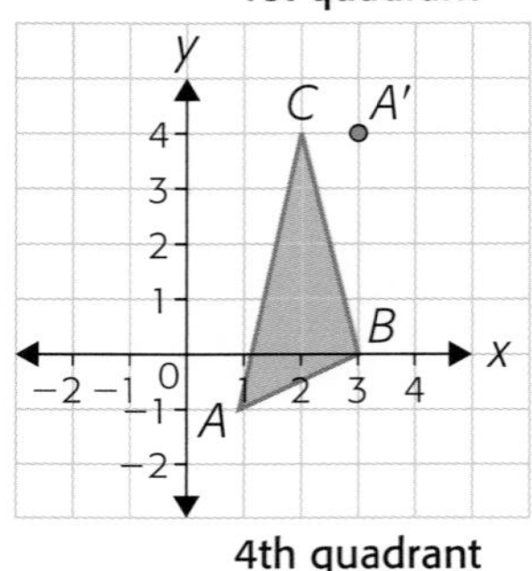

B Practising

3. Determine the vertices of $A'B'C'D'$ after each transformation of $ABCD$.

a) a reflection across the x-axis

b) a reflection across the y-axis

4. Fazel says that if you reflect a triangle in the x-axis and then in the y-axis, the image of the triangle will be the same as if you did the reflections in the opposite order. Do you think he is right? Use the coordinates of three different triangles to support your opinion.

5. a) Describe the translation that moves vertex A to $A'(3, 4)$.

b) State the images of B and C after the same translation.

6. The vertices of $\triangle XYZ$ are $X(0, -4)$, $Y(0, 0)$, and $Z(3, 3)$. Determine the image vertices if $\triangle XYZ$ is translated 3 units to the right and 2 units down.

7. Describe the translation that moves

a) $ABCD$ to $A'B'C'D'$

b) $A'B'C'D'$ to $A''B''C''D''$

c) $ABCD$ to $A''B''C''D''$

8. The vertices of $\triangle PQR$ are $P(-2, -1)$, $Q(2, 1)$, and $R(0, 4)$. Determine the vertices of the image after a translation that moves vertex P to vertex Q.

9. $\triangle DEF$ is transformed to $\triangle D''E''F''$ by applying the same translation two times. The coordinates of D are $(-5, -3)$.

a) Describe the translation.

b) Write the coordinates of vertices E and F.

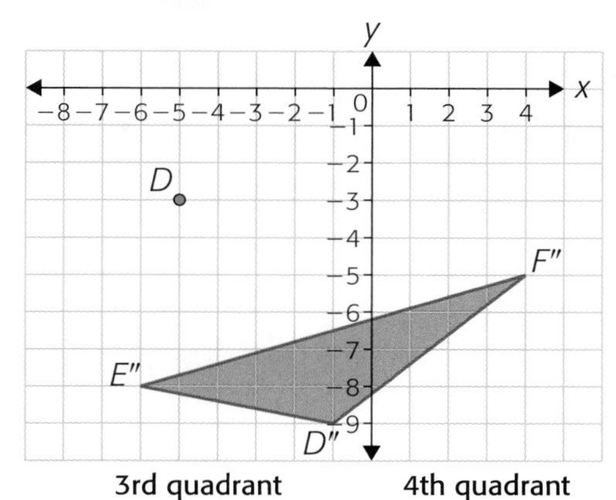

10. How can you use only the coordinates of the vertices to show that $\triangle A'B'C'$ is **not** the image of $\triangle ABC$ after a translation?

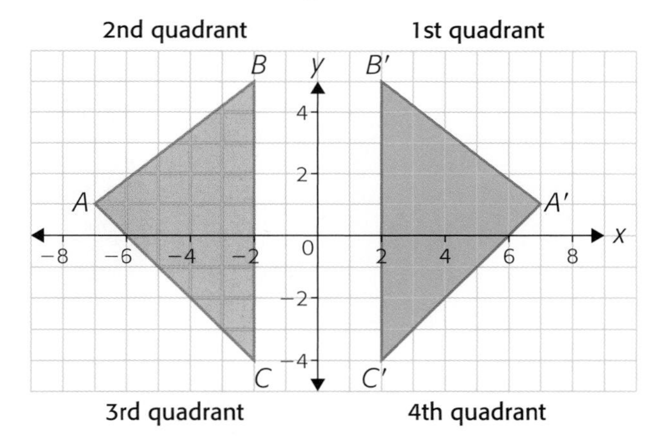

11. Two vertices of a square are $P(-2, 4)$ and $Q(4, 4)$.

a) State two possible sets of coordinates for the other two vertices.

b) Draw your two squares on grid paper.

c) Describe the translation that would move the upper square to the lower square.

12. A shape is completely in the 1st quadrant. Where could it be after a translation? Where could it be after a reflection?

7.4 Rotations

YOU WILL NEED

- centimetre grid paper
- a protractor
- a ruler

GOAL

Perform and describe rotations in all four quadrants of a Cartesian plane.

LEARN ABOUT the Math

Ashley saw a Celtic design in an ad. She decided to create a geometric design like it using rotations.

How can Ashley use rotations to create a geometric design?

centre of rotation

a fixed point around which other points in a shape rotate in a clockwise (cw) or counterclockwise (ccw) direction; the centre of rotation may be inside or outside the shape

A. Copy this design onto a Cartesian coordinate system. Use the **origin** as the **centre of rotation** for a 90° cw turn.

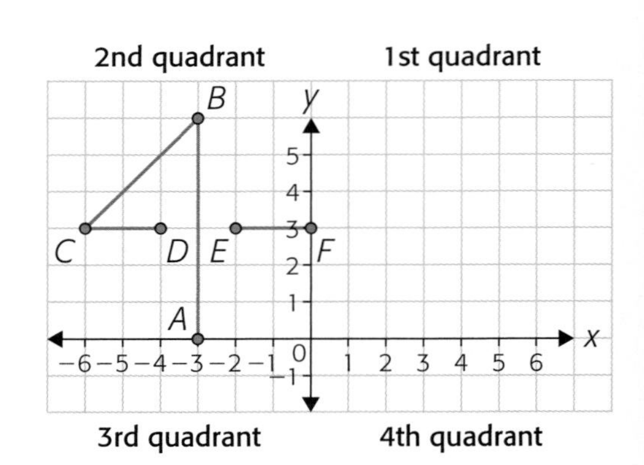

B. Draw a **line segment** from the origin to D. Place a protractor so that 0 is on the line segment and the centre is on the origin. Draw a line to mark 90°.

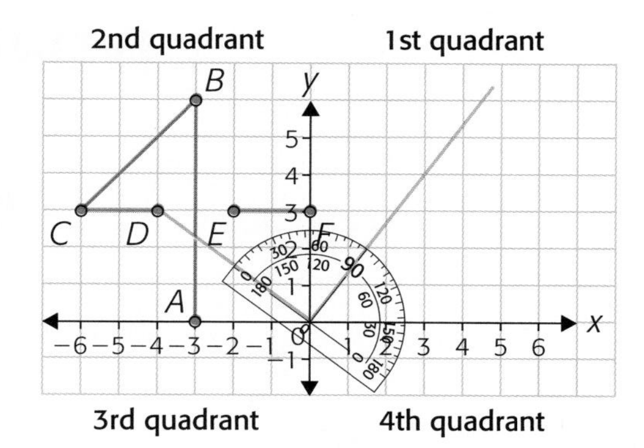

C. Put the point of a compass on the origin, and draw an arc from D to the 90° line. Label the point where the arc touches the line D'.

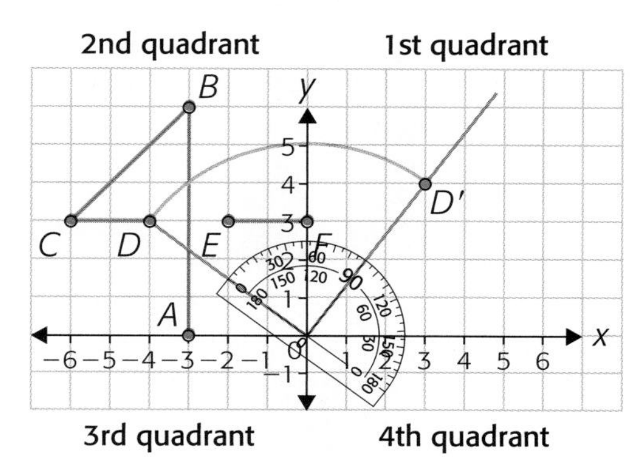

D. Repeat parts B and C, but with points A, B, C, E, and F, to rotate these points 90° cw around the origin. Add the necessary lines between the image points to create the design in the 1st quadrant.

E. Rotate the design in the 1st quadrant 180° cw around the origin.

F. Rotate the design in the 3rd quadrant 90° ccw around the origin to complete the geometric design.

Reflecting

G. Why is it important that the new segments be just as far from the centre of rotation as the original segments?

H. Suppose that a shape in the 2nd quadrant is rotated 180° cw around the origin. Which quadrant will the image be in?

I. What three pieces of information are used to describe a rotation?

WORK WITH the Math

Example | Describing rotations

Describe how to create the logo at the right using rotations.

1st quadrant

4th quadrant

Jessica's Solution

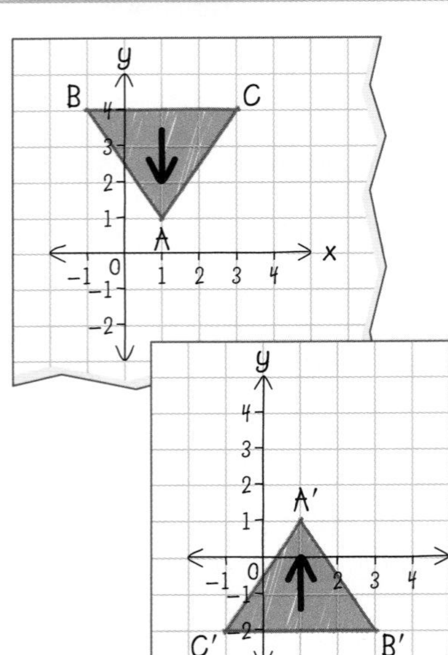

I decided to make the top triangle first. The vertices are $A(1, 1)$, $B(-1, 4)$, and $C(3, 4)$.

I rotated ΔABC 180° cw around (1, 1) to create the image, $\Delta A'B'C'$.

I decided to make the bottom triangle next.
To describe a rotation, I need to state the centre of rotation, the direction (cw or ccw), and the number of degrees.
The image vertices are $A'(1, 1)$, $B'(3, -2)$, and $C'(-1, -2)$.

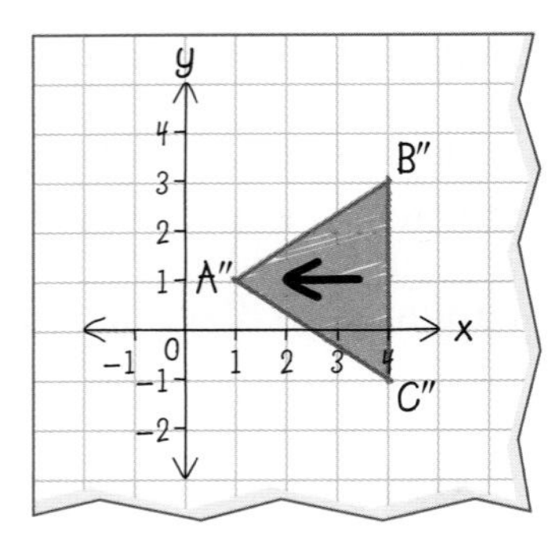

I rotated $\Delta A'B'C'$ 90° ccw around (1, 1) to create $\Delta A''B''C''$.

Then I made the third triangle. The vertices of the third triangle are $A''(1, 1)$, $B''(4, 3)$, and $C''(4, -1)$.

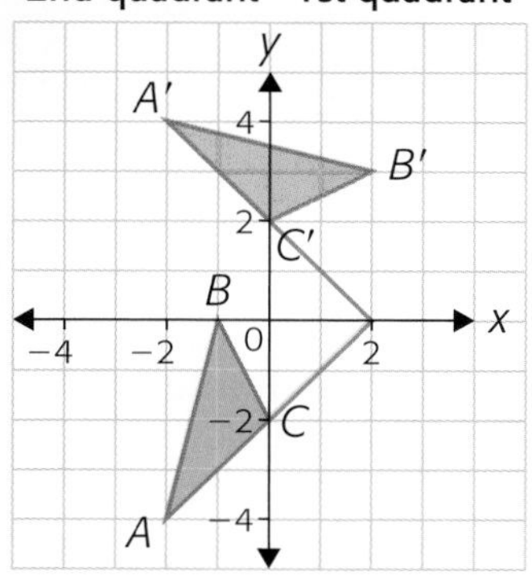

A Checking

1. $\triangle ABC$ has been rotated.
   a) What are the coordinates of the centre of rotation?
   b) What is the direction and degree of the rotation?

B Practising

2. The vertices of $\triangle DEF$ are $D(2, 3)$, $E(1, 5)$, and $F(-1, 1)$. Determine the vertices of the image after $\triangle DEF$ has been rotated 90° ccw around the origin.

3. a) Rotate rectangle $QRST$ 90° cw around the origin.
   b) Label the vertices of the image.
   c) How could you have predicted that the image would be taller than it is wide?

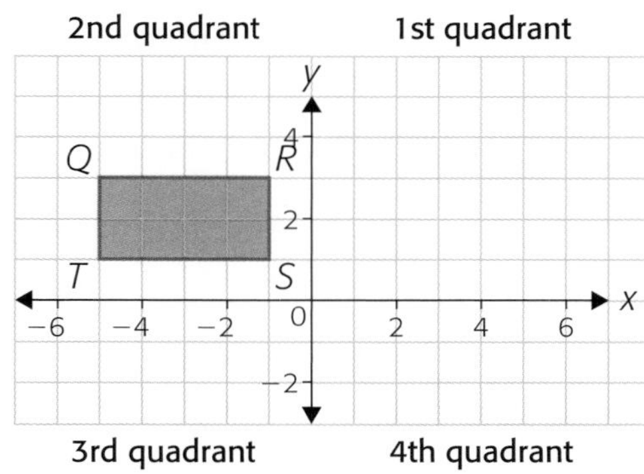

4. Suppose that your teacher tells you that the minute hand on the clock will rotate 45° while you write a math quiz. If the quiz starts at 9:00, at what time does it end? What is the angle between the starting and ending positions of the second hand?

5. a) Draw a triangle on grid paper. Label the vertices X, Y, and Z.
   b) Rotate $\triangle XYZ$ 180° cw around X. Label the vertices of the image X', Y', and Z'.

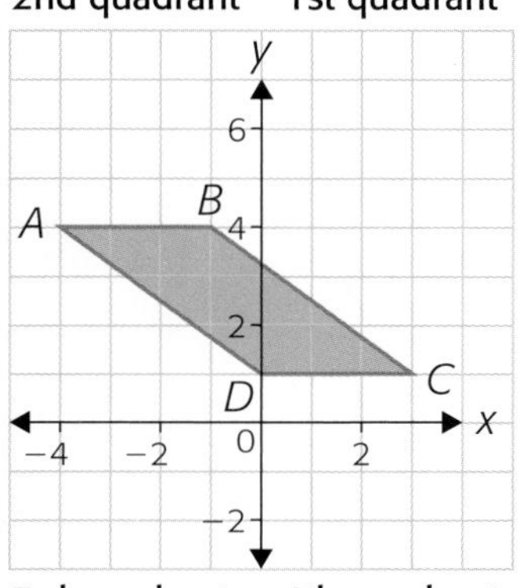

6. a) Rotate quadrilateral $ABCD$ 180° ccw around vertex D. Write the coordinates of the image vertices.
   b) Suggest a different rotation you could use to create the same image you created in part (a). Justify your suggestion.

7. Explain the steps you would use to rotate a shape in the 1st quadrant so that its image is in the 3rd quadrant.

Chapter 7

Mid-Chapter Review

Frequently Asked Questions

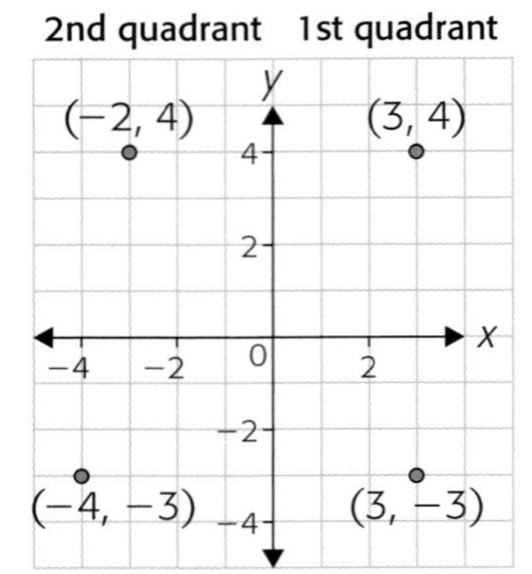

Q: How can you describe a point on a Cartesian coordinate system?

A: A set of two numbers is used to describe a point on a Cartesian coordinate system. The first number tells you how far to move right or left from the origin (0, 0). The second number tells you how far to move up or down from the origin.

Q: How can you tell whether a shape is the image of another shape after each transformation?

- **a translation**
- **a reflection**
- **a rotation**

A: Each transformation produces an image that is congruent to its pre-image.

Transformation	Relationship between vertices of pre-image and vertices of image	Example
translation	Each pre-image vertex is moved the same distance in the same direction. The image faces the same way as the pre-image.	
reflection	Each pre-image vertex is the same distance from the reflection line as its image vertex. The image faces the opposite way to the pre-image.	
rotation	The vertices of the pre-image and the image are the same distance from the point that is the centre of rotation. $\angle AXA'$, $\angle BXB'$, and $\angle CXC'$ are all the same.	

Practice

Lesson 7.1

1. Create a shape with four vertices, all in the 1st quadrant. Label the vertices using letters and coordinates. Describe a translation that would result in each image vertex being in a different quadrant.

Lesson 7.2

2. Plot the points $A(-1, -2)$, $B(-4, 2)$, $C(0, 0)$, $D(4, 7)$, and $E(3, -5)$ on a Cartesian coordinate system.

3. Write the letter of the point in question 2 that matches each description.

a) located at the origin

b) in the 2nd quadrant

c) farthest to the right

d) lowest

Lesson 7.3

Reading Strategy

Use pictures to show what you know about each transformation.

4. a) Draw $\triangle ABC$, with vertices $A(0, 0)$, $B(4, 0)$, and $C(0, 3)$.

b) Translate $\triangle ABC$ 6 units to the left and 2 units up. Determine the coordinates of the image vertices.

c) Reflect $\triangle ABC$ across the x-axis. Determine the coordinates of the image vertices.

Lesson 7.4

5. Describe a single transformation that would move parallelogram $HIJK$ to each image. If possible, give more than one answer for each image.

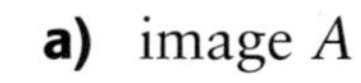
a) image A

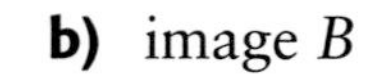
b) image B

2nd quadrant

1st quadrant

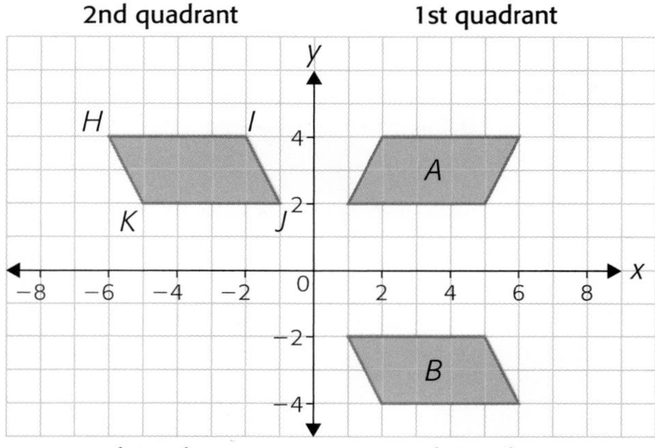

3rd quadrant

4th quadrant

7.5 Communicate about Transformations

YOU WILL NEED

- grid paper
- a compass
- a ruler

GOAL

Discuss mathematical ideas using mathematical terms.

LEARN ABOUT the Math

Nick asked Pavlo to check an entry in his math portfolio. In the entry, Nick described how the yellow triangle was transformed to create the blue triangle.

How can Nick improve his description?

Nick's Entry

I knew that it couldn't be *just* a slide.

I thought that a 90° turn was used because A′C′ is horizontal, but AC is vertical.

I used a 90° turn, and the triangle ended up in the second quadrant.

Then I saw that I *just* had to reflect across the *y*-axis. This worked.

Pavlo's Questions and Suggestions

- How did you know this?
- Why did you say "slide" instead of "translation"?
- What did you mean by "it"?

- Why did you think a 90° turn had to be used?
- Why did you say "turn" instead of "rotation"?

- What was your centre of rotation?
- Did you rotate clockwise or counterclockwise?
- You might want to draw a diagram and describe the coordinates after each transformation.

- How did you know that you could reflect?

A. What other questions could you ask to help Nick improve his description?

B. Rewrite Nick's description in response to Pavlo's questions and suggestions. Use the Communication Checklist.

Reflecting

C. How did Pavlo's questions and suggestions help Nick improve his communication about the transformed triangle?

D. Which parts of the Communication Checklist did Nick cover well?

Communication *Checklist*

✔ Did you explain your thinking clearly?

✔ Did you use correct mathematical language?

✔ Did you support your description with diagrams?

WORK WITH the Math

Example | Describing a transformation

Describe how the yellow triangle was transformed to create the green triangle.

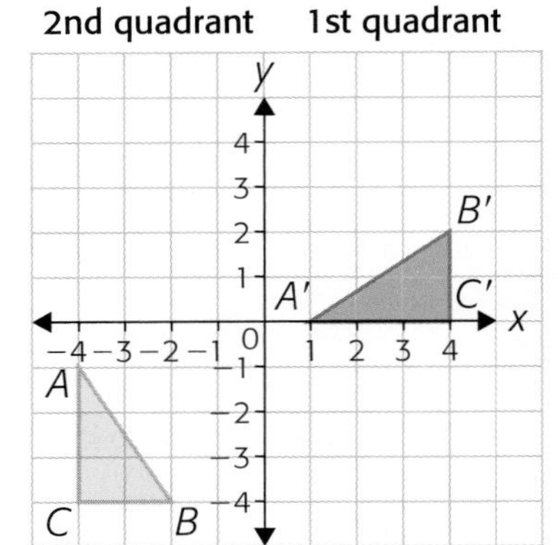

Ashley's Solution

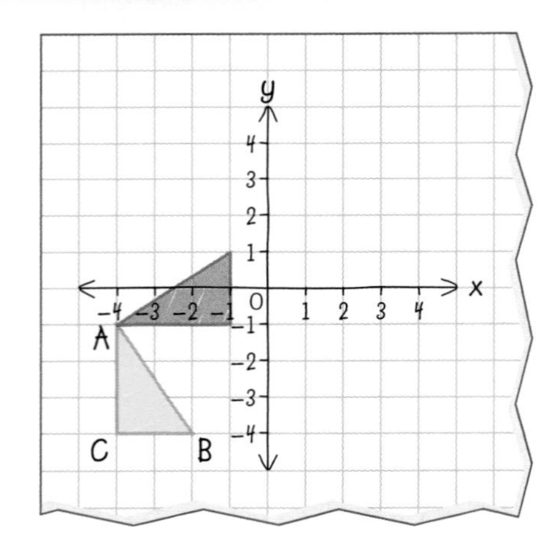

I noticed that C' is to the right of A'. To get C to the right of A, I rotated $\triangle ABC$ 90° ccw around vertex A.

$A(-4, -1) \rightarrow (-4, -1)$

$B(-2, -4) \rightarrow (-1, 1)$

$C(-4, -4) \rightarrow (-1, -1)$

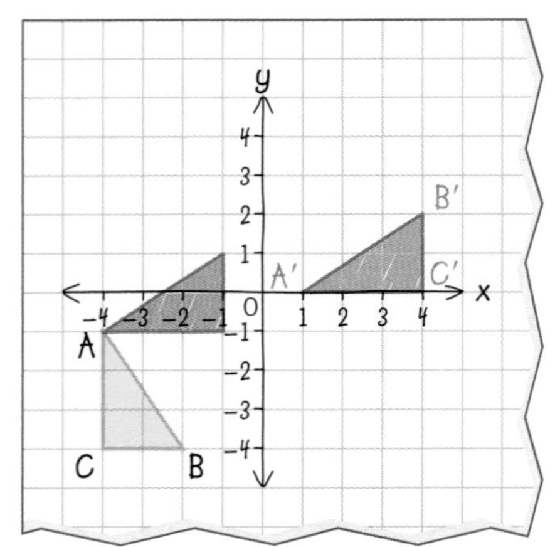

To get the rotated image of $\triangle ABC$ into the 1st quadrant, I translated it 5 units to the right and 1 unit up.

$(-4, -1) \rightarrow (1, 0)$

$(-1, 1) \rightarrow (4, 2)$

$(-1, -1) \rightarrow (4, 0)$

This is one way to describe the transformation. Looking over my work, I can see other ways to describe the transformation.

A Checking

1. **a)** Plot four different points on a Cartesian coordinate system. Connect the points to create a polygon.
   b) Transform your polygon to another position on the grid.
   c) Use mathematical language to describe the transformation.

B Practising

2. Improve Diane's description of the transformation, using the Communication Checklist to help you.

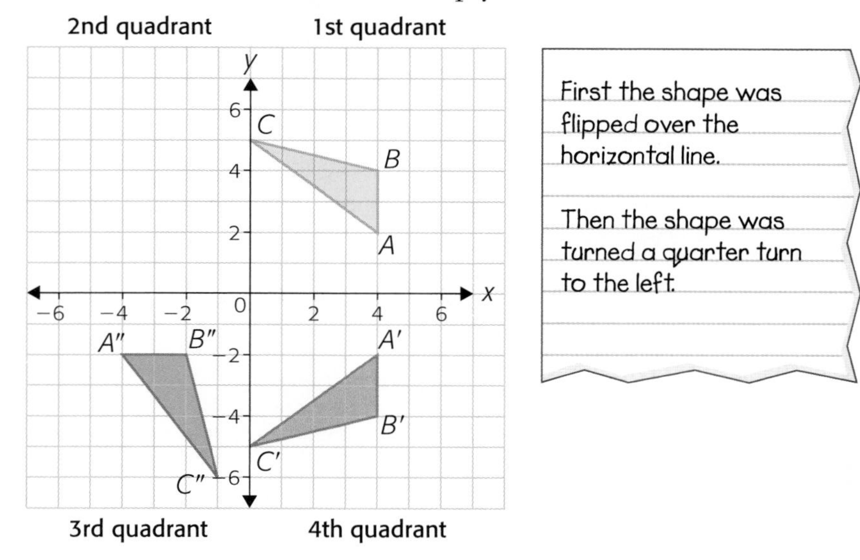

3. Describe the transformation $\triangle ABC \rightarrow \triangle A''B''C''$ in question 2 in a different way than Diane did.

4. **a)** Draw a parallelogram in the third quadrant of a Cartesian coordinate system.
   b) Draw a congruent parallelogram in another quadrant.
   c) Describe how you would transform your parallelogram in part (a) to create your parallelogram in part (b).
   d) Use the Communication Checklist to check your answer in part (c). How could you improve your description?

MATH GAME

Transformational Golf

Number of players: 2

YOU WILL NEED
- grid paper

How to Play

1. Each player designs a hole for a golf course on a Cartesian coordinate system. The hole must include
   - a tee and a green in different quadrants
   - hazards (trees, water, and sand)
   - a par value to tell how many moves are needed to get from the tee to the green

   The ball can be moved using any combination of translations, reflections, and rotations.
   - You may not rotate or translate through a hazard.
   - The centre of a rotation cannot be in a hazard.
   - Only the *x*-axis or *y*-axis can be a line of reflection over a hazard.
2. Players exchange designs. Each player describes the transformations they would use to get the ball from the tee to the green.
3. The player who has the lowest score wins.

Pavlo's Turn

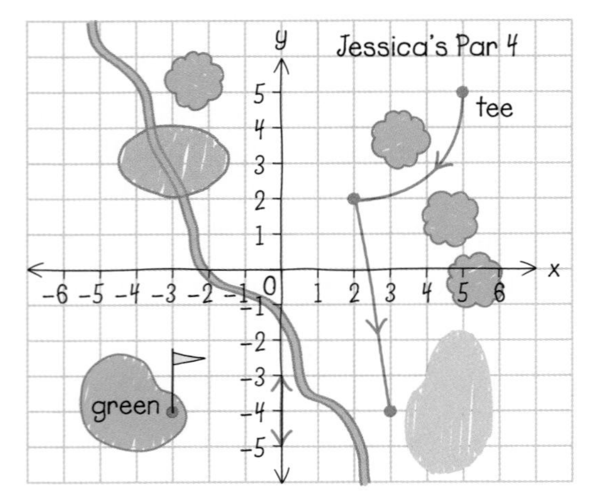

First I rotated the ball 90° cw around point (2, 5).
Then I translated the ball 1 unit to the right and 6 units down.
My last transformation was a reflection across the y-axis.
That's 3 moves. I'm 1 under par!

7.6 Perpendicular Bisectors

YOU WILL NEED

- a compass
- a protractor
- a ruler
- a transparent mirror

GOAL

Construct perpendicular bisectors.

LEARN ABOUT the Math

Pavlo and Nestor are camping with their families at different campsites in Mount Robson Provincial Park. They want to find a meeting spot that is the same distance from both of their campsites.

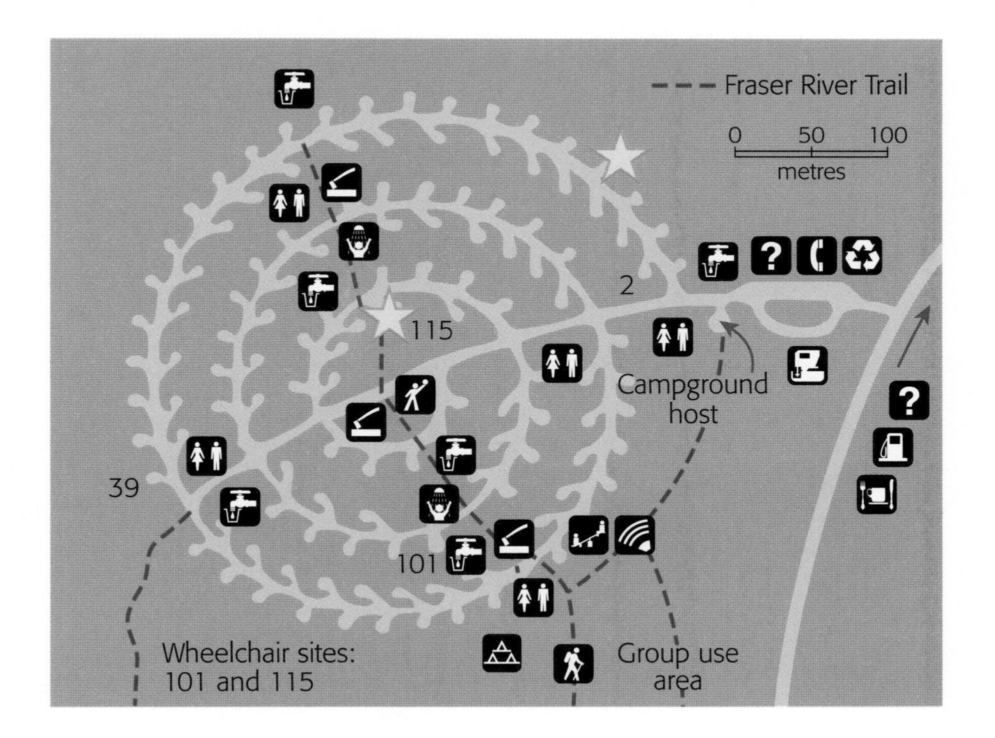

How can Pavlo and Nestor determine a meeting spot?

Example 1 | Using a fold

How can Pavlo and Nestor choose a meeting spot that is the same distance from both of their campsites?

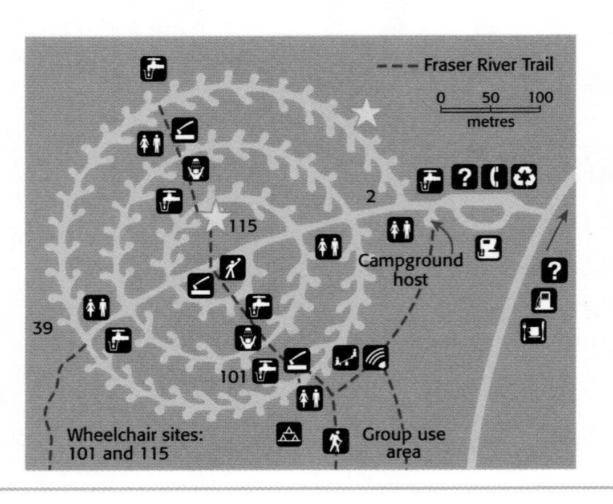

Pavlo's Solution

I labelled the campsites *X* and *Y* on a map of the park. I drew a line segment from *X* to *Y*.

I folded the map so that *X* was on top of *Y*. Then I drew a line along the crease.

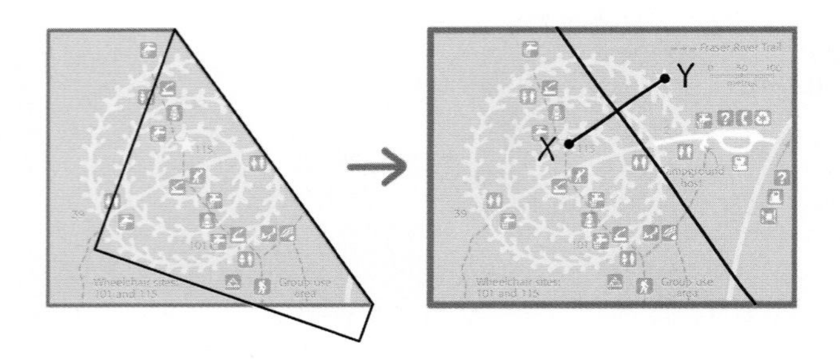

intersection point
the point where two lines or line segments cross each other; for example, QR intersects ST at intersection point E

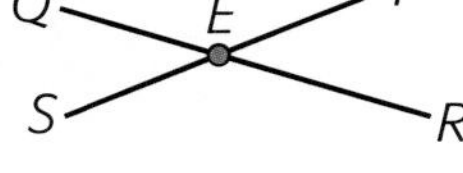

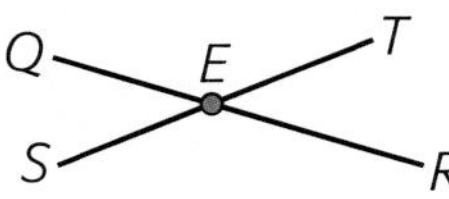

perpendicular bisector
a line that intersects a line segment at 90° and divides it into two equal lengths

perpendicular bisector

A B

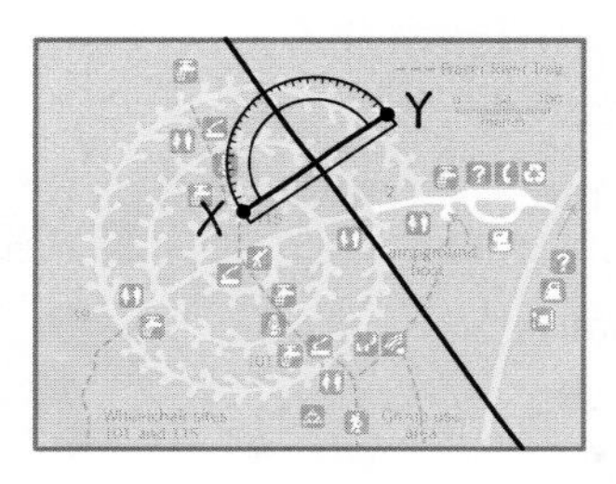

I placed the centre of my protractor at the **intersection point** of the crease and XY. The angle between the crease and XY measures 90°.

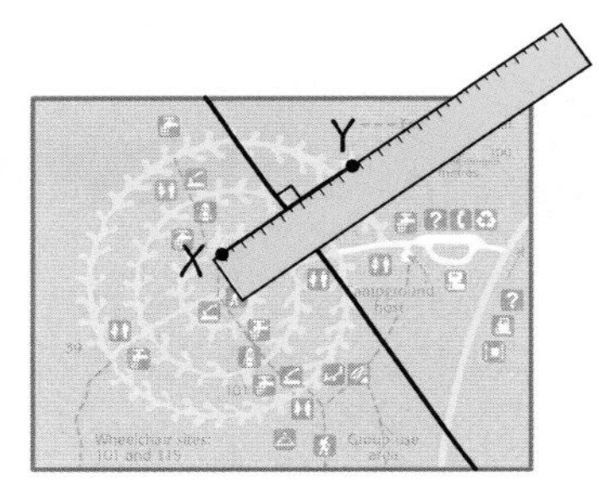

I used a ruler to check that the crease divides XY in half. The crease is the **perpendicular bisector** of XY.

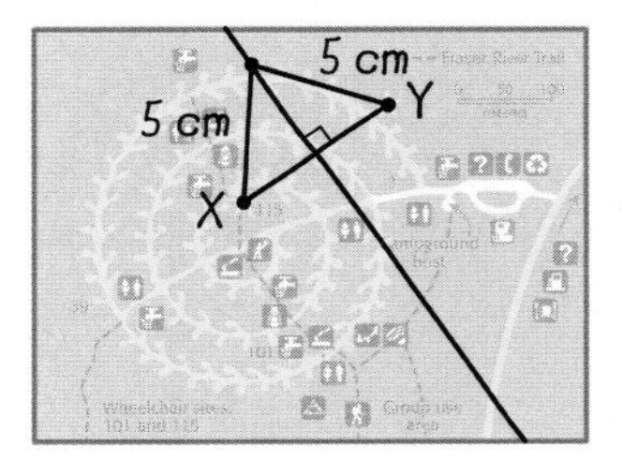

I also used a ruler to measure the distance from other points on the crease to X and Y. All the points are the same distance from both campsites.

It looks like we can choose a meeting place anywhere on the perpendicular bisector.

Communication | Tip

In a diagram, perpendicular line segments are indicated by a little square. In writing, perpendicular line segments are indicated by the symbol $\perp$. For example, $AB \perp CD$.

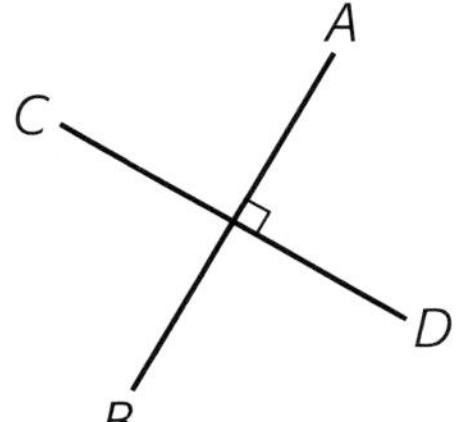

Example 2 | Using a transparent mirror

How can Pavlo and Nestor choose a meeting spot that is the same distance from both of their campsites using a transparent mirror?

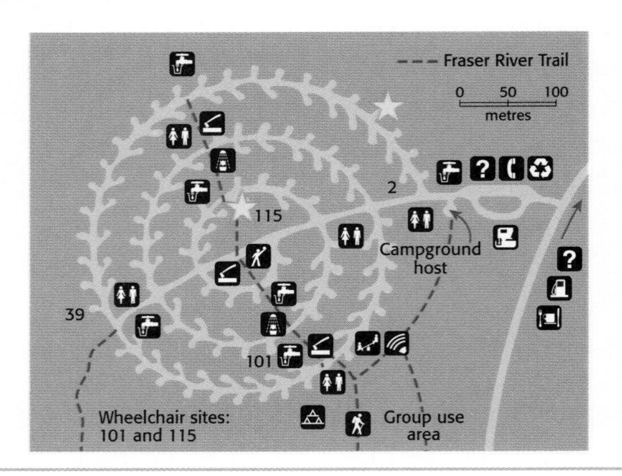

Nestor's Solution

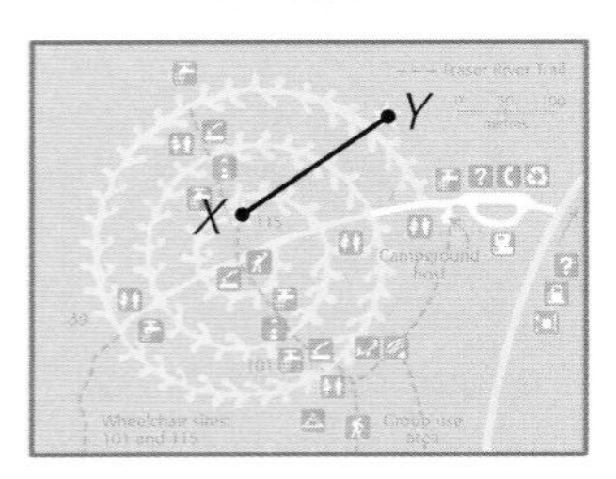

I labelled the campsites X and Y on a map of the park. I joined X and Y with a line segment.

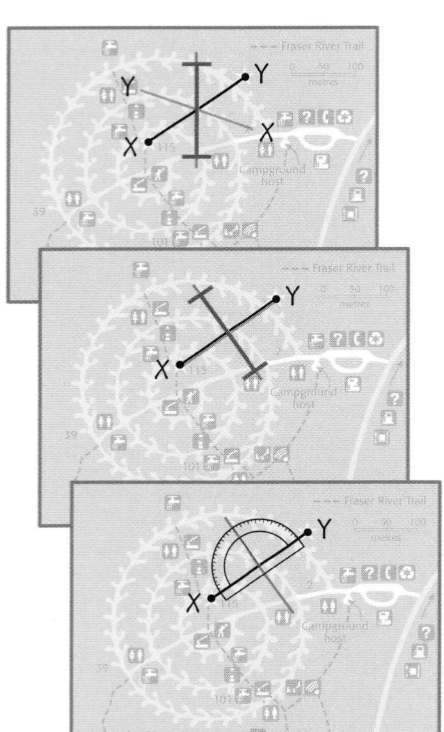

I positioned a transparent mirror across XY.

I moved the transparent mirror until the reflection of X lined up with Y. Then I drew along the edge of the mirror. Since this is the reflection line, I know that it divides XY in half.

I used a protractor to check that the angle is 90°. The line of reflection is the perpendicular bisector of XY.

The point where the reflection line crosses XY is the same distance from both campsites.

Reflecting

A. Why does it make sense that the perpendicular bisector of a line segment reflects one end of the line segment onto the other end?

B. How are Pavlo's method and Nestor's method for creating a perpendicular bisector alike? How are they different?

WORK WITH the Math

Example 3 | Using a compass

How can Pavlo and Nestor choose a meeting spot using a compass?

Solution

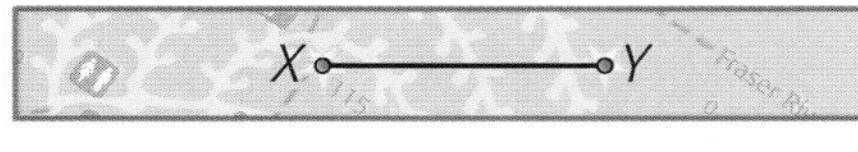

Label the campsites X and Y on the map. Draw a line segment between them.

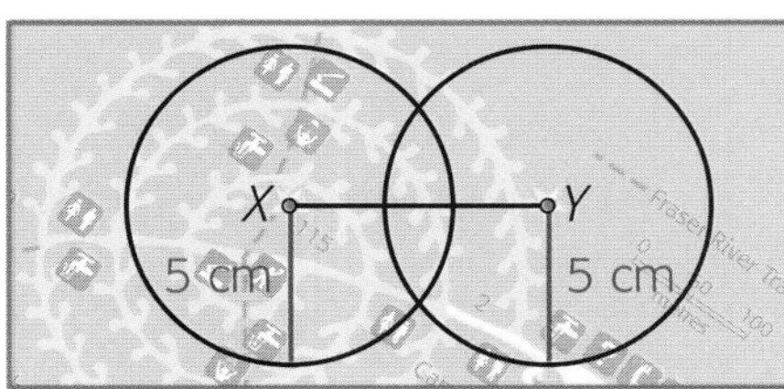

Using a compass, draw two overlapping circles with the same radius centred at X and Y.

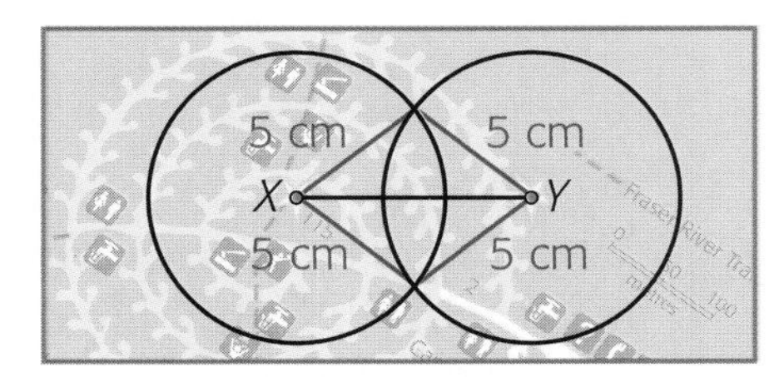

The two points where the circles cross are the same distance from X as they are from Y since the circles have the same radius.

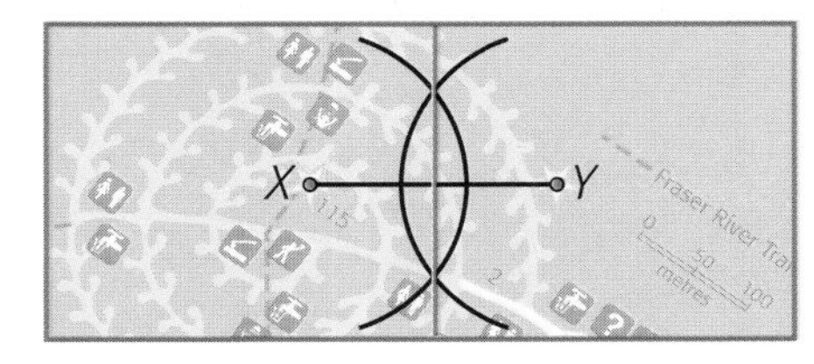

Draw a line segment through the two points. Check that the line segment meets XY at a 90° angle and divides XY into two equal lengths. If it does, it is the perpendicular bisector.

The meeting spot can be one of the points where the circles cross or the point on XY that crosses the line through them.

Example 4 | Using a protractor

Yan and Julie want to choose a practice field that is about the same distance from both of their dorms at soccer camp. How can Julie use a protractor to construct the perpendicular bisector?

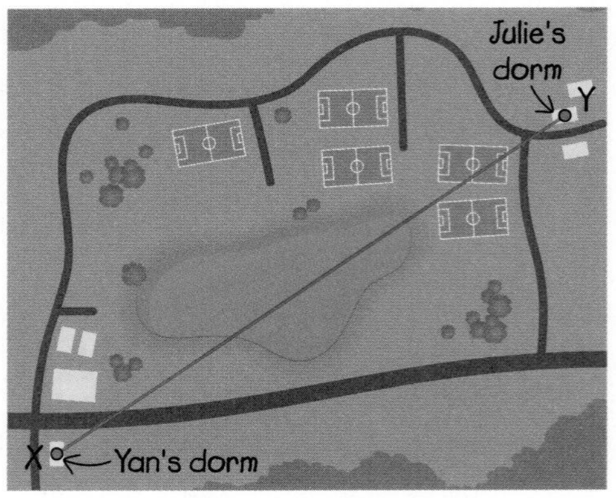

Solution

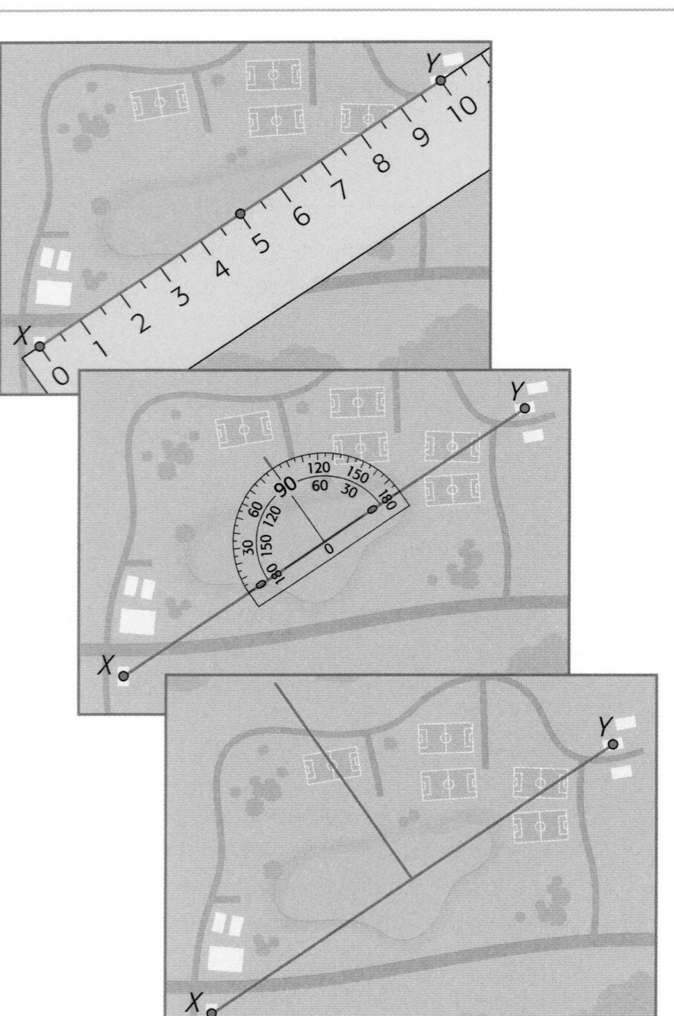

Label the dorms X and Y. Connect X and Y with a line segment.
Measure the length of XY. Mark the centre.

Place your protractor on XY, with its centre at the midpoint. Mark 90°.

Draw a line from the midpoint of XY to the 90° mark. This is the perpendicular bisector of XY.

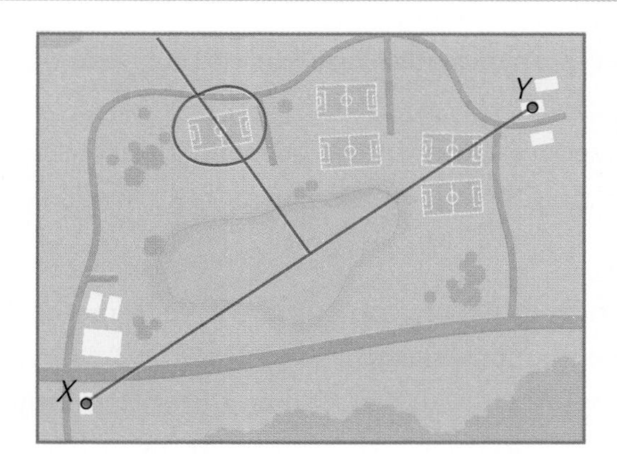

This practice field that is circled is close to the perpendicular bisector, so it is about the same distance from both dorms.

A Checking

1. Draw each line segment. Then construct the perpendicular bisector.

a) *A* ——— *B*
6 cm

b) *C* ——— *D*
7 cm

c)

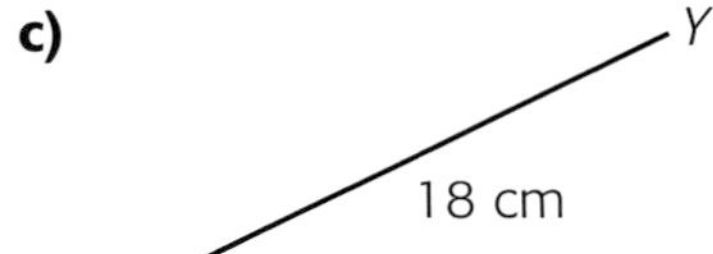

d)

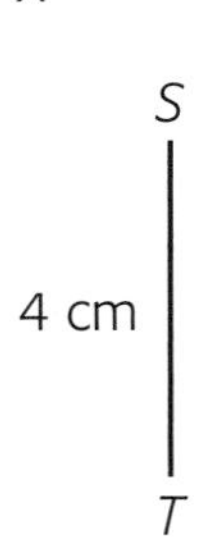

B Practising

2. Which diagram shows a perpendicular bisector?

a)

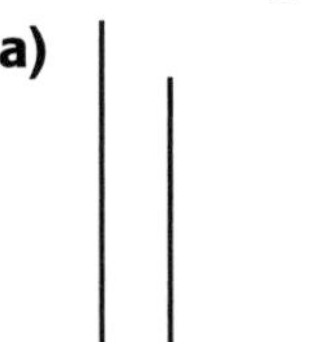

b)

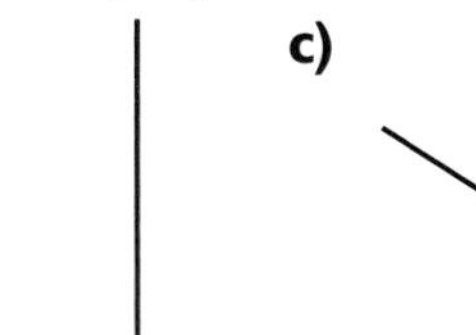

c) **d)**

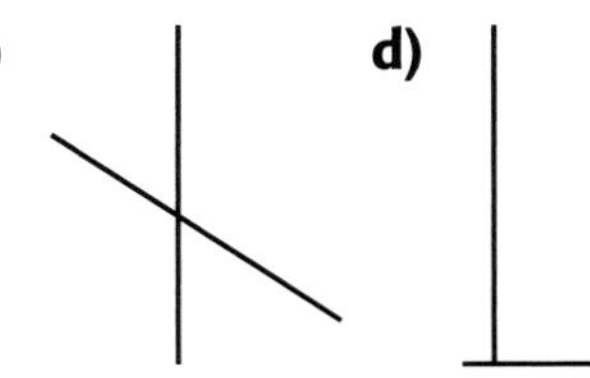

3. Draw a line segment that is each length. Then construct the perpendicular bisector.

a) 10 cm **b)** 6.5 cm **c)** 8.75 cm **d)** 5.5 cm

Reading Strategy

Predict the answer to the question. How did you make your prediction? Look at the examples to check your prediction.

4. **a)** Draw a triangle and label the vertices A, B, and C.
   b) Construct the perpendicular bisector of each side of the triangle.
   c) Use the intersection point of the perpendicular bisectors as the centre of a circle that passes through A. What do you notice?

5. Describe a situation in which you could use each method to construct a perpendicular bisector.
   a) folding paper
   b) using a compass and ruler
   c) using a protractor and ruler
   d) using a transparent mirror

6. Draw a line segment of any length and label the end points.
   a) Construct the perpendicular bisector.
   b) List the steps you followed in part (a).
   c) How can you prove that the line segment you created in part (a) is the perpendicular bisector?

7.7 Parallel Lines

YOU WILL NEED
- plastic stir sticks
- a compass
- a ruler
- a transparent mirror

Construct parallel line segments.

LEARN ABOUT the Math

Ashley is designing a lift for the school play. The lift will move up, **parallel** to the floor, allowing an actor to appear to rise in the air.

How can Ashley and Jessica accurately draw parallel lines for the platform of the lift?

A. Make an X by joining two stir sticks at their midpoints with a pushpin. Use a ruler to draw a quadrilateral that just touches the stir sticks.

B. Measure the angles of the quadrilateral with a protractor. Measure the side lengths. What kind of quadrilateral is it? Which sides are parallel?

C. Make a different X with the stir sticks. Repeat parts A and B.

D. How can you use the stir sticks to draw two parallel line segments that are a given distance apart?

Communication | *Tip*

Parallel line segments are indicated by the symbol ||. For example, *AB* || *CD* means that *AB* and *CD* are parallel.

Reflecting

E. How can you be sure that two line segments are parallel?

F. How does the stir stick model help you construct parallel line segments?

WORK WITH *the Math*

Example 1 | Constructing parallel line segments

Use what you know about rectangles to construct parallel line segments.

Ashley's Solution: Using a protractor

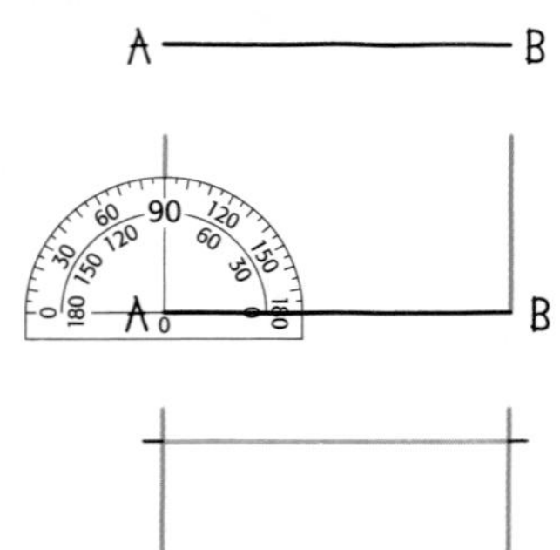

First I drew line segment *AB* using a ruler.

Then I used my protractor to draw a 90° angle at each end of *AB*. The 90° angles are perpendicular to *AB*.

I used my ruler to mark the same distance on each vertical line. I connected the marks to create a rectangle.

The top and bottom of the rectangle are parallel. The left and right sides are also parallel.

Jessica's Solution: Using a transparent mirror

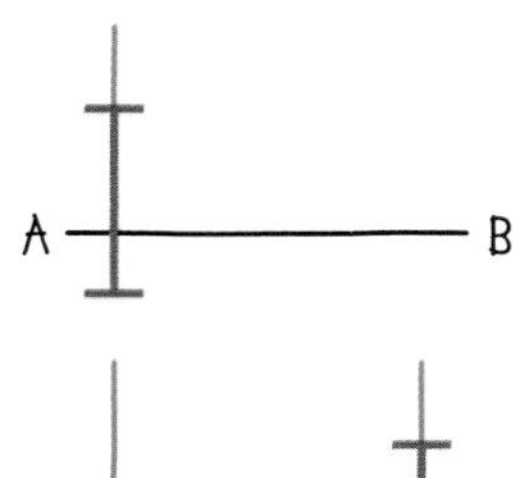

I placed a transparent mirror over line segment AB. When the reflection of AB lined up with AB, I drew a line segment along the edge of the mirror. This line segment is perpendicular to AB.

I moved the transparent mirror to a different spot on AB and drew another perpendicular line segment.

The two perpendicular line segments are parallel, just like the sides of a rectangle.

Example 2 | Using perpendicular bisectors

Construct parallel line segments using the properties of parallel lines.

Nick's Solution

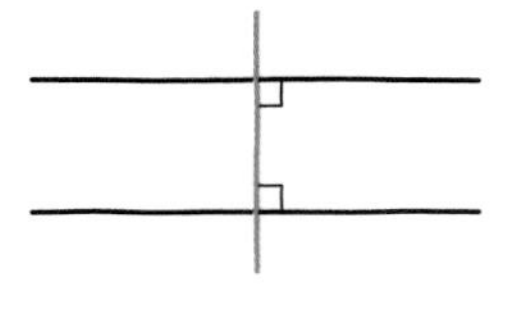

I noticed that when I drew a line perpendicular to one line, it was also perpendicular to any parallel lines. I decided to use perpendicular bisectors.

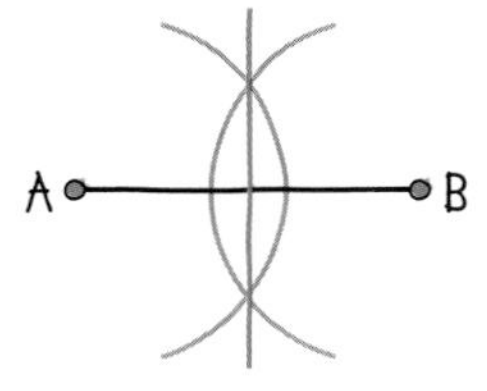

First I drew line segment AB. Then I constructed the perpendicular bisector of AB.

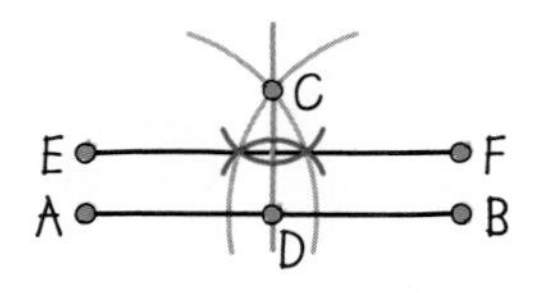

I labelled points C and D on the perpendicular bisector. Then I constructed the perpendicular bisector of CD and called it EF. $EF \parallel AB$.

A Checking

1. Trace the line segments. Show that two of the line segments are parallel.

B Practising

2. Draw and label a line segment that is 6 cm long. Construct a second line segment that is parallel to your first line segment.

3. Explain how you can use the following tools to check if two lines are parallel.

a) stir sticks
b) protractor
c) transparent mirror
d) ruler

4. For each object, trace two parallel line segments. Check that they are parallel. Then construct another line segment that is parallel to both.

a)

b)

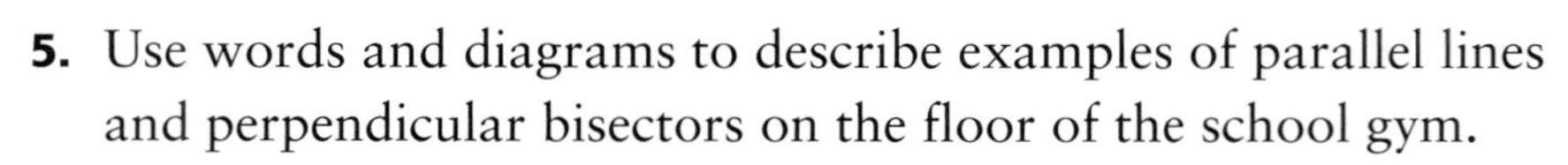

5. Use words and diagrams to describe examples of parallel lines and perpendicular bisectors on the floor of the school gym.

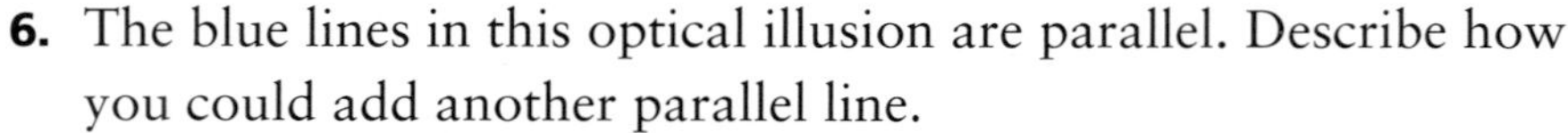

6. The blue lines in this optical illusion are parallel. Describe how you could add another parallel line.

7.8 Angle Bisectors

YOU WILL NEED
- paper
- scissors
- a compass
- a ruler
- a protractor
- a transparent mirror

GOAL

Construct angle bisectors.

LEARN ABOUT the Math

Nick needs a protractor for his homework, but he left his protractor at school.

How can Nick create a protractor?

A. Use a compass to draw a circle on a piece of paper. Cut out the circle and fold it in half.

B. Cut along the fold line to create a semicircle. Label the ends of the semicircle 0° and 180°.

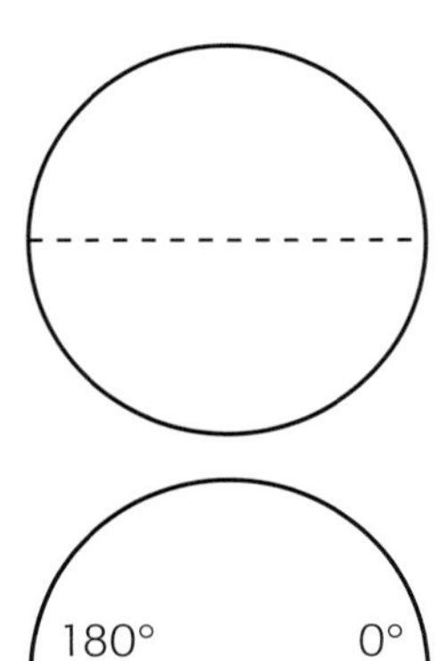

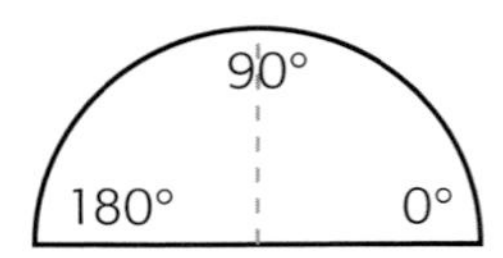

C. Fold the semicircle again and label the perpendicular bisector 90°.

D. Fold the semicircle once more to create an **angle bisector** for each right angle. Label the fold lines with the correct degrees.

angle bisector

a line that cuts an angle in half to form two equal angles

Reflecting

E. How does folding create an angle bisector?

F. How are perpendicular bisectors and angle bisectors similar?

G. How can you check that a line segment actually bisects an angle?

WORK WITH the Math

Example | Constructing an angle bisector

Draw the bisector of $\angle ABC$.

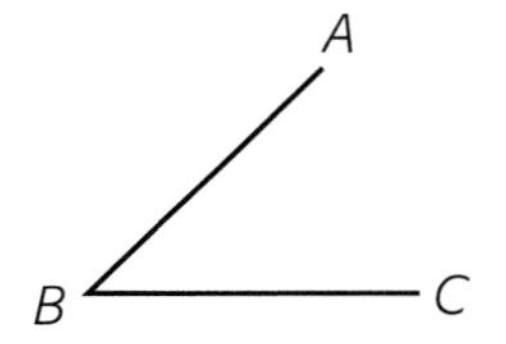

Gail's Solution: Using a transparent mirror

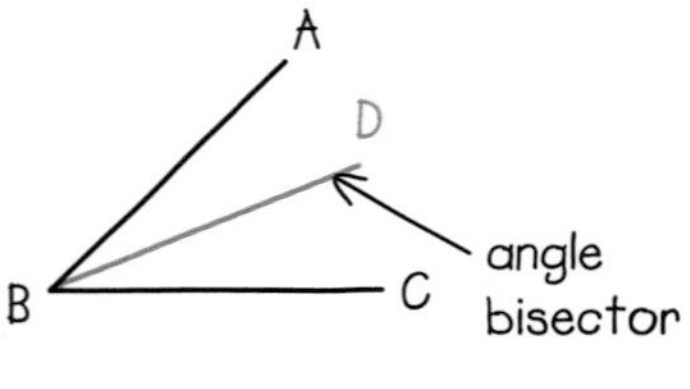

Since an angle bisector makes two equal angles, I can think of it as a reflection line. $\angle ABD$ is reflected to $\angle CBD$.

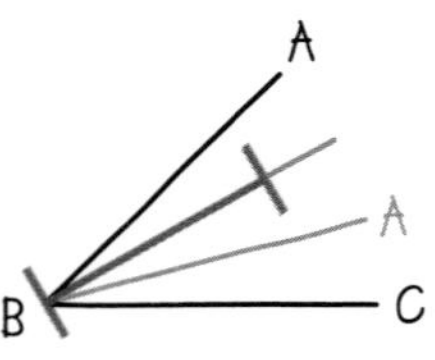

I placed a transparent mirror so that it passed through *B*.

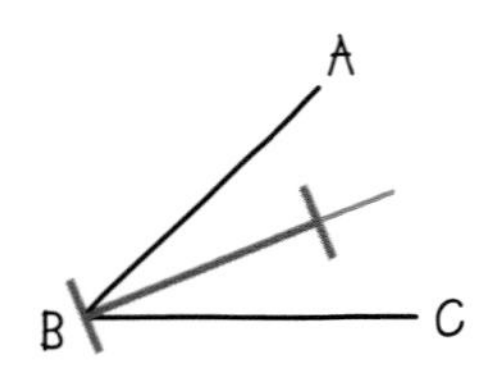

Keeping one end at *B*, I moved the transparent mirror until the reflection of *AB* lined up with *BC*. I drew a line along the edge of the mirror to create the angle bisector.

Ashley's Solution: Using a compass

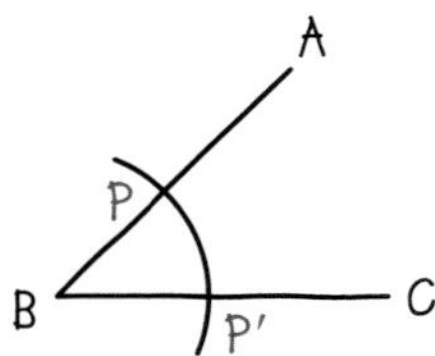

I placed my compass point on point *B*. I drew an arc that crossed *AB* and *BC*. If I reflected *P* in the angle bisector, its image would be *P′*.

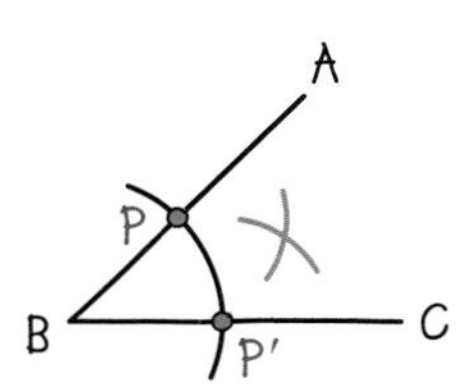

I drew arcs in the angle by placing my compass point first on *P* and then on *P′*. These arcs are reflections of each other in the angle bisector. The point where they cross gets reflected to itself, so it must be on the bisector.

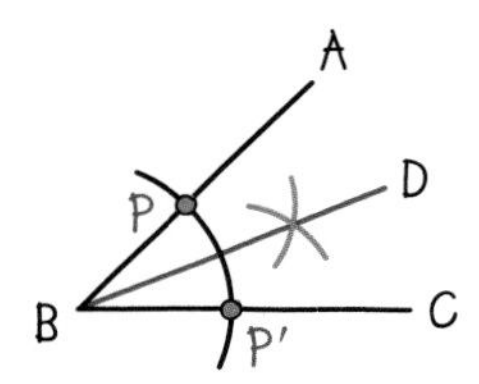

I drew a line from point *B* through the intersecting arcs to construct the angle bisector, *BD*.

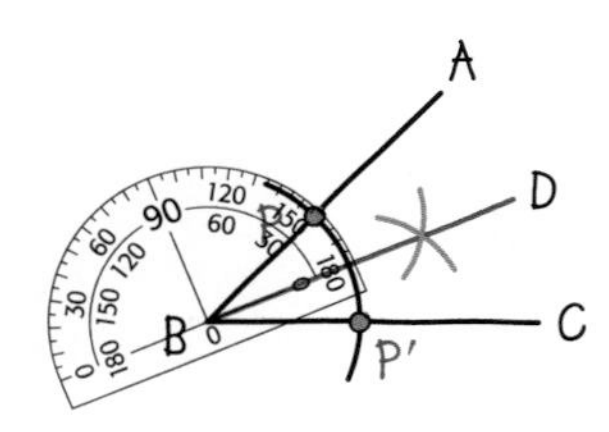

I measured the angles with a protractor to check my work. ∠*ABD* and ∠*DBC* are the same size, so *BD* is definitely the angle bisector.

A Checking

1. Which diagrams show an angle bisector?

a)

b) 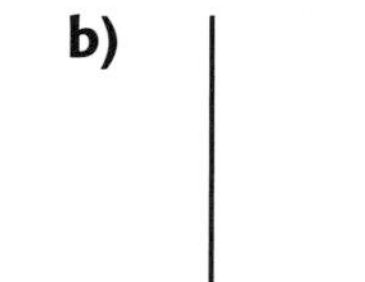

c) 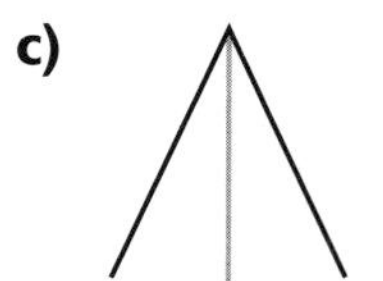

d) 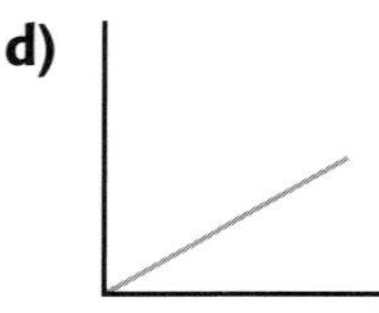

2. Draw an 80° angle. Construct the angle bisector.

B Practising

3. Draw an acute angle and bisect it.

4. Draw an obtuse angle and bisect it.

5. Use a protractor to draw each angle. Then construct the angle bisector. Use a different method for each part.

a) 90° **b)** 160° **c)** 200°

6. **a)** Use a ruler to draw any triangle.

b) Construct the bisector for each angle in your triangle.

c) What do you notice about the bisectors?

7. Identify the angle bisectors in each picture.

a) 

b) 

c) 

8. Construct the angle bisector for a 60° angle using at least two different methods.

CURIOUS MATH

Napoleon's Theorem

A. Draw a right triangle. Colour it blue.

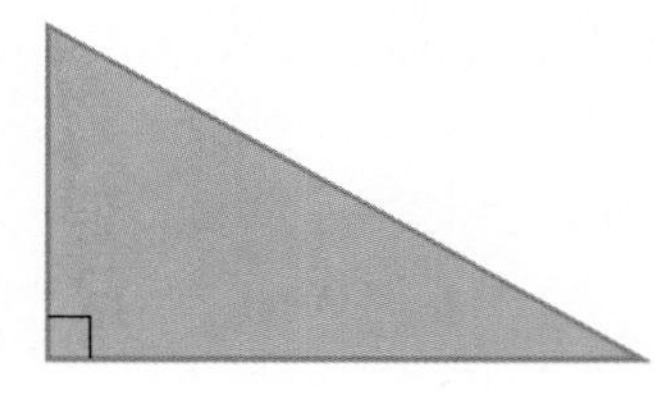

B. Construct an equilateral triangle on each side of the blue triangle by drawing 60° angles. Colour these triangles orange.

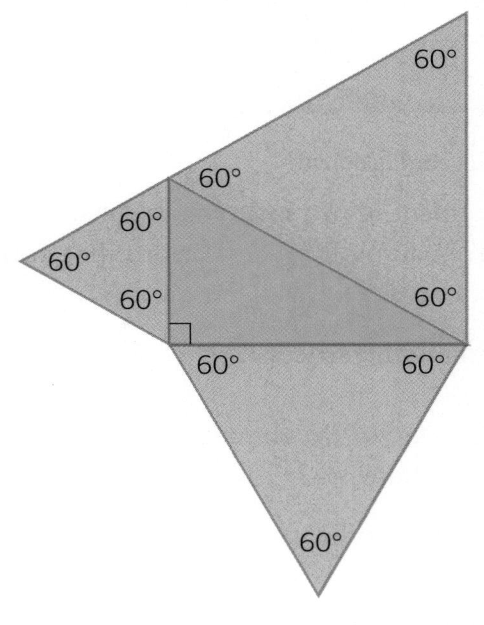

C. Construct the bisectors of all three angles in each orange triangle. Mark the centre where the bisectors meet.

D. Join the centres of the orange triangles. What kind of triangle does this create? How do you know?

E. Repeat steps A to D using other right triangles. Compare your findings with your classmates' findings. Do you think the result will always be the same?

Chapter Self-Test

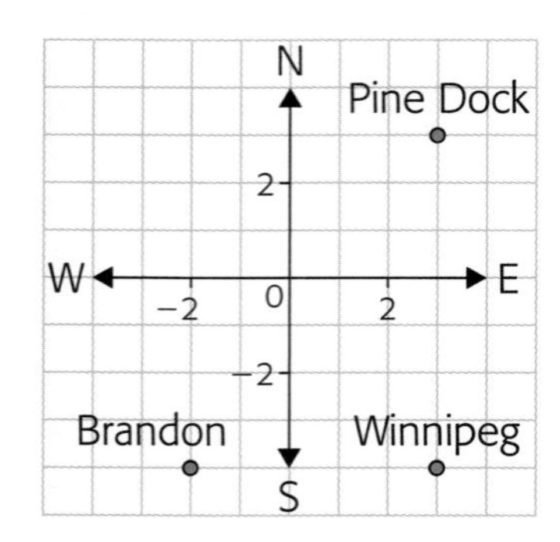

1. **a)** Record the coordinates for each city.
   b) Find the distance between Brandon and Winnipeg, measured in grid squares.
   c) Repeat part (b) for Winnipeg and Pine Dock.

2. **a)** Draw $\triangle XYZ$ on grid paper. Translate $\triangle XYZ$ 3 units to the right and 2 units up to produce $\triangle X'Y'Z'$.

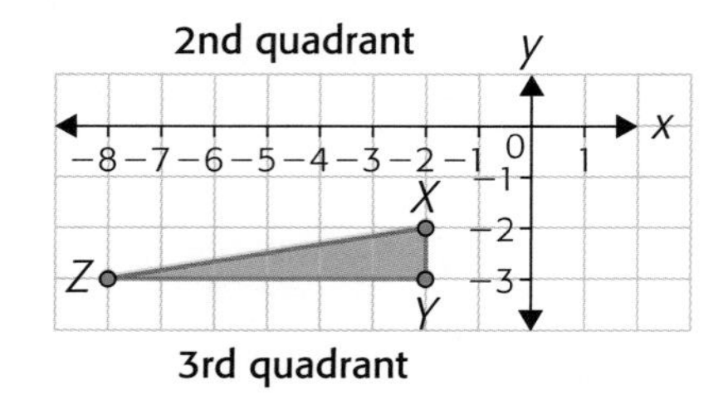

   b) Extend line segment XY to form line segment LM.
   c) Reflect $\triangle X'Y'Z'$ across LM, and record the coordinates of the image vertices.

3. **a)** Draw a polygon with vertices $D(2, 2)$, $E(-1, 4)$, $F(-2, -1)$, and $G(3, -2)$.
   b) Rotate the polygon 90° cw about the origin.
   c) Record the coordinates of D', E', F', and G'.

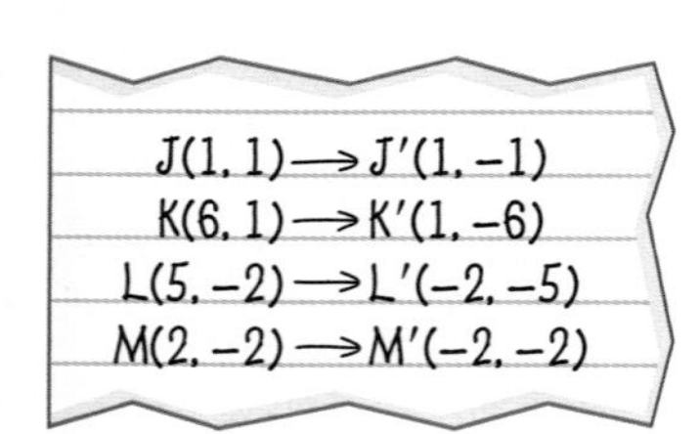

4. Describe two different ways to achieve the transformation of the shape $JKLM$.

5. Draw a line segment AB. Construct the perpendicular bisector of AB and another line segment that is parallel to AB. Explain the steps you used.

6. Draw an acute angle, a right angle, and an obtuse angle with a protractor. Construct the bisector of each angle. Use at least two different methods.

What Do You Think Now?

Revisit What Do You Think? on page 283. How have your answers and explanations changed?

Chapter 7

Chapter Review

Frequently Asked Questions

Q: How do you construct a perpendicular bisector?

A1: Fold a line segment end to end to find the midpoint. The crease creates the perpendicular bisector of the line segment.

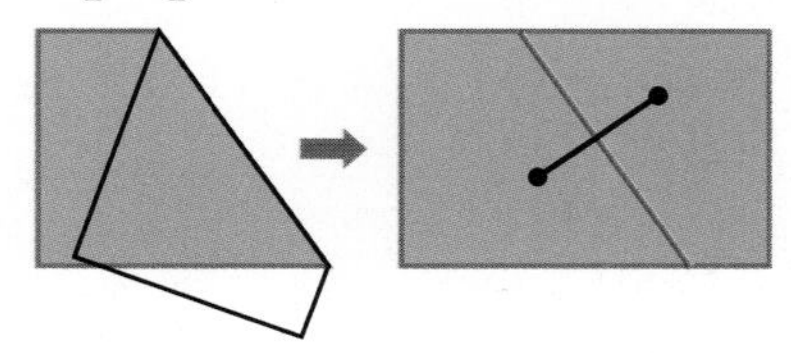

A2: Use a transparent mirror to reflect one endpoint of a line segment onto the other endpoint. Draw along the edge of the mirror.

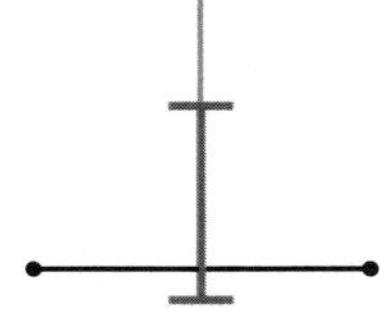

A3: Use a compass to draw intersecting circles from each end of a line segment. The line that joins the points of intersection is the perpendicular bisector.

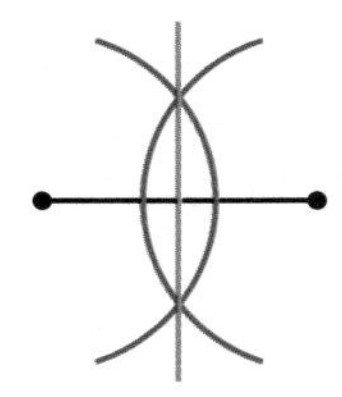

A4: Use a protractor to draw a 90° angle at the midpoint of a line segment.

Q: How do you construct parallel line segments?

A1: Draw a rectangle using a transparent mirror, a protractor, or an X made with two line segments that are the same length and cross at their midpoints. Lines along the top and bottom, or along the sides, are parallel.

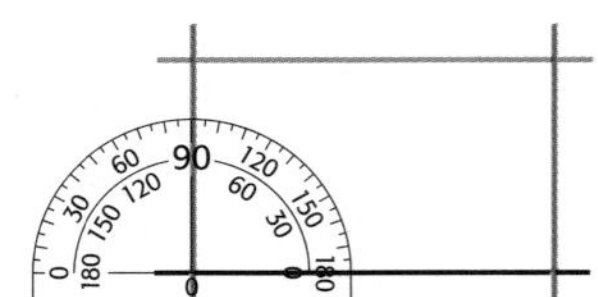

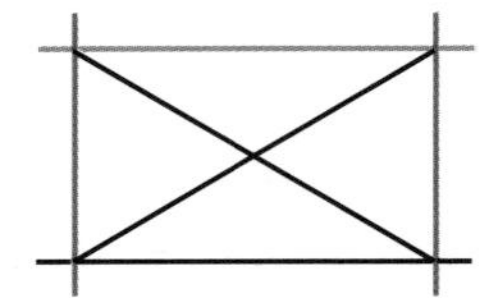

A2: Construct the perpendicular bisector of a line segment. Construct the perpendicular bisector of the first perpendicular bisector. The original line segment and the second perpendicular bisector are parallel.

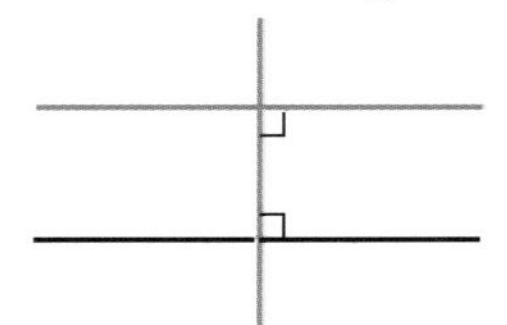

Q: How do you construct an angle bisector?

A1: Fold the rays of the angle on top of each other. The crease is the angle bisector.

A2: Place a transparent mirror in the angle so that one ray reflects onto the other. Draw along the edge of the mirror.

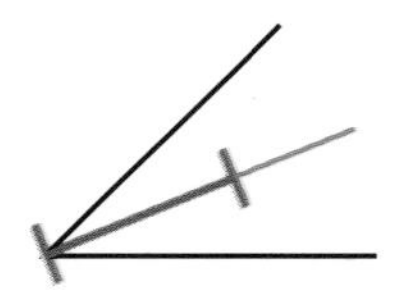

A3: Use a compass, with its point on the vertex of the angle, to draw an arc across both arms of the angle. Move the compass point to the points where the arc and the rays meet, and draw two intersecting arcs. Then draw a line from the intersection of the arcs to the vertex of the angle. This line is the angle bisector.

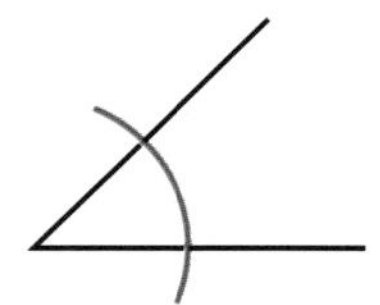
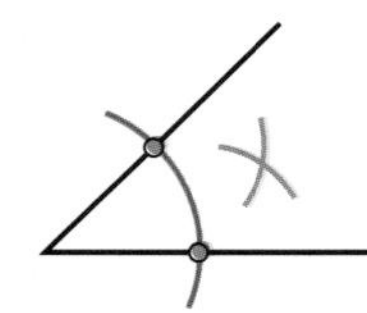
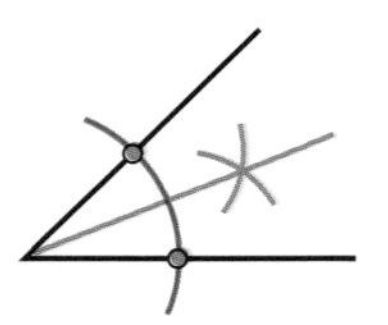

Practice

Lesson 7.2

1. Which of the following points matches each description? Explain how you know.

$(-14, 0)$, $(0, 0)$, $(14, 0)$, $(0, 14)$, $(0, -14)$

a) farthest right

b) farthest left

c) lowest down

d) highest up

Lesson 7.3

2. a) Draw quadrilateral $ABCD$ with vertices $A(0, 2)$, $B(3, 1)$, $C(3, -2)$, and $D(-1, -1)$.

b) Reflect $ABCD$ in the y-axis to produce $A'B'C'D'$.

c) Determine the coordinates of $A'B'C'D'$.

d) Translate $A'B'C'D'$ 2 units to the left and 1 unit up to produce $A''B''C''D''$.

e) Determine the coordinates of $A''B''C''D''$.

3. a) Draw a triangle anywhere in the 1st quadrant. Label the vertices and name their coordinates.

b) Describe a translation that will produce an image of your triangle in the 3rd quadrant. Label the vertices of the image and name the coordinates.

c) Describe a reflection that will produce an image of the image in the 2nd quadrant. Label the vertices of the new image and name its coordinates.

Lesson 7.4

4. $\triangle ABC$ has coordinates $A(-1, 3)$, $B(-2, 0)$, and $C(1, -1)$.

a) Draw $\triangle ABC$.

b) Rotate $\triangle ABC$ 90° ccw about B.

5. How can you transform triangle 1 to match triangle 2? Describe as many ways as you can.

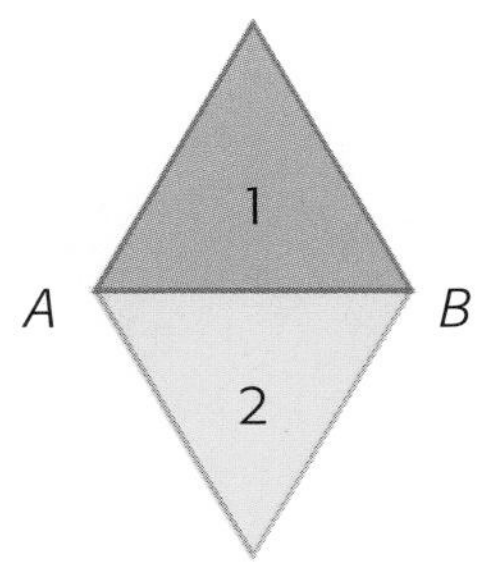

Lesson 7.5

6. A figure has vertices $A(2, 0)$, $B(6, 0)$, $C(7, 3)$, and $D(3, 3)$. The image of the figure after a transformation has vertices $A'(-1, -4)$, $B'(-5, -4)$, $C'(-6, -1)$, and $D'(-2, -1)$.

a) Draw the figure and its image on a coordinate grid.

b) Describe how to create the image using transformations. Explain your thinking.

Lesson 7.6

7. a) Draw two line segments that are 8 cm long. Label one line segment AB and the other line segment CD.

b) Construct the perpendicular bisectors of the two line segments using different methods.

Lesson 7.7

8. Name three examples of parallel line segments.

9. Construct a pair of parallel line segments.

Lesson 7.8

10. Copy the following angles. Construct the bisector of each angle.

a)

b)

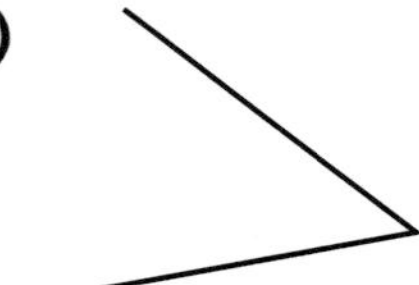

c)

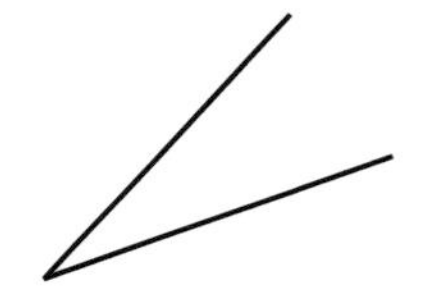

d)

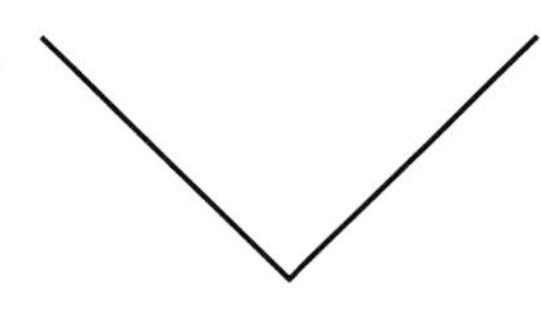

11. Describe examples of translations, reflections, rotations, perpendicular bisectors, parallel line segments, and angle bisectors in this quilt square.

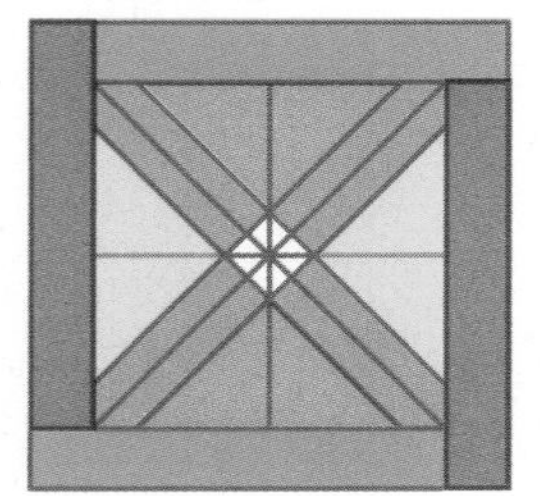

Chapter 7

Chapter Task

YOU WILL NEED
- a tangram set
- grid paper

Tangram Puzzle Pals

Your class is participating in an e-mail puzzle exchange. Each student creates a tangram design on a Cartesian coordinate system. They e-mail directions for constructing their design to their puzzle pal.

Task | Checklist

✔ Are all of your designs polygons?

✔ Did you use correct mathematical language?

✔ Did you label your sketches?

✔ Did you include coordinates, parallel lines, perpendicular lines, angle bisectors, and transformations in your directions?

How many tangram designs can you create and describe for a puzzle pal?

A. Create a tangram design in the shape of a polygon.

B. Draw your design on a Cartesian coordinate system.

C. Label the vertices with capital letters. Label the polygons with lower-case letters.

D. Write directions for your puzzle pal. Be sure to include coordinates, parallel lines, perpendicular lines, angle bisectors, and transformations.

E. Repeat steps A to D several times with different designs.

Chapters 4–7

Cumulative Review

Note: Select ALL the correct answers to each question.
Use 3.14 as an approximate value for π in all calculations.

1. The 13 girls in Susan's class make up close to 45% of the class. How many students are in Susan's class?
A. 13 **B.** 58 **C.** 29 **D.** 6

2. George answered 34 out of 40 questions correctly on an exam. What percent of the questions did he answer correctly?
A. 35% **B.** 40% **C.** 14% **D.** 85%

3. Eliza scored 90% on an exam with 40 questions. How many questions did she answer correctly?
A. 30 **B.** 7 **C.** 36 **D.** 97

4. Mary bought a pair of jeans on sale for 25% off. The original price of the jeans was $79. What was the sale price before tax?
A. $25 **B.** $54 **C.** $59.25 **D.** $40.99

5. Anwar and Ben ate dinner at a restaurant. The bill was $67. They left a $13 tip. About what percent of the bill was the tip?
A. 10% **B.** 15% **C.** 20% **D.** 25%

6. Which decimal is equivalent to 14%?
A. 0.14 **B.** 1.4 **C.** 140 **D.** 14.0

7. Which fraction is equivalent to 98%?
A. $\frac{98}{100}$ **B.** $\frac{98}{10}$ **C.** $\frac{100}{98}$ **D.** $9\frac{8}{10}$

8. A crane operator has to turn the crane 60°. What fraction of a circle is 60°?
A. $\frac{1}{2}$ **B.** $\frac{1}{3}$ **C.** $\frac{1}{4}$ **D.** $\frac{1}{6}$

9. A circle has a diameter of 14 cm. What is the best estimate for the circumference of the circle?
A. 14 cm **B.** 28 cm **C.** 42 cm **D.** 56 cm

10. Which circle has a circumference of 20.1 cm?

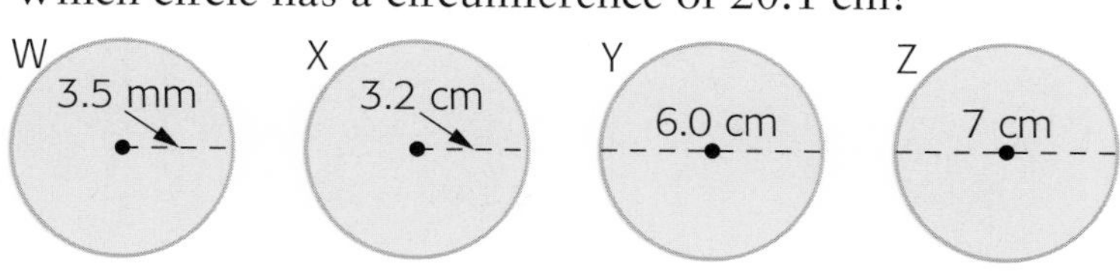

A. W **B.** X **C.** Y **D.** Z

F
4.5 cm
H 6.2 cm G

11. Which circle in question 10 has an area of 28.3 cm^2?

A. W **B.** X **C.** Y **D.** Z

12. What is the area of $\triangle FGH$?

A. 27.9 cm^2
B. 10.7 cm^2
C. 14.0 cm^2
D. 14.0 cm

J K
2.5 cm
4.5 cm
M 4.1 cm L

13. What is the area of parallelogram *JKLM*?

A. 10.3 cm^2
B. 1.3 cm
C. 10.3 m^2
D. 5.6 cm

14. Which expressions have a value of 9?

A. $+4 + (+5)$
B. $+4 + (-5)$
C. $(-4) + (+5)$
D. $(+4) - (-5)$

15. Which set of integers **cannot** complete the equation
$\blacksquare - \blacksquare + \blacksquare = -8$?

A. 8, 16, 0
B. 19, 32, 5
C. 156, 264, 100
D. 16, 16, 8

16. What is the sum of $(+8) + (-8)$?

A. $+1$ **B.** -1 **C.** 2 **D.** 0

W Y
X Z

17. Which diagram at the left shows a perpendicular bisector?

A. W **B.** X **C.** Y **D.** Z

18. Which point is farthest left on a Cartesian plane?

A. $(-11, 0)$ **B.** $(0, -11)$ **C.** $(11, 0)$ **D.** $(0, 11)$

19. A figure with coordinates $A(2, 0)$, $B(6, 0)$, $C(7, 3)$, and $D(3, 3)$ is transformed. The coordinates of the image are $A'(-2, 0)$, $B'(-6, 0)$, $C'(-7, -3)$, and $D'(-3, -3)$. What was the transformation?

A. a rotation only
B. a flip only
C. a slide only
D. a rotation and a slide

SCC
42
CHAMPIONSHIPS
NORTH HA
SCC
521
CHAMPIONSHIPS

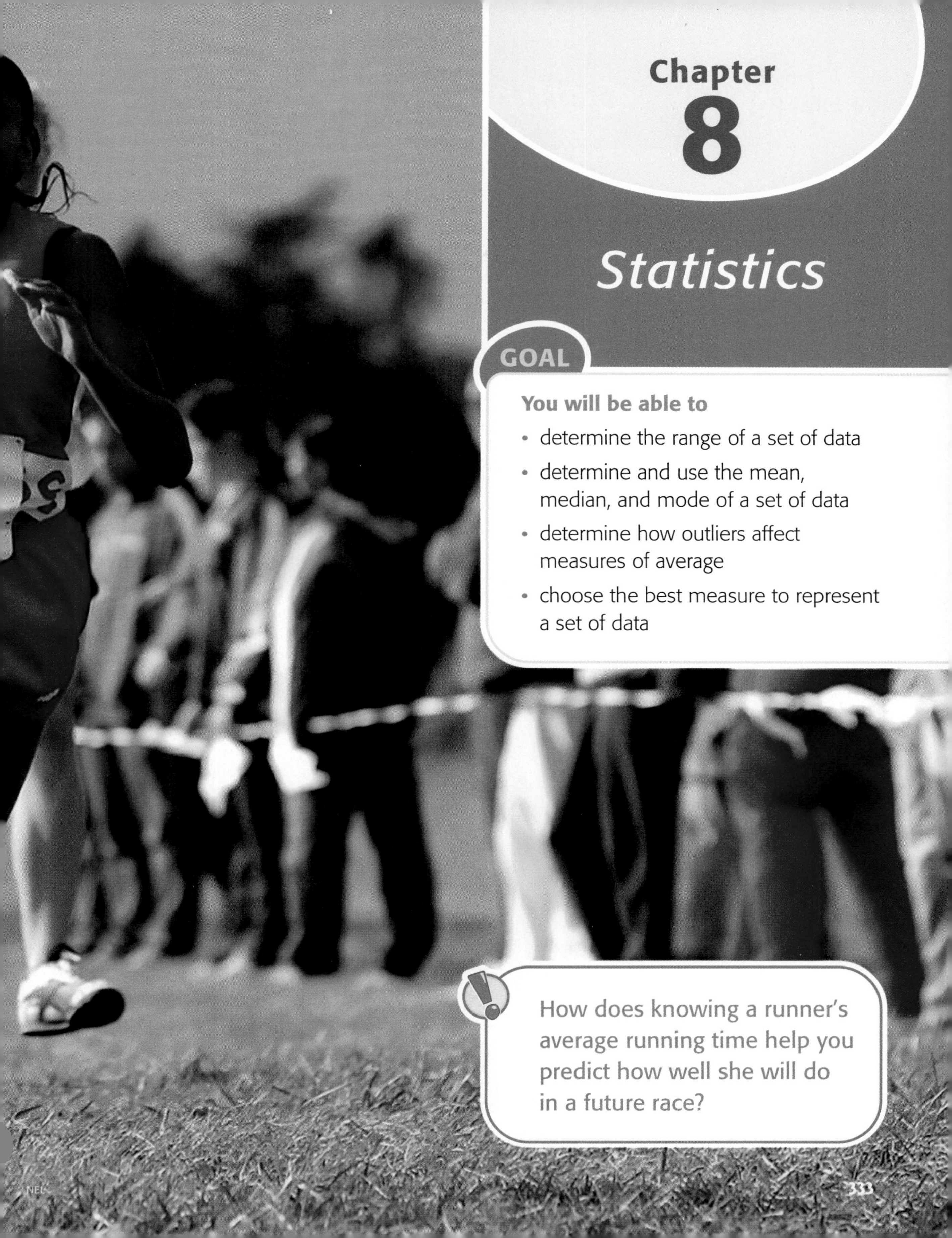

Chapter 8

Statistics

GOAL

You will be able to

- determine the range of a set of data
- determine and use the mean, median, and mode of a set of data
- determine how outliers affect measures of average
- choose the best measure to represent a set of data

How does knowing a runner's average running time help you predict how well she will do in a future race?

Chapter 8

Getting Started

YOU WILL NEED
- grid paper
- a ruler
- a calculator

Long Names

Jessica said, "I think most girls have longer names than boys do. Jessica and Katarina are longer names than Nick and Hans." Pavlo said, "But Cho and Gail are short girls' names, and Brandon is a long boy's name."

Are most girls' names longer than most boys' names?

A. Make a list of your classmates' names.

B. Record the number of letters in each student's name in a tally chart.

Girls		Boys	
Number of letters in name	Number of names	Number of letters in name	Number of names
2	I	2	
3	IIII	3	III
4		4	

C. Represent your results on a graph. You can use one graph with both sets of data shown on it or two different graphs. Make sure that you fully label your graph.

D. In your class, which are longer, boys' names or girls' names?

E. Do you think that the results would be the same for other classes in your school? Explain why or why not.

What Do You Think?

Decide whether you agree or disagree with each statement.
Be ready to explain your decision.

1. Susie scored 9.4, 9.2, and 9.1 on her gymnastics routine. Chandra scored 9.1, 9.1, and 9.5. Susie did better.

2. When playing Scrabble, you got 10, 8, 14, 6, 9, 10, 12, 25, and 9 on your first nine turns. Your average score is 9 since it's the middle value.

3. Joven asked the first eight students who came into a room how many hockey cards they have. They said that they have 1, 2, 10, 10, 10, 16, 20, and 100 cards. The next student is likely to have 10 cards.

4. Marie's marks on six tests were 61, 73, 82, 88, 88, and 88. Her average must be about 80.

8.1 The Range of a Set of Data

GOAL

Arrange a set of data in order and determine its range.

LEARN ABOUT the Math

A physical education teacher has put the students in her class into two teams for baseball. Now she wants to make sure that the two teams are about the same physically. She asks the students to measure their heart rate, height, and mass.

Team 1	Heart rate (beats/min)	Height (m)	Mass (kg)
Shandra	78	1.60	45
Mike	72	1.70	59
Allison	74	1.62	48
Mark	69	1.78	66
Brian	62	1.81	63
Jason	68	1.73	60
Janice	79	1.56	44
Devon	72	1.69	59
Leslie	80	1.56	44
Charlene	84	1.52	41

Team 2	Heart rate (beats/min)	Height (m)	Mass (kg)
Sandeep	70	1.72	60
Marcia	70	1.54	46
Rosa	72	1.64	50
Loralie	76	1.62	45
Imran	64	1.80	61
Cedric	71	1.75	59
Eric	74	1.65	58
Taylor	74	1.83	62
Maureen	76	1.69	58
Carolyn	73	1.69	52

Which team's members are more alike physically (mass, height, and heart rate)?

A. Arrange the heart rates for the students in each team in increasing order using a **line plot.**

B. Compare the **range** of the heart rates for both teams.

C. Repeat parts A and B for the heights and masses of the students in each team.

D. Which team's members are more similar? Explain.

range

the difference between the greatest and least value in a set of data; for example, the range of 6, 7, 7, 8, and 9 is 3, because $9 - 6 = 3$

Reflecting

E. How similar are the two teams in terms of height, mass, and heart rate?

F. Why does knowing the range not tell you the greatest or least values?

G. Suppose that the data for one group has a smaller range than the same type of data for another group. What do you know about the groups?

Work with the Math

Example | Calculating the range of a set of data

Here are the highest peaks in each province or territory in Western Canada and Northern Canada. What is the range of the peaks?

Mountain	Height (m)	Mountain	Height (m)
Baldy Mountain, MB	832	Mount Logan, YT	5959
Cypress Hills, SK	1468	unnamed peak, NT	2773
Mount Columbia, AB	3747	Barbeau Peak, NU	2616
Fairweather Mountain, BC	4663		

Ashley's Solution

832, 1468, 2773, 2616, 3747, 4663, 5959

I wrote out the values.

832, 1468, 2616, 2773, 3747, 4663, 5959

I arranged the values in increasing order. I ordered them by looking at the thousands, and then at the hundreds.

5959 m – 832 m = 5127 m
The range is 5127 m.

I subtracted the least value from the greatest value to calculate the range.

A Checking

1. Calculate the range of each set of data.
   a) 6, 10, 8, 3, 7, 21
   b) 3226, 3390, 2855, 1955
   c) 12.6, 8.3, 4.5, 2.2, 21.3, 15.4
   d) 80, 70, 90, 85, 130, 200

B Practising

2. Determine the range of gasoline prices in Whitehorse, Northwest Territories, from March 2002 to March 2006.

Date	March 2002	March 2003	March 2004	March 2005	March 2006
Price (¢/L)	73.2	87.7	89.0	97.4	100.4

3. List a set with five different values and a range of 15.

4. The 10 driest cities in Canada are listed in the following table. What is the range of days with no precipitation?

City	Days with no precipitation each year	City	Days with no precipitation each year
Brandon, MB	251	Medicine Hat, SK	266
Calgary, AB	252	Moose Jaw, SK	256
Estevan, SK	251	Regina, SK	251
Kamloops, BC	258	Saskatoon, SK	253
Lethbridge, AB	263	Swift Current, SK	253

5. This table lists the brain masses of different mammals.

Mammal	human	baboon	monkey	camel	dolphin
Brain mass (g)	1400	140	100	680	1700
Mammal	kangaroo	cat	raccoon	rabbit	squirrel
Brain mass (g)	56	30	39	12	6

a) Calculate the range of masses.

b) What factors might account for the range of masses?

6. Judy's class collected pennies for charity and put them in six jars. Nicolas's class had four jars of pennies.

Jars in Judy's class	1	2	3	4	5	6
Number of pennies	500	652	873	998	1090	343

Jars in Nicolas's class	1	2	3	4
Number of pennies	237	984	252	894

a) Calculate the range of pennies for both classes.

b) What do you notice about the two ranges?

c) What do the ranges tell you about these sets of data? What do the ranges not tell you?

8.2 The Median and Mode of a Set of Data

Determine the median and the mode of a set of data.

LEARN ABOUT the Math

Here are some of Wayne Gretzky's statistics as a hockey player.

Year	Team	Games played	Points	Trophies
1979–80	Edmonton Oilers	79	137	LBM, HM
1980–81	Edmonton Oilers	80	164	AR, HM
1981–82	Edmonton Oilers	80	212	AR, HM, LBP
1982–83	Edmonton Oilers	80	196	AR, HM, LBP
1983–84	Edmonton Oilers	74	205	AR, HM, LBP
1984–85	Edmonton Oilers	80	208	AR, HM, CS
1985–86	Edmonton Oilers	80	215	AR, HM, LBP
1986–87	Edmonton Oilers	79	183	AR, HM
1987–88	Edmonton Oilers	64	149	CS
1988–89	Los Angeles Kings	78	168	HM
1989–90	Los Angeles Kings	73	142	AR
1990–91	Los Angeles Kings	78	163	AR. LBM
1991–92	Los Angeles Kings	74	121	
1992–93	Los Angeles Kings	45	65	
1993–94	Los Angeles Kings	81	130	AR, LBM
1994–95	Los Angeles Kings	48	48	
1995–96	Los Angeles Kings	62	81	

median

a representative value of a set of data; the middle value of the ordered data.
For example, for the set 2, 3, 4 the median is 3; for the set 2, 3, 4, 5 the median is 3.5.

mode

a representative value of a set of data; the value or item that occurs most often in a set of data.
For example, for the set 1, 5, 6, 6, 6, 7 the mode is 6; for the set 1, 1, 5, 6, 6, 7 the modes are 1 and 6; for the set 1, 2, 5, 6, 7, 8 there is no mode.

A sportscaster wants to report the typical number of games that Wayne Gretzky played for each team in a year.

What values would be reasonable to report?

A. Order from least to greatest the games that Wayne Gretzky played each year for the Oilers.

B. Determine the **median** of this set of data.

C. Determine the **mode** of this set of data.

D. Determine the median and the mode for the games that Wayne Gretzky played for the Kings.

E. If you were the sportscaster, which values from parts B, C, and D would you report as the typical number of games played for the two teams?

Reflecting

F. Why are the median and the mode both good ways to represent a set of data?

G. Did you use the mode or the median for the values you would report? Why?

LBM: Lady Byng Memorial Trophy, awarded for sportsmanship

HM: Hart Memorial Trophy, awarded to the Most Valuable Player (MVP)

AR: Art Ross Trophy, awarded to the highest scorer each season

LBP: Lester B. Pearson Trophy, awarded to the MVP as voted by peers

WORK WITH the Math

Example 1 | Using an odd number of data values

The following table shows the mileages of the most fuel-efficient compact cars in 2006. Jessica's mom wants to buy a new compact car with good fuel mileage. Which cars should she consider?

Car	Mileage in city (litres for each 100 km)	Car	Mileage in city (litres for each 100 km)
1	6.4	6	6.1
2	6.2	7	7.0
3	7.1	8	7.2
4	6.9	9	7.1
5	6.8		

Jessica's Solution

6.1, 6.2, 6.4, 6.8, (6.9), 7.0, 7.1, 7.1, 7.2
The middle value is 6.9, so the median is 6.9.

I ordered the mileages from least to greatest. There are 9 values, so the median is the 5th value.

The mode is 7.1.

The mode is the value that occurs most often in a set of data. 7.1 occurs twice.

My mom should consider cars 1, 2, 5, and 6.

These cars have fuel mileage that is less than the median and the mode.

Example 2 | Using an even number of data values

Nestor, Gail, and Nick planted seeds as part of their science project. After two weeks, they measured the heights of the seedlings in centimetres. Determine the median and the mode of the heights. Which value is more typical of the heights?

Nestor's Solution

39
42, 44, 44, 44, 47, 47
50, 59, 59
61, 64
73, 75, 76, 77
87, 88, 89
90, 90, 92, 98, 98, 98
105, 108
120

I grouped the 2-digit numbers by their tens and the 3-digit numbers by their hundreds and tens. This made the heights easier for me to analyze. I counted each height as I listed it. There are 28 heights. The median is the value in the middle, so the median is halfway between the 14th and 15th values. The 14th value is 75. The 15th value is 76.

The median height is 75.5 cm.

75.5 is halfway between 75 and 76.

There are two modes, 44 cm and 98 cm.

Both 44 and 98 occur three times. This is more than any other value occurs. They are the modes.

The median, 75.5 cm, represents the data better than the modes.

The heights are distributed quite evenly. Most of them are between 44 cm and 98 cm. This means the modes are not typical values. I decided that the median represents the data better. It is more typical of the heights.

A Checking

1. Determine the median and mode of each set of data.
   a) 230, 225, 230, 252, 239, 243
   b) 52.6, 63.4, 46.5, 56.2, 62.2, 65.2, 60.8

2. Determine the median and mode of this set of data.
   18, 19, 19, 12, 17, 19, 18, 18, 18, 25

3. Construct a set of data with six values, a median of 12, and a mode of 10.

B Practising

4. Determine the median of each set of data.

a) 4, 8, 2, 9, 3, 3, 0

b) 32, 88, 13, 54, 84

c) 80%, 69%, 72%, 86%, 91%, 42%

d) 312, 221, 873, 992, 223, 224

5. Determine the mode of each set of data.

a) 7, 8, 9, 9, 8, 6, 6, 9, 8, 4

b) 18, 19, 19, 12, 17, 16, 18, 18, 12, 16

c) 4.3, 7.1, 8.8, 7.1, 7.2, 7.6, 4.3, 7.1, 8.8, 7.0

d) B, G, F, G, G, A, F, F, C, D

6. a) Determine the median of the points that Wayne Gretzky scored each year for the Oilers.

b) Determine the median of the points that he scored each year for the Kings.

c) Compare your answers for parts (a) and (b). Why might you have expected the first answer to be greater even before you did the calculation?

7. Andrew asks each student in his class which type of movie he or she likes best: comedy, action-adventure, romance, animated, or other. Will he use the mode or the median to report his results? Explain why.

8. a) The mode of 59, 85, 72, 42, 62, 72, 53, 59, 63, and ■ is 72. Determine the missing value.

b) The median of 15, 17, 13, 19, 20, 33, 22, 12, 18, and ■ is 18.5. Is it possible to determine the missing value? Explain.

9. Charlene measured and recorded the heights of 12 plants: 32 cm, 45 cm, 82 cm, 99 cm, 15 cm, 102 cm, 75 cm, 15 cm, 15 cm, 75 cm, 2 cm, and 75 cm. Then one plant died, and she removed the height of this plant from the data. The median height is now 45 cm. Which height did Charlene remove?

Reading Strategy

What do you know about median and mode that can help you solve the problem?

10. This table shows the medals that Canadians have won at the Winter Olympic Games from 1976 to 2006.

	Year								
Medal	**1976**	**1980**	**1984**	**1988**	**1992**	**1994**	**1998**	**2002**	**2006**
gold	1	0	2	0	2	3	6	7	7
silver	1	1	1	2	3	6	5	4	10
bronze	1	1	1	3	2	4	4	6	7

a) Determine the median and mode for each medal.

b) Which measure—the median or the mode—represents each medal better? Explain your answer.

11. Simone did a survey in her school. She asked how many students in each class ride the bus to school. She wrote down her results, as shown below.

Number of students in each class who ride the bus:
2, 2, 2, 5, 10, 12, 15, 15, 16, 4, 3, 5, 21, 20, 18, 5, 6, 5, 22, 24, 28

Which measure—the median or the mode—represents the data better? Explain your choice.

8.3 The Mean of a Set of Data

YOU WILL NEED
- coloured counters
- grid paper

GOAL

Determine the mean of a set of data.

LEARN ABOUT the Math

Ashley scored the following points in seven basketball games: 9, 7, 0, 12, 11, 8, 9. Ashley's coach wants to know the typical number of points that Ashley scores.

What value might be a good description of Ashley's performance?

Example 1 | Determining the mean using a graph

I determined my **mean** score using a bar graph.

Ashley's Solution

mean

a representative value of a set of data. The mean is determined by sharing the sum of the data evenly among the values in the set.
For example, the five values in the set 3, 6, 8, 14, 9 have a sum of 40. The mean is 8 ($40 \div 5 = 8$).

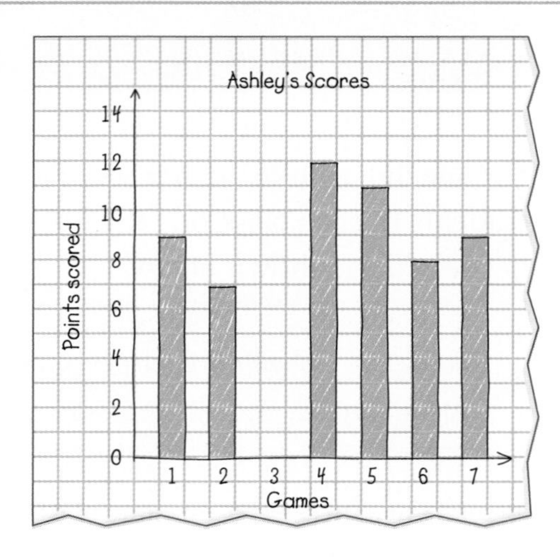

I decided to share my scores over all my games using a bar graph.
I drew a bar graph of my scores.

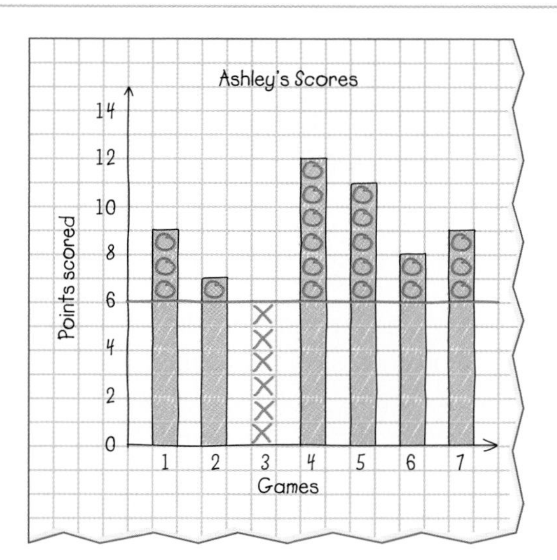

I used a ruler to guess and test where the scores might all be the same. I drew a horizontal line at 6 points. This didn't work because there were more filled squares above the line than empty squares below the line.

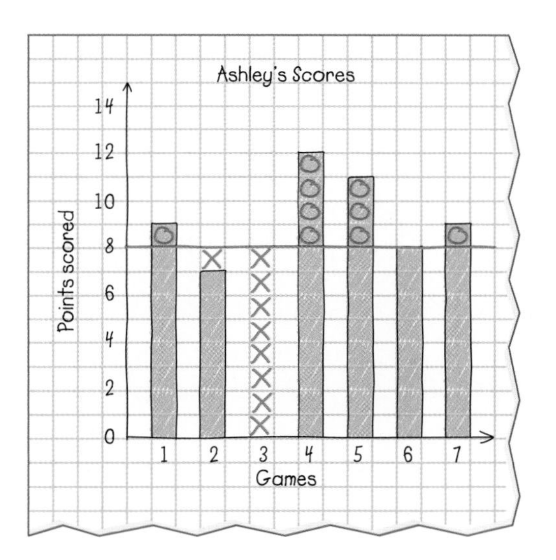

Then I drew a horizontal line at 8 points. This did work, because there is the same number of filled squares above the line as empty squares below the line. The line shows that I scored a mean of 8 points in each game.

My mean score is 8 points per game.

Communication | *Tip*

You may hear people talk about the "average" of a set of data—for example, the "average height" of the students in a class. Usually, they are talking about the mean. The "average" doesn't have to be the mean, however. It can also be the median or the mode. To be clear, it's best to say "mean" instead of "average" when you are talking about the mean.

Example 2 | Determining a mean using counters

I determined the typical number of points that Ashley scores using counters.

Pavlo's Solution

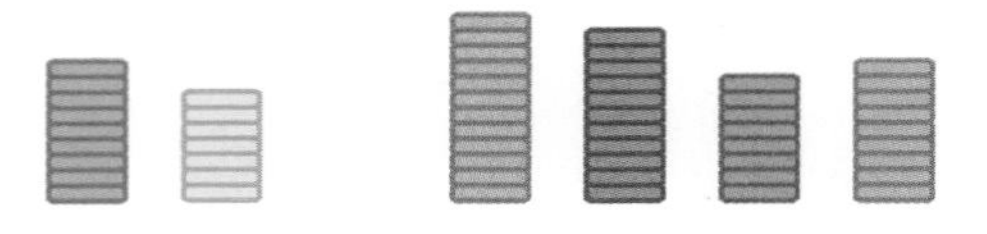

If Ashley scored the same number of points every game, then all of her games would be typical. I decided to rearrange the points to see how many she'd get if she scored the same number every game.
I represented each score with a pile of counters.

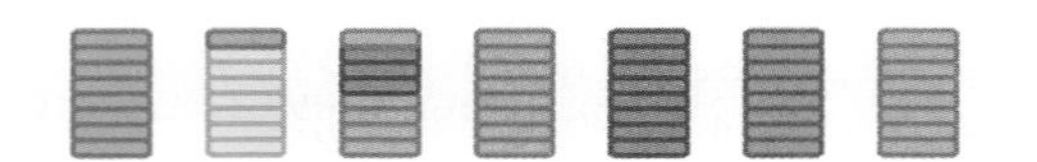

This shows what Ashley would have scored if she had scored the same number of points in every game, but her total points were the same. I figured it out by shifting the counters until the piles were all the same height.

Ashley's typical score is 8 points per game.

There are 8 counters in each pile.

Example 3 | Determining the mean by computation

I determined Ashley's mean score by computation.

Nestor's Solution

I can share Ashley's scores over all her games by adding them and then dividing the sum by the number of games.

$9 + 7 + 0 + 12 + 11 + 8 + 9 = 56$

First I added Ashley's scores.

$56 \div 7 = 8$

Ashley's mean score is 8 points per game.

Then I divided the sum to share the number of scores equally among all the games.

Reflecting

A. Why might Ashley's coach want to know the typical number of points that Ashley scores?

B. Explain why Ashley, Pavlo, and Nestor got the same value.

WORK WITH *the Math*

Example 4 | Choosing the median or the mean

This table shows the medals that Canadians have won at the Jeux de la francophonie. Determine the mean and median of each type of medal. Which value represents the data better?

	Year				
Medal	**1989**	**1994**	**1997**	**2001**	**2005**
gold	9	14	10	12	4
silver	15	10	14	8	6
bronze	20	15	13	18	8

Gail's Solution

gold: 4, 9, (10), 12, 14 — median = 10
silver: 6, 8, (10), 14, 15 — median = 10
bronze: 8, 13, (15), 18, 20 — median = 15

I ordered the values for each medal. The median is in the middle. Since there are 5 values, the median is the 3rd value.

gold:
sum = 9 + 14 + 10 + 12 + 4 = 49
mean = 49 ÷ 5 = 9.8 or about 10
silver:
sum = 15 + 10 + 14 + 8 + 6 = 53
mean = 53 ÷ 5 = 10.6 or about 11
bronze:
sum = 20 + 15 + 13 + 18 + 8 = 74
mean = 74 ÷ 5 = 14.8 or about 15

I calculated the mean for each medal by adding all of the values and dividing by 5. I answered to the nearest whole because you cannot win a fraction of a medal.

gold: mean = 10 and median = 10
silver: mean = 11 and median = 10
bronze: mean = 15 and median = 15
The median and the mean are either similar or the same. They both represent the data well.

A Checking

1. Determine the mean of each set of data to one decimal place.
   a) 18, 22, 22, 17, 30, 18, 12
   b) 19.0, 23.8, 25.3, 17.5, 14.0

B Practising

2. Determine the mean of each set of data to the nearest whole number.
   a) 3, 5, 10, 23, 7, 2, 0, 1
   b) 121, 147, 1000, 19, 1012

3. The Calgary Stampede had a record attendance in 2001. Determine the mean number of visitors per day.

Calgary Stampede Attendance for 2001

Day	July 4	July 5	July 6	July 7	July 8	July 9
Attendance	31 610	86 308	110 411	150 907	93 927	104 635
Day	July 10	July 11	July 12	July 13	July 14	
Attendance	133 753	100 074	127 557	125 458	132 052	

4. These are the ages of the members of a children's choir:
   9, 10, 11, 7, 14, 11, 10, 8, 7, 7, 11, 11
   a) What is the mean age?
   b) Two new members have joined the choir. They are both 7 years old. What is the mean age now?
   c) Why did the mean age decrease?

5. The Arctic Winter Games are held every two years. The following table shows the number of medals won by the Northwest Territories from 1998 to 2006.

Year	1998	2000	2002	2004	2006
Northwest Territories	190	173	76	107	105

   a) Determine the mean number of medals won.
   b) Determine the median number of medals won.
   c) Which value better represents the number of medals won? Explain.

6. Why are you more likely to use the mode to describe the average shoe size worn by Grade 7 boys in your school, but the mean to tell the average daily temperature over a period of one week?

7. A set of values has a sum of 84 and a mean of 12. How many values are in the set?

8. Five sisters all do volunteer work. Last month, they did volunteer work for a mean of 16 h. Four of them worked for 16, 18, 12, and 14 h. For how many hours did the fifth sister work?

9. In one week, five students in a study group read 1, 2, 2, 3, and 12 books. When one student moved to another class, the mean number of books read became 2. Which student moved? Explain your reasoning.

10. In 2002, about 1 151 000 people had cable television. In 2003, about 1 393 000 people had cable television.

a) What was the mean number of new subscribers per month in 2003?

b) Why might a cable television company be interested in this information?

11. Suppose that the mean of six values is 48. Does one of the values have to be 48? Explain why or why not. Give an example to support your answer.

Reading Strategy

What can you infer from the problem to help you find the correct mean?

12. Jean-Pierre works part time in a school supplies store. Each day, for 25 days, he recorded the number of calculators that were sold. On one day, he recorded that 36 calculators were sold when really 86 were sold. He calculated the mean number of calculators sold as 72. What is the correct mean?

13. The class with the greatest mean sales in a spring fundraiser will win a prize. The mean for Eric's class is $148. The mean for Natalia's class is $152. Natalia's sales total $150. If Natalia moved to Eric's class, the mean for each class would increase. Explain why.

14. Is it possible to have a set of data in which the median and the mean are the same? Explain.

Mid-Chapter Review

Frequently Asked Questions

Q: How do you calculate the range of a set of data?

A: Subtract the least value from the greatest value in the set. For example, the range of 2, 5, 7, 9, 15, 26, 9, and 1 is 25, because $26 - 1 = 25$.

Q: How do you determine the mode of a set of data?

A: The mode is the value that occurs most often in a set of data. The data may or may not be numerical. A set of data can have zero, one, or more than one mode. For example, for the set

A, B, A, C, A, B, B, D
the modes are A and B.

For the set
12, 20, 20, 24, 25, 39
the mode is 20.

Q: How do you determine the median of a set of data?

A: Arrange the data in numerical order, from least to greatest. If the set of data has an odd number of values, the median is the middle value. For example, the median of 11, 13, 14, 15, 16, 18, and 20 is 15. If the set has an even number of values, the median is halfway between the two middle values. For example, the median of 13, 14, 15, 17, 18, and 20 is 16, because 16 is halfway between 15 and 17.

Q: How do you calculate the mean of a set of data?

A: Add the values in the set, and then divide the sum by the number of values in the set. For example, the mean of 8, 5, 9, 6, and 7 is 7, because $8 + 5 + 9 + 6 + 7 = 35$ and $35 \div 5 = 7$.

Practice

Lesson 8.1

1. The amount of fresh fruit eaten by the average Canadian each year is shown. What is the range of the amount of fruit eaten?

Year	1993	1995	1998	2001	2004
Fresh fruit eaten (to nearest kilogram)	117	121	122	124	133

2. The depths of the Great Lakes are shown. What is the range of the depths?

Lake	Erie	Huron	Michigan	Superior	Ontario
Depth (m)	64	229	282	406	244

Lesson 8.2

3. Ten students wrote short stories and received these letter grades: A, B, B, A, B, B, C, C, B, A. What is the mode?

4. Determine the median and mode of this set of data:
4.5, 4.7, 4.9, 5.5, 1.3, 1.5, 2.7, 3.9, 4.9, 2.7, 5.6.

5. The heights of 12 plants are 32 cm, 45 cm, 82 cm, 99 cm, 15 cm, 102 cm, 75 cm, 15 cm, 15 cm, 75 cm, 2 cm, and 75 cm. One plant died and was removed from the group. The median is now 45 cm, and the mode is now 15 cm. Which plant was removed?

Lesson 8.3

Year	Time (s)
1896	12.0
1900	11.0
1904	11.0
1908	10.8
1912	10.8
1920	10.8
1924	10.6
1928	10.8
1932	10.3
1936	10.3

6. The winners of the men's 100 m sprint, and their times, for the first 10 Olympic Games are listed in the table at the left.

a) Determine the mean and median of the times.

b) Are the median and mode of this set of data good predictors of the likely results in the next Olympics?

7. A set of values has a sum of 112 and a mean of 14. How many values are in the set?

8. Six shoppers spent a mean amount of \$59. Five of them spent \$38, \$51, \$56, \$82, and \$60. How much did the sixth shopper spend?

8.4 Exploring Statistics

Use statistics.

EXPLORE the Math

statistics

the collection, organization, and interpretation of data

Meteorologists collect data about the weather and use **statistics** to interpret that data so they can make predictions.

This table shows the annual average snowfall for major cities in Western and Northern Canada and in Eastern Canada.

Western or Northern city	Annual snowfall (to nearest centimetre)	Eastern city	Annual snowfall (to nearest centimetre)
Calgary, AB	135	Charlottetown, PE	338
Edmonton, AB	130	Fredericton, NB	295
Iqaluit, NU	108	Halifax, NS	261
Regina, SK	107	Montreal, QC	214
Victoria, BC	47	Ottawa, ON	221
Whitehorse, YT	145	Québec, QC	337
Winnipeg, MB	115	St. John's, NL	322
Yellowknife, NT	144	Toronto, ON	135

What are good values to represent the annual snowfall for all of Western and Northern Canada and for all of Eastern Canada?

CURIOUS MATH

When Is a Low Score Not a Bad Score?

Rosy's sister, Fatouma, entered a math contest for Grade 9 students. There was a prize of $1000 for the student with the top mark.
Fatouma did not win the prize, but she was happy to score $\frac{21}{50}$. Rosy was surprised that Fatouma was happy.
Here are all of the scores for the math contest. The scores are in order from least to greatest and marked with percentiles. A percentile tells what percent of the data is less than or equal to a value.

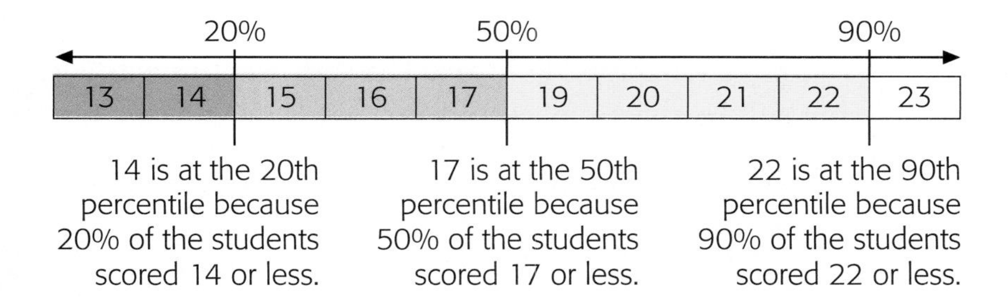

1. What was the least score? What was the highest score?
2. What is the range of the scores?
3. At what percentile is a score of 17?
4. At what percentile is a score of 23?
5. What score is at the 10th percentile?
6. Explain why Fatouma was happy with her score.

8.5 Outliers

YOU WILL NEED

- a calculator

Identify the outliers in a set of data.

LEARN ABOUT the Math

The cafeteria staff at Nick's school prepare 400 meals each day, but there is always some food left over. The staff want to waste less food, but still be able to meet students' needs most of the time. They recorded how many meals were bought for 15 school days.

Day	1	2	3	4	5	6	7	8
Number of meals	320	325	299	298	326	315	320	311
Day	9	10	11	12	13	14	15	
Number of meals	295	272	120	265	278	288	296	

How many meals should the staff prepare each day?

Example 1 | Identifying the outlier using a line plot

I identified the outlier in the data and decided not to include that value when calculating the mean.

Nick's Solution

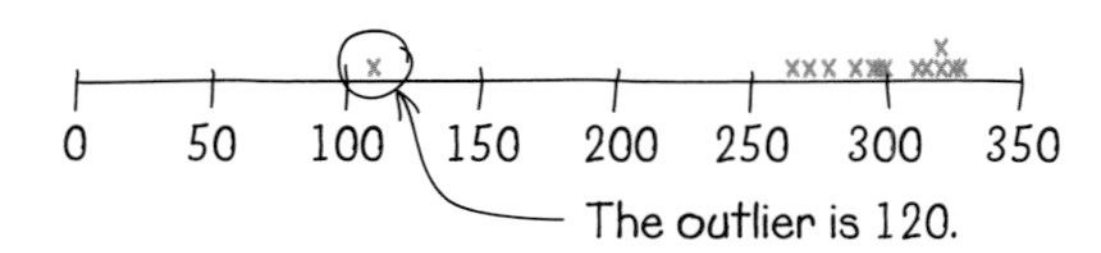

I represented the values on a line plot. I used a line plot because it helped me see how close the values are to each other.

The values are very close together, except for day 11. This value is the **outlier**.

outlier

a data value that is far from the other data values

3 2 0 [+] 3 2 5 [+] 2 9 9 [+] 2 9 8
[+] 3 2 6 [+] 3 1 5 [+] 3 2 0 [+] 3 1 1
[+] 2 9 5 [+] 2 7 2 [+] 1 2 0 [+] 2 6 5
[+] 2 7 8 [+] 2 8 8 [+] 2 9 6
[=] 4328 [÷] 1 5 [=]

288.5333333

The mean with the outlier is 289, to the nearest whole number.

I calculated the mean with the outlier. I added all 15 values and divided by 15. I answered to the nearest whole number because I had to have a whole number of meals.

4328 – 120 = 4208

4 2 0 8 [÷] 1 4 [=]

300.5714286

The mean without the outlier is 301, to the nearest whole number.

I calculated the mean without the outlier. I could have added all the values again, but it was easier to subtract the outlier from the sum.
I divided by 14 because I wanted the mean of 14 values. I answered to the nearest whole number.

With the outlier, the mean is 289. If 289 meals had been prepared on each of the 15 days, there would not have been enough meals on 10 days.
Without the outlier, the mean is 301. If 301 meals had been prepared each day, then there would not have been enough meals on only 6 days.
It is better to use the mean without the outlier to predict the number of meals to prepare.
The staff should prepare 301 meals.

Including the outlier moves the mean farther away from the centre, where most of the values are. Not including the outlier brings the mean closer to the centre of the data.

Example 2 | Identifying the outlier using a graph

I identified the outlier in the data, and decided to use the mode to make my prediction.

Jessica's Solution

I made a graph of the values.

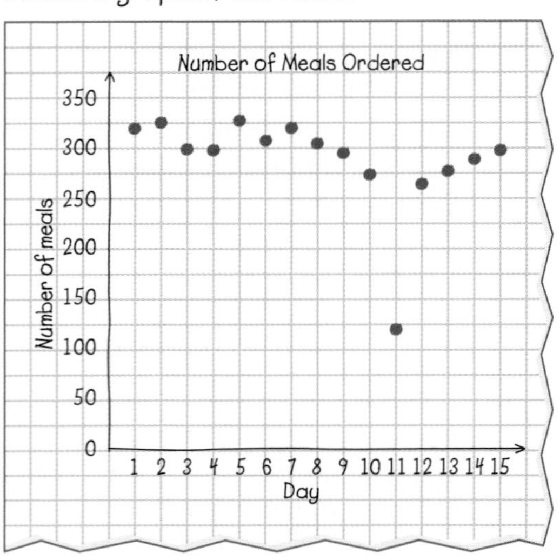

The values for the number of meals are close to each other, except for the value on day 11. This value is far from the other values.

I chose to use the median and the mode to predict the number of meals to serve, because I thought these values would not be affected as much by the outlier as the mean would be.

The outlier is 120.

120
265
272, 278
288
295, 296, 298, 299
311, 315
320, 320, 325, 326

I ordered the values.
There are 15 values, so the median is the 8th value, 298.

Without 120, there is one less value, so the median is now between 296 and 298.
The new median is 297.

I removed the outlier and determined the median. 297 is halfway between 296 and 298.

With the outlier, the median is 298. Without the outlier, the median is 297.

The median is not affected very much when the outlier is removed.

With the outlier, the mode is 320. Without the outlier, the mode is also 320.

The mode is not affected when the outlier is removed.

If 298 meals had been prepared, there would not have been enough meals on 7 days.
If 320 meals had been prepared, there would not have been enough meals on only 2 days.
The staff should prepare 320 meals each day.

The mode is the best measure to make sure that enough meals are prepared.

Reflecting

A. When would the mode be affected by removing an outlier?

B. Why would you omit an outlier when determining the mean of a set of data?

WORK WITH the Math

Example 3 | Analyzing the effect of removing data

Pavlo entered a math competition and received the following marks on 10 tests: 55%, 99%, 75%, 75%, 75%, 82%, 90%, 84%, 88%, 80%. He has two options for calculating his final score.

- **Option A: Calculate the mean without the least and greatest marks.**
- **Option B: Calculate the mean of all the marks.**

Which option should Pavlo choose?

Solution

a) The least and greatest marks are 55 and 99.
$75 + 75 + 75 + 82 + 90 + 84 + 88 + 80 = 649$
$649 \div 8 = 81$ to the nearest whole number
Pavlo's score using Option A is 81%.

Calculate the mean using Option A.
Add the data without 55 and 99.
Divide the sum by 8 because there are 8 tests.

b) $55 + 99 + 649 = 803$
$803 \div 10 = 80$ to the nearest whole number
Pavlo's score using Option B is 80%.

Calculate the mean using Option B.
Add the least and greatest marks to the total.
Divide by the total number of tests.

Pavlo should chose Option A because it gives the higher score, 81.

The mean is 1 mark higher when the least and greatest marks are not used.

A Checking

1. Ricardo asked 13 students how many hours they spent on a computer each week. These are his results:
   14, 18, 16, 19, 21, 14, 2, 18, 14, 15, 23, 17, 15
   a) Represent the data in a line plot.
   b) Identify the outlier in the data.
   c) Determine the mean, median, and mode, including the outlier.
   d) Determine the mean, median, and mode, not including the outlier.

B Practising

2. Vivian Starlight sells packages of beads by mass. The masses of nine packages are 245 g, 265 g, 256 g, 54 g, 272 g, 254 g, 242 g, 264 g, and 258 g. Vivian asks Emily, her little sister, to calculate the mean mass of these bead packages. What answer should Emily give?

3. A company employs 16 people. The chief executive earns $200 000 per year. The director earns $150 000 per year. The two supervisors each earn $100 000 per year. The four managers each earn $50 000 per year, and the eight factory workers each earn $35 000 per year.
   a) Identify any outliers in the salaries.
   b) Determine the mean salary, median salary, and mode salary, including the outliers.
   c) Determine the mean salary, median salary, and mode salary, not including the outliers.
   d) The director wants to attract new factory workers. You have determined six different average salaries. Which one of these average salaries should the director use to advertise the company's average salary? Explain.
   e) One factory worker wants a raise. Which of the six average salaries should she use to support her request? Explain.

4. Robert received the following marks on six quizzes:
   25%, 75%, 75%, 80%, 77%, 82%.
   What argument can Robert use to persuade his teacher that his first quiz should not count on his final mark?

5. Todd recorded his dad's golf scores over the summer. In 12 games, his dad scored 98, 87, 92, 85, 81, 88, 91, 80, 187, 94, 89, and 90. His dad told him that a lower score is better in golf.

a) Calculate the mean score with and without the outlier.

b) Which mean score should Todd report to his dad? Explain your answer.

6. Yesinia's classmates sold magazine subscriptions to raise money for a sailing trip. Ten students participated. They raised $25, $150, $165, $135, $133, $154, $160, $145, $158, and $150. The students were hoping to have an average of $150 in sales. Which average should they report? Explain your choice.

7. The lifespans of different types of shrew are listed in the following table. What is the average lifespan of a shrew? Explain your choice.

Type of shrew	Lifespan (in years)
Forest shrew	1.0
Alpine shrew	1.3
Common shrew	2.0
Smoky shrew	1.0
Lesser shrew	2.0
Vagrant shrew	1.3
Long-tailed shrew	2.0
Pygmy shrew	2.0
House shrew	2.5
Tree shrew	12.0

8. Courtney says that it is cheating to eliminate outliers when you calculate averages. When might she be right? When might she be wrong?

8.6 Communicate about Data

YOU WILL NEED

- a calculator

GOAL

Explain why one measure represents a set of data better than another.

LEARN ABOUT the Math

Ashley's science teacher challenged the students to build little cars powered by elastic bands. Ashley recorded the distance each student's car travelled, in metres:
7.0, 6.4, 8.3, 10.0, 5.5, 4.6, 8.2, 6.7,
7.0, 9.1, 7.5, 9.4, 25.0, 8.6, 30.7, 6.0
Ashley explained which measure of average represented the data best.

How can Ashley improve her explanation?

Ashley's Explanation

1. I plotted the distances in a bar graph because a bar graph makes it easier to see how the values are arranged.

Gail's Questions

How does this help you?

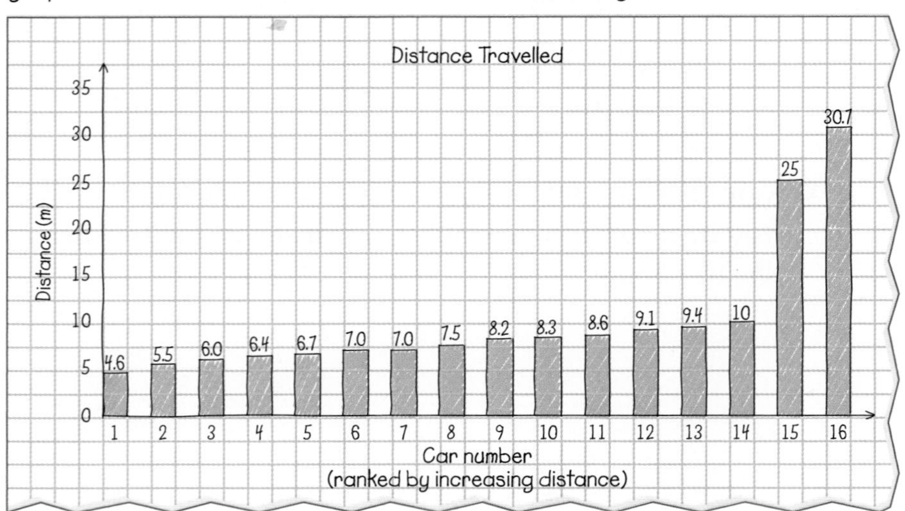

2. I calculated the mean to one decimal place.
   160.0 ÷ 16 = 10.0 m

How did you calculate the mean?

3. I calculated the mean without the two greatest numbers.
   104.3 ÷ 14 = 7.5 m

Why did you do this? Is it fair to do this?

4. I used the bar graph to locate the median.

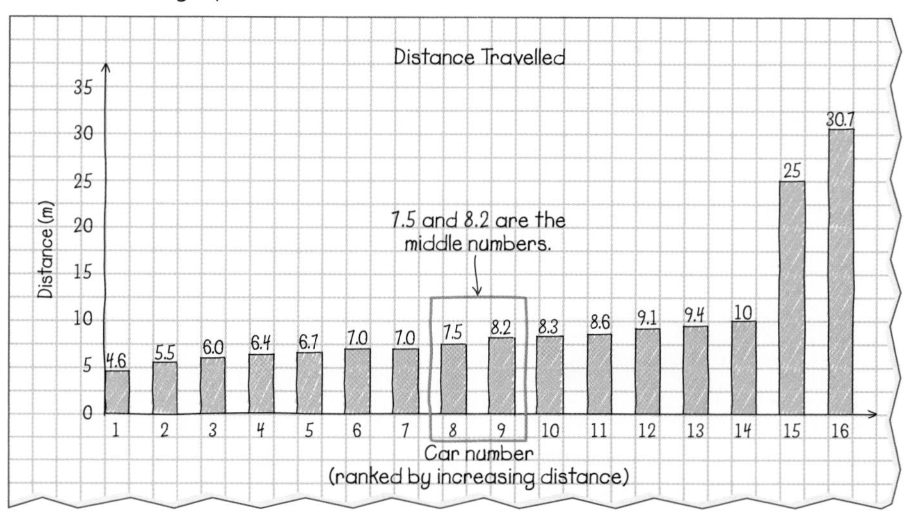

The median is 7.9.

5. The mode is 7.0 m.
6. The best measure of average is the median, 7.9 m.

Why did you choose the median as the best measure of average?

Communication *Checklist*

- ✔ Are the graphs appropriate for the data?
- ✔ Did you include all the important details?
- ✔ Did you make reasonable conclusions?
- ✔ Did you justify your conclusions?
- ✔ Were you convincing?

Reflecting

A. What other questions would you ask about Ashley's explanation?

B. Rewrite Ashley's explanation. Include the answers to Gail's questions and answers to your questions.

C. Which part of the Communication Checklist did Ashley cover well? Explain your answer.

WORK WITH the Math

Example | Choosing the best average

Janine is practising the shot put. Here are the results of her last 10 attempts:

Attempt	1	2	3	4	5	6	7	8	9	10
Distance (m)	8.5	8.2	8.5	8.4	8.5	5.5	8.6	8.5	8.3	8.6

Do you think that Janine will put the shot 8.5 m on track and field day?

Solution

The mean is 8.2. The median is 8.5. The mode is 8.5.

Janine had one very short distance, 5.5 m. This distance lowered the mean below the value that you would expect. Most of Janine's attempts are close to the 8.5 m distance. Even the shorter attempts were close to 8.5 m. The median and the mode show this better than the mean does so they are the best measures to use for predicting. Based on these two measures, Janine will probably throw about 8.5 m on track and field day.

A Checking

1. How much milk should the school order each day? Improve Judy's solution using the Communication Checklist.

Judy's Solution

I gathered data and calculated the mean, median, and mode.

Day	White milk (cartons)	Chocolate milk (cartons)
Monday	45	70
Tuesday	61	50
Wednesday	54	45
Thursday	65	52
Friday	68	62

	White milk (cartons)	Chocolate milk (cartons)
mode	no mode	no mode
median	61	52
mean	59	56

The cafeteria should buy 61 cartons of chocolate milk and 56 cartons of white milk each day.

B Practising

2. Roger asked 15 students how many hours of TV they watched each week. Here are his results:
14, 16, 12, 14, 14, 11, 20, 12, 10, 16, 15, 17, 5, 15, 10
a) Determine the mean, median, and mode of these values.
b) Roger said, "If I watched 2 h of TV each day, I'd be an average TV watcher." Is he correct? Explain your reasoning.

3. Asha, Peter, and Winnie are the captains of the school math teams. They wrote their contest results in this table.

	Contest								
Captain	**#1**	**#2**	**#3**	**#4**	**#5**	**#6**	**#7**	**#8**	**#9**
Asha	82	82	88	100	77	81	87	83	83
Peter	84	84	90	71	78	87	89	88	86
Winnie	85	85	85	81	81	85	82	85	83

a) Whose math team is best, based on the mean? Explain.
b) Whose team is best, based on the median? Explain.
c) Whose team is best, based on the mode? Explain.
d) Which measure would you choose to determine whose team is the best? Why might someone else disagree with you?

4. Melanie found this information about forest fires started by lightning.

Western and Northern Canada	Number of fires	Eastern Canada	Number of fires
Manitoba	105	Newfoundland and Labrador	14
Saskatchewan	180	Prince Edward Island	0
Alberta	425	Nova Scotia	27
British Columbia	842	New Brunswick	20
Yukon Territory	14	Québec	74
Northwest Territories	253	Ontario	168

a) Represent the data in a graph.
b) Are more fires started by lightning in Western and Northern Canada or in Eastern Canada? Explain.

MATH GAME

What's the Average?

YOU WILL NEED
- game cards
- 5 dice

The goal of this game is to determine the mean, median, and mode of the numbers you roll with five dice and to find one of these values on your game card.

Number of players: 2 to 4

How to Play

1. Players have their own game cards and take turns rolling five dice.
2. On your turn, determine the mean, mode, and median of four of the numbers you rolled. (Do not round to whole numbers.)
3. If possible, put a check mark in an empty box beside the correct mean, mode, or median on your game card.
4. If you cannot find an empty box that matches one of these values, put an X in any empty box.
5. When all the cards are filled, the player with the most check marks is the winner.

Example	Mean	Mode	Median	Action
Gail's roll	4	6	4.5	Gail could put a check mark beside a mean of 4 or a mode of 6. Both boxes were empty, so she chose the mean of 4.
Nick's roll	4	4	4	Nick could put a check mark beside a mean of 4, a mode of 4, or a median of 4. The only empty box he had was the median of 4, so he chose that.
Ashley's roll	3.5	none	3.5	Ashley's mean and median were not whole numbers, and she did not have a mode, so she could not put a check mark on her game card. She chose to put an X beside the median of 6.

Gail's Card	
Mean	**✓/✗**
1	
2	
3	
4	✓
5	
6	
Mode	**✓/✗**
1	
2	
3	
4	
5	
6	
Median	**✓/✗**
1	
2	
3	
4	
5	
6	

Chapter **Self-Test**

1. A biologist is studying gulls. He measured and recorded these wingspans, in centimetres:
   132, 145, 162, 135, 142, 122, 138, 124, 135, 140, 128, 122, 145, 138, 139, 122, 146, 150, 167, 128, 134, 147, 151, 122
   Determine the range and mean of these wingspans.
2. Determine the median and mode of each set of data.
   a) 43, 49, 46, 47, 42, 39, 52, 41, 44
   b) 135, 148, 168, 154, 148, 152, 169, 170
3. The median of a set of data is 10. Does 10 have to be one of the values in the set? Use an example to support your answer.
4. Does every set of data have a mode? Use an example to support your answer.
5. Jonathan's scores for seven bowling games are 110, 120, 134, 126, 132, 124, and 122. What score does he need on the eighth game to keep the same mean score?
6. Consider this set of data: 525, 575, 495, 63, 450, 560, 500. Which of the following values would change the mean by the greatest amount if it were added to the set? Explain.
   A. 1500 **B.** 499 **C.** 1
7. **a)** Determine the median, mean, and mode of the Calgary June temperatures.
   b) Joan says that the average temperature for June was 33 °C. Did she use the median, mean, or mode?
   c) Which measure do you think represents the data the best? Explain.

Calgary Daily High Temperatures in June

19°C	22°C	18°C	23°C	21°C
20°C	20°C	18°C	21°C	24°C
25°C	24°C	27°C	28°C	26°C
24°C	25°C	26°C	27°C	25°C
26°C	27°C	30°C	31°C	33°C
33°C	33°C	30°C	33°C	27°C

What Do You Think Now?

Revisit What Do You Think? on page 335. How have your answers and explanations changed?

Chapter Review

Frequently Asked Questions

Q: How can you identify an outlier in a set of data?

A: You can plot the data in a line plot or on a graph. Look for values that are far apart from the other values. For example, consider the following set of data: 5, 20, 21, 20, 23. For this set of data, the value 5 is an outlier.

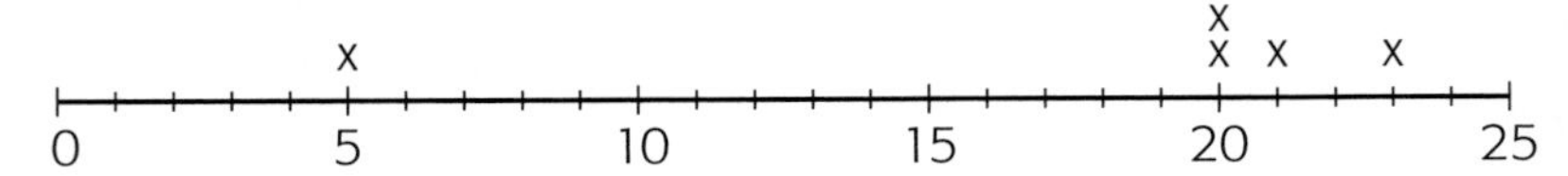

Q: What is the effect on the mean, median, and mode when you don't include an outlier?

A: The mean and the median may change slightly. The mode is unlikely to change. For example, consider the following set of data: 5, 20, 21, 20, 23. For this set of data, the mean is 17.8, the median is 20, and the mode is 20. When the outlier, 5, is not included, the mean is 21, the median is 20.5, and the mode is 20. These results represent the data better.

Q: When would you use the mode, mean, or median to represent a set of data?

A: In some situations, all three measures may represent the data well. In other situations, you may need to choose which measure will represent the data best. For example:

- Use the mode when the data are not numerical or when you are interested in which value occurs most often.
- Use the mean when you think all the values should be considered. For example, the mean of 77%, 88%, 75%, and 80% is 80%.

- You might choose to use the median when most of the values are together, but there are some outliers. For instance, suppose the ages of 11 cousins in a family are 11, 12, 12, 12, 13, 13, 14, 14, 14, 25, and 31. The median age, 13, represents the data better than the mean age, 16.

Practice

Lesson 8.1

1. Determine the range of each set of data.
   a) 25, 87, 92, 29, 33, 98, 19, 33, 45
   b) 446, 440, 440, 442, 444, 442, 440, 443, 440

Lesson 8.2

2. Determine the median and mode of each set of data.
   a) 4, 8, 8, 9, 3, 4, 4   **b)** 125, 83, 115, 94, 109, 115, 89, 104

Lesson 8.3

3. Rosa is in a bowling league. She had these scores:
132, 118, 122, 106, 94, 94, 112, 118, 104, 120, 108, 104, 96, 122, 130, 116, 104, 118, 106, 124
   a) Display Rosa's scores on a line plot.
   b) Determine the range of her scores.
   c) Determine the mean of her scores.

4. Calculate the means and medians of 1, 2, 3, ..., 15 and 1, 2, ..., 21. What do you notice?

5. Each line plot shows the number of books that have been read by students in a reading club. Does the mean, median, or mode represent each set of data best?

a)
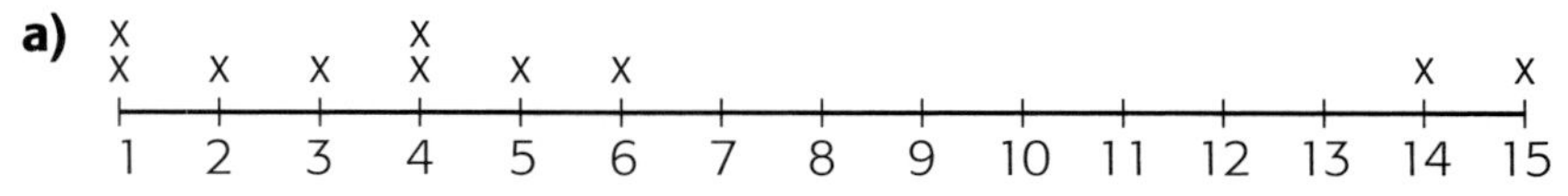

b)
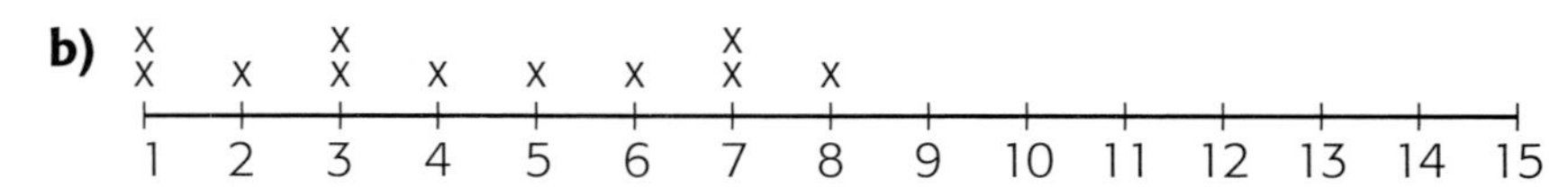

c)
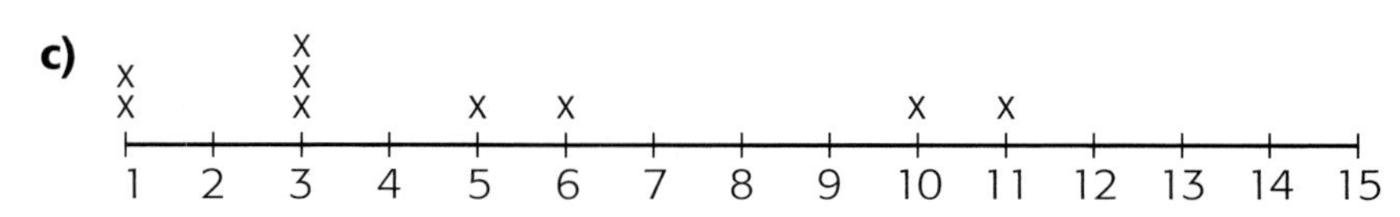

Lesson 8.4

6. Why might you use the mean to describe the average monthly temperature in your community, but the mode to describe the pant size that a store sells most often?

Lesson 8.5

7. The following numbers of rooms are rented at a hotel each night for two weeks:
35, 44, 40, 37, 33, 45, 34, 34, 43, 99, 38, 39, 43, 48

a) Identify the outlier.

b) The hotel manager will use the mean of the data to predict the number of rooms to prepare each night. Should the hotel manager use the mean with the outlier or without it?

Lesson 8.6

8. Sandra asks 20 people entering a music store how old they are. Here are her results:
17, 25, 33, 38, 24, 8, 45, 27, 27, 15, 26, 37, 8, 4, 38, 14, 42, 17, 25, 31

a) Represent her data in a graph.

b) Would you use the mean, median, or mode to describe the most common age of the people entering the music store? Explain.

9. These are Shirley's golf scores this year:
118, 112, 116, 120, 112, 117, 96, 90, 90, 92, 81, 83, 92, 92, 92, 90

a) Determine the mean, mode, and median of Shirley's golf scores.

b) Which measure represents Shirley's golf scores the best? Explain your choice.

10. A bookstore offers a "scratch-and-win" card to each customer who buys more than $50 worth of books. One thousand cards are worth $5 each. One hundred cards are worth $10 each. Ten cards are worth $20 each, and one card is worth $1000. Which measure—the mean, median, or mode—best represents the average value of a card? Explain your choice.

Chapter Task

Task | Checklist

- ✔ Did you include all the important details?
- ✔ Did you explain why you chose a particular measure to best describe your results?
- ✔ Did you make reasonable conclusions?
- ✔ Did you include the result of your comparison with other groups in your class?
- ✔ Were you convincing?

Measuring Reflex Speed

How quickly can you react? Test your reaction speed!

Does everyone have the same reaction speed?

A. Hold a centimetre ruler at the end marked 30 cm. Have your partner place his or her thumb and forefinger near the end marked 0 cm, without touching the ruler.

B. Without warning your partner, let go of the ruler. Record the centimetre mark at which your partner catches it.

C. Repeat step B nine times.

D. Switch roles with your partner, and repeat steps A to C.

E. Determine the range, mean, median, and mode of each set of reaction times.

F. Determine which measure in step E best represents the data. Explain.

G. Compare your reaction time with the reaction times of the other students in your class.

H. Report your own results and your comparison in step G.

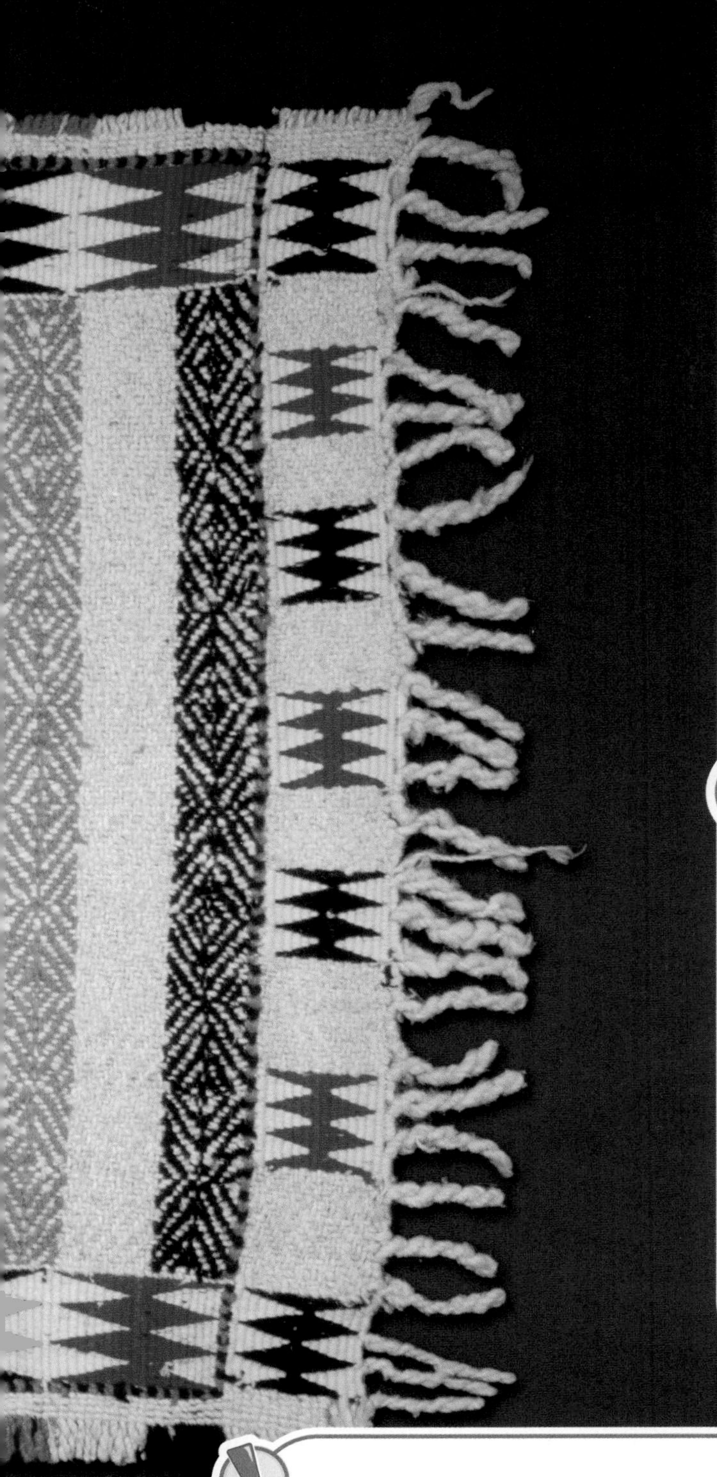

Chapter 9

Linear Relations and Linear Equations

GOAL

You will be able to

- describe a pattern rule using a linear relation
- represent a linear relation using an algebraic expression
- evaluate an expression given the value of a variable
- describe the relationship between a pattern, its table of values, and its graph
- solve a problem represented by a linear equation and verify the solution

What is the relationship between the number of black stripes in the centre of the chief's blanket and the number of black border pieces? Is the relationship between the number of red stripes and the number of red border pieces the same?

Getting Started

YOU WILL NEED
- a calendar page for one month
- grid paper
- a ruler

Finding Calendar Patterns

What number patterns can you find in the calendar?

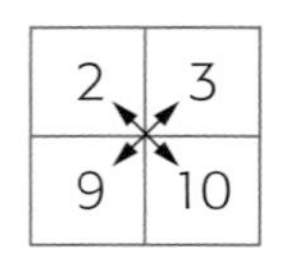

A. Copy the calendar page. Draw a box around any 2×2 square. Add the pairs of numbers along the diagonals. What do you notice?

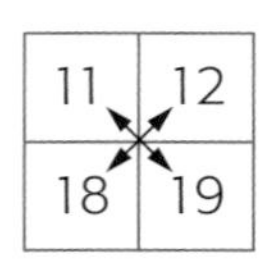

B. Now choose two other 2×2 squares. Add the pairs of numbers along the diagonals. What pattern do you find?

C. Add the numbers in the columns in each of the three squares. What pattern do you find?

D. Add the numbers in the rows in each square. What pattern do you find?

E. Why do the patterns in the squares work the way they do?

F. Repeat parts A to E for 3×3 squares in the calendar.

What Do You Think?

Decide whether you agree or disagree with each statement.
Be ready to explain your decision.

1. To predict the number of cubes in figure 6, you could use a table of values.

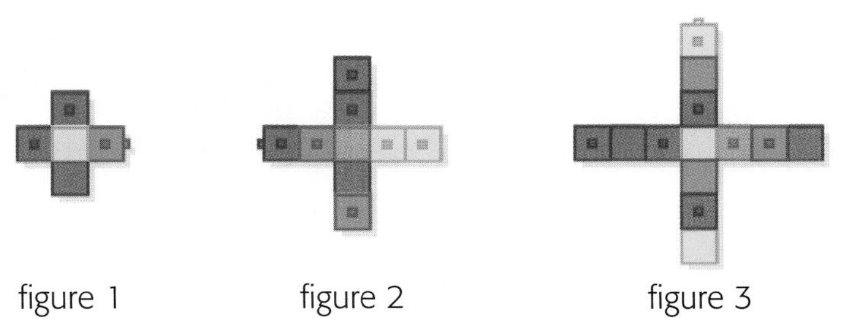

figure 1 figure 2 figure 3

2. When you write the **formula** for the area of a rectangle, you must always use l and w as the **variables**.

3. Starting with the **equation** $2r = 8$, you can create many different equations with the same solution.

4. A computer program gives the output shown for the inputs 1 to 3. To know the output for 10, you need to know the outputs for 1 to 9.

Input	1	2	3	4	5	6	7	8	9	10
Output	7	13	19							

9.1 Writing a Pattern Rule

YOU WILL NEED
- coloured square tiles

GOAL

Write a pattern rule using numbers and variables.

LEARN ABOUT the Math

Ryan made this pattern using coloured tiles.

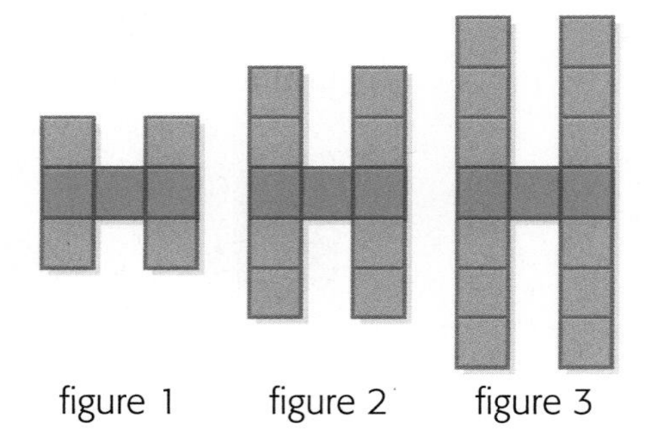

How can you write the pattern rule using numbers and variables?

A. Complete the table.

Figure number	Number of green tiles	Number of orange tiles	Total number of tiles
1	3	4	7
2	3	8	11
3			15
4			
5			
6			

B. Use words to describe the **relation** between the number of orange tiles in a figure and its figure number.

relation

a property that allows you to use one number to get information about another number. For example, the perimeter of a square is 4 times the length of one side, so if you know the length of one side of the square, you can determine the perimeter. This relation can be represented by the formula $P = 4s$ or by a table of values.

Side length (cm)	Perimeter (cm)
1	4
2	8
3	12
4	16

constant term

a quantity that does not change; for example, in $2 \times n + 5$, 5 is a constant term

numerical coefficient

the number that is the multiplier of a variable; for example, in $2 \times n + 5$, 2 is the numerical coefficient of n

C. Represent the figure number using the **variable** n. Write an **algebraic expression** that tells how to calculate the number of orange tiles in figure n.

D. How many green tiles are in figure n?

E. Write an algebraic expression to represent the total number of tiles in figure n.

F. Identify the **constant term** and the **numerical coefficient** in your algebraic expression.

G. Why is your expression from part E a **pattern rule**?

Communication | Tip

- Sometimes an algebraic expression is just called an expression.
- When you multiply a variable by a number or another variable, omit the multiplication sign. For example, write $2a$ instead of $2 \times a$, and write ab instead of $a \times b$.
- A variable can be represented either by a capital letter or a lower-case letter; for example, $A = b + 2$. You can choose any letter as a variable, but you may want to choose a letter that reminds you of the quantity it represents; for example, n for figure number.

Reflecting

H. How did looking at the coloured tiles help you to write your algebraic expression in part E?

I. What do the constant term and the numerical coefficient of your expression tell you about the pattern?

J. You have described the same relation with figures, a table of values, words, and a pattern rule. Which description do you prefer? Explain your choice.

WORK WITH the Math

Example 1 | Writing a pattern rule

Write a pattern rule to represent the relation between the number of blocks in any figure in this pattern and its figure number, *n*.

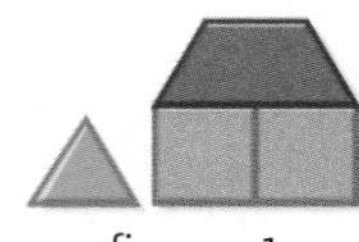

figure 1

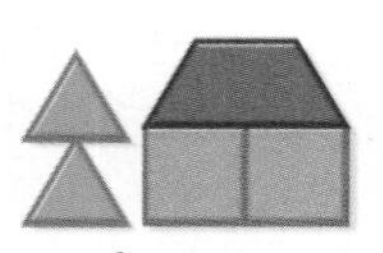

figure 2

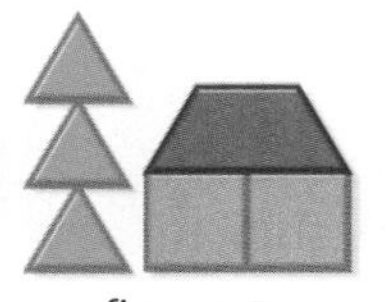

figure 3

Ryan's Solution

I used b to represent the number of blocks in a figure.

I used n to represent the figure number. My pattern rule is $b = n + 3$.

I noticed that the number of triangles changed in each figure. The number of triangles is the same as the figure number.

Each figure also had 3 other blocks that did not change. That means the constant term is 3.

Example 2 | Visualizing a pattern in different ways

Write a pattern rule using an algebraic expression for the number of tiles in any figure in this pattern.

figure 1

figure 2

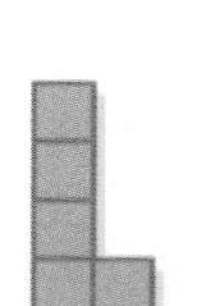

figure 3

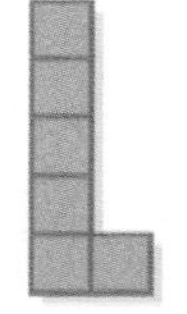

figure 4

Oshana's Solution

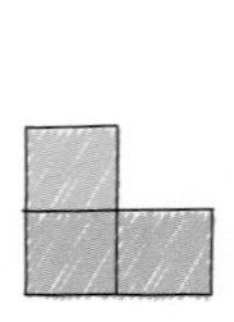

figure 1

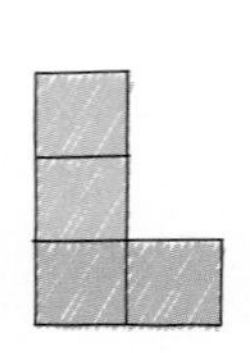

figure 2

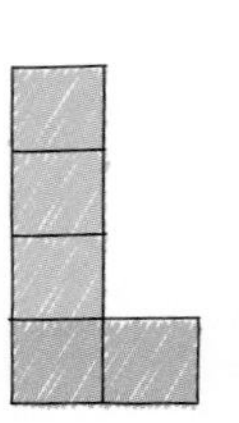

figure 3

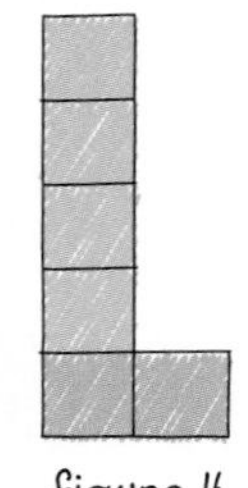

figure 4

I drew the pattern.

There are always 2 tiles in the base. I coloured them blue.

The top increases in each figure. I coloured the tiles in the top green.

I used T to represent the number of tiles in a figure and n to represent the figure number.

I wanted to relate the number of tiles to the figure number *n*.

The number of blue tiles is always 2.

I used the algebraic expression $2 + n$ to create the pattern rule.

The figure number is the same as the number of green tiles.

My pattern rule is $T = 2 + n$.

The pattern rule says that the number of tiles in a figure is the number of blue tiles plus the number of green tiles.

Jacob's Solution

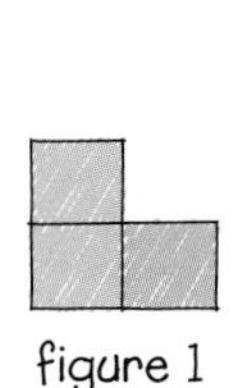

figure 1

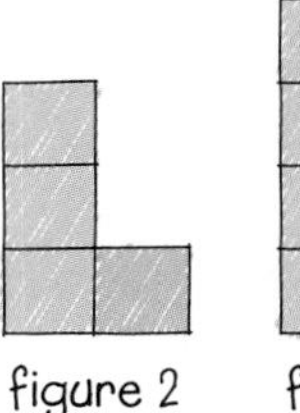

figure 2

figure 3

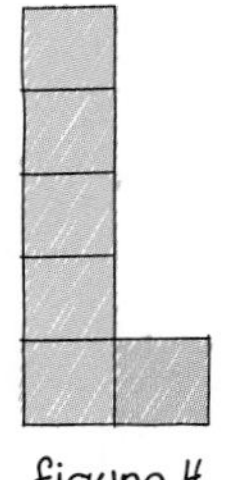

figure 4

I drew the pattern.

I coloured the vertical tiles green.

The number of vertical tiles increases in each figure.

There is always 1 tile remaining. I coloured the 1 remaining tile blue.

I used T to represent the number of tiles in a figure and f to represent the figure number.

I used the algebraic expression $f + 1$ to create the pattern rule.

In each figure, the number of green tiles is 1 more than the figure number.

My pattern rule is $T = (f + 1) + 1$.

The last 1 represents the 1 blue tile in each figure.

Example 3 | Predicting a pattern rule

Write a pattern rule to represent the relation between the number of tiles in any figure in this pattern and its figure number, n.

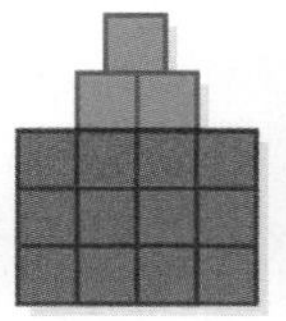

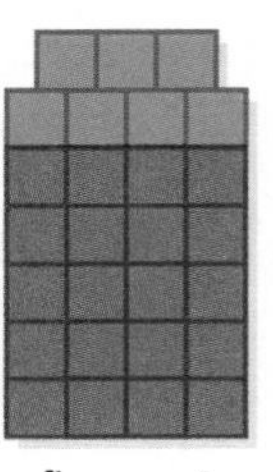

figure 1 figure 2 figure 3 figure 4

Sarah's Solution

Figure number	Number of tiles
1	9
2	15
3	21
4	27

+6, +6, +6

The number of tiles in each figure increases by 6 each time (2 blue, 2 purple, and 2 green). That's how the 6-times table works too.

n	$6n$
1	6
2	12
3	18

+6, +6

Figure number	Number of tiles	6n	Difference
1	9	6	3
2	15	12	3
3	21	18	3
4	27	24	3

I compared the number of tiles in each shape with $6n$.

The number of tiles in figure n is always 3 greater than $6n$.

The rule for the number of tiles in figure n is $T = 6n + 3$.

I can say the rule as, "Multiply the figure number by 6 and then add 3."

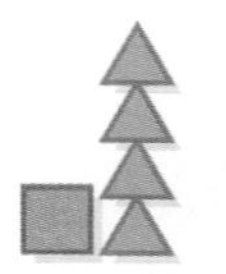

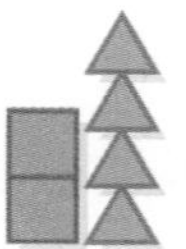

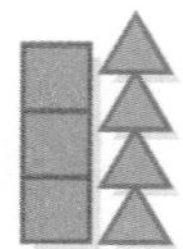

figure 1 figure 2 figure 3

A Checking

1. Write a pattern rule using an algebraic expression for the number of tiles in any figure in the pattern at the left.

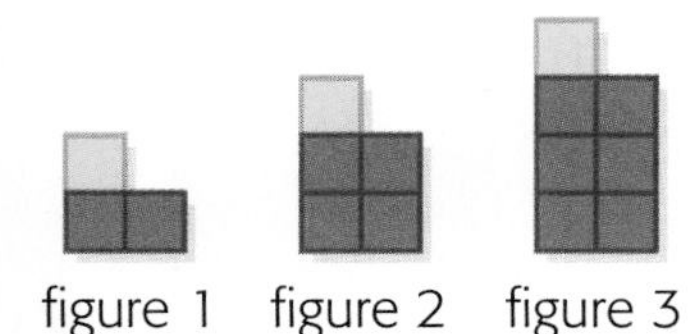
figure 1 figure 2 figure 3

2. **a)** What stays the same and what changes in the tile pattern at the left?
   b) Write a pattern rule in words.
   c) Write a pattern rule using an algebraic expression for the number of tiles in any figure.
   d) Identify the numerical coefficient and the constant term in your expression.

B Practising

figure 1

figure 2

figure 3

3. **a)** Complete the table for the pattern at the left.

Figure number	1	2	3	4	5
Number of triangles	4	5			

   b) Describe in words the relation between the number of triangles in a figure and its figure number.
   c) Write a pattern rule using an algebraic expression to represent this relation.

4. Anne, Sanjay, and Robert wrote different pattern rules for the same pattern. Explain each student's reasoning.

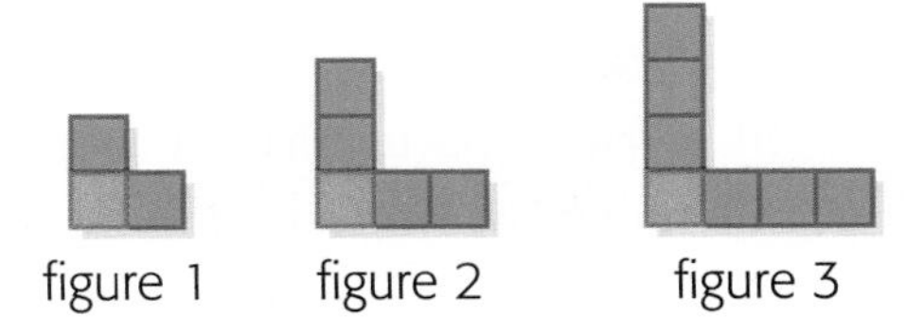
figure 1 figure 2 figure 3

Anne: "My pattern rule is $T = n + 1 + n$."

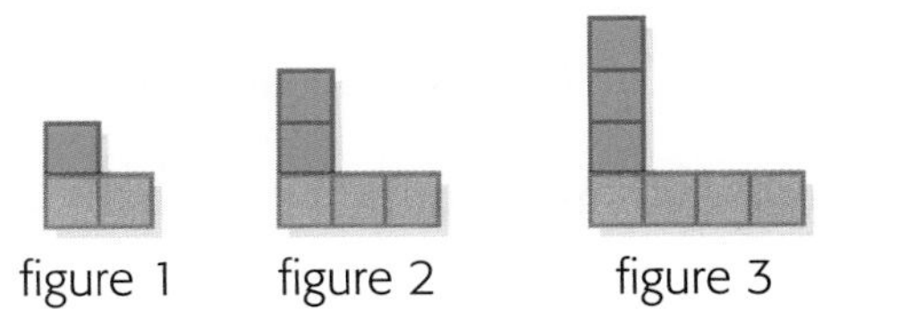
figure 1 figure 2 figure 3

Sanjay: "My pattern rule is $T = n + (n + 1)$."

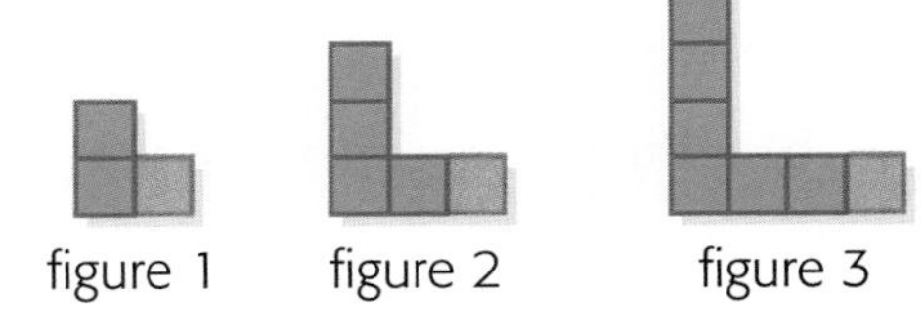
figure 1 figure 2 figure 3

Robert: "My pattern rule is $T = 2n + 1$."

5. Kyle and Tynessa coloured the same pattern of tiles differently.
Kyle's colouring:

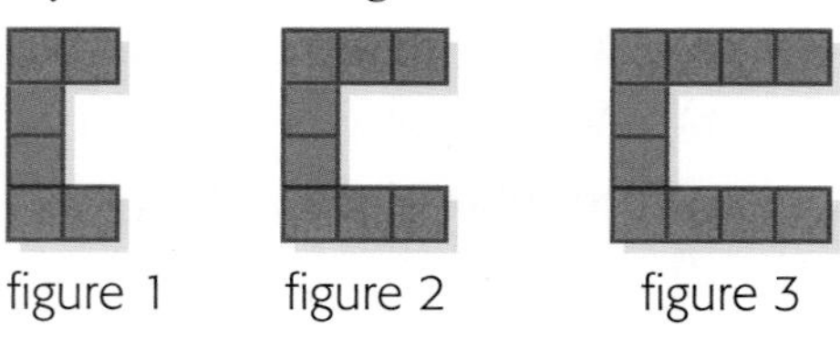

Tynessa's colouring:

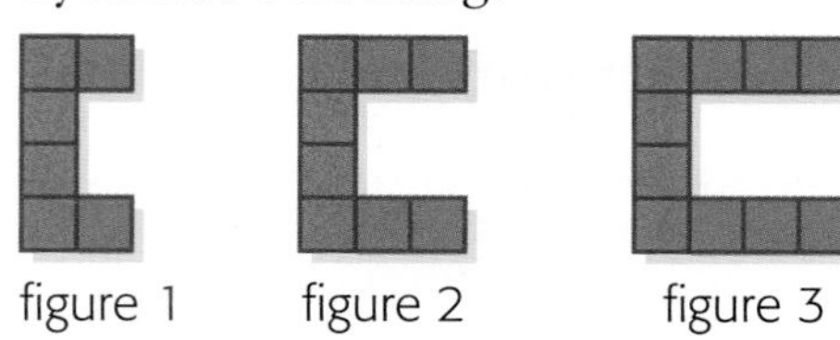

a) Write a pattern rule using an algebraic expression based on Kyle's colouring.

b) Write a pattern rule using an algebraic expression based on Tynessa's colouring.

c) Identify the constant term and the numerical coefficient in each expression.

d) Why must Kyle's and Tynessa's pattern rules be the same, even though their algebraic expressions look different?

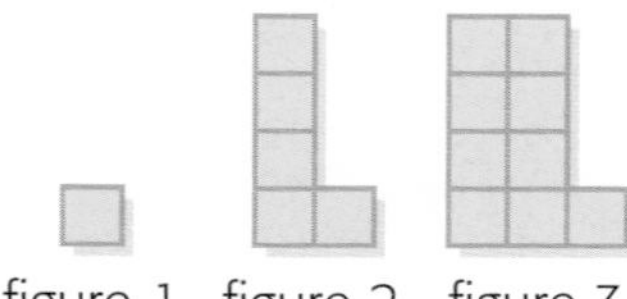

6. a) Draw the next two figures in the tile pattern at the left.

b) Write a pattern rule using an algebraic expression for the number of tiles in any figure.

c) Identify the constant term and the numerical coefficient in your expression.

d) What do the constant term and the numerical coefficient tell you about how the pattern grows?

7. Is there a figure with exactly 257 tiles in each pattern? Explain.

a) $T = 2n + 1$ **b)** $T = 2n + 4$

8. Suppose that you have a pattern rule with an algebraic expression.

a) What does the constant term tell you about the pattern?

b) What does the numerical coefficient tell you about the pattern?

Reading Strategy

Complete an Understanding What I Read chart for each term you don't understand in question 8.

CURIOUS MATH

Creating Number Tricks Using Algebra

How can you model number tricks?

A.

Try this trick.	**Get the picture.**	**Here's the algebra!**
Think of a one-digit number.		n
Multiply by 6.		$6n$
Add 10.	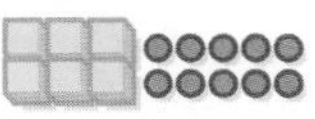	$6n + 10$
Divide by 2.		
	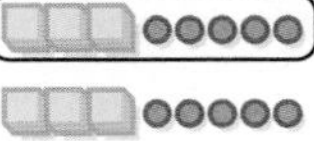	$3n + 5$
Subtract 5.		$3n$
Divide by 3.		n

What's the answer? Always your starting number!

B.

Try this trick.	**Get the picture.**	**Here's the algebra!**
Think of a one-digit number.		a
Multiply by 6.		$6a$
Add 10.		$6a + 10$
Subtract the original number.	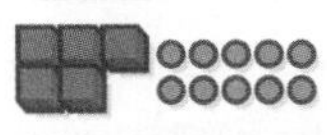	$5a + 10$
Divide by 5.	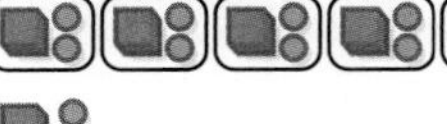	
		$a + 2$
Subtract the original number.		2

What's the answer? Always 2!

1. Finish the trick below so that the answer is always the original number.

Try this trick.	**Get the picture.**	**Here's the algebra!**
Think of a one-digit number.		y
Multiply by 10.	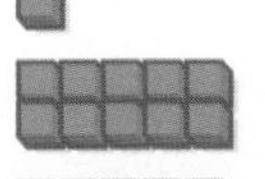	$10y$
Add 10.		$10y + 10$
Divide by ■.		
Subtract ■.		

2. Make up a trick of your own. Use pictures and algebra to show how it works. Try it with a classmate.

9.2 Evaluating an Expression to Solve a Problem

YOU WILL NEED
- a calculator

Create and evaluate an expression to solve a problem.

LEARN ABOUT the Math

Denis and Nayana are helping to organize a school trip for 260 students to Regina.

- Swift Buses charges $7 per student.
- Zim Buses charges $6 per student, plus $500.

Denis and Nayana decide to calculate the charge for each company.

Which company charges less?

Example 1 | Evaluating an expression in one step

Create an expression to represent what Swift charges for any number of students. Determine the charge for 260 students using your expression.

Denis's Solution

I used n to represent the number of students.

$7n$

From the description, I knew that there would be a $7 charge for each student.

$= 7(260)$

$= 1820$

To evaluate my expression, I substituted 260 for n because there are 260 students.

Swift will charge $1820 for 260 students.

Communication | *Tip*

- Use brackets when you substitute a number for a variable. This will prevent you from running numbers together. For example, to evaluate $2a$ for $a = 10$, write $2(10)$.
- Write each step in a calculation directly under the previous step. Line up the equal signs. This makes the calculation easier to read and check. For example,

$$\begin{aligned} 2a + 5 &= 2(10) + 5 \\ &= 20 + 5 \\ &= 25 \end{aligned}$$

Example 2 | Evaluating an expression in two steps

Create an expression to represent what Zim charges for any number of students. Determine the charge for 260 students using your expression.

Nayana's Solution

Number of students	Zim's charge ($)	Pattern
0	500	500 + 0(6)
1	506	500 + 1(6)
2	512	500 + 2(6)
3	518	500 + 3(6)
4	524	500 + 4(6)

I created a table of values for Zim's charges. Then, I looked for a pattern in the values.

I saw that the table started at 500 and the value increased by 6 with each row.

Each value is 500 more than 6 times the number of students.

I used n to represent the number of students.

$$\begin{aligned} &500 + 6n \\ &= 500 + 6(260) \\ &= 500 + 1560 \\ &= 2060 \end{aligned}$$

Zim will charge $2060 for 260 students.
$1820 is less than $2060, so Swift will charge less.

My expression has a constant term of 500 and a numerical coefficient of 6.
To evaluate my expression, I substituted 260 for *n* because there are 260 students.

Reflecting

A. Each company's charge was described in words. How else did Denis and Nayana describe the relation between the charge and the number of students?

B. Why was Denis able to evaluate his expression with just one arithmetic operation, while Nayana needed two operations?

WORK WITH the Math

Example 3 | Solving a patterning problem

Jasmin made a pattern using blue pattern blocks. How many blocks are in figure 20?

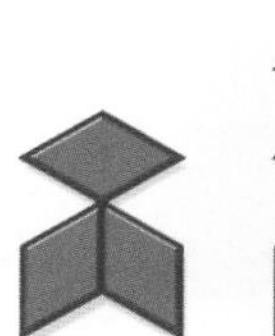
figure 1

figure 2

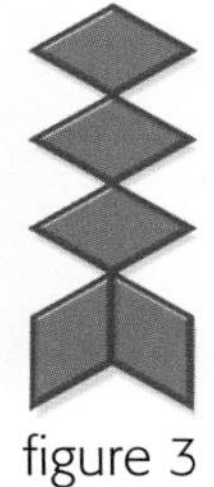
figure 3

Solution

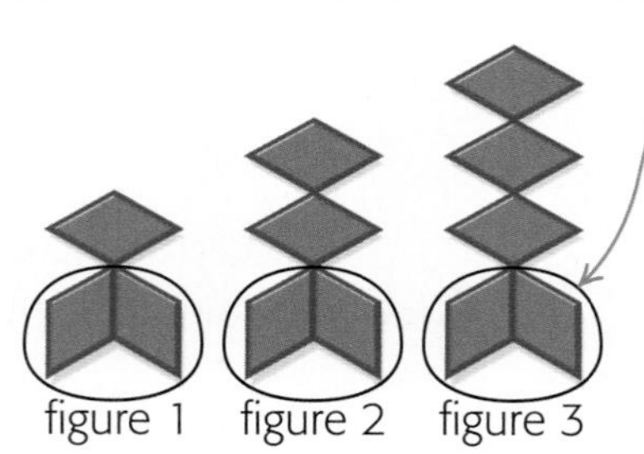

Each figure starts with 2 blocks at the bottom.
Figure 1 has 3 blocks.
Figure 2 has 4 blocks.
Figure 3 has 5 blocks.
Each figure has 2 more blocks than its figure number.

Use n to represent the figure number.

$n + 2$

$= (20) + 2$ — Substitute 20 for n.

$= 22$ — There are 22 blocks in figure 20.

A Checking

1. Evaluate each expression for $d = 5$.

a) $6d$ **b)** $5d - 1$ **c)** $d + 1$ **d)** $3(d + 2)$

2. Write an expression to represent the cost to rent a sled for a base fee of \$35, plus \$12 per hour.

B Practising

3. Evaluate each expression for $a = 3$ and $b = 5$.

a) $3a$ **b)** $8b$ **c)** $9a$ **d)** $2(b - 1)$

4. Aisha did t sets of weightlifting, except the last time when she stopped 2 reps from the end of the last set. There are 8 reps in each set.

a) Write an expression to represent how many reps Aisha did.

b) Suppose that $t = 4$. Calculate how many reps she did.

5. Evaluate the expression $6(b - 1) + 3$ for $b = 4$. Show and explain all the steps.

6. Write an expression for each cost.

a) \$4 to sharpen each pair of skates for a class skating party

b) hamburgers at \$3 each

c) \$2 per hour plus \$5 to rent skates

d) hats on sale for \$10 each

7. Each figure in the pattern is made from green, blue, purple, and yellow tiles. Each expression tells the number of tiles of one colour in a figure. Match each expression to its colour.

A. $2n$ **B.** $2n + 4$ **C.** $2n - 1$ **D.** $n + 2$

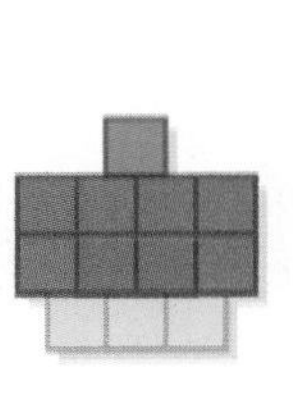
figure 1

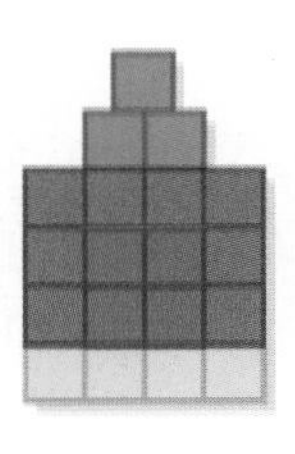
figure 2

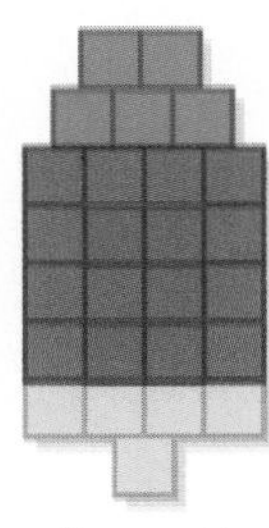
figure 3

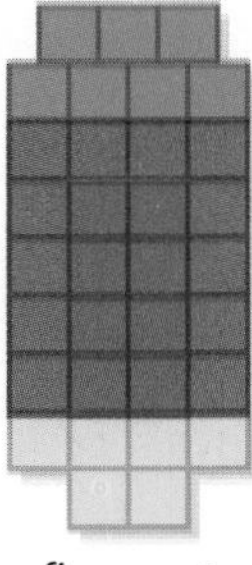
figure 4

8. Samantha works in the snack bar at a community centre. She earns \$8 an hour. One weekend, she was paid a bonus of \$50.

a) Write an expression to represent her total earnings for h hours.

b) On that weekend, she worked for 15 h. Calculate how much she earned. Show your work.

9. Jerry sells wool caps at a booth. He earns \$25 a day, plus \$2 for each cap that he sells. On Monday, he sold 17 caps.

a) Create a table of values to show Jerry's daily earnings when he sells 0, 1, 2, 3, 4, and 5 caps.

b) Write an expression to describe Jerry's daily earnings.

c) Calculate how much money Jerry earned on Monday.

10. A box of DVDs costs \$56. Winnie can use \$3 coupons to reduce the price.

a) Write an expression to describe the amount that Winnie would pay if she used c coupons.

b) Suppose that Winnie has 5 coupons. How much will she pay?

11. a) Complete the table.

Term number (figure number)	Picture	Term value (number of stars)
1	☆ ☆☆	3
2	☆☆ ☆☆☆	5
3	☆☆☆ ☆☆☆☆	7
4		
5		

b) Write a rule for this pattern. Use n for the term number in your expression.

c) Predict the value of term 8.

12. A banquet hall charges a flat rate of \$1000, plus \$30 per guest. Suppose that there is a party at the banquet hall every night. Why would the owner of the banquet hall find it useful to create an algebraic expression to calculate the bill for each party?

9.3 Exploring Possible Values

YOU WILL NEED

- pattern blocks

GOAL

Explore solving a relation with more than one variable.

EXPLORE the Math

This chart shows the cost of different groups of pattern block shapes. Your class wants to buy 100 of each shape.

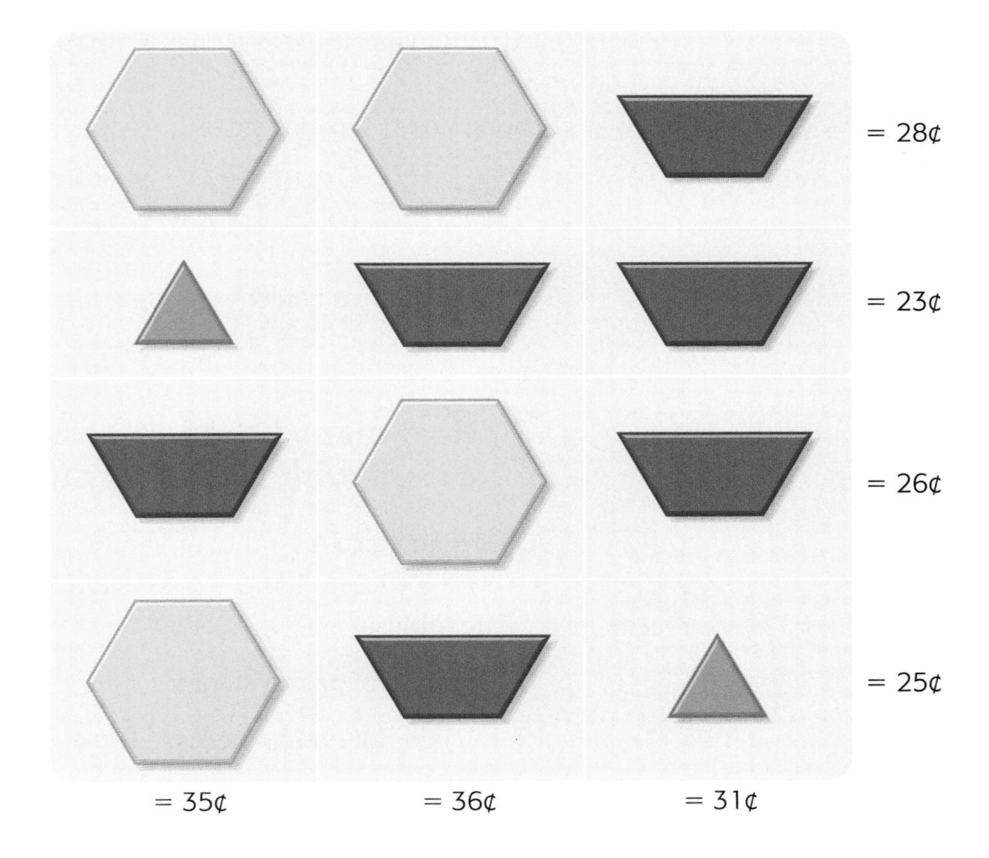

How much does each shape cost? How much will your class need to spend?

9.4 Linear Relations and Their Graphs

YOU WILL NEED

- grid paper
- a ruler
- triangular pattern blocks

Graph a linear relation and describe properties of the graph.

LEARN ABOUT the Math

Megan is designing straight paths for the school garden. She thinks there is a relation she can use to predict how many paving stones and how many border pieces she will need for each path. She will need 12 paving stones for the first path.

1 paving stone — 6 border pieces
2 paving stones — 8 border pieces
3 paving stones — 10 border pieces
4 paving stones — 12 border pieces

How many border pieces will Megan need for a path with 12 paving stones?

A. Megan started a table of values to show how the number of border pieces changes as she adds paving stones. Complete the table.

Number of paving stones	1	2	3	4	5	6	7	8
Number of border pieces	6	8	10					

B. Write a relation that tells how to calculate the number of border pieces when you know the number of paving stones.

C. Megan began to plot the data from the table as a **scatter plot**. She used "Number of paving stones" and "Number of border pieces" as the **coordinates** for each point. Complete the graph.

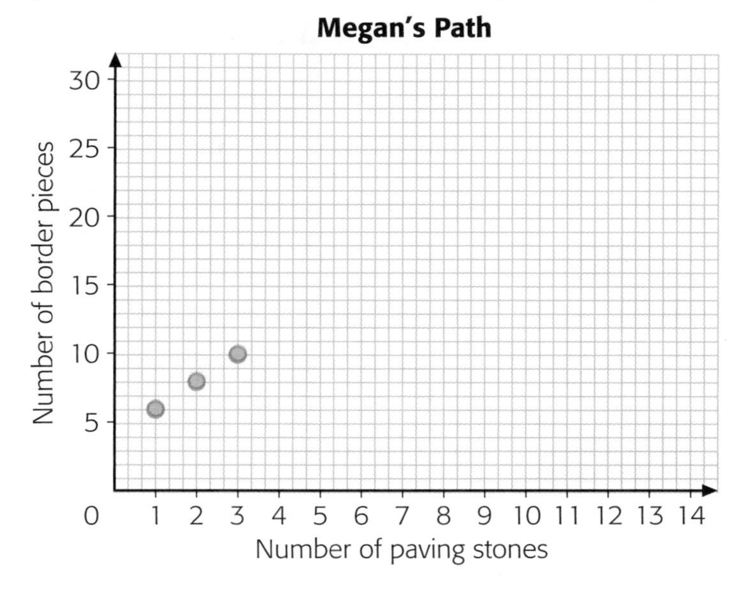

D. Extend the pattern to include a point on the vertical axis. Use a ruler. How many paving stones does this point represent? How many border pieces does this point represent?

linear relation

a relation whose plotted points lie on a straight line

E. By how many units does the graph rise each time one paving stone is added?

F. Megan's path will have 12 paving stones. Predict the number of border pieces she will need using your graph.

G. Check your answer by extending the table of values in part A.

Reflecting

H. How did you use the table of values to graph this relation?

I. Look at your graph in part D. How does it show that the relation between the number of paving stones and the number of border pieces is a **linear relation?**

J. Why does it make sense that the graph goes up by the same amount for each additional paving stone?

WORK WITH the Math

Example 1 | Graphing a linear relation using a table

The rule $T = 4n + 3$ describes the relation between the figure number n and the number of tiles in the figure in this pattern.

a) Graph the relation. Why can you say it is a linear relation?

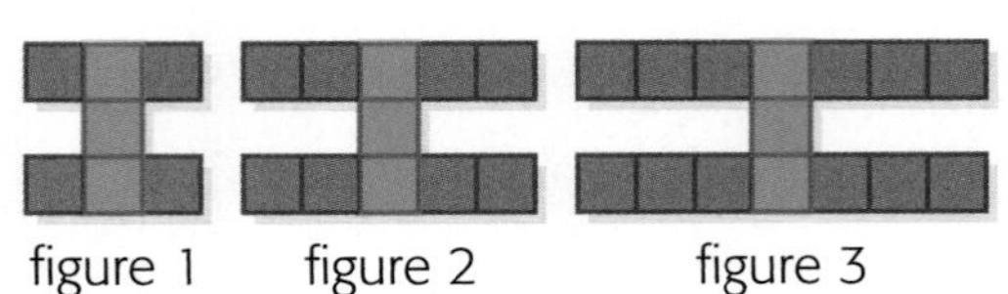

b) Describe some of the patterns in the graph. Relate these pattterns to the pattern rule.

Ryan's Solution

a)

Figure number, n	Number of tiles, 4n + 3
1	7
2	11
3	15
4	4(4) + 3 = 19
5	4(5) + 3 = 23
6	4(6) + 3 = 27
7	4(7) + 3 = 31
8	4(8) + 3 = 35

I made a table of values.

I used $T = 4n + 3$ to extend the table.

I used the values as coordinates for the points on the graph.

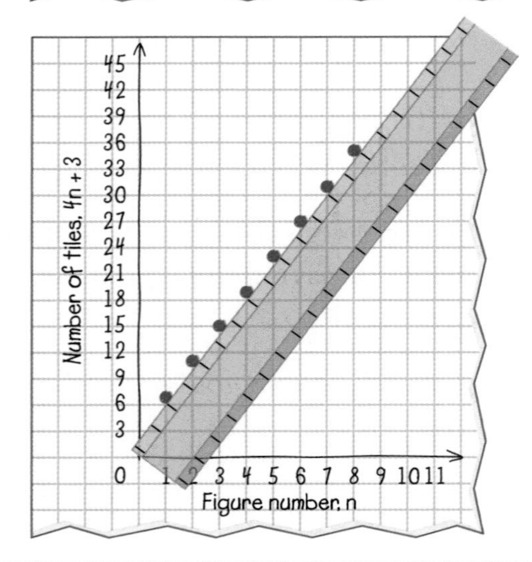

The data points fall along a straight line, so the relation is linear.

b)

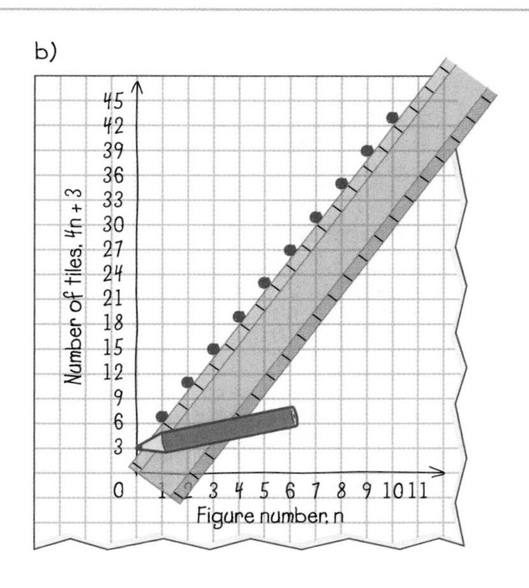

Each time the figure number increased by 1 unit, the graph increased by 4 units. This was because each figure increased by 4 square tiles from the figure before it. There are no points between the points I plotted, because I can't use part of a paving stone.

I extended the pattern to make a point on the vertical axis at 3.
There is no figure number 0, but I imagine it would look like this:

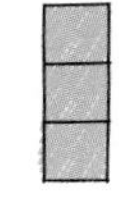

These three tiles are represented by the constant term.

Example 2 | Solving a problem using a graph

A new factory makes golf carts. The graph shows the number of carts made each day. If this pattern continues, how many carts will the factory make on day 15?

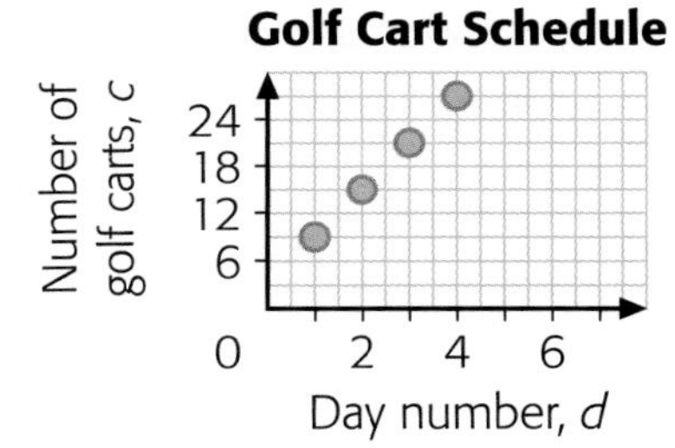

Sarah's Solution

I used the graph to create a pattern rule. I used c to represent the number of carts and d to represent the day number.
$c = 6d + ?$

The points are in a straight line, so I think the other points will be on the same line.

There are 6 more golf carts made each day.

Day, d	Value of 6d	Value from graph	Value of 6d + 3
1	6	9	9
2	12	15	15
3	18	21	21
4	24	27	27

So I used a table to compare the value of $6d$ to the value on the graph.
The values on the graph are 3 greater than the values of $6d$. I tried $c = 6d + 3$ by adding another column to the table. The values match.

$c = 6d + 3$
$= 6(15) + 3$
$= 93$

I substituted 15 into the pattern rule.
On day 15, the factory will make 93 golf carts.

Example 3 | Matching a linear relation to its graph

Match each linear relation to its graph.

Relation A: $y = 2x + 3$ Relation B: $y = 3x + 2$

Graph A

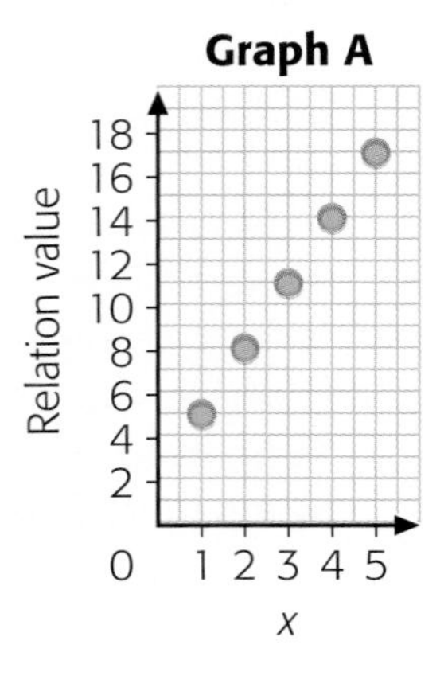

Graph B

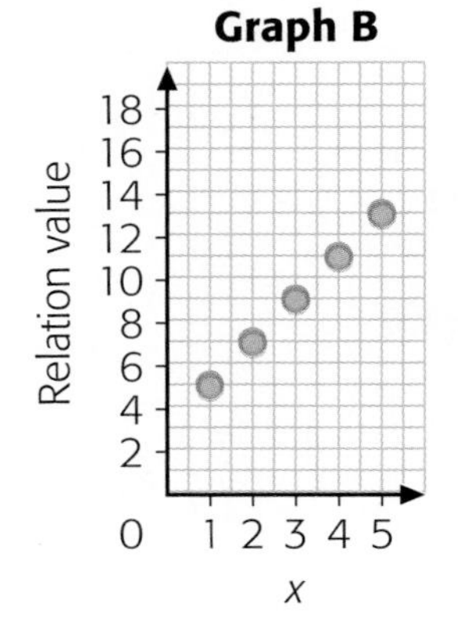

Graph C

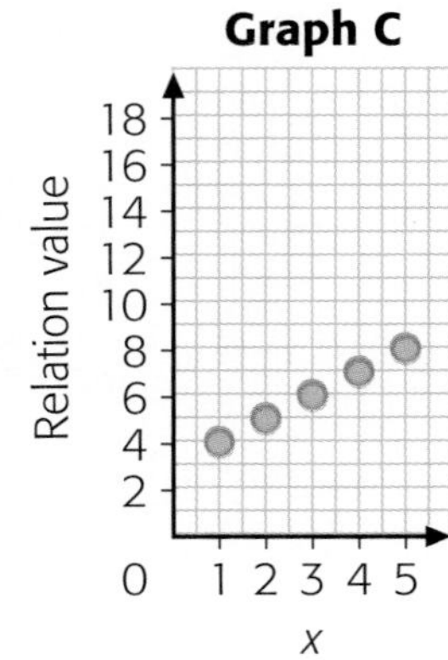

Jacob's Solution

I made a table of values for each relation.

x	2x + 3
1	5
2	7
3	9
4	11
5	13

x	3x + 2
1	5
2	8
3	11
4	14
5	17

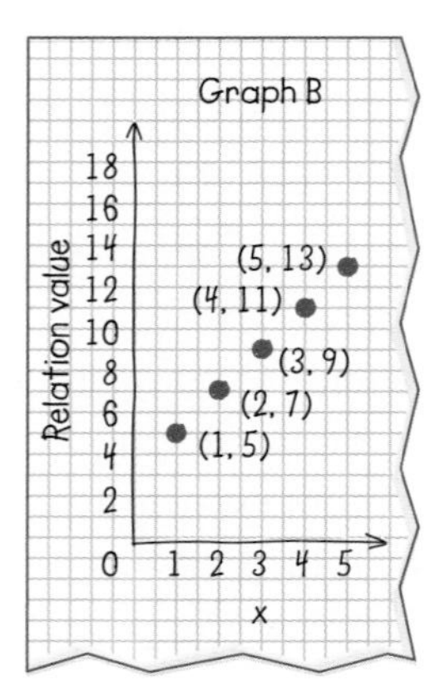

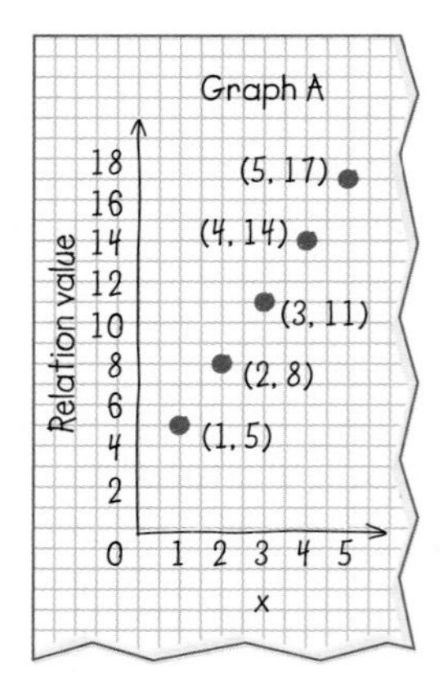

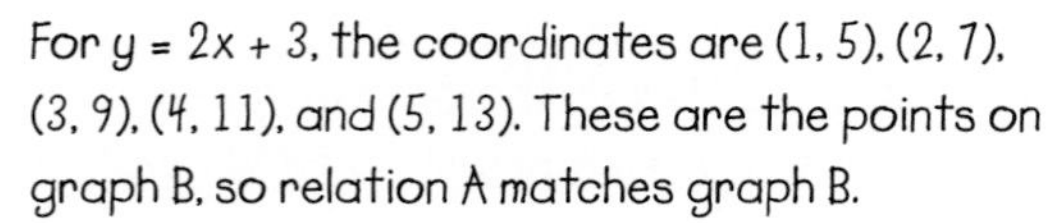

For $y = 2x + 3$, the coordinates are (1, 5), (2, 7), (3, 9), (4, 11), and (5, 13). These are the points on graph B, so relation A matches graph B.

For $y = 3x + 2$, the coordinates are (1, 5), (2, 8), (3, 11), (4, 14), and (5, 17). These are the points on graph A, so relation B matches graph A.

A Checking

1. Graph the points in this table of values.

b	1	2	3	4
$2b - 2$	0	2	4	6

2. a) Create a table of values for the relation $y = n + 3$.
b) Graph $y = n + 3$ using your table of values.

B Practising

3. Create a table of values for each linear relation.
a) $y = 3n + 1$ **b)** $y = 5n + 3$ **c)** $y = 3n + 5$

4. Graph each linear relation in question 3 using your tables of values.

5. Graph these linear relations on the same set of axes. Use a different colour for each relation.
a) $y = 2n + 5$ **c)** $y = 2n + 3$
b) $y = 2n + 7$ **d)** $y = 2n + 1$

6. How are the graphs in question 5 alike? How are they different?

7. Graph these linear relations on the same set of axes. Use a different colour for each relation.
a) $y = n + 3$ **c)** $y = 3n + 3$
b) $y = 2n + 3$ **d)** $y = 4n + 3$

8. How are the graphs in question 7 alike? How are they different?

9. Match each linear relation to its graph.
A. $y = b + 3$ **B.** $y = 2b + 4$ **C.** $y = 2b$

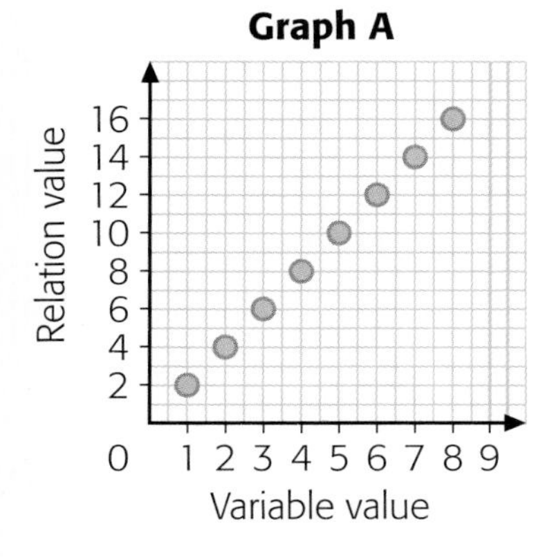

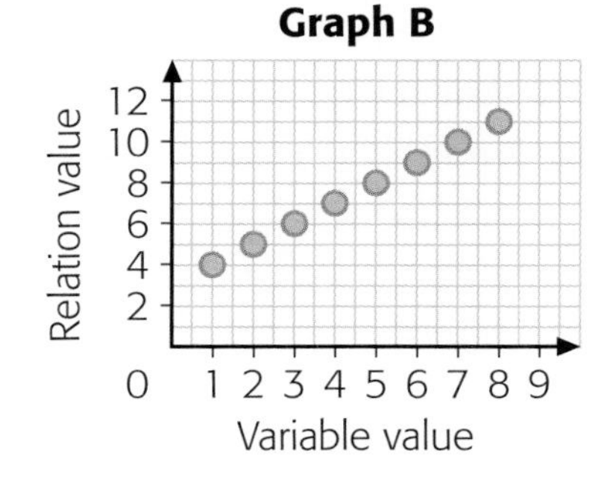

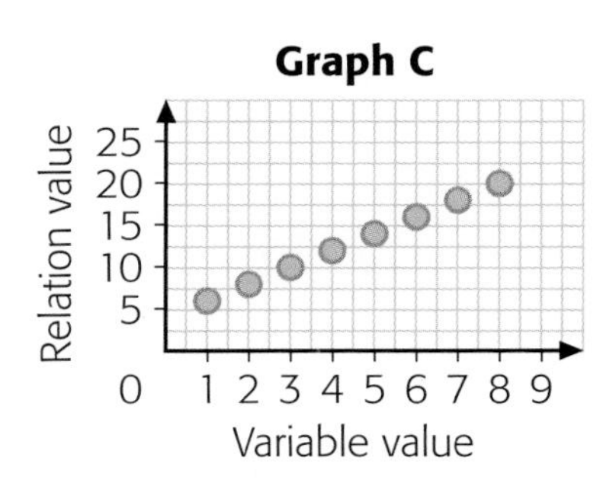

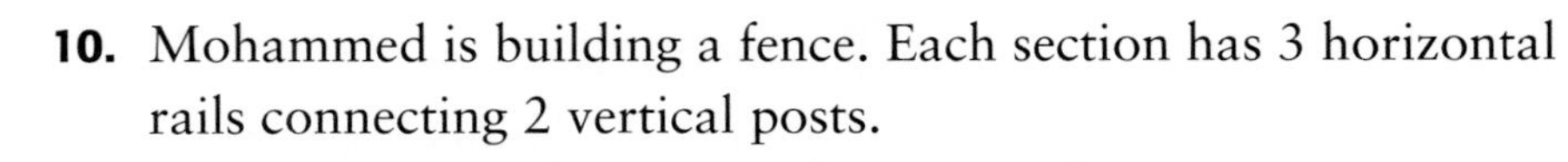

10. Mohammed is building a fence. Each section has 3 horizontal rails connecting 2 vertical posts.

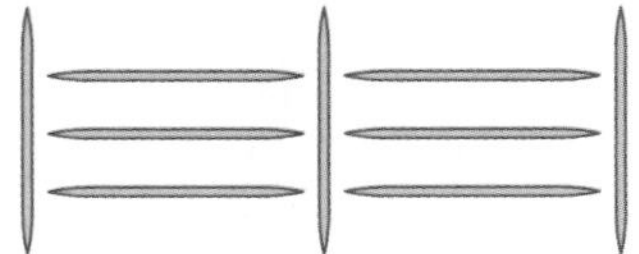

a) Write a rule for the number of rails Mohammed will need, based on the number of posts.

b) Graph the relation described by your pattern rule.

c) Mohammed's fence will have 10 posts. Determine how many rails he will need using your graph.

11. Mohammed is building another fence.

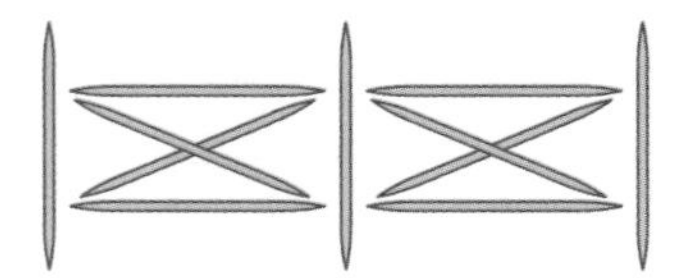

a) How is the pattern rule for this fence different from the pattern rule for the fence in question 10?

b) How are the graphs different?

12. a) Write a pattern rule to represent this toothpick pattern.

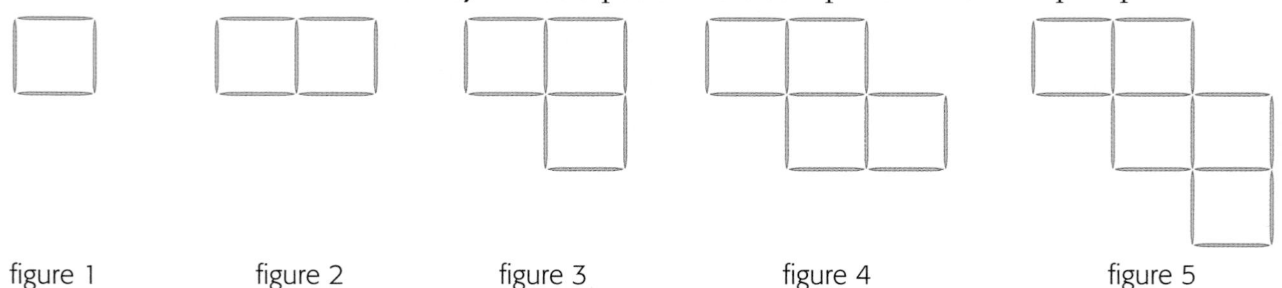

figure 1 figure 2 figure 3 figure 4 figure 5

b) Graph the relation between figure n and the number of toothpicks needed to make the figure.

13. a) Write a pattern rule for the pattern 6, 11, 16, 21, 26, … that relates each term to its term number.

b) Graph the relation between the terms and their term numbers.

14. Kaitlyn is making a flower-bed border with triangular paving stones and border pieces, like those Megan used for her path. Kaitlyn drew this graph.

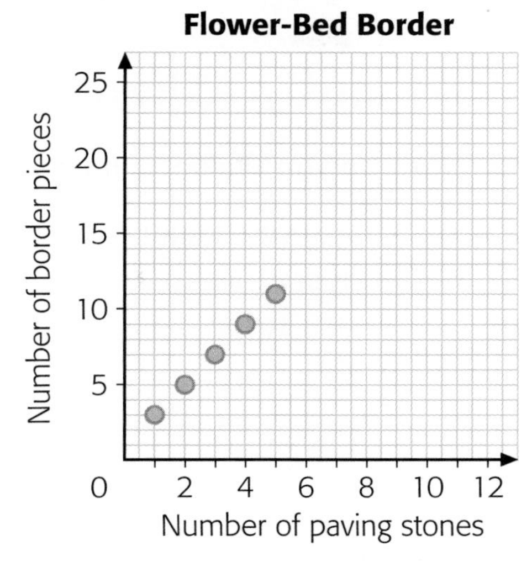

a) What relation does the graph show?

b) Write a pattern rule for this relation.

c) How can you determine the length of each border piece?

15. a) Draw a pattern of tiles that matches each rule.

A. $y = n + 5$

B. $y = 5n$

C. $y = 3n + 1$

D. $y = 2n + 3$

b) Graph each pattern rule.

c) Describe how the constant term and the numerical coefficient of the variable in each expression affect the graph and the figures in the geometric pattern.

16. A pattern rule can be written using an expression like ■x + ●. How will the graph of the rule be affected by changing the values of ■ and ●?

Chapter 9

Mid-Chapter Review

Frequently Asked Questions

Q: How do you evaluate an expression?

A: Substitute a number for the variable, and then use order of operations to calculate. For example, you can evaluate $2n + 1$ for $n = 4$ as follows:

$$\begin{aligned} 2n + 1 &= 2(4) + 1 \\ &= 8 + 1 \\ &= 9 \end{aligned}$$

Q: How do you graph a linear relation?

A: Make a table of values, and then use it to plot points on a scatter plot. One variable tells the horizontal position of the point, and the other variable tells its vertical position. For example, graph $f = 3n + 2$.

n	$3n + 2$
1	5
2	8
3	11
4	
5	17
6	

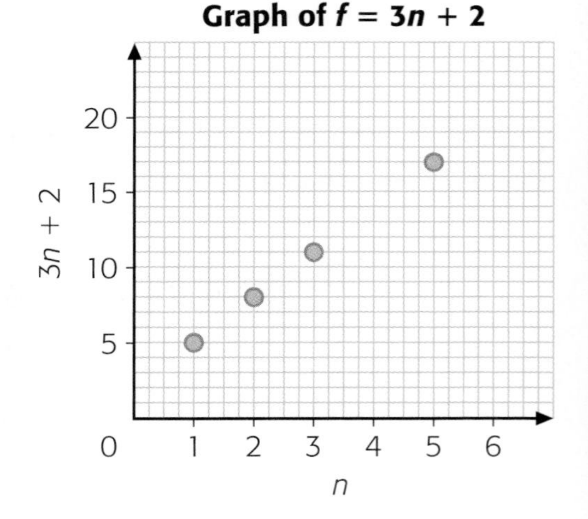

Q: How can you use the plotted points of a linear relation to determine other points of the relation?

A: Place a ruler along the plotted points. Other points in the relation will also lie on the line made by the ruler. For example, for the graph of $f = 3n + 2$, you can use a ruler to see that (4, 14) and (6, 20) are also points in the relation.

Practice

Lesson 9.1

1. Write a pattern rule using an algebraic expression for the number of tiles in any figure in this pattern.

Figure number	Picture	Number of tiles
1		3
2		6
3		9

Lesson 9.2

2. a) Draw the next two figures in this pattern.

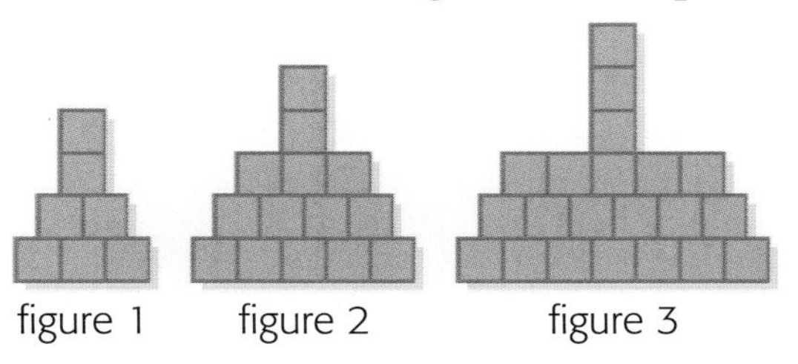

b) Write a pattern rule using an algebraic expression for the number of tiles in any figure in this pattern.

c) Predict the number of tiles used in figure 10.

3. Emma and Alex coloured the same pattern of tiles differently.

Emma's colouring: Alex's colouring:

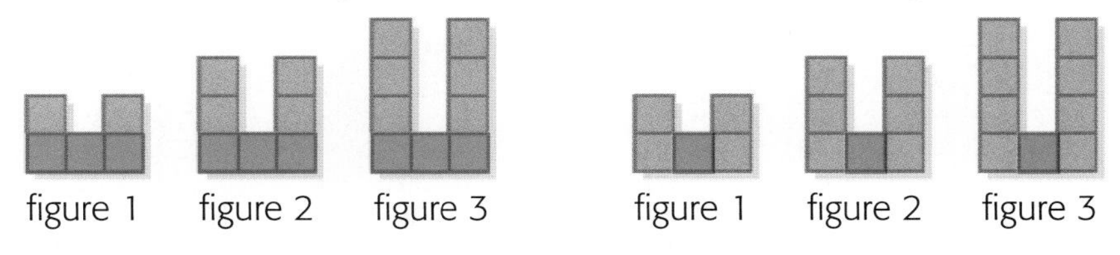

a) Write a pattern rule using an algebraic expression for each colouring.

b) Identify the constant term and the numerical coefficient in each expression.

c) Describe what the constant term and the numerical coefficient in each expression tell you about the pattern.

4. The cost to rent skates is $3, plus $2 per hour.
   a) Write an expression that tells the cost to rent skates for any number of hours.
   b) Determine the cost to rent skates for 8 h.

Lesson 9.4

5. The table of values and the graph show the relation between the hours that Erin works and her earnings. Enter the missing numbers in the table of values.

Hours worked	Dollars earned
1	
	6
3	
4	
	9
6	
7	
	12

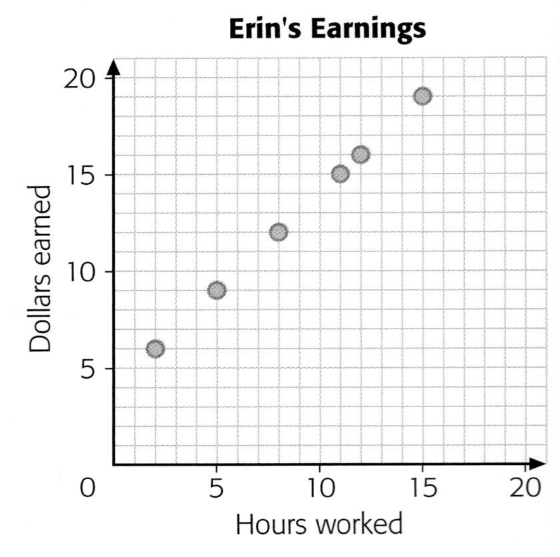

6. Graph these linear relations on the same set of axes. Use a different colour for each relation.
   a) $y = 3n + 2$ b) $y = 3n - 1$ c) $y = 3n$

7. How are the graphs in question 6 alike? How are they different?

8. a) Write a pattern rule for the number of toothpicks in each figure.

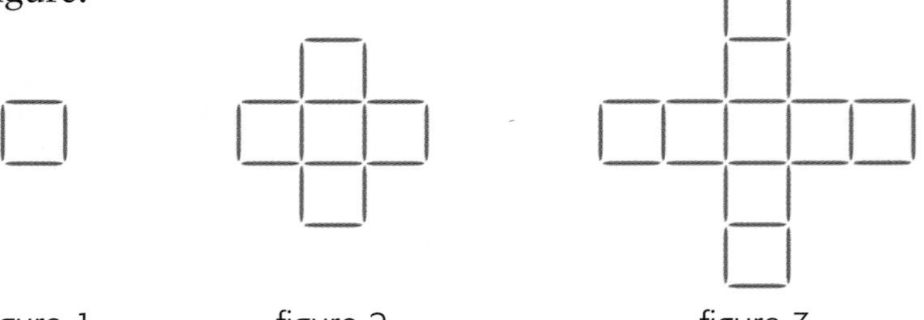

   b) Graph the relation described by the rule.
   c) Predict the number of toothpicks in figure 7 using the graph.

9.5 Solving Equations Using Mental Math

YOU WILL NEED

- toothpicks

GOAL

Solve a problem by solving a related equation.

LEARN ABOUT the Math

Megan and Oshana are building this toothpick pattern. They have 28 toothpicks.

figure 1 figure 2 figure 3

equation

a statement that two quantities or expressions are equivalent; for example, $4 + 2 = 6$ and $6x + 2 = 14$

solution to an equation

a value of a variable that makes an equation true; for example, the solution to $6x + 2 = 14$ is $x = 2$

What is the largest figure they can build?

A. Write a pattern rule for the number of toothpicks in figure n.

B. Write an **equation** to represent the problem.

C. Your equation may look like ■ × **variable** + ■ = 28. What is the value of the ■ × **variable** part?

D. What is the value of your variable?

E. Which figure has 28 toothpicks?

F. Check your **solution to the equation.**

Reflecting

G. How are your pattern rule in part A and your equation in part B alike? How are they different?

H. Think about your equation. What meaning does each part of the equation have when you connect it to the problem?

I. How did you use mental math to calculate the solution?

WORK WITH *the Math*

Example 1 | Solving a problem using an equation

Irene breeds and sells rabbits. One day, she sold half of her rabbits. Then, she sold one more. She still had 13 rabbits. How many rabbits did she have to start?

Denis's Solution

I used r to represent the number of rabbits she started with.

$\frac{r}{2} - 1 = 13$

$\frac{r}{2}$ represents the number of rabbits left after half are sold. I still need to subtract 1 for the rabbit sold later.
After all the rabbits were sold, there were 13 left.

$\frac{r}{2} = 14$

If I subtract 1 from something and get 13, I must have started with 14. This means that $\frac{r}{2}$ must equal 14.

$r = 28$

The number you divide by 2 to get 14 is 28.

Verify the solution:
Suppose that Irene started with 28 rabbits. If she sold half, she would have 14 left. If she sold 1 more, she would have 13. This matches what the problem said.

I substituted my solution back into the original problem.

The solution $r = 28$ is correct. Irene started with 28 rabbits.

Example 2 | Solving a sharing problem using an equation

Scott and his 4 friends mowed lawns together last summer. They split their earnings equally, and each person received $75. Represent the situation with an equation. Determine the total amount of money they earned using your equation.

Nayana's Solution

$\frac{m}{5} = 75$

I used m to represent the money that was shared. The friends divided the money 5 ways.

$m = 5 \times 75$

$m = 375$

The friends earned $375.

The 5 friends each got $75, so the total amount is 5 times $75.

A Checking

1. Solve. Verify your solutions.

a) $n + 6 = 13$

b) $w - 11 = 22$

c) $9p = 63$

d) $2n + 3 = 15$

e) $\frac{x}{3} = 9$

f) $\frac{y}{4} = 7$

2. Jamie wants to know which figure in this pattern has exactly 43 tiles.

figure 1

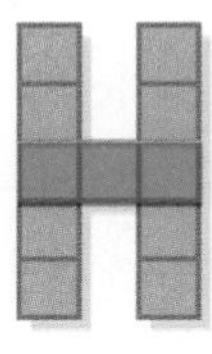

figure 2

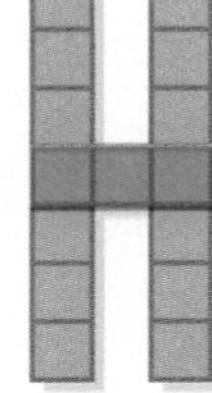

figure 3

a) Write an equation to represent Jamie's problem.

b) Solve the equation.

c) Check your solution. Show what you did.

B Practising

3. Solve each equation.

a) $7b = 84$

b) $11 = q - 4$

c) $8 + z = 30$

d) $\frac{w}{10} = 20$

e) $22 = m + 2$

f) $35 = n - 5$

4. Solve each equation.

a) $23 = 2m + 3$

b) $42 = 6a - 6$

c) $9n - 4 = 32$

d) $5n + 5 = 40$

5. a) Explain each step in this solution.

$$6 + 5m = 16$$

Step 1: $5m = 10$

Step 2: $m = 2$

b) How can you verify that the solution $m = 2$ is correct?

6. Look again at Jamie's pattern in question 2. Can you build a figure in this pattern with exactly 39 tiles? Explain.

7. a) Write a pattern rule to represent the number of tiles in each figure in this pattern.

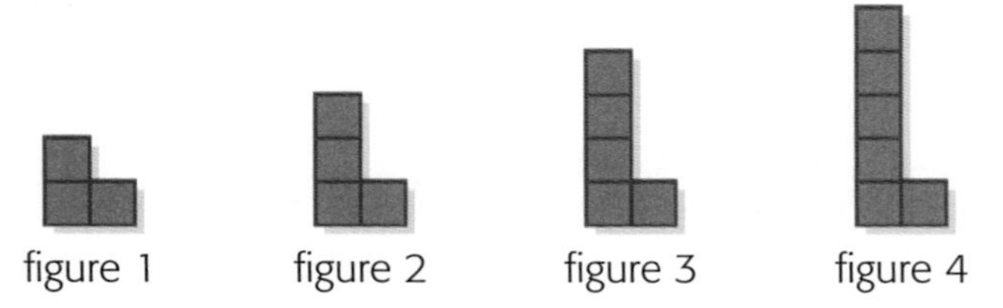

b) Albert wants to build the figure with 24 tiles in this pattern. Write an equation you can solve to determine the number of the figure with 24 tiles.

c) Solve your equation.

d) Verify your solution by drawing the figure and counting the tiles.

e) Determine which figure in this pattern has 21 tiles, using your equation. Describe the figure with 21 tiles.

8. a) Loretta wants to build the figure with 28 pattern blocks in the following pattern. Write an equation you can solve for the number of this figure.

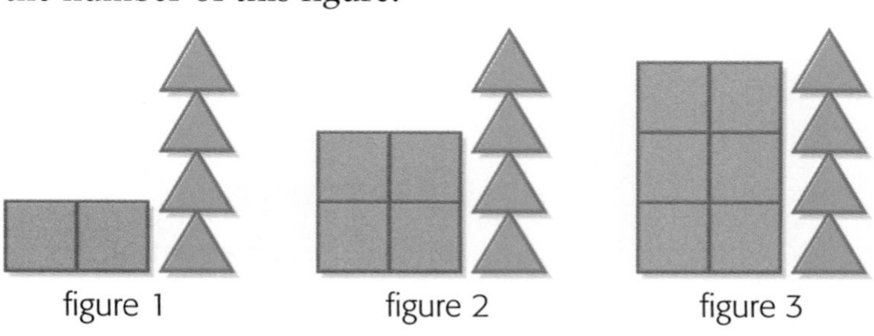

b) Solve your equation and verify your solution.

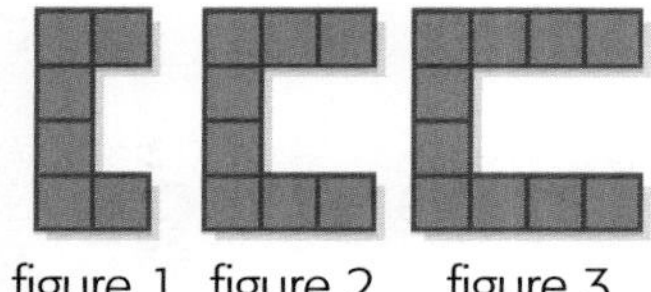
figure 1 figure 2 figure 3

9. a) Wilmer wants to build the figure with exactly 30 tiles in the pattern at the left. Write an equation you can solve for the number of the figure.

b) Solve your equation and verify your solution.

10. To rent a movie, a company charges \$2, plus \$1 per day.

a) Write a pattern rule to represent the cost, c, of renting a movie for d days.

b) Write an equation to answer the question, "If you have \$9, for how many days can you rent a movie?"

c) Solve your equation and verify your solution.

11. Susan has \$25. She is going to spend \$4 on a book, and then \$3 per day on lunch.

a) Write an equation to answer the question, "For how many days can Susan buy lunch?"

b) Solve your equation and verify your solution.

12. Kevin says to Zach, "I am thinking of a number. If you double it and then subtract 1, the result is 7."

a) Write an equation to determine Kevin's number.

b) What steps can you use to solve the equation? Explain.

13. What is the greatest number of squares you can build with 100 toothpicks using this pattern?

figure 1 figure 2 figure 3

14. What is the greatest number of triangles you can build with 100 toothpicks using this pattern?

figure 1 figure 2 figure 3 figure 4

15. Look at the linear relation ■x + ● = ◆. Suppose that you know the value each geometric symbol represents. What steps would you use to solve for x using mental math?

9.6 Solving Equations Using Models and Drawings

YOU WILL NEED

- integer tiles, coloured counters, or coloured cubes

GOAL

Model and solve problems using pictorial and concrete methods.

LEARN ABOUT the Math

Sarah showed her classmates the following number trick:

1. Pick a whole number.
2. Multiply the number by 2.
3. Add 5 to the result.

Jacob said, "My answer is 17."

Sarah used the equation $2n + 5 = 17$.
She said, "You started with 6."
She was correct.

How can you represent the steps in Sarah's solution?

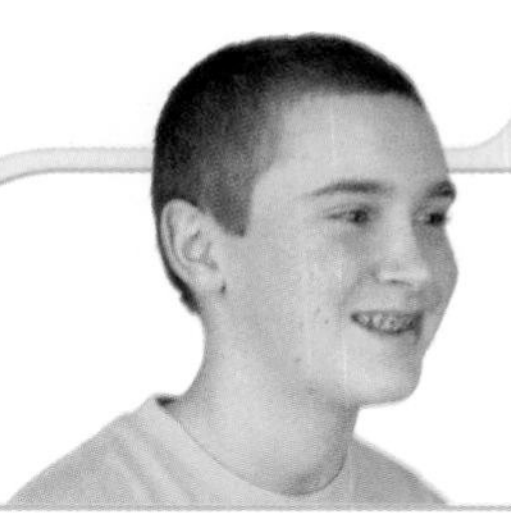

Example 1 | Using concrete materials

Represent the steps in Sarah's solution using cubes and counters.

Jacob's Solution

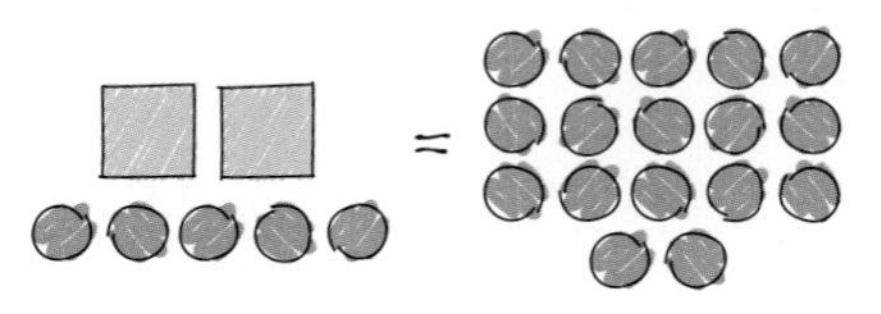

I modelled the equation. I used a [cube] to represent each n and a [counter] to represent each 1.

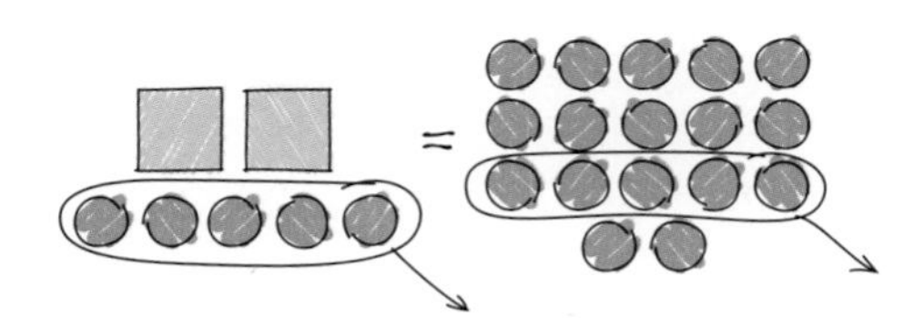

I removed 5 red counters from each side.

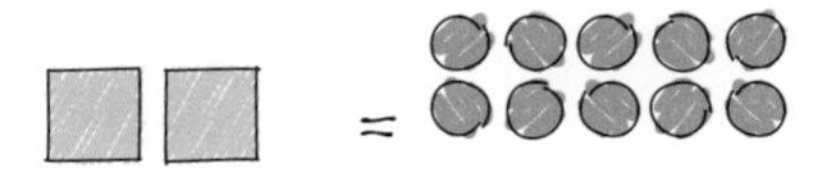

That kept the sides equal.

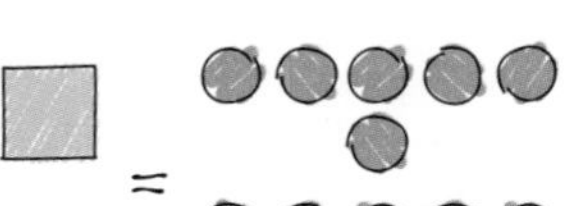

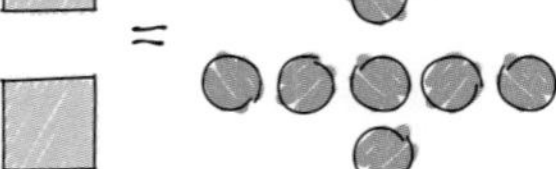

I split the pieces on each side into 2 equal groups.

There were still 2 green n cubes on the left side and 12 counters on the right.

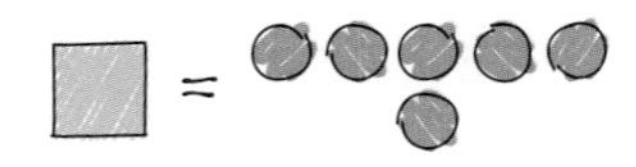

$n = 6$

Each green n cube had the same value as 6 counters.

Example 2 | Using a drawing

Represent the steps in Sarah's solution using a drawing.

Megan's Solution

n	n	5
17		

I drew identical rectangles to represent each side of the equation. Then I split one to show the two n terms and the constant term, 5.

n	n	5
12		5

The two n pieces had to have a value of $17 - 5 = 12$.

n	n	5
6	6	5

Each n had to have a value of 6.

So, $n = 6$.

Reflecting

A. How do Jacob's model and Megan's drawing show each step needed to solve the equation?

WORK WITH the Math

Example 3 | Modelling and solving integer equations

Model and solve each equation.

a) $x + (-2) = (-3)$ **b)** $x + (-2) = (+3)$ **c)** $x + (+2) = (-3)$

Solution

a) $x + (-2) = (-3)$

$x = (-1)$

b) $x + (-2) = (+3)$

$x = (+5)$

c) $x + (+2) = (-3)$

$x = (-5)$

Example 4 | Solving an equation by dividing

Tom shared his candy with 4 friends. Everyone got 3 pieces. Represent the situation with an equation.
Solve the equation to determine the number of pieces that Tom began with.

Solution

Use x to represent the total number of pieces of candy.
Draw 5 columns, because each person got $\frac{1}{5}$ of the candy.

$\frac{x}{5}$	$\frac{x}{5}$	$\frac{x}{5}$	$\frac{x}{5}$	$\frac{x}{5}$
3	3	3	3	3

Each person got 3 pieces.

The equation $\frac{x}{5} = 3$ represents the situation.

x
15

Tom began with 15 pieces of candy.

A Checking

1. Represent each equation using a drawing or a model with counters. Then solve each equation.

a) $p - 9 = 15$ **b)** $5w - 2 = 13$ **c)** $z + (-5) = (-2)$

B Practising

2. Represent and solve each equation.

a) $p + 8 = 10$ **c)** $x - 7 = 4$ **e)** $x + (-5) = (-1)$

b) $2h + 6 = 12$ **d)** $\frac{c}{6} = 2$ **f)** $y + (-4) = (-3)$

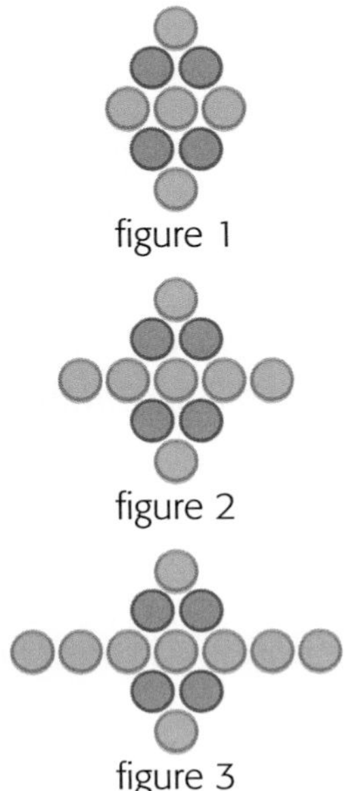
figure 1
figure 2
figure 3

3. a) Write a pattern rule for the number of counters in figure n of the pattern shown at the left.

b) Write an equation to solve the problem, "Which figure has exactly 73 counters?"

c) Solve your equation. Show what you did.

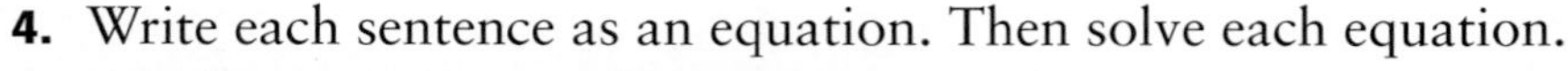

4. Write each sentence as an equation. Then solve each equation.

a) The sum of a number and 19 is 35.

b) Eight times a number is 192.

c) When you multiply a number by 9 and subtract 16, the result is 47.

5. Andrea has $73 in her bank account. She takes out $5 every week.

a) Write a linear relation to show the amount of money in Andrea's account after w weeks.

b) Write an equation to represent the number of weeks before Andrea has $58 left in her account.

c) Solve your equation. Show what you did.

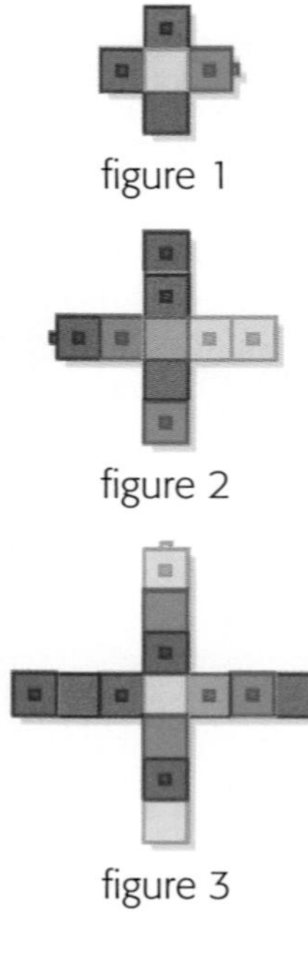

figure 1

figure 2

figure 3

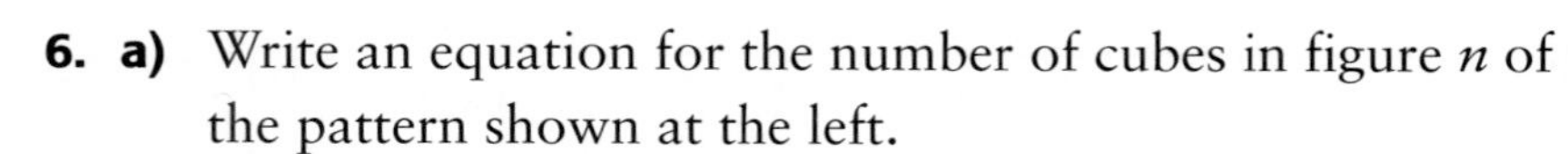

6. a) Write an equation for the number of cubes in figure n of the pattern shown at the left.

b) Which figure has exactly 25 cubes?

c) Does any figure have exactly 16 cubes? Explain.

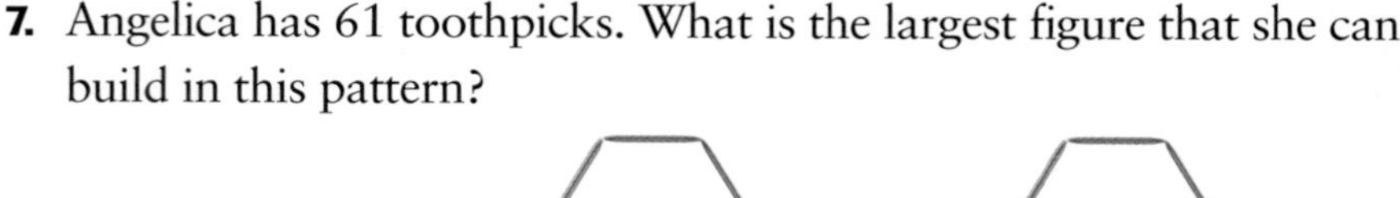

7. Angelica has 61 toothpicks. What is the largest figure that she can build in this pattern?

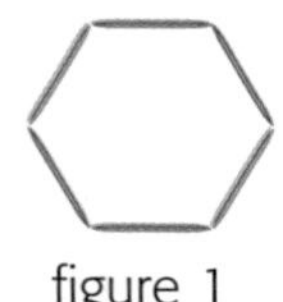

figure 1

figure 2

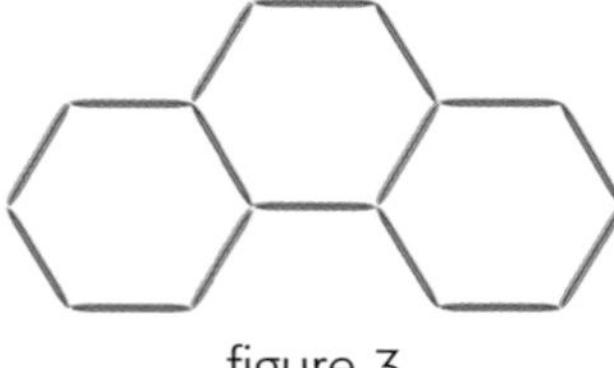

figure 3

8. A computer program gives the output shown for the inputs 1 to 3.

Input	1	2	3	4	5	6	7	8	9	10
Output	7	13	19							

a) Write the calculation rule that the program uses.

b) Write an equation to answer the question, "What input will give an output of 61?"

c) Solve the equation. Show what you did.

9. Suppose that you have to solve an equation. When is it better to use a drawing to represent the solution? When is it better to use concrete materials, such as counters?

MATH GAME

The Number Game

The goal is to guess what expression another player has made.

Number of players: 2 to 4

How to Play

1. Take turns being the Rule Maker. The Rule Maker writes an expression with one variable, but does not show it to the other players.
2. The Rule Maker asks a player for a number. The Rule Maker substitutes this number into the expression and tells the result. The player who gave the number then tries to figure out the rule.
3. If the rule is incorrect, the Rule Maker asks the next player for a number.
4. The Rule Maker continues to ask for numbers until a player figures out the rule.
5. Play until everyone has been the Rule Maker. The player with the greatest score wins.

Scoring

1. The Rule Maker receives 1 point for each incorrect rule.
2. The player who figures out the rule receives the same number of points as the Rule Maker for that round, plus 10 extra points.

Oshana's Turn

Nayana was the Rule Maker.
Denis said 2, and the result was 7. Denis's rule was incorrect.
Jacob said 3, and the result was 9. Jacob's rule was incorrect.
Then it was my turn.
I said 4, and the result was 11.
I figured out that the expression was $2n + 3$. I was right!
Nayana got 2 points, and I got $2 + 10 = 12$ points.

9.7 Solving Equations by Graphing

YOU WILL NEED
- grid paper
- a ruler

GOAL

Model and solve problems using tables of values and graphs.

LEARN ABOUT the Math

Every week, Denis deposited \$2 in his bank account. On his birthday, he deposited an extra \$15. His new bank balance was \$105.

How many deposits did Denis make?

Example 1 | Using a table of values

Determine how many deposits Denis made using a table of values.

Ryan's Solution

I used d to represent the number of deposits.
$2d + 15 = 105$

I wrote an equation to represent the problem.

Guess for d	Value (\$)	Comment
43	101	too low
46	107	too high
45	105	correct

I made a table of values for $2d + 15 = 105$.

I tried values for d until I got the correct answer.

I knew that d had to be less than 50 since $100 + 15$ is more than 105. So, I started with $d = 43$.

Denis made 45 deposits.

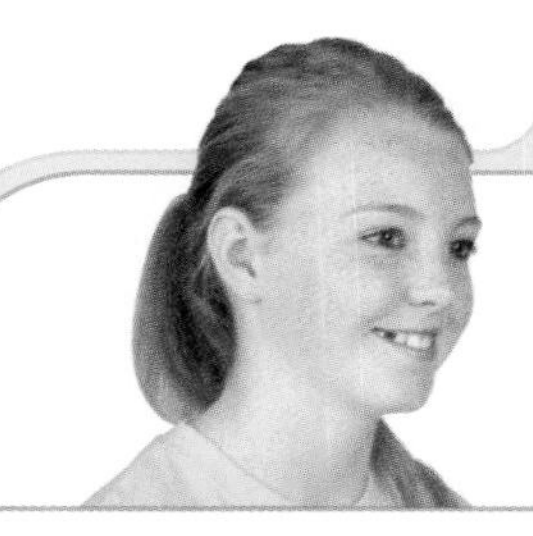

Example 2 | Drawing a graph

Determine how many deposits Denis made using a graph.

Sarah's Solution

d	2d + 15
10	35
20	55
30	75
40	95

I made a table of values.

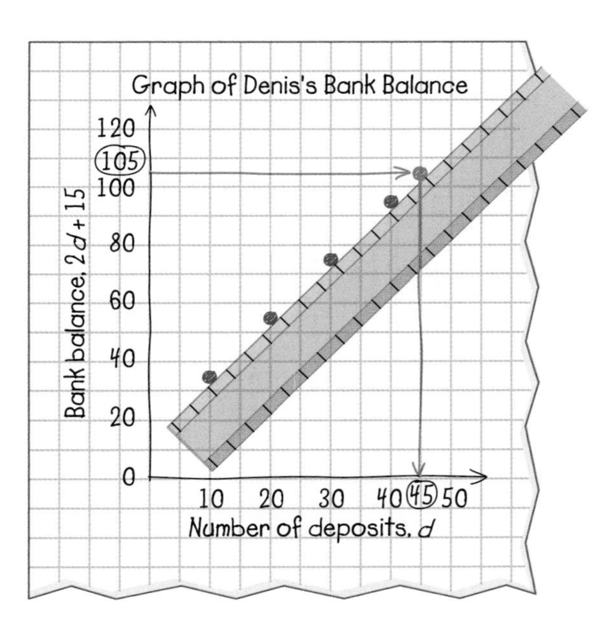

Then, I graphed the points.

The balance was $105, so I drew a line from 105 across the graph. I put the ruler along the plotted points and looked for the intersection. I drew a new point there.

I drew a line down from the new point on the graph.

The line met the *d*-axis at 45.

Denis made 45 deposits.

Reflecting

A. How does Sarah's method of drawing a horizontal line and then a vertical line solve the equation?

WORK WITH *the Math*

Example 3 | Solving a patterning problem

Determine which figure in this pattern has exactly 39 tiles, using a graph.

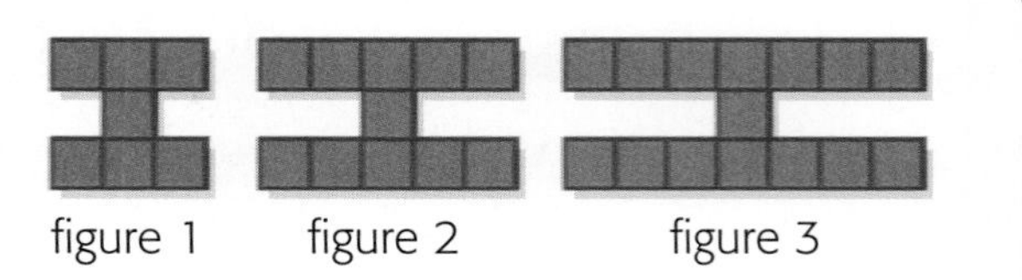

Solution

Use n to represent the figure number.

Figure number (term number)	Number of tiles (term value)
1	7
2	11
3	15
4	19
n	$4n + 3$

(+4 between each successive term value)

Figure 9 has 39 tiles.

Graph the pattern rule $4n + 3$.

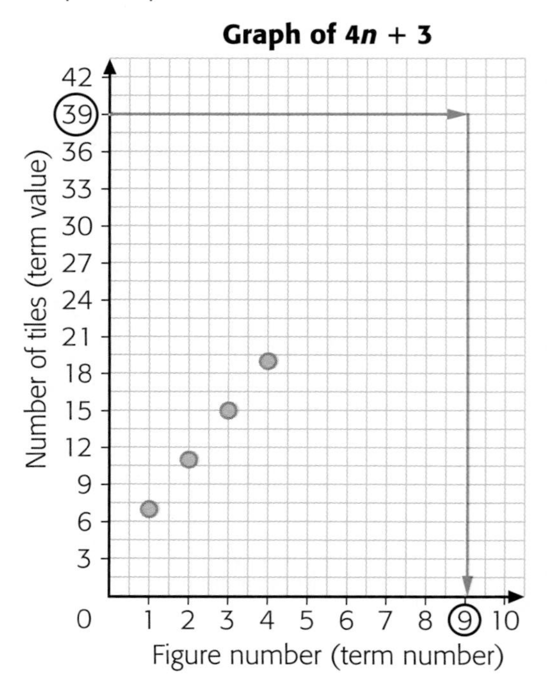

A Checking

1. Solve $2n + 3 = 17$ using the graph.

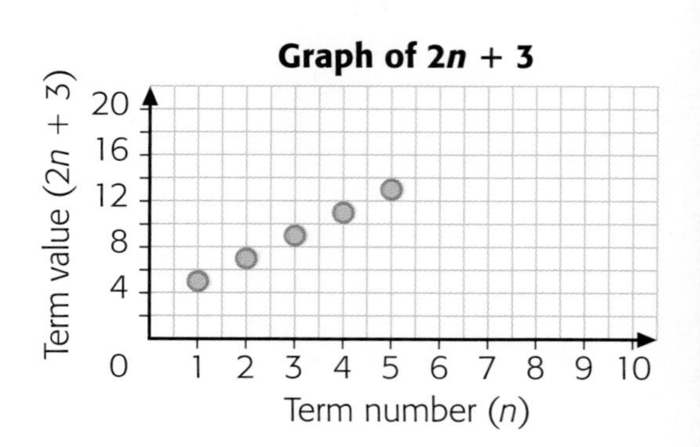

B Practising

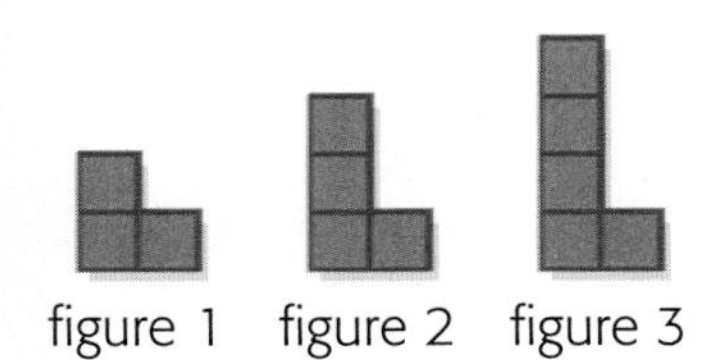

2. a) Make a table of values for the pattern at the left.
   b) Write a pattern rule for the number of tiles in each figure.
   c) Write an equation to determine which figure has 22 tiles.
   d) Solve your equation.

3. a) Make a table of values for this pattern.

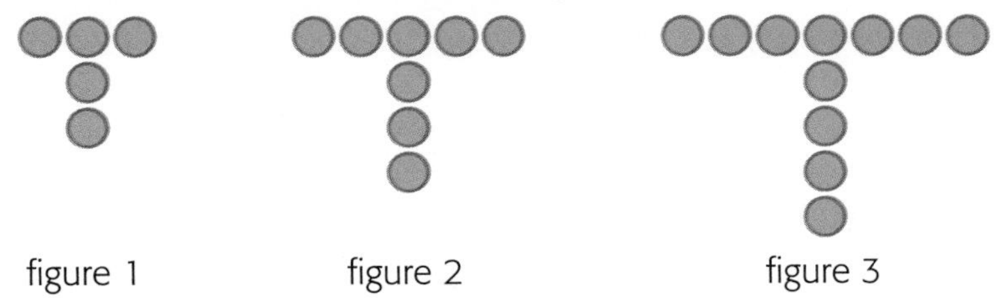

   b) Write a pattern rule for the number of counters in each figure.
   c) Write an equation to determine which figure has 23 counters.
   d) Solve your equation.

4. This graph shows David's bank balance.

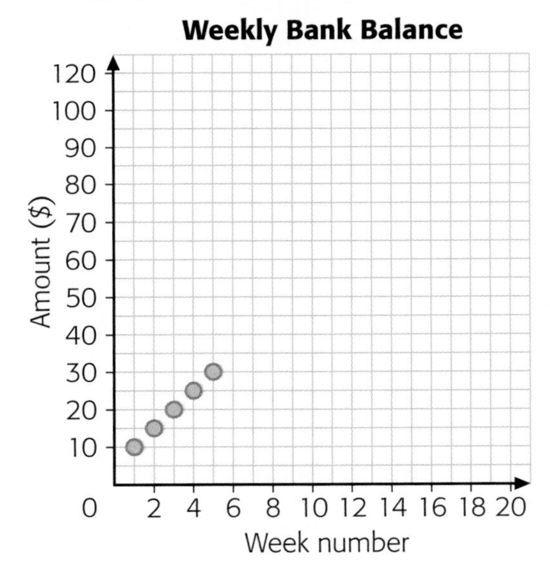

   a) Make a table of values from the graph.
   b) Create a pattern rule to represent David's bank balance at w weeks.
   c) Write an equation to determine when his bank balance is $60.
   d) Solve your equation.
   e) When will David's bank balance be $100?
   f) What will it be after 20 weeks?

5. Which figure in each pattern has exactly 97 toothpicks?

a)

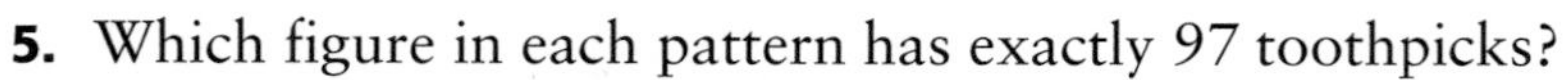

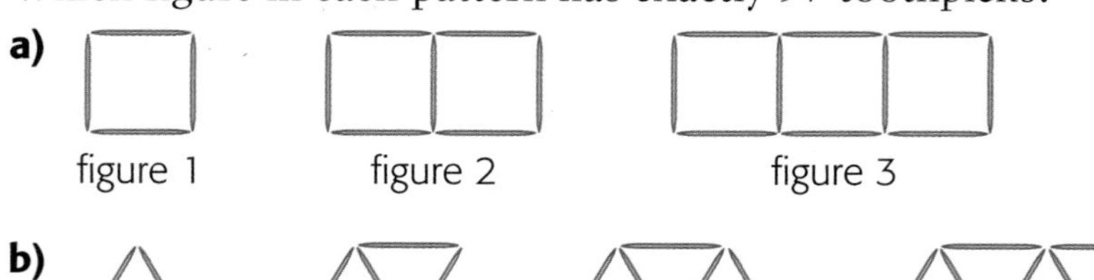

b)

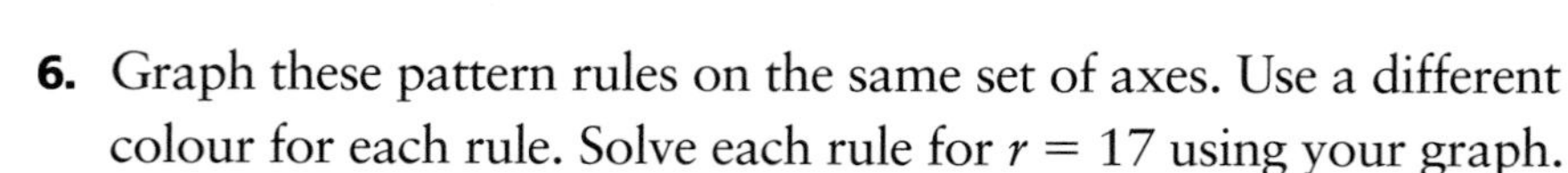

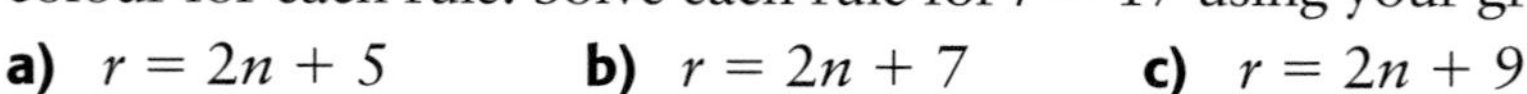

6. Graph these pattern rules on the same set of axes. Use a different colour for each rule. Solve each rule for $r = 17$ using your graph.

a) $r = 2n + 5$ **b)** $r = 2n + 7$ **c)** $r = 2n + 9$

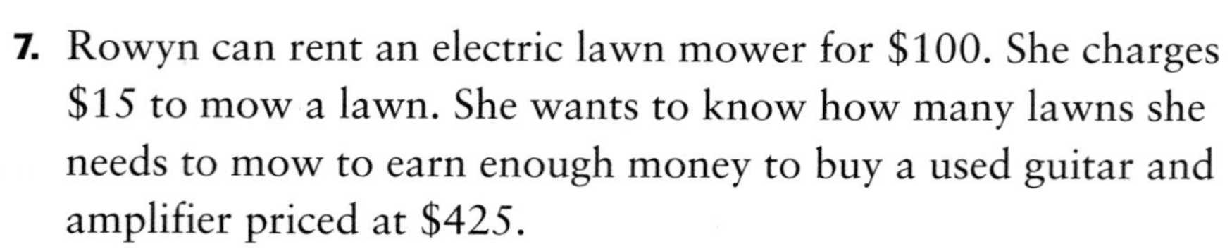

7. Rowyn can rent an electric lawn mower for \$100. She charges \$15 to mow a lawn. She wants to know how many lawns she needs to mow to earn enough money to buy a used guitar and amplifier priced at \$425.

a) Graph this situation. Put the number of lawns Rowyn might mow on the horizontal axis and the amount she will earn on the vertical axis.

b) Write an expression that relates Rowyn's earnings to the number of lawns she mows.

c) Solve an equation to determine how many lawns Rowyn needs to mow.

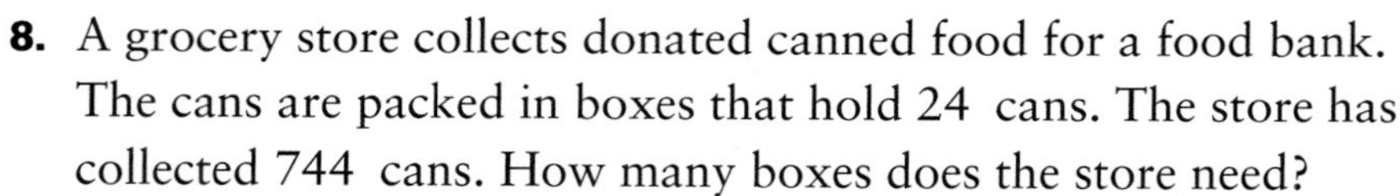

8. A grocery store collects donated canned food for a food bank. The cans are packed in boxes that hold 24 cans. The store has collected 744 cans. How many boxes does the store need?

a) Graph this situation. Put the number of boxes on the horizontal axis and the number of cans on the vertical axis.

b) Determine the number of boxes needed using your graph.

c) Write an expression to relate the number of boxes needed to the number of cans.

d) Solve an equation to determine the number of boxes needed.

e) You have solved this problem in two ways. How else could you have solved it?

9. Suppose that an equation looks like ■x + ● = 12. Describe how you could use the graph of y = ■x + ● to solve the equation.

9.8 Communicate the Solution of an Equation

YOU WILL NEED
- counters
- lightweight containers

GOAL

Use models, words, and symbols to record and explain the steps in solving an equation.

LEARN ABOUT the Math

Jacob is using a drawing to represent the steps needed to solve $4n + 3 = 15$. Megan is asking questions to help Jacob improve his explanation.

How can Jacob improve his explanation?

Jacob's Explanation

I represented the equation with a picture of a balance scale.

I represented each step in the solution with more pictures.

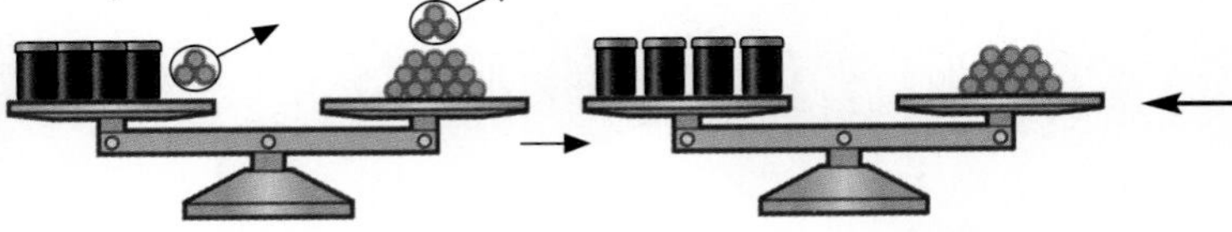

This picture represents
$4n + 3 - 3 = 15 - 3$.

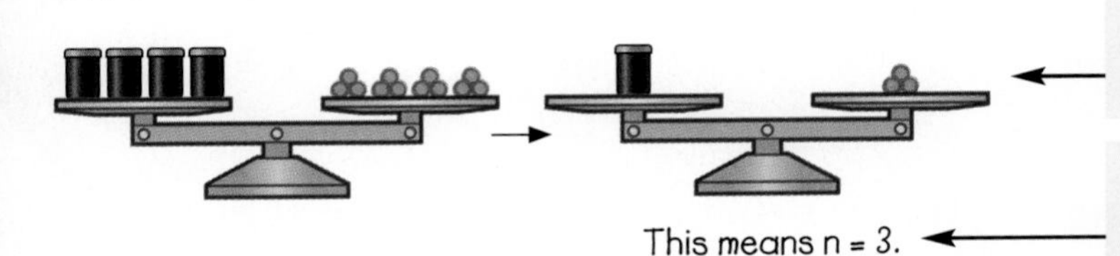

This means $n = 3$.

Megan's Questions

How did you know what to put on each side of the balance scale?

Why did you subtract the 3 counters from each side first?

What does this drawing represent?

What step did you use to go from $4n = 12$ to $n = 3$? You didn't explain it.

How can you show that your solution is correct?

Communication Checklist

- ✔ Did you show each step in your reasoning?
- ✔ Did you use a model or picture to illustrate or justify your reasoning?
- ✔ Did you record your solution using mathematical symbols?
- ✔ Did you use words and pictures that were clear and correct?

A. Use Megan's questions and comments to improve Jacob's explanation.

B. What parts of the Communication Checklist did Megan deal with in her questions?

Reflecting

C. How does using a balance model make Jacob's explanation easier to understand?

D. Suppose that Jacob had used a real balance scale, real containers, and real counters to demonstrate his solution. Why might his demonstration not work out exactly?

E. Which part of Jacob's solution was most difficult to explain? Why?

***WORK WITH** the Math*

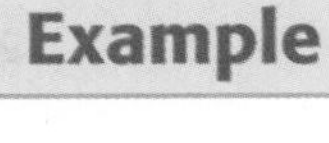

Example | Illustrating the solution of an equation

The same number of counters is in each bag. How many counters are in each bag? Explain your solution.

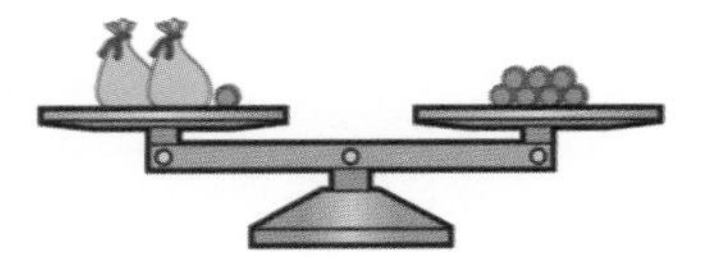

Megan's Solution: Using a balance model

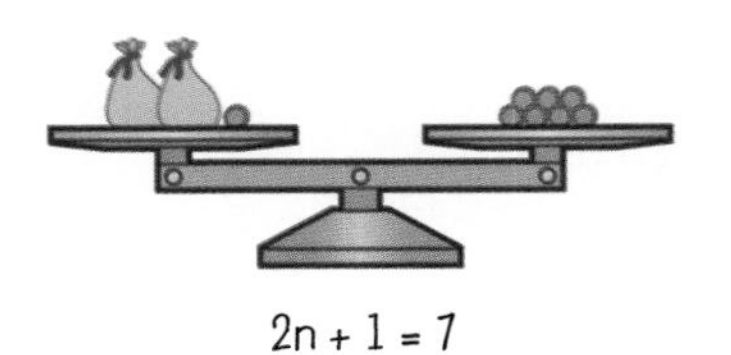

$2n + 1 = 7$

I wrote the balance problem as an equation.

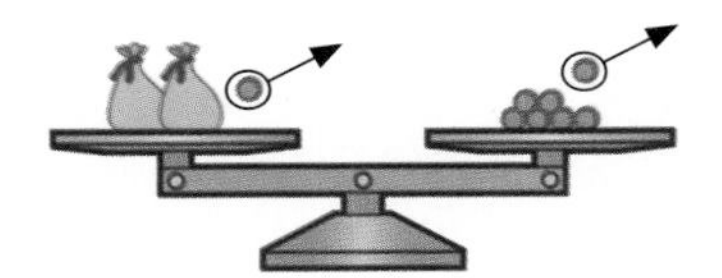

I imagined removing the counter from the left pan.
I had to remove 1 counter from the right pan to keep the scale balanced.

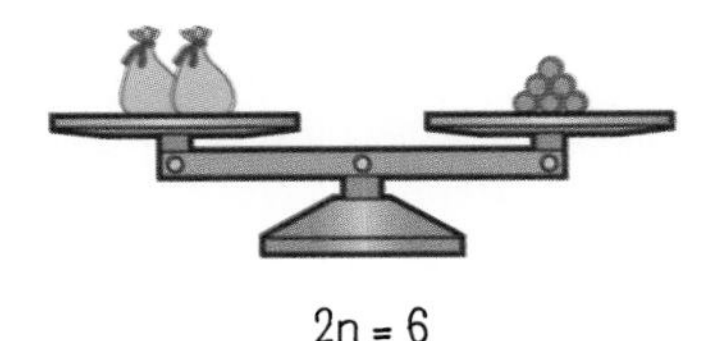

$2n = 6$

This made the equation $2n = 6$.

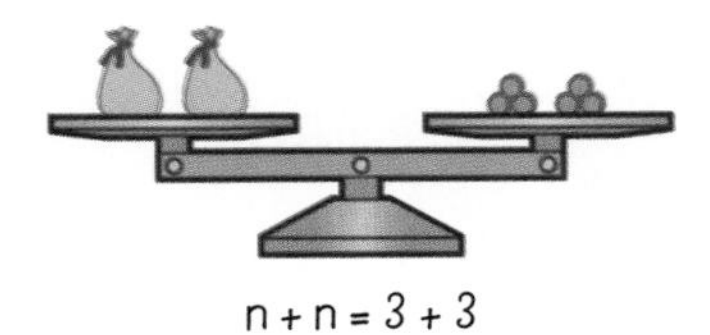

$n + n = 3 + 3$

I regrouped the counters on the right pan into 2 equal groups.

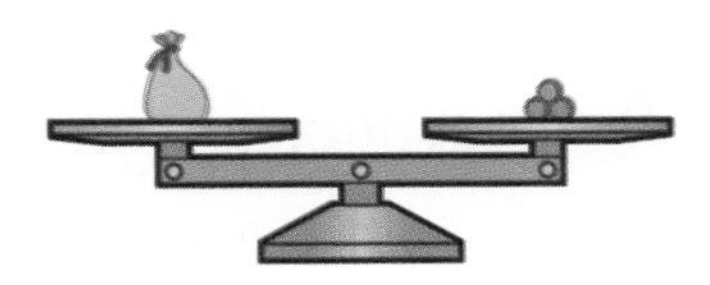

$n = 3$

Each bag contains 3 counters.

Each container is balanced by 3 counters.

A Checking

1. Use a balance model and the Communication Checklist to improve this solution.

$$3c + 1 = 10$$

Step 1: $3c = 9$

Step 2: $c = 3$

B Practising

2. Draw a balance model to illustrate each step used to solve this problem.

$$4c = 12$$

$$c + c + c + c = 3 + 3 + 3 + 3$$

$$c = 3$$

3. Write and solve an equation for each balance problem. Explain each step.

a)

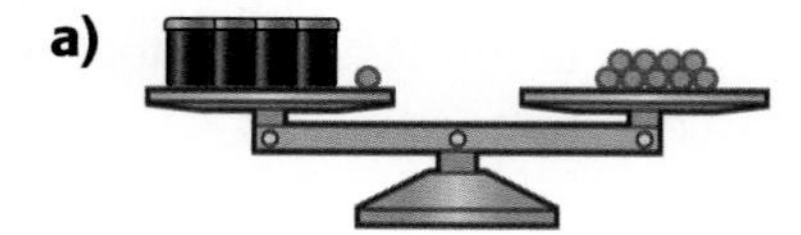

b)

c)

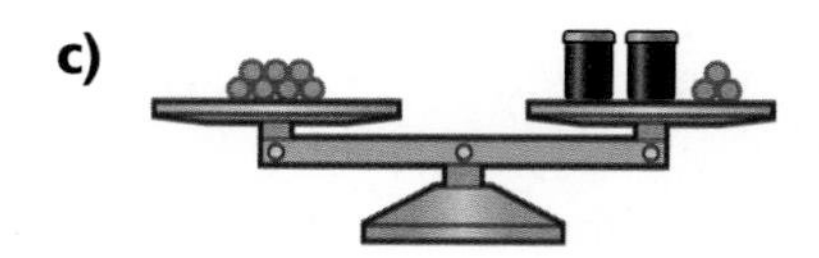

4. Solve each equation. Explain each step.

a) $3x + 5 = 11$

b) $x + (-5) = (-1)$

c) $2z = 8$

d) $\frac{a}{5} = 10$

e) $(-8) = b + (+3)$

f) $19 = 4b + 3$

5. Why is it important to explain your steps clearly when describing how you solved an equation?

Chapter 9

Chapter Self-Test

1. Write a rule for this pattern.

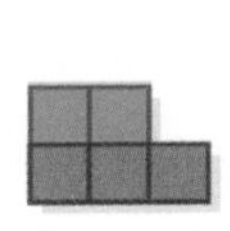
figure 1

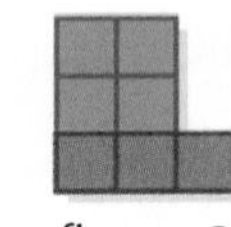
figure 2

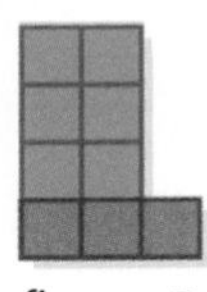
figure 3

2. A membership in a store's book club costs \$10. Members can buy paperbacks for \$6 each.
   a) Write an expression for the cost of paperbacks for a book club member, including the cost of a membership.
   b) Write the equation that you should solve to determine the number of books a member can buy for \$106.
   c) Solve your equation. Show each step.

Graph of $3n + 7$

$3n + 7$: 60, 50, 40, 30, 20, 10

n: 0, 5, 10, 15

3. Evaluate $9a + 7$ for $a = 5$. Show your work.

4. Solve $5a + 2 = 17$. Show each step.

5. Solve $3n + 7 = 52$ using the graph at the left.

6. Which figure in this pattern has exactly 161 counters?

figure 1

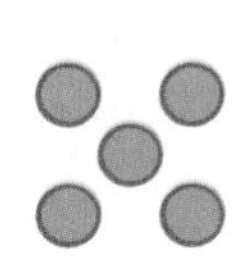
figure 2

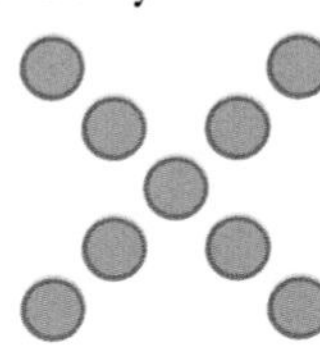
figure 3

7. Solve each equation. Explain each step.
   a) $6x = 78$
   b) $n + (-2) = (+5)$
   c) $6p + 1 = 19$
   d) $\frac{r}{5} = 10$

What Do You Think Now?

Revisit What Do You Think? on page 375. How have your answers and explanations changed?

Chapter Review

Frequently Asked Questions

Q: What is the difference between an expression and an equation?

A:

An expression ...	**An equation ...**
... is like a word phrase.	... is like a word sentence.
... may contain one or more operations but does not have an equal sign.	... may contain one or more operations and does have an equal sign.
... can be evaluated by substituting a number for each variable and then calculating.	... can be solved by determining the values of the variables that make the equation true.
Examples: $3n$, $b + 4$, $2p - 7$	Examples: $3n = 6$, $b + 4 = 13$, $2p - 7 = 37$

Q: How can you solve an equation?

A1: You can use mental math and reason out the solution by working backward. For example, to solve $26 = 3b + 5$, you can reason as follows:

- Since you add 5 to $3b$ to get 26, $3b$ must be 21.
- Three times a number is 21, so the number must be 7.
- Verify your answer by substituting the value you got for the variable into the original equation. Both sides of the equation should have the same value. If not, try again.

$$26 = 3b + 5$$
$$21 = 3b$$
$$7 = b$$

Verify.

Left side:	Right side:
26	$3b + 5$
	$= 3(7) + 5$
	$= 21 + 5$
	$= 26$ ✔

A2: You can illustrate each step with a model or drawing. For example, to solve $3n + 2 = 17$, you can use a balance model.

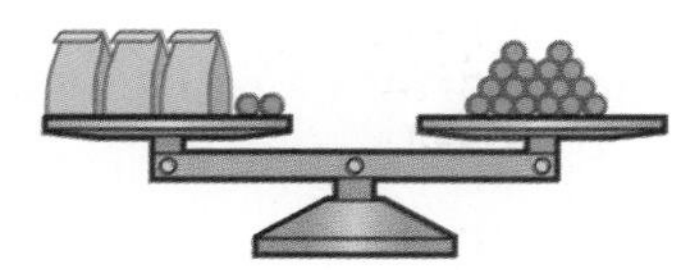

n represents the number of counters in each bag.
$3n + 2 = 17$

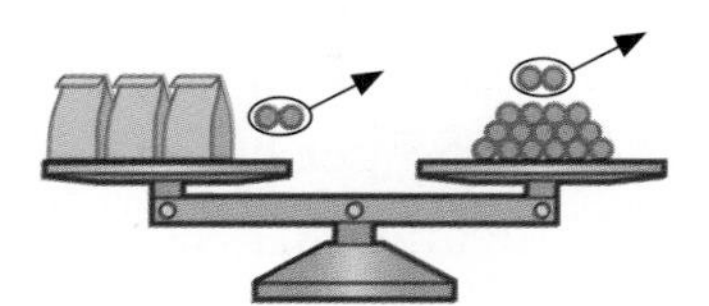

$3n + 2 - 2 = 17 - 2$

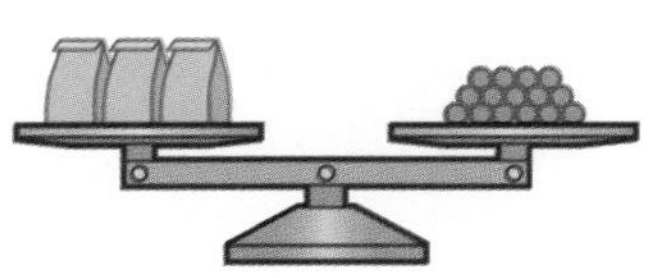

$3n = 15$

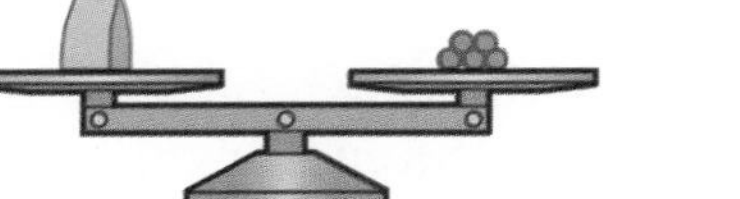

$n = 5$

Each bag contains 5 counters.

A3: You can use a table of values and a graph. For example, to solve $2x + 3 = 25$, make a table of values. The coordinates of the points are (1, 5), (4, 11), and (7, 17). Plot these points.

x	1	4	7
$2x + 3$	5	11	17

Draw a line from 25 on the vertical axis. Place a ruler beside the dots. Put a dot where the ruler and the 25 line meet. Draw a line down from this point to the horizontal axis. The value on the horizontal axis is the solution. From the graph, $x = 11$.

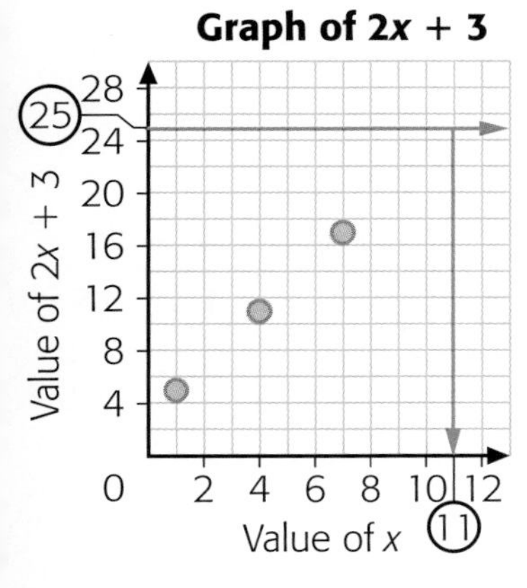

Practice

Lesson 9.1

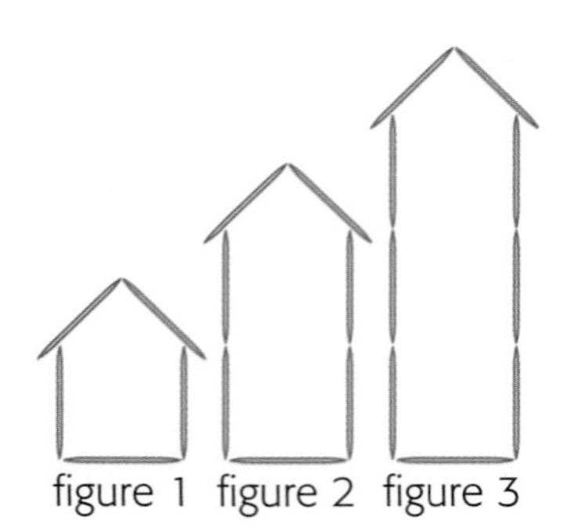

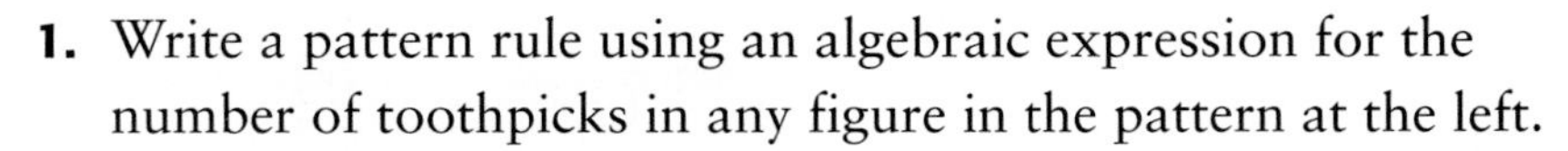
1. Write a pattern rule using an algebraic expression for the number of toothpicks in any figure in the pattern at the left.

Lesson 9.2

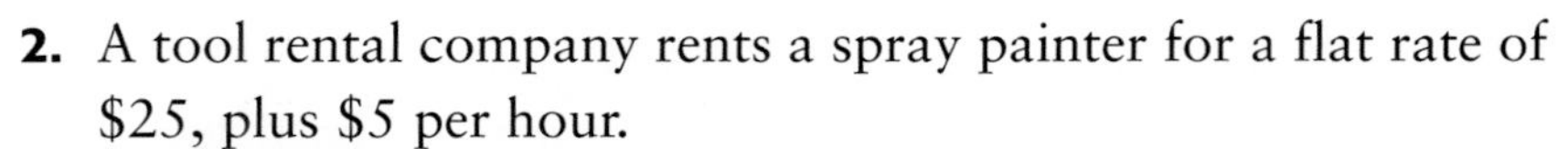
2. A tool rental company rents a spray painter for a flat rate of \$25, plus \$5 per hour.

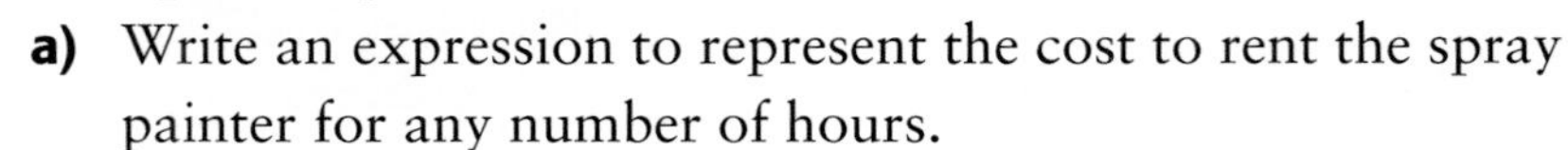
   a) Write an expression to represent the cost to rent the spray painter for any number of hours.
   b) Determine the cost to rent the spray painter for 9 h.

Lesson 9.4

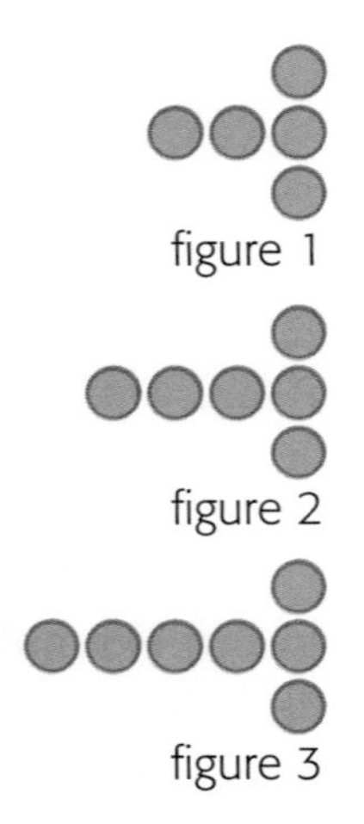

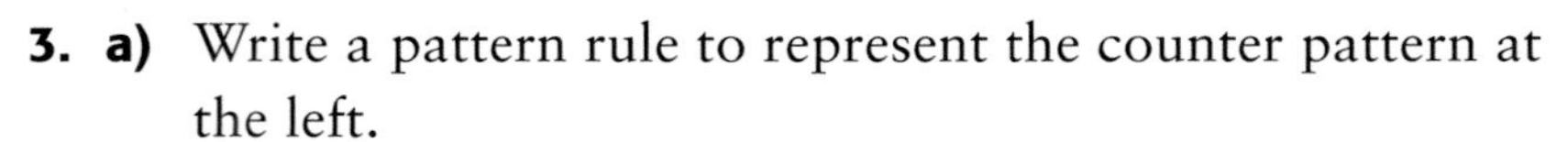
3. **a)** Write a pattern rule to represent the counter pattern at the left.
   b) Graph the relation that the rule represents.
   c) Determine the number of counters in figure 5 using your graph.

Lesson 9.5

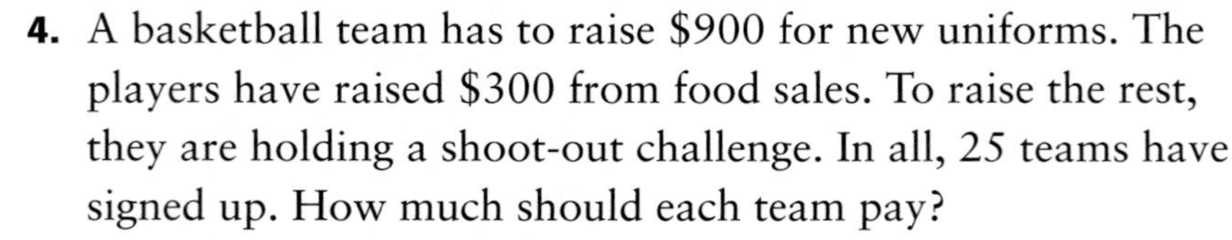
4. A basketball team has to raise \$900 for new uniforms. The players have raised \$300 from food sales. To raise the rest, they are holding a shoot-out challenge. In all, 25 teams have signed up. How much should each team pay?

   a) Create an equation to represent this problem.
   b) Solve your equation using mental math.
   c) Check your solution. Show what you did.

Lesson 9.6

5. Solve each equation.

a) $2x + 1 = 13$	**c)** $4w + 3 = 15$	**e)** $2w + 8 = 24$
b) $3a + 4 = 19$	**d)** $c + (+3) = (-5)$	**f)** $3x + 10 = 25$

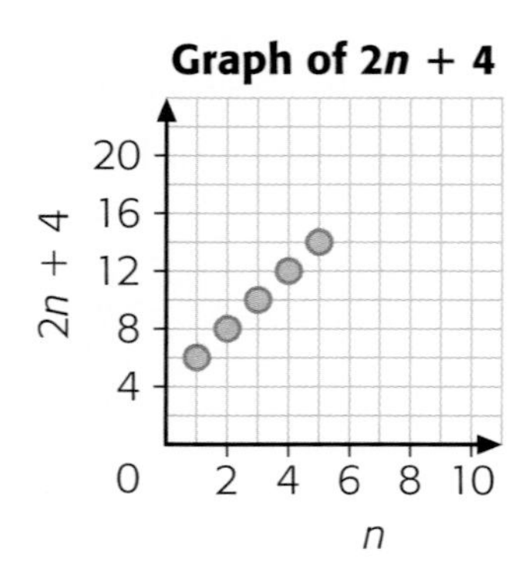

Lesson 9.7

6. Solve $2n + 4 = 20$ using the graph. Explain what you did.

Chapter Task

Task | Checklist

- ✔ Did your drawings show clearly how your pattern worked?
- ✔ Did you record your solution using mathematical symbols?
- ✔ Did you check your equation and your solution?
- ✔ Did you show each step in your reasoning?
- ✔ Did you make sure that your solution was clear and easy to understand?

Names, Patterns, and Equations

In art class, students are making mosaic tile patterns based on the initials in their names.

What patterns can you create using one of your initials as a starting figure?

A. Build one of the letters in your name using linking cubes or coloured square tiles. (This will be the starting figure in your pattern.)

B. Write a rule that tells the number of tiles needed for each figure in your pattern. Use the rule to build the next two figures in your pattern.

C. Use colour to show which parts of your pattern rule change with every figure and which part stays the same.

D. Pose a question about your pattern that can be answered by solving an equation. Write the equation.

E. Solve the equation to answer your question. Illustrate each step in your solution with a drawing or model.

F. Show that your solution to the equation is correct.

1
2
3
5
6
7
8
9
10
11
12

Chapter 10

Probability

GOAL

You will be able to

- conduct probability experiments
- describe probabilities using ratios, fractions, and percents
- determine all the possible outcomes for a probability experiment using a tree diagram, an organized list, or a table
- compare theoretical and experimental probabilities

Suppose that you are conducting probability experiments. What is the probability of getting a 6 in each experiment?

Getting Started

YOU WILL NEED
- 2 six-sided dice
- counters

In this chapter, assume that a die is a cube numbered 1 to 6, unless it is described differently.

Lucky Seven

Matthew and Fiona are playing Lucky Seven.

Is Lucky Seven a fair game?

Lucky Seven Rules

1. Play with a partner.
2. Place eight counters in a pile between you.
3. Each of you rolls a die.
4. If the sum of the two dice is 5, 6, 7, or 8, Player 1 gets a counter. If the sum is any other number, Player 2 gets a counter.
5. The winner is the player with the most counters after eight rounds.

A. Play Lucky Seven with a partner. Decide who is Player 1 and who is Player 2. Play two rounds. Record the results.

Roll sum	Player 1	Player 2
7	✓	
10		✓

The ✓ shows which player won a counter.

B. Predict which is true:
- Player 1 is more likely to win.
- Player 2 is more likely to win.
- The two players are equally likely to win.

C. Roll another six times. Record who wins.

D. You have now rolled eight times. Record the **probability** of each player winning a counter as a ratio in the form number of counters won : number of rolls.

E. Combine your results with the results of two other pairs. Use the combined data to write a ratio for the probability of Player 1 winning a counter.

F. Use the combined data to write a ratio for the probability of Player 2 winning a counter.

G. How accurate was your prediction in part B? Is Lucky Seven a fair game? Explain why or why not.

What Do You Think?

Decide whether you agree or disagree with each statement. Be ready to explain your decision.

1. The probability of getting a tail when tossing a fair coin is the same as the probability of rolling an even number with a fair die.
2. The probability of rolling two 1s on two dice is twice as great as the probability of rolling one 1 on one die.
3. The experimental probability of a result will always be close to the theoretical probability of the result.

10.1 Exploring Probability

YOU WILL NEED

- 2 six-sided dice

GOAL

Determine the experimental probability of an event.

event

a set of one or more outcomes in a probability experiment; for example, the event of rolling an even number with a six-sided die consists of the outcomes of rolling a 2, a 4, and a 6

EXPLORE the Math

Julie and Nolan are playing a game.

- They each roll two dice.
- Julie adds her numbers.
- Nolan subtracts his numbers (lower from higher).
- They each roll lots of times.

They want to compare the ratios for the two **events.**

Is it more likely that Julie will roll a sum of 8 or that Nolan will roll a difference of 2?

10.2 Representing Probabilities as Fractions and Percents

YOU WILL NEED

- a spinner with 20 sections, a pencil, and a paper clip
- 3 coins

GOAL

Express probabilities using fractions, percents, and number lines.

LEARN ABOUT the Math

There are 20 students in a class: 13 boys and 7 girls. The teacher makes a spinner with all their names on it. The boys' names are in blue sections, and the girls' names are in green sections. Before the teacher calls on a student, she spins to select a name.

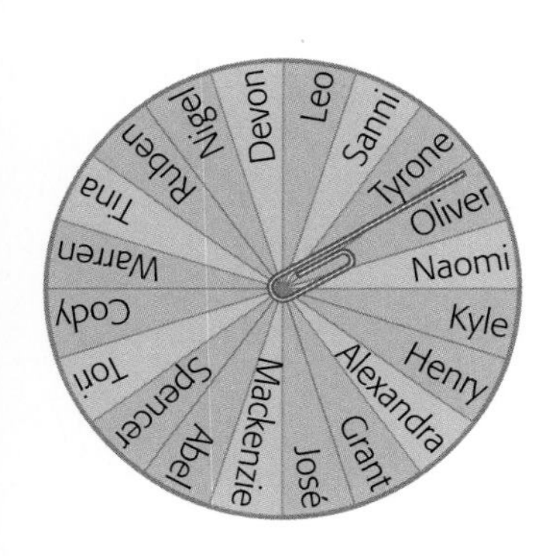

favourable outcome

the desired result in a probability experiment

experimental probability

in a probability experiment, the ratio of the number of observed favourable outcomes to the number of trials, or repetitions, of the experiment

What is the probability of selecting a girl's name in 100 spins?

A. Spin a spinner like the one shown 10 times. After each spin, record whether the **favourable outcome** of selecting a girl's name occurred.

B. What fraction of the 10 spins represents the **experimental probability** of selecting a girl's name? Write this fraction as a percent.

C. Show the experimental probability of selecting a girl's name on the following probability line. How would you change this line to show the probability as a percent?

impossible ← less likely | more likely → certain

$0 \quad \frac{1}{4} \quad \frac{1}{2} \quad \frac{3}{4} \quad 1$

D. Explain why selecting a girl's name and selecting a boy's name are not **equally likely outcomes** when using the spinner.

theoretical probability

the ratio of the number of favourable outcomes to the number of possible equally likely outcomes; for example, the theoretical probability of tossing a head on a coin is $\frac{1}{2}$, since there are 2 equally likely outcomes and only 1 is favourable

E. Write the **theoretical probability** of selecting a girl's name as a ratio, a fraction, and a percent.

F. Predict the number of times you might select a girl's name in 100 spins. Explain.

Reflecting

G. The probability line in part C begins with the label 0 and ends with the label 1. Why are these labels appropriate?

H. Did you use the fraction or the percent to predict the number of times a girl's name would be selected in 100 spins? How did you use it?

I. Why do the ratio, fraction, and percent all represent the same probability?

Communication | *Tip*

Instead of writing the words "probability of tossing a coin and getting heads," you can write P(heads); for example, $P(\text{heads}) = \frac{1}{2}$, or 0.5, or 50%.

WORK WITH the Math

Example | Representing an experimental probability

The first baby born in a hospital on each of the previous four days was a boy. Is the probability that a boy will be the first baby born on the next two days closer to $\frac{1}{2}$ or $\frac{1}{4}$?

May

sun	mon	tues	wed	thurs	fri	sat
1	2	3	4	5	6	7
8	9	10	11	12 ?	13 ?	14
15	16	17	18	19	20	21

Max's Solution

Heads and tails in a coin toss are equally likely outcomes. Boys and girls are about equally likely, too. I tossed coins to model the problem, and then estimated the probability.

Trial number	Both heads	Not both heads
1		✓
2	✓	
30		
Total	7	23

Since I had to think about two days, I tossed two coins and recorded the results. I made a head represent a boy and a tail represent a girl. If I tossed both heads, that meant a boy was born first on both days.

I tossed the two coins 30 times.

I calculated the probability that a boy would be born first on the next two days to be $P(2 \text{ boys}) = 7:30 = \frac{7}{30}$.

I wrote the experimental probability as a fraction. The numerator showed the number of favourable outcomes, and the denominator showed the total number of **trials**.

$7 \div 30 = 0.233333...$

I estimated this as 0.23, which is 23%.

It's easier to compare $\frac{7}{30}$ and $\frac{1}{4}$ as percents than as fractions.

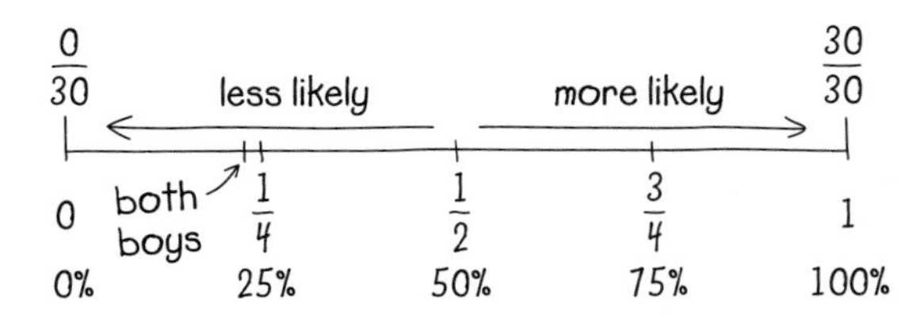

I showed the probability on a probability line. Instead of impossible, I wrote 0% and $\frac{0}{30}$. Instead of certain, I wrote 100% and $\frac{30}{30}$. 23% is about halfway between 0 and $\frac{1}{2}$.

My probability line shows that the probability of the first baby born on the next two days being a boy is closer to $\frac{1}{4}$ than $\frac{1}{2}$. But I should probably combine my data with someone else's data since you should always repeat an experiment as many times as you can.

A Checking

1. Suppose that the class on the spinner had five more boys and five more girls. How would you calculate the probability of selecting a girl's name as a fraction? As a percent? As a ratio?

2. Roll a die 20 times. Record each roll and the experimental probability of each event as a ratio, a fraction, and a percent.
   a) rolling a 5
   b) rolling an even number
   c) not rolling a 4, 5, or 6
   d) rolling a 1

B Practising

3. Joe read that the theoretical probability of winning a certain game is 30%.
   a) Write this probability as a ratio or a fraction.
   b) Show it on a probability line.

Reading Strategy

Ask three questions to help you understand this problem.
Share your questions with a partner.

4. Predict whether each theoretical probability below is closer to 10%, $\frac{1}{6}$, 50%, or 90%. Then test your prediction by rolling a die 20 times and reporting the experimental probability as a percent.
   a) P(roll is less than 6)
   b) P(roll is a 2)
   c) P(roll is more than 4)

5. Show the theoretical probability of each event on a probability line.
   a) getting a tail when tossing a coin
   b) rolling a prime number with a six-sided die

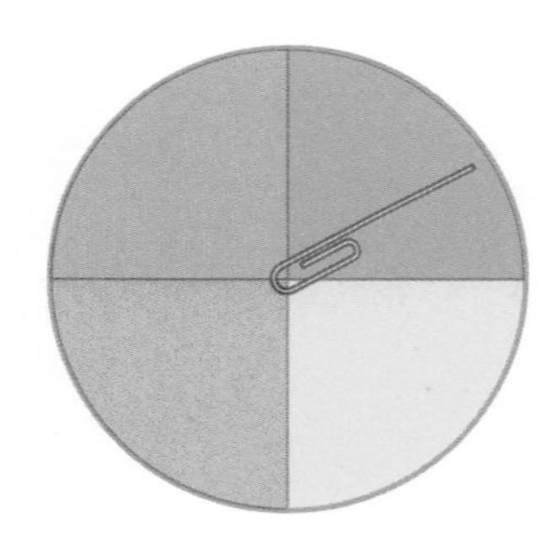

6. The four coloured areas on the spinner at the left are the same size. This means that the pointer is equally likely to land on all colours. Write each theoretical probability as a fraction and as a percent.
   a) P(yellow)
   b) P(green or yellow)
   c) P(black)
   d) P(not green)

M A T H E M A T I C S

7. Show each theoretical probability for the cards at the left on a probability line.
   a) P(vowel)
   b) P(consonant)
   c) P(letter with curved parts)

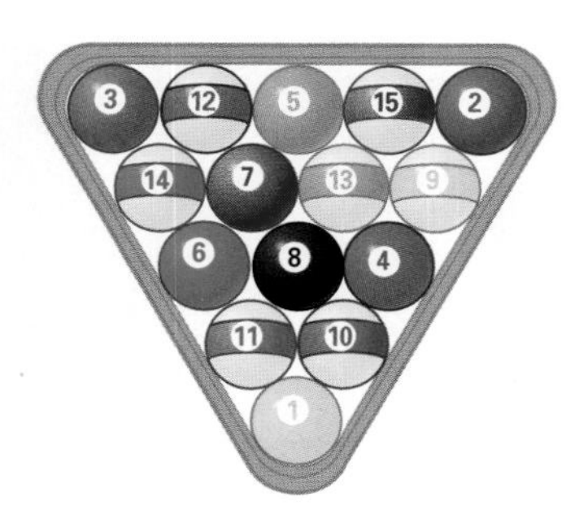

8. One ball is chosen at random from the rack of balls shown. Calculate each theoretical probability as a fraction or a ratio.
   a) $P(\text{black})$
   b) $P(10)$
   c) $P(\text{odd number})$
   d) $P(\text{even number})$
   e) $P(\text{solid purple, black, or orange})$
   f) $P(\text{number less than } 20)$

9. List the events in question 8 with a theoretical probability greater than 40%.

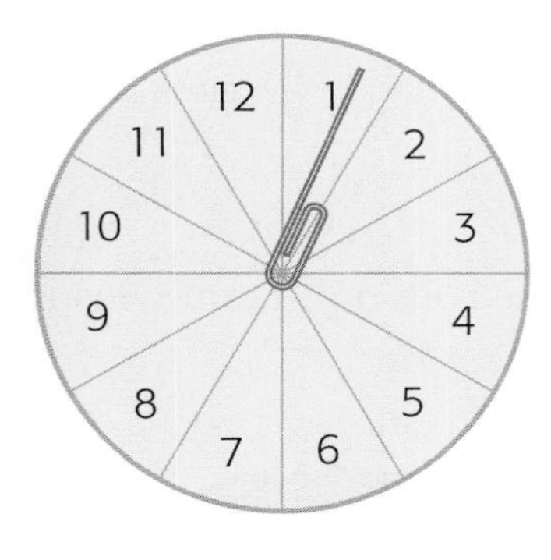

10. Use the spinner. Write the theoretical probability of each event to the nearest percent.
    a) $P(\text{multiple of } 3)$
    b) $P(\text{factor of } 12)$
    c) $P(\text{prime number})$
    d) $P(3, 5, \text{ or } 8)$
    e) $P(\text{number less than } 12)$
    f) $P(\text{multiple of } 5)$

11. Describe an event to match each probability.
    a) 50% b) 25% c) $\frac{1}{31}$ d) $\frac{5}{6}$ e) 0 f) 1

12. A 10-sided die has sides numbered 1 to 10.
    a) What fraction represents $P(\text{rolling an } 8)$?
    b) What percent represents $P(\text{rolling an } 8)$?
    c) How many 8s would you expect to roll in 100 rolls?
    d) Did you use the fraction from part (a) or the percent from part (b) to answer part (c)?

13. Describe what each statement means.
    a) The probability of the statement "I will win the race" is 0.
    b) The probability of the statement "I will win the race" is 100%.
    c) The probability of the statement "I will win the race" is $\frac{5}{10}$.

10.3 Probability of Independent Events

YOU WILL NEED

- 2 six-sided dice
- cards numbered 1 to 6

Determine probability by identifying the sample space.

LEARN ABOUT the Math

Yan and Liam each roll a die. Yan wins if she rolls a 4. Liam wins if the sum of both their rolls is 4. Otherwise, it's a tie.

Is Yan more likely to win than Liam?

A. Yan created the following chart to show all the possible outcomes from rolling two dice. She uses W when she wins, L when she loses, and T when she ties. Complete the chart to show the experiment's **sample space.**

sample space

all the possible outcomes in a probability experiment

		Yan's roll					
		1	2	3	4	5	6
Liam's roll	1	T	T	L	W	T	T
	2				W		
	3				W		
	4				W		
	5				W		
	6				W		

I roll 4 and Liam rolls 2.

B. Calculate who is more likely to win the game.

C. Suppose that Liam and Yan change the game. Liam draws a card from a deck of five cards numbered 1 to 5, looks at the card, and puts it back in the deck. Then Yan draws a card. Yan still wins if she draws a 4, and Liam still wins if the sum of their draws is 4. List all the possible outcomes in this sample space.

D. Who is more likely to win the new game?

Reflecting

E. How could you have predicted that there would be 36 outcomes in the sample space in part A?

F. How do you know that Yan's chart in part A includes all the possible outcomes for the game?

G. In a third version of the game, Liam does not put his card back. Why were Yan's and Liam's card draws in part C **independent events,** but their draws in the new game not independent events?

independent events

two events are independent events if the probability of one is not affected by the probability of the other; for example, if you toss a coin and roll a die, the events are independent. The result of rolling the die does not depend on the result of tossing the coin.

WORK WITH the Math

Example | Using an organized list

Fiona's hockey team keeps a cooler full of apple juice, orange juice, cranberry juice, and water. The team mom pulls out bottles for players without looking. Fiona wondered what the probability is that the next two drinks that are pulled out will be the same.

Fiona's Solution

I used A for apple juice, C for cranberry juice, W for water, and O for orange juice. Then I listed all the combinations of two drinks possible. I listed them as first drink - second drink.

I used an organized list to see all the possible combinations of drinks that might occur.

A - A	C - A	W - A	O - A
A - C	**C - C**	W - C	O - C
A - W	C - W	**W - W**	O - W
A - O	C - O	W - O	**O - O**

If both drinks in an outcome were the same, I highlighted them in green. I counted the total number of outcomes and the number that I had highlighted in green.

P(2 of the same drink) = $\frac{4}{16}$

The probability is $\frac{4}{16}$ or $\frac{1}{4}$, which is 25%.

There were 16 outcomes, but only 4 had both drinks the same.

A Checking

1. One experiment involves spinning a spinner and tossing a coin. Another experiment involves taking two coloured balls, one after the other, from a bag. Which experiment has outcomes that involve independent events? Explain your choice.

2. Suppose that you roll two dice. What is the theoretical probability of each event?

a) sum of 8

b) sum of 7

c) sum of 3

Second roll \ First roll	1	2	3	4	5	6
1	2	3				
2	3	4				
3	4					
4	5					
5	6					
6	7					

B Practising

3. Suppose that you roll two dice. What is the theoretical probability of each event?

a) difference of 3 **b)** difference of 1 **c)** difference of 0

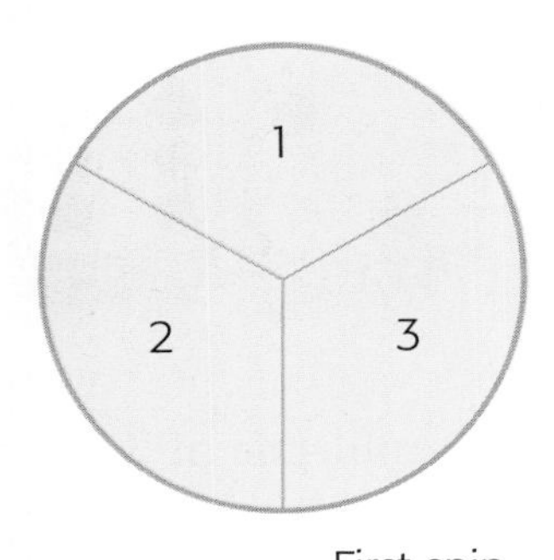

Second spin \ First spin	1	2	3
1			
2			
3			

4. Imagine spinning the spinner at the left twice.

a) Does the chart show all the possible outcomes? Explain.

b) How could you have predicted that there would be nine outcomes with two spins?

c) What is the theoretical probability of the sum of the two spins being an even number?

d) What is the theoretical probability of the sum of the two spins being greater than 2?

5. Deanna and Carol are playing a game. They roll a die twice and add the numbers they roll. A sum of 5 scores a point.

a) What is the probability of rolling a sum of 5?

b) What is the probability that Deanna will roll a sum greater than 5 on her next turn?

c) Why are the dice rolls independent events?

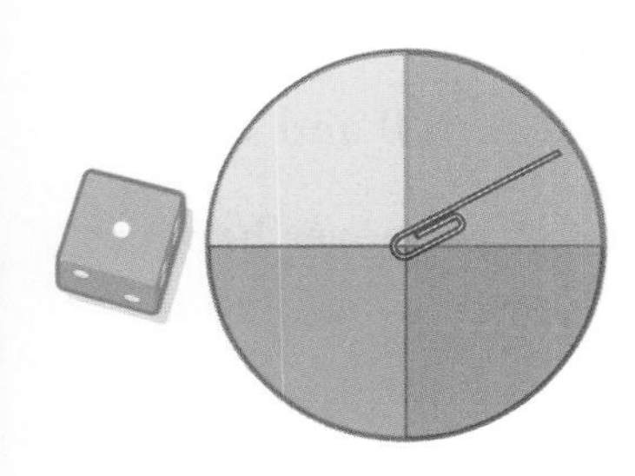

6. Suppose that you spin the spinner at the left and then roll the die. Determine the probability of each event.

a) *P*(yellow and 3)

b) *P*(yellow and anything except 3)

c) *P*(purple and even)

7. a) Describe a probability experiment with two independent events.

b) Describe a probability experiment with two events that are not independent.

Mid-Chapter Review

Frequently Asked Questions

Q: How can you describe a probability with numbers?

A: You can describe it as a ratio that compares the number of favourable outcomes to the number of possible outcomes. The ratio compares a part to a whole, so you can also write it as a fraction or a percent.

For example, the probability of rolling a multiple of 3 with a six-sided die can be written as $P(3 \text{ or } 6) = 2:6$. You could also write this as the fraction $\frac{2}{6}$, or $\frac{1}{3}$. Since $\frac{1}{3} = 0.3333 \ldots$, the probability is about 33%. You could show this on a probability line.

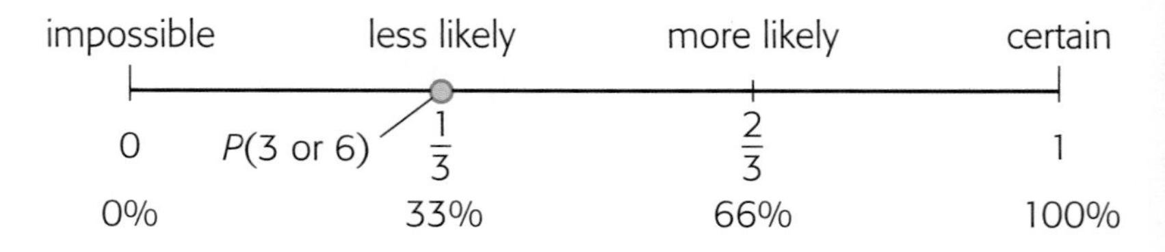

Q: Why must the value of a probability be between 0 and 1?

A: The least probability describes an event that never happens, or happens zero times. Therefore the least probability is

$$\frac{0}{\text{number of possible outcomes}} = 0.$$

The greatest probability describes an event that always happens. This means that the probability is 100%, or

$$\frac{\text{number of possible outcomes}}{\text{number of possible outcomes}} = 1.$$

Q: When are two events independent?

A: Two events are independent when the result of one event has no effect on the result of the other event.

For example, remove one ball from a bag, record its colour, put it back, and then repeat. The probability of removing the pink ball on the first draw is $\frac{1}{5}$. The probability of removing it on the second draw is still $\frac{1}{5}$. The two draws are independent events.

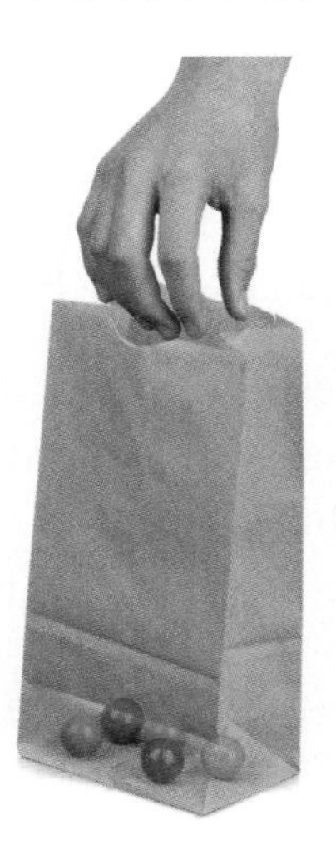

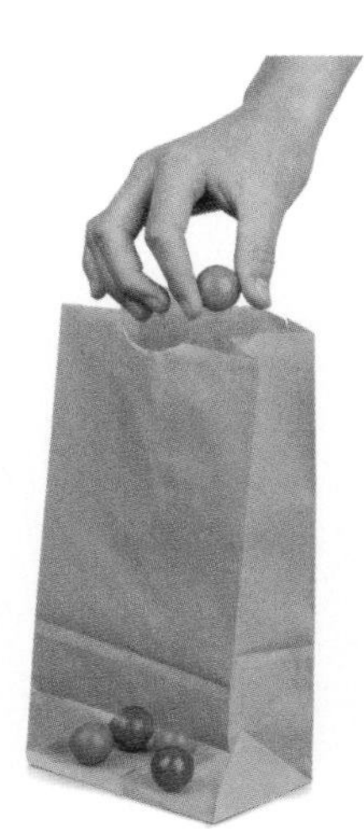

Now draw the pink ball first, but don't put it back. There is now no pink ball in the bag. The probability of drawing pink on the second draw is 0. These events are not independent.

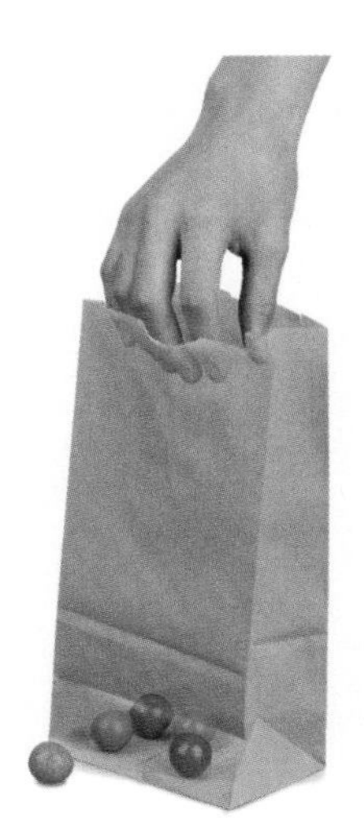

Practice

Lesson 10.2

1. Fred shuffles the cards numbered 2 through 10 from a deck of cards. He then draws a card. Determine the theoretical probability of each event as a fraction and a percent, to the nearest whole number.
   a) $P(\text{drawing a } 10)$
   b) $P(\text{drawing a red card})$
   c) $P(\text{drawing a red } 10)$
   d) $P(\text{drawing an odd card})$
   e) $P(\text{drawing a card less than } 11)$
   f) $P(\text{drawing a king})$

2. Katya rolled a regular six-sided die 16 times. Her experimental probabilities for three events are given:
   $P(\text{even number}) = \frac{9}{16}$ $P(\text{less than } 4) = \frac{8}{16}$ $P(\text{exactly } 6) = \frac{1}{16}$
   a) Which result matches the theoretical probability?
   b) Which result is close to, but not identical to, the theoretical probability?
   c) Which result is far from the theoretical probability?

3. A bag contains two red marbles, three green marbles, and seven black marbles. One marble is removed from the bag.
   a) Write $P(\text{green})$ as a fraction and as a percent.
   b) Predict the number of times a green marble will be selected if this experiment is carried out 50 times.

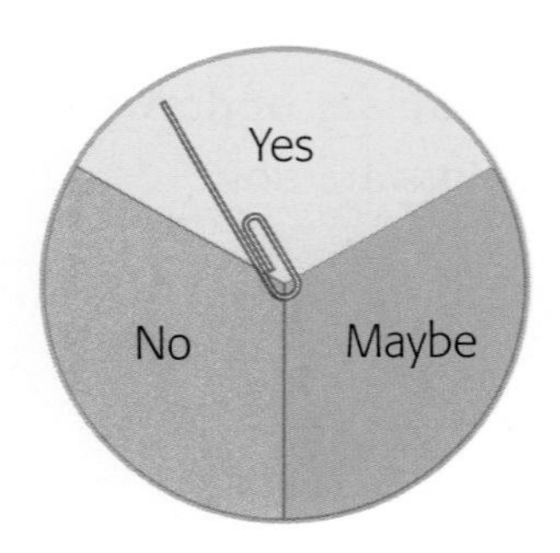

4. Raj is conducting an experiment. He spins the spinner at the left twice for each trial.
   a) List all the possible outcomes for a trial.
   b) Determine the probability of getting the same spin result in both spins of a trial.
   c) Determine the probability of not getting a Yes in two spins.

Lesson 10.3

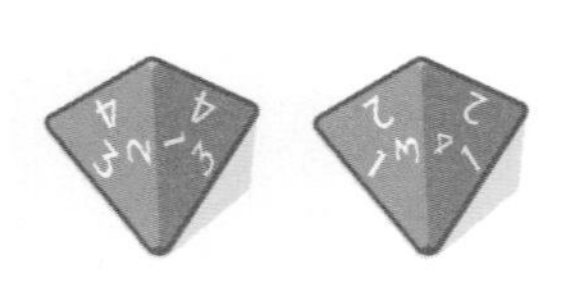

5. Two four-sided dice, each numbered 1 to 4, are rolled.
   a) List all the possible outcomes in the sample space of this experiment.
   b) Explain why the rolls of the dice are independent events.
   c) Determine the probability that the sum of the dice will be 5.

MATH GAME

On a Roll

YOU WILL NEED

- two dice

The goal of this game is to be the first player to make 10 correct predictions.

Number of players: 2 to 4

How to Play

1. One player rolls two dice and calculates the product of the numbers rolled.
2. All the players predict whether the product of the next roll will be greater than, less than, or equal to this product.
3. The next player rolls the dice. Players who made a correct prediction score 1 point.
4. Players take turns rolling the dice and calculating the product. The game continues until a player has 10 points.

Roll	Result of roll	Product	My score	My prediction for next roll
1	3, 4	12		greater
2	3, 5	15	1	equal
3	1, 1	1	1 + 0 = 1	greater

10.4 Solve Problems Using Organized Lists

YOU WILL NEED
- play money: loonies, dimes, and quarters

Solve a problem using an organized list to identify the sample space.

LEARN ABOUT the Math

Julie is waiting for the school bus. She would like to buy a drink and a snack while waiting. She has five coins in her wallet. She knows that they must be quarters, dimes, or loonies, but she doesn't remember how many of each she has. For fun, she decides not to look, and to figure out the probability that she can buy only a snack or only a drink, but not both.

What is the probability that Julie will be able to buy only one item?

1 Understand the Problem

- I have five coins.
- Each coin is either a loonie, a dime, or a quarter.
- There may be more than one of some types of coins.
- There may be none of some types of coins.
- The snacks are $2.00 each, and the drinks are $2.00 each. This means that if the total value of the coins is at least $2.00 but less than $4.00, I can buy only one item.

2 Make a Plan

I'll write all the possible combinations of five coins in an organized list. This will help me see what combinations have a value of at least $2.00 and less than $4.00. I'll create my table using a pattern, so I won't miss or repeat any combinations.

③ Carry Out the Plan

Loonies	Quarters	Dimes	Total value	Summary of possible outcomes	
5	0	0	$5.00	with 5 loonies,	
				1 combination	
4	1	0	$4.25	with 4 loonies,	
4	0	1	$4.10	2 combinations	
3	2	0	$3.50	with 3 loonies,	I highlighted the
3	1	1	$3.35	3 combinations	combinations with
3	0	2	$3.20		a total value of
2	3	0	$2.75	with 2 loonies,	at least $2.00
2	2	1	$2.60	4 combinations	and less than $4.00.
2	1	2	$2.45		There are 8 of
2	0	3	$2.30		these combinations
1	4	0	$2.00	with 1 loonie,	
1	3	1	$1.85	5 combinations	There are
1	2	2	$1.70		21 different
1	1	3	$1.55		combinations,
1	0	4	$1.40		and 8 of these
0	5	0	$1.25	with no loonies,	combinations
0	4	1	$1.10	6 combinations	allow me to buy
0	3	2	$0.95		only one item.
0	2	3	$0.80		The probability of
0	1	4	$0.65		being able to buy
0	0	5	$0.50		only one item is $\frac{8}{21}$.

③ Look Back

I checked my table to make sure that I didn't miss any combinations. I counted to make sure that I had the same number of combinations with two quarters as I had with two loonies.

Reflecting

A. What pattern did Julie use?

B. How did using the pattern and organized list make it more likely that Julie listed all the possible combinations with no repeats?

WORK WITH the Math

Example | Solving a problem with an organized list

In a school checkers tournament, a win is worth 5 points, a tie is worth 2 points, and a loss is worth 1 point. If two players have the same number of points, then the player with more wins than ties is ranked higher. Yan has 10 points. What is the probability that she has more wins than ties?

Matthew's Solution

1 Understand the Problem

This is the information I know:

- Yan has 10 points.
- There could be some losses.
- Wins are worth 5 points, ties are worth 2 points, and losses are worth 1 point.

2 Make a Plan

I'll list all the combinations of wins, losses, and ties that add to 10 points. I'll start by looking at the number of possible wins. Then I'll think about ties and losses.

3 Carry Out the Plan

Combination for 10	Number of wins	Number of ties	Number of losses
5 + 5	2	0	0
5 + 2 + 2 + 1	1	2	1
5 + 2 + 1 + 1 + 1	1	1	3
5 + 1 + 1 + 1 + 1 + 1	1	0	5
2 + 2 + 2 + 2 + 2	0	5	0
2 + 2 + 2 + 2 + 1 + 1	0	4	2
2 + 2 + 2 + 1 + 1 + 1 + 1	0	3	4
2 + 2 + 1 + 1 + 1 + 1 + 1 + 1	0	2	6
2 + 1 + 1 + 1 + 1 + 1 + 1 + 1 + 1	0	1	8
1 + 1 + 1 + 1 + 1 + 1 + 1 + 1 + 1 + 1	0	0	10

There are 10 ways to score 10 points.

Only two ways have more wins than ties.

The probability of having 10 points and more wins than ties is $\frac{2}{10}$.

4 Look Back

There are patterns in the columns for wins, ties, and losses.
The patterns lead me to think that I have listed all the possible combinations.

A Checking

1. Suppose that you have two coins in your pocket. Each coin is either a penny, a nickel, a dime, or a quarter. The coins may have the same value.

a) How many different combinations are possible? The order in which you count the coins does not matter.

b) How many of these combinations sum to less than 20¢?

c) What is the probability that the two coins sum to less than 20¢?

B Practising

2. In a baseball tournament, teams get 5 points for a win, 3 points for a tie, and 1 point for a loss. Nathan's team has 29 points.

a) Show all the different combinations of wins, ties, and losses for Nathan's team using an organized list.

b) What is the probability that Nathan's team had more losses than ties?

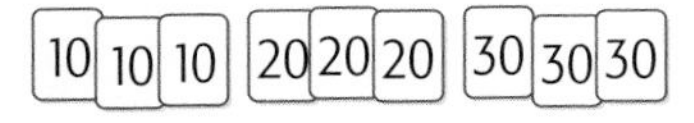

3. Phil has the deck of nine cards at the left. Phil picks one card. He returns the card to the deck and picks another card. Then he multiplies the first card by the second card.

a) Show all of Phil's possible products.

b) Calculate the probability that Phil's product is over 500.

4. Each morning, John is the first to take one of these four jobs from the family daily job jar. What is the probability that he will get to walk the dog on both Monday and Tuesday?

5. Create a problem that can be solved using an organized list. Provide a complete solution.

10.5 Using Tree Diagrams to Calculate Probability

YOU WILL NEED
- 2 six-sided dice
- counters
- grid paper

GOAL

Determine probabilities using a tree diagram.

LEARN ABOUT the Math

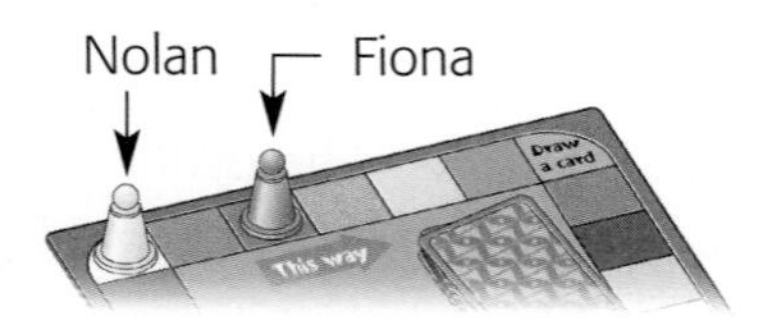

Nolan and Fiona are playing a board game with two counters and dice. Nolan is two spaces behind Fiona. They each roll a die and move forward the number of spaces rolled.

What is the probability that Nolan and Fiona will land on the same space?

tree diagram

a way to record and count all combinations of events, using lines to form branches to connect the two parts of the outcome; for example, the following tree diagram shows all the combinations that can happen if you toss a coin twice

1st toss	2nd toss	1st toss	2nd toss
H	H (HH)	T	H (TH)
	T (HT)		T (TT)

A. Nolan drew a **tree diagram** to show all the possible outcomes of rolling the two dice. Complete his diagram. How could you predict that there would be 36 branches?

Nolan's roll	Fiona's roll	Same space?	Nolan's roll	Fiona's roll	Same space?
	1 (orange)			1 (orange)	✓(orange/orange)
	2 (yellow)			2 (yellow)	
1	3 (green)		3	3 (green)	
(brown)	4 (blue)		(orange)	4 (blue)	
	5 (purple)			5 (purple)	
	6 (grey)			6 (grey)	
	1 (orange)			1	
	2 (yellow)			2	
2	3 (green)		4	3	
(red)	4 (blue)		(yellow)	4	
	5 (purple)			5	
	6 (grey)			6	

The ✓ means that we landed on the same space.

B. Count the outcomes for which Nolan and Fiona land on the same space.

C. Calculate the theoretical probability of both students landing on the same space. Write it as a fraction.

Reflecting

D. Why does each branch represent one outcome?

E. How did you use the tree diagram to determine the numerator and the denominator of the probability fraction?

F. How does using a tree diagram describe the sample space?

WORK WITH the Math

Example | Calculating using a tree diagram

Suppose that you spin the spinner twice. What is the probability of getting the blue section both times?

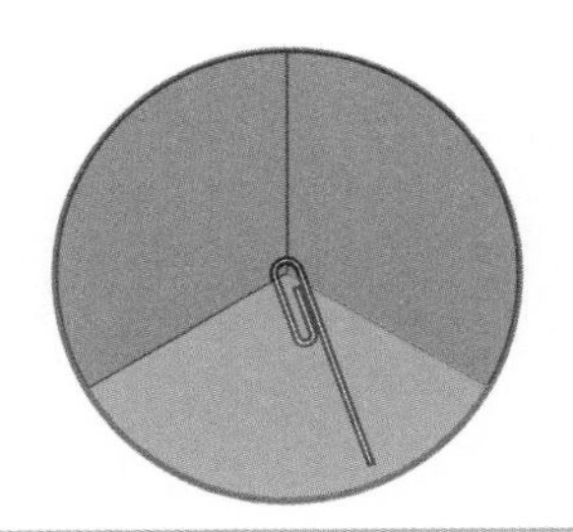

Max's Solution

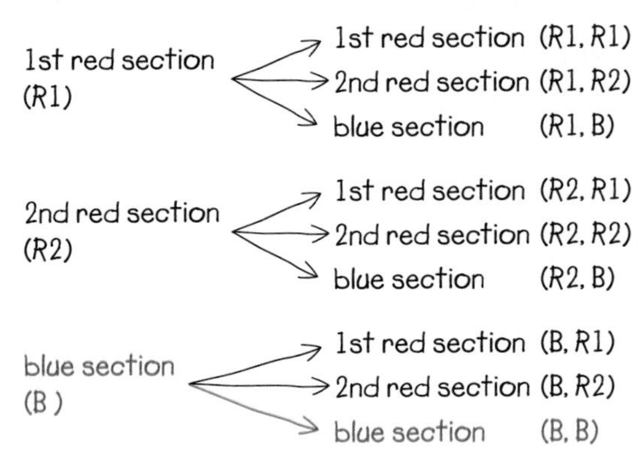

I assumed that each section has an equal chance of happening.

I listed all the possibilities in a tree diagram. I used R1 for one red section, R2 for the other red section, and B for the blue section.

The 9 branches represent 9 equally likely outcomes.

Only 1 of the 9 branches starts with the blue section and ends with the blue section, so 1 of the 9 outcomes is favourable.

P(blue section twice) = $\frac{1}{9}$

A Checking

1. Determine the theoretical probability that Nolan and Fiona will land on spaces next to each other. Use the tree diagram you made for the game Nolan and Fiona played.

B Practising

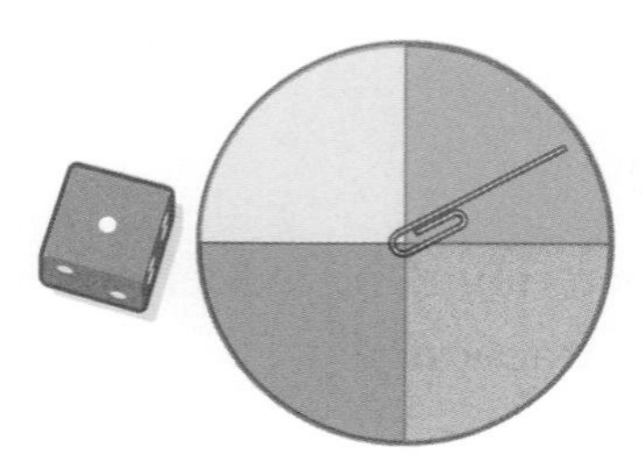

2. Suppose that you roll the die and spin the spinner at the left.
   a) Show all the possible outcomes in the sample space using a tree diagram.
   b) Calculate *P*(anything but 5 and yellow).

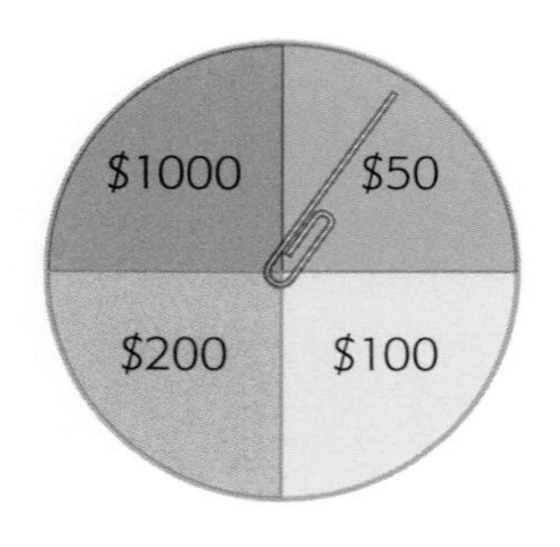

3. Kaycee has won a contest. To determine the amount of her prize, she must spin this spinner twice. She will receive the sum of her two spins.
   a) Show all the possible outcomes by creating a tree diagram.
   b) What is the probability that Kaycee will receive more than the minimum amount but less than the maximum amount?
   c) What is the probability that Kaycee will receive more than $500?
   d) What is the probability that Kaycee will receive between $200 and $400?

4 **a)** Suppose that the spinner is spun twice. List all the possible outcomes in a tree diagram.
   b) Determine the theoretical probability that the difference of the numbers will be 1.
   c) Determine the theoretical probability that the product of the numbers will be 4.
   d) Determine the theoretical probability that the second number will be 2 greater than the first number.

5. Omar has three T-shirts: one red, one green, and one yellow. He has two pairs of shorts: one red and one black. Answer the following questions using a tree diagram.

a) How many different outfits can Omar put together?
b) What is the probability that Omar's outfit will include a red T-shirt or red shorts?
c) Are choosing a T-shirt and shorts independent events? Explain.

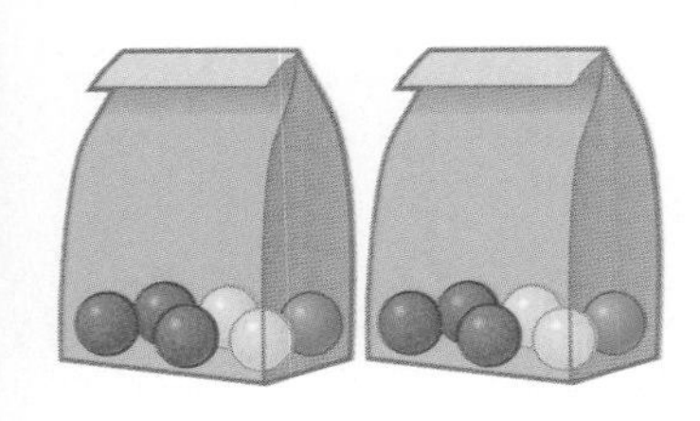

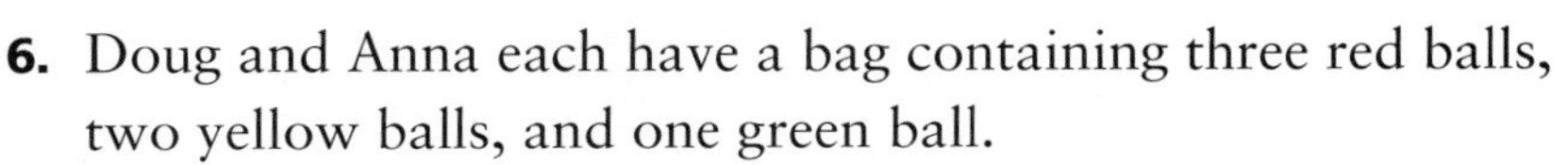

6. Doug and Anna each have a bag containing three red balls, two yellow balls, and one green ball.
In Doug's experiment, he takes one ball from the bag, puts it back, and then takes another ball.
In Anna's experiment, she takes one ball from the bag, and then takes another ball without returning the first ball to the bag.
a) Draw a tree diagram for Doug's experiment.
b) Determine the probability that Doug will draw one red ball and one green ball using your tree diagram.
c) Why does Doug's experiment involve independent events, while Anna's experiment does not?

7. A probability experiment involves adding the numbers rolled on a four-sided die (with the numbers 1, 2, 3, and 4) and on a six-sided die.
a) Describe the sample space for this experiment using an organized list or a tree diagram.
b) Determine P(sum is less than 5).

8. How can you use multiplication to predict the number of branches on a tree diagram?

10.6 Comparing Theoretical and Experimental Probabilities

YOU WILL NEED

- a four-section spinner

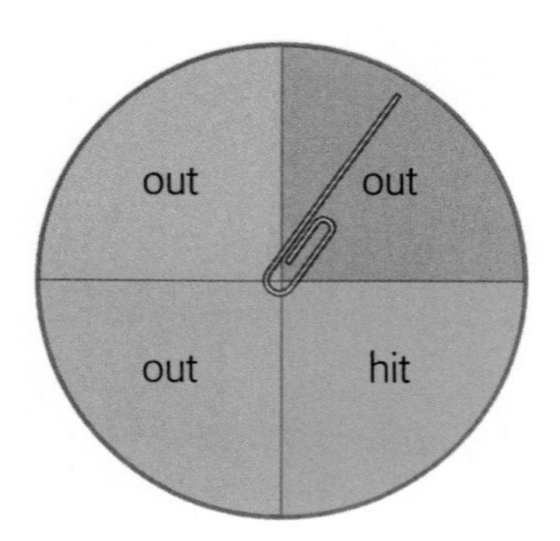

GOAL

Compare theoretical and experimental probability for two independent events.

LEARN ABOUT the Math

Julie and Liam are playing a baseball board game in which a spinner determines whether a player gets a hit or strikes out.

How does the theoretical probability that Julie will get two hits in her first two spins compare with the experimental probability?

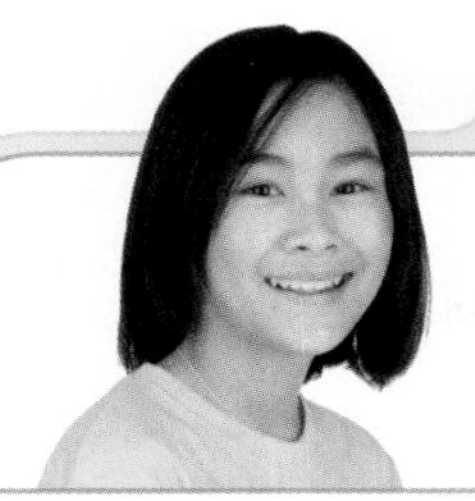

Example 1 | Using a tree diagram

I listed all the possibilities in a tree diagram.

Yan's Solution

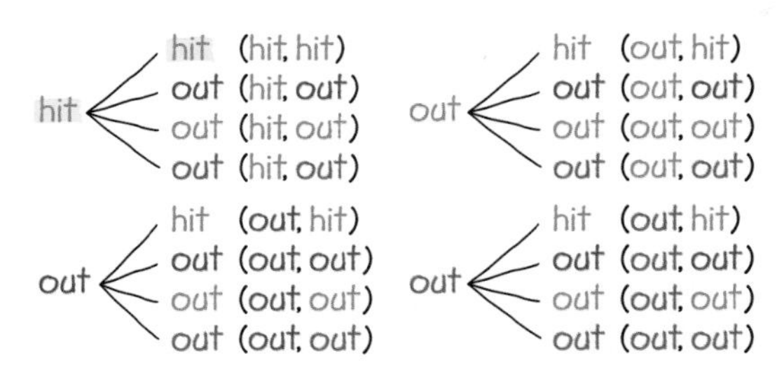

I coloured each result so I could tell the section the spinner landed in.

There is only one outcome that means two hits.

Only 1 of the 16 outcomes has two hits.
The theoretical probability is

$P(H, H) = \frac{1}{16} = 0.0625$, or about 6%.

There are 16 outcomes, but only 1 with two hits.

Example 2 | Using an organized list

I did an experiment to determine the experimental probability.

Matthew's Solution

1st spin	2nd spin
OUT	OUT
OUT	OUT
OUT	OUT
OUT	HIT
HIT	HIT
OUT	OUT
OUT	OUT
HIT	HIT
HIT	HIT
HIT	OUT

1st spin	2nd spin
HIT	OUT
HIT	OUT
OUT	OUT
HIT	HIT
OUT	OUT
OUT	HIT
HIT	HIT
HIT	OUT
OUT	OUT
OUT	OUT

I carried out 20 trials, and I spun the spinner twice in each trial. Two hits in a row happened in 5 trials.

I suspect that there are too many HIT, HITs. I wonder if something is wrong with the spinner. I might check it. I'll also see what results my classmates got.

There were 5 results of HIT, HIT in 20.

$P(H, H) = \frac{5}{20} = 0.25$ or 25%.

Example 3 | Using a simulated spinner

I located a double spinner simulation.

Fiona's Solution

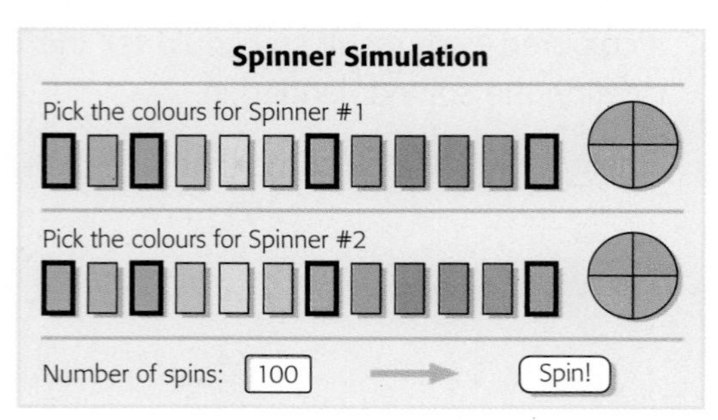

I set the simulation to spin 100 times.

I used yellow to represent a hit. If two yellow sections came up in a spin, then I had two hits in a row.

Because the spinner lets me, I could spin 1000 times and get a better experimental result.

Spinner #1: ▲▲▲▲ Spinner #2: ▲▲▲▲
Spins: 100

1.▲▲	2.▲▲	3.▲▲	4.▲▲	5.▲▲	6.▲▲	7.▲▲	8.▲▲	9.▲▲	10.▲▲
11.▲▲	12.▲▲	13.▲▲	14.▲▲	15.▲▲	16.▲▲	17.▲▲	18.▲▲	19.▲▲	20.▲▲
21.▲▲	22.▲▲	23.▲▲	24.▲▲	25.▲▲	26.▲▲	27.▲▲	28.▲▲	29.▲▲	30.▲▲
31.▲▲	32.▲▲	33.▲▲	34.▲▲	35.▲▲	36.▲▲	37.▲▲	38.▲▲	39.▲▲	40.▲▲
41.▲▲	42.▲▲	43.▲▲	44.▲▲	45.▲▲	46.▲▲	47.▲▲	48.▲▲	49.▲▲	50.▲▲
51.▲▲	52.▲▲	53.▲▲	54.▲▲	55.▲▲	56.▲▲	57.▲▲	58.▲▲	59.▲▲	60.▲▲
61.▲▲	62.▲▲	63.▲▲	64.▲▲	65.▲▲	66.▲▲	67.▲▲	68.▲▲	69.▲▲	70.▲▲
71.▲▲	72.▲▲	73.▲▲	74.▲▲	75.▲▲	76.▲▲	77.▲▲	78.▲▲	79.▲▲	80.▲▲
81.▲▲	82.▲▲	83.▲▲	84.▲▲	85.▲▲	86.▲▲	87.▲▲	88.▲▲	89.▲▲	90.▲▲
91.▲▲	92.▲▲	93.▲▲	94.▲▲	95.▲▲	96.▲▲	97.▲▲	98.▲▲	99.▲▲	100.▲▲

There were 7 results that represented two hits in a row in 100 trials. The experimental probability is $P(H, H) = \frac{7}{100} = 0.07$ or 7%.

My experimental probability and Yan's theoretical probability are very close.

Reflecting

A. Why might the experimental probability be different from the theoretical probability?

B. Why do you think Fiona's data might be more reliable than Matthew's?

WORK WITH the Math

Example 4 | Comparing probabilities

A bag holds two yellow cubes, one blue cube, and one red cube. In an experiment you pick one cube from the bag, replace it, and then pick a second cube. Repeat this experiment 20 times. Compare the experimental and theoretical probabilities of drawing two cubes that are the same colour.

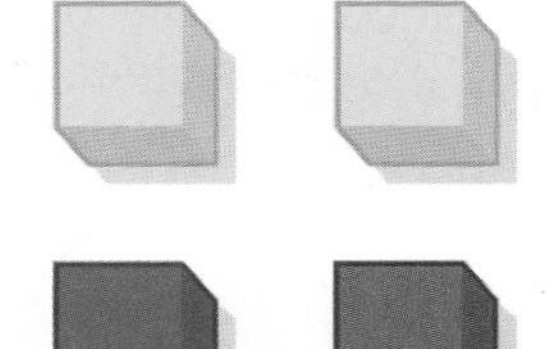

Solution

Y1 → Y1 (Y1, Y1); Y2 (Y1, Y2); R (Y1, R); B (Y1, B)

R → Y1 (R, Y1); Y2 (R, Y2); R (R, R); B (R, B)

Y2 → Y1 (Y2, Y1); Y2 (Y2, Y2); R (Y2, R); B (Y2, B)

B → Y1 (B, Y1); Y2 (B, Y2); R (B, R); B (B, B)

Draw a tree diagram to represent the different ways to remove the cubes. Use Y1 and Y2 for the yellow cubes, R for the red cube, and B for the blue cube.

There are 16 possible outcomes. Only 6 show cubes of the same colour.
$P(\text{2 cubes the same colour}) = \frac{6}{16}$
$= 0.375$, or about 38%

Write the theoretical probability as a percent so that it can be easily compared with the experimental probability.

In the spreadsheet experiment
- 0 and 1 represent yellow
- 2 represents red
- 3 represents blue

1st draw	0	3	3	3	0	2	1	2	1	3
2nd draw	0	0	1	3	3	3	1	3	3	1
1st draw	1	2	3	0	3	0	2	0	2	3
2nd draw	2	1	2	1	0	1	2	2	0	0

Make a spreadsheet for 20 draws. Use the random number generator. The favourable combinations will be
- 0-0, 0-1, 1-0, and 1-1 (both yellow)
- 2-2 (both red)
- 3-3 (both blue)

Run the experiment. Highlight the favourable combinations in the results.

There are 20 trials and 6 favourable outcomes.
$P(\text{2 cubes the same colour}) = \frac{6}{20} = 0.3$
or 30%

In a spreadsheet, you can repeat the experiment as many times as you like quickly and easily.

Reading Strategy

Summarize what you know about experimental and theoretical probability. Use a Venn diagram.

A Checking

1. A bag holds two red cubes, one blue cube, and one yellow cube. Darth is going to pick one cube from the bag, replace it, and then pick a second cube.

a) Calculate the theoretical probability that Darth will pick two different-coloured cubes.

b) Conduct the experiment 20 times. Compare the experimental probability with your answer in part (a).

c) Combine your results with those of your classmates. Compare the new experimental probability to your answer in part (a).

B Practising

2. a) What is the theoretical probability of rolling an even number on a die?

b) Roll a die 20 times. Combine your results with the results of four other students. Compare the experimental probability of rolling an even number with the theoretical probability.

3. a) Suppose that you roll two dice. What is the theoretical probability that both numbers will be a multiple of 3?

b) Conduct an experiment with at least 20 trials. What is your experimental probability for the event in part (a)?

c) Why might the experimental probability be different from the theoretical probability?

d) Combine your results with the results of other students. What is the experimental probability now?

4. a) Suppose that you roll a die twice. What is the theoretical probability that you will roll a number greater than 3 before you roll a number less than 3?

b) Compare the theoretical probability with an experimental probability. Use at least 20 trials.

c) How might you set up this experiment using computer technology?

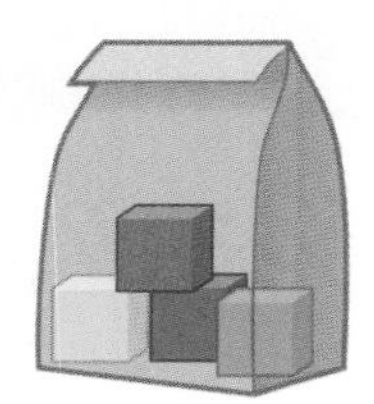

5. Anthony removes a block from the bag at the left, checks its colour, and puts it back. He then removes another block.

a) What is the probability that Anthony will remove the red block on his second try?

b) Why are the first and second block removals independent events?

c) Do an experiment to determine an experimental probability for removing red on the second try. Combine your results with the results of other students to have more data. Compare your combined data with the theoretical probability.

6. How can you change the experiment in question 5 so that it does not involve independent events?

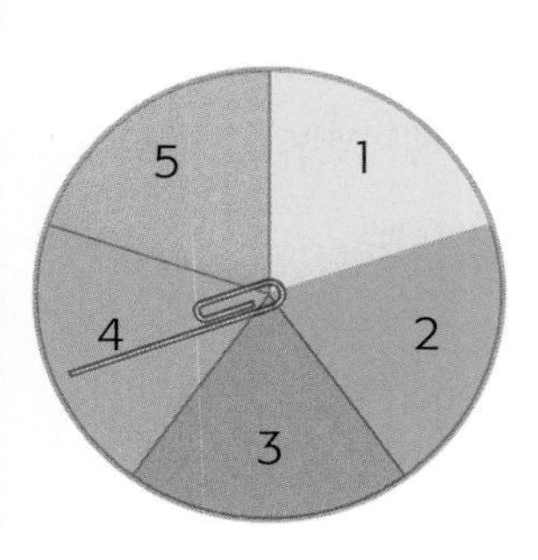

7. a) Determine the theoretical probability that when you spin this spinner twice, the product of the two spins will be an even number.

b) Do an experiment to determine the experimental probability of the product being an even number.

c) Compare your results as a class. What happened to the experimental probability as the number of trials increased?

8. Suppose that you roll a 12-sided die and toss a coin.

a) Determine the theoretical probability of rolling an even number and tossing a head.

b) Do an experiment to calculate the experimental probability of rolling an even number and tossing a head.

c) Compare your answers in parts (a) and (b).

9. a) Mykola has calculated that the theoretical probability of a certain outcome in an experiment is 37%. He conducts the experiment five times and gets the following experimental probabilities for the outcome: 97%, 80%, 85%, 100%, and 92%. What advice would you give Mykola?

b) Mae wants to determine the experimental probability that all three children in a family will be girls. She determined that the probability is 25%. What advice would you give Mae?

CURIOUS MATH

SIMPSON'S PARADOX

Suppose that you have two bags. Each bag contains some blue marbles and some black marbles. If you draw a blue marble from a bag, you win.

Here are two situations to investigate:

Situation A

Marbles	Bag 1	Bag 2
blue	5	3
black	6	4

Situation B

Marbles	Bag 1	Bag 2
blue	6	9
black	3	5

1. In both situations, you have a better probability of winning with bag 1. Explain why.
2. Suppose that you place the marbles from bag 1 of both situations into a single bag. Calculate the probability of winning using this bag.
3. Suppose that you place the marbles from bag 2 of both situations into a single bag. Calculate the probability of winning using this bag.
4. How is the probability of winning using combined bags different from the probability of winning using separate bags?

Chapter 10

Chapter Self-Test

1. Write each probability as a fraction, a ratio, and a percent, based on Keith's rolls of a die.

Keith's Rolls of a Die

First 10 rolls	4	5	2	3	1	2	6	4	2	3
Next 10 rolls	2	1	1	3	1	6	5	4	6	4
Next 10 rolls	1	2	3	6	4	5	1	2	1	3

a) P(even number in the first 10 rolls)
b) P(odd number in all 30 rolls)
c) P(number less than 3 in the first 20 rolls)

2. Write each probability for Bridget's spins as a fraction.

Bridget's 25 Spins

2	3	3	1	4	1	2	5	1	2	2	3	1
1	2	4	5	2	4	1	1	2	3	3	1	

a) spinning a 2
b) spinning a 5
c) spinning a 1
d) spinning an even number

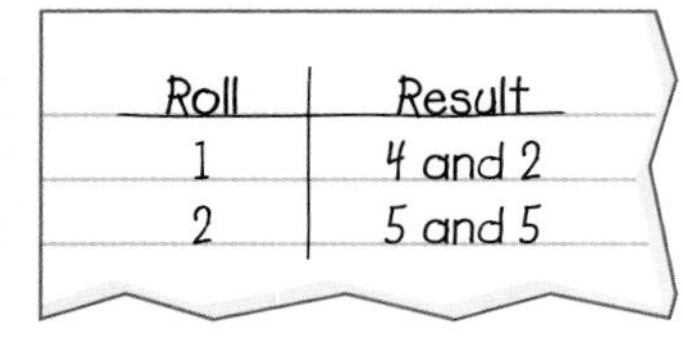

Roll	Result
1	4 and 2
2	5 and 5

3. Roll two dice 20 times. Record the result of each roll. Write each experimental probability as a percent.
a) two numbers greater than 3
b) two prime numbers
c) a sum of 3

4. You have cards numbered 1 to 5. In experiment A, you select a card, return it to the deck, and then select another card. In experiment B, you select one card and then select another card. Why does experiment A involve independent events, while experiment B does not?

5. Two identical dice are rolled at the same time. What is the theoretical probability of each event?
   a) 4 and 3
   b) 2 and another even number
   c) two consecutive numbers
   d) two numbers whose sum is a multiple of 3
   e) two numbers whose sum is a multiple of 5
   f) two numbers 3 apart

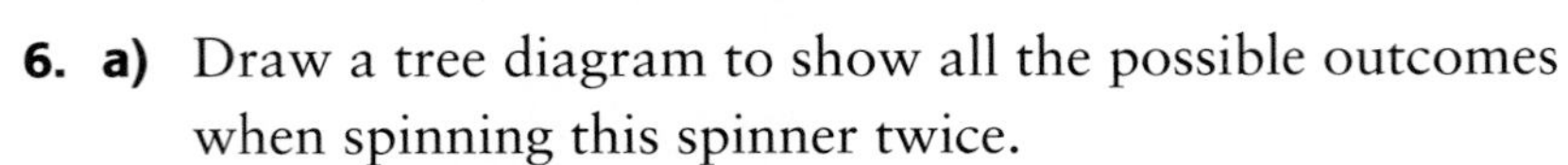

6. a) Draw a tree diagram to show all the possible outcomes when spinning this spinner twice.
   b) Determine the probability of spinning the same number twice. Use the tree diagram you drew in part (a).
   c) Determine the probability of spinning two numbers with a difference less than 3. Use your tree diagram.

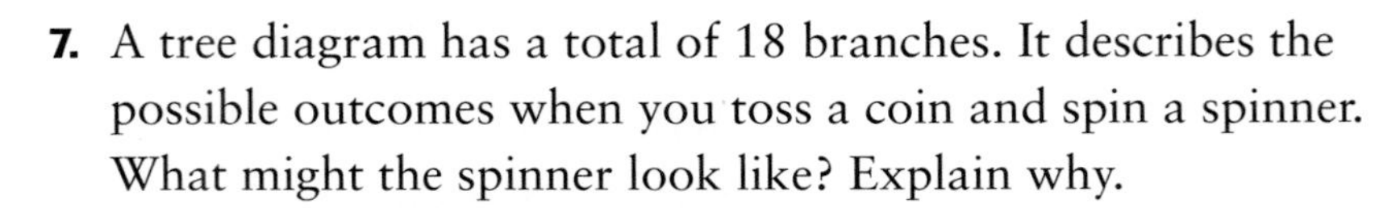

7. A tree diagram has a total of 18 branches. It describes the possible outcomes when you toss a coin and spin a spinner. What might the spinner look like? Explain why.

8. Roll two dice 20 times. Record the product of the numbers you get for each roll.
   a) Write the experimental probability that the product will be even.
   b) Write the theoretical probability that the product will be even.
   c) Which probability is greater, experimental or theoretical?
   d) Suppose that you rolled 100 times, and your results did not seem to match the theoretical probability. What might be the reason?

9. In an experiment, a card is drawn from a deck of 10 cards numbered 1 through 10. Describe an event with each probability.
   a) 0 b) 1 c) $\frac{1}{2}$ d) 20% e) 4:10 f) 7:10

What Do You Think Now?

Revisit What Do You Think? on page 429. How have your answers and explanations changed?

Chapter Review

Frequently Asked Questions

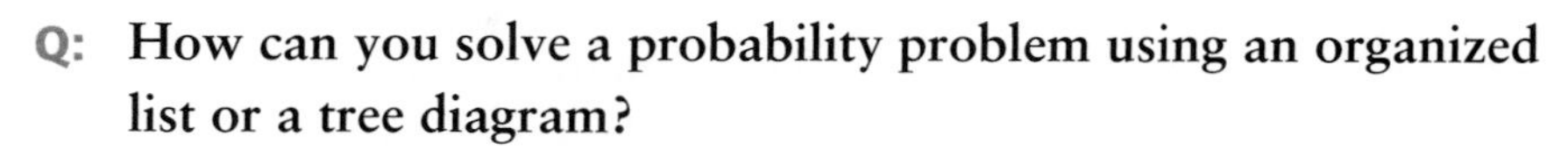

Q: How can you solve a probability problem using an organized list or a tree diagram?

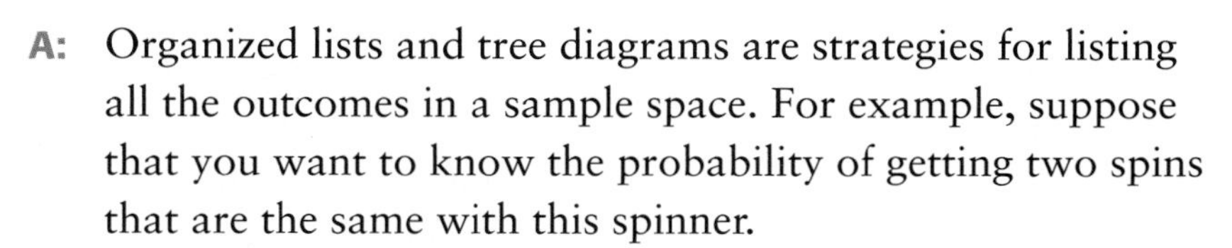

A: Organized lists and tree diagrams are strategies for listing all the outcomes in a sample space. For example, suppose that you want to know the probability of getting two spins that are the same with this spinner.

You can create an organized list to show the sample space and highlight the favourable outcomes.

1st spin is 1, 2nd spin is 1	1st spin is 2, 2nd spin is 1	1st spin is 3, 2nd spin is 1
1st spin is 1, 2nd spin is 2	**1st spin is 2, 2nd spin is 2**	1st spin is 3, 2nd spin is 2
1st spin is 1, 2nd spin is 3	1st spin is 2, 2nd spin is 3	**1st spin is 3, 2nd spin is 3**

$P(\text{both spins the same}) = \frac{3}{9} = \frac{1}{3}$

You can also use a tree diagram to represent all the outcomes, and then identify the favourable outcomes.

1 → ① (1, 1)
1 → 2 (1, 2)
1 → 3 (1, 3)

2 → 1 (2, 1)
2 → ② (2, 2)
2 → 3 (2, 3)

3 → 1 (3, 1)
3 → 2 (3, 2)
3 → ③ (3, 3)

$P(\text{both spins the same}) = \frac{3}{9} = \frac{1}{3}$

Practice

Lesson 10.2

1. Suppose that you randomly choose an integer from 1 to 100. Write each probability as a fraction and a percent.

a) P(number is even)

b) P(number has two digits)

c) P(number is a multiple of 10)

d) P(number is a multiple of 9)

2. Supppose that you randomly choose another integer from 1 to 100. Describe an event with each probability.

   a) 25% **b)** 0 **c)** 100%

Lesson 10.3

3. Imagine predicting the weather for the next two days using the weather spinner at the left.

   a) Explain why the spins are independent events.

   b) Explain why rainy, sunny, and cloudy are not equally likely events.

Lesson 10.4

4. Conduct an experiment in which you draw one card and spin the spinner once. List all the outcomes in the sample space. Then determine each theoretical probability using your list.

   a) *P*(greater than 7 and C) **b)** *P*(ace and 5)

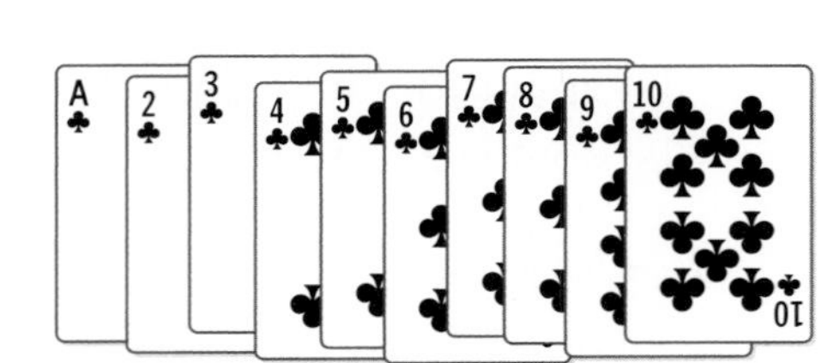

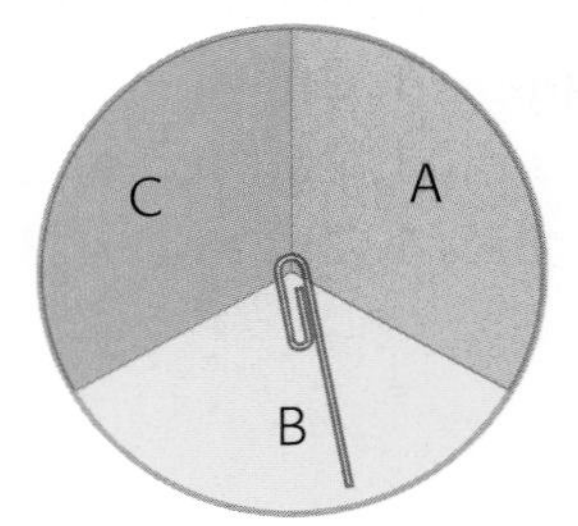

Lesson 10.5

5. Consider an experiment in which you spin the spinner at the left once and toss a coin. Determine the sample space for the experiment by drawing a tree diagram. Then use your tree diagram to determine each probability.

   a) *P*(7 and H) **b)** *P*(odd and T)

Lesson 10.6

6. Roll one die twice.

   a) Determine the theoretical probability that the numbers rolled will be in increasing order.

   b) Determine the experimental probability of the outcome from part (a) by carrying out an experiment using 36 trials.

   c) Explain why the theoretical probability in part (a) might be different from the experimental probability in part (b).

Chapter Task

Task | Checklist

- ✔ Did you make sure that your tree diagram represented all the possible outcomes?
- ✔ Did you conduct the experiments an appropriate number of times?
- ✔ Did you explain your thinking?
- ✔ Did you support your conclusions?

Winning Races

Fiona, Julie, and Yan are the best runners in their school. They always come in first, second, or third in races. Each comes in first in 2 km races about $\frac{1}{3}$ of the time.

What is the probability that Julie will win both 2 km races in the June competitions?

A. Determine the theoretical probability that Julie will win both races using a tree diagram.

B. Explain why Julie's running experiment is a fair way to determine the experimental probability that Julie will win both races.

Julie's Running Experiment
Roll a die.
- If the result is 1 or 2, Fiona wins.
- If the result is 3 or 4, I win.
- If the result is 5 or 6, Yan wins.

Roll twice.
Repeat this experiment 25 times.

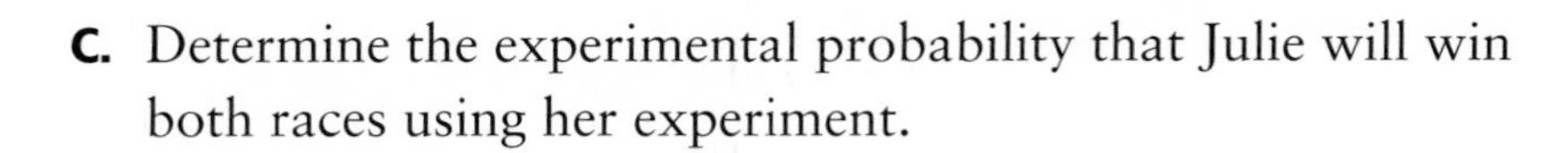

C. Determine the experimental probability that Julie will win both races using her experiment.

D. How do the probabilities in parts A and C compare? Which probability do you think is more accurate? Why?

E. Suppose that Julie trains really hard so she can win $\frac{1}{2}$ of the races. Each of the other two girls now wins only $\frac{1}{4}$ of the races. Would the tree diagram you drew in part A help you determine Julie's new probability of winning both races? Explain.

A Knight Island Otter's Diet
other
crabs
mussels
clams

Chapter 11

Circle Graphs

GOAL

You will be able to

- analyze and interpret data presented in a circle graph
- decide what kind of data is best displayed in a circle graph
- construct a circle graph using various methods

What can you determine from the circle graph?

Getting Started

Making Decisions

Nolan and Nestor conducted a survey to find out which activity, out of four different activities, their classmates would choose to do in their spare time.

They graphed their results.

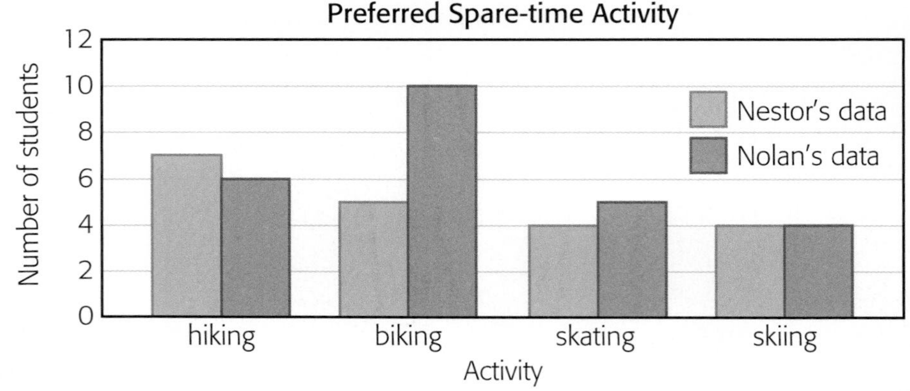

What can you conclude about the data in the graph?

A. How many students are in each class? How do you know?

B. Which activity do Nolan's classmates prefer? Which activity do Nestor's classmates prefer?

C. Create a table that shows the percent of each group that prefers each activity.

D. Combine the two groups. What percent of the combined group prefers each activity?

E. Which activity would you choose for each class if you had to plan a field day? Which activity would you choose for the combined classes? Explain.

What Do You Think?

Decide whether you agree or disagree with each statement.
Be ready to explain your decision.

1. The results of a survey to choose a new school colour are easy to interpret quickly by looking at the data in the following chart.

   What should be the new school colour?
   red (R) blue (B) orange (O)
   RRBOBORBOBBORBBOROBBRORB
   ORBORORRRBORROOBRRBOROOR

2. A graph is always a good way to show how individual amounts relate to the whole.

3. When you change the vertical scale on a bar graph, the highest bar on the original graph may not be the highest bar on the new graph.

4. The number of people about whom data was collected can always be determined by looking at a bar graph.

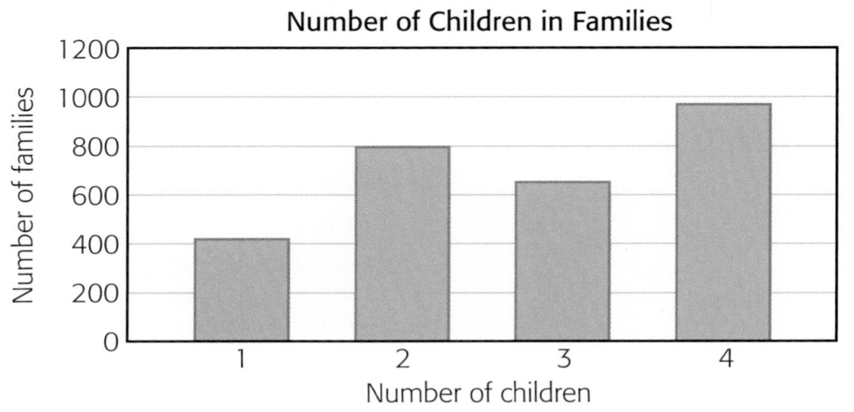

11.1 Interpreting Circle Graphs

Read and analyze the information in a circle graph.

LEARN ABOUT the Math

A video download site surveyed a large group of people, then made the following graph using the data.

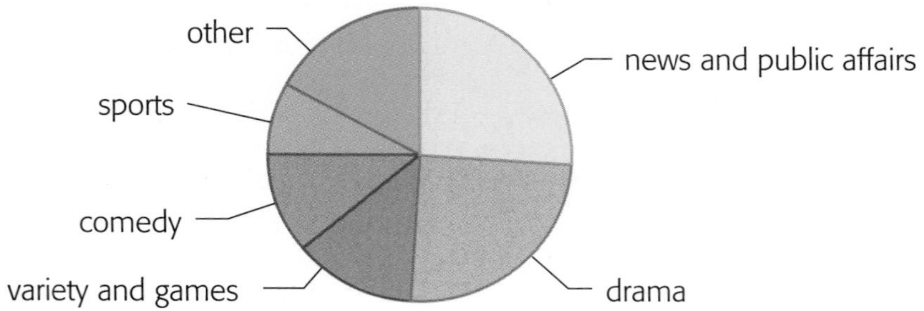

What can you learn from the data in the graph?

A. Why do you think the video site used these categories of viewing to gather its data in the **circle graph?**

B. Can you tell how many people were surveyed by looking at the graph? Does it matter how many people were surveyed?

C. Which section in the graph is about three times as large as another section? What can the larger section tell you about these types of programs?

D. List three other comparisions you can make using the data in the circle graph.

circle graph
a graph that shows how parts make up a whole

E. Out of 1000 people, about how many watch drama? Explain how you made your estimate.

F. What else can you conclude from the circle graph?

Reflecting

G. How might someone use the data in the circle graph?

H. Why is a circle graph a good way to communicate this kind of data?

WORK WITH the Math

Example 1 | Analyzing a circle graph

Kevin graphed the weekly sales of chocolate milk in his school. What can you determine from his circle graph?

Chocolate Milk Sold in a Week

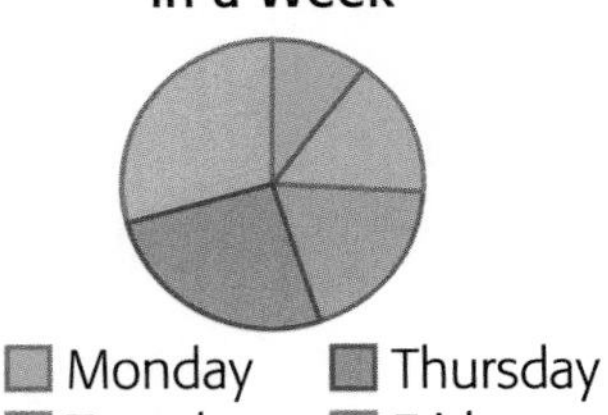

Nayana's Solution

I determined the following:

- A different amount of chocolate milk is sold each day.
  The sections are different sizes.
- The amounts sold increase every day from Monday to Friday.
  The sections increase in size from Monday to Friday.
- More than half the chocolate milk is sold on the last two days of the week.
  More than half the circle is for Thursday and Friday.
- If you order for a week in which Friday is a holiday, reduce your order by $\frac{1}{4}$.
  More than $\frac{1}{4}$ of the circle is for the amount sold on Friday.
- If you order for a week in which Monday is a holiday, reduce your order by $\frac{1}{10}$.
  About $\frac{1}{10}$ of the circle is for the amount sold on Monday.

Example 2 | Calculating amounts from a circle graph

Ashley saw this circle graph in the newspaper.

Ashley's older sister has a monthly income of about $2000. Ashley wants to know how much her sister should be spending in each budget category.

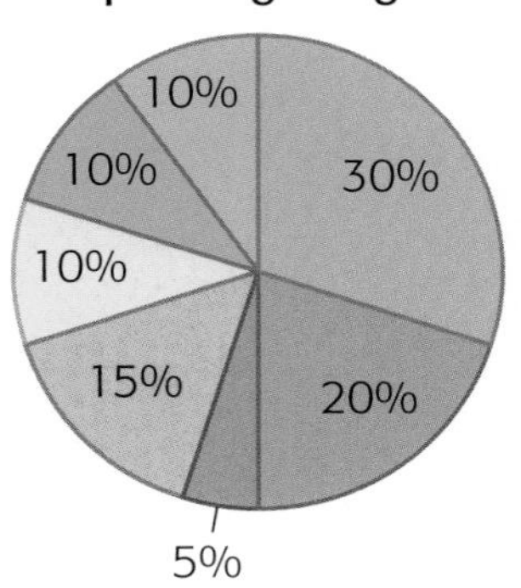

Ashley's Solution

My sister should be spending the following amounts, based on the circle graph:

• Recreation and Education: $200	I know that 10% of $2000 is $200 since 10% is $\frac{1}{10}$.
• Housing and Utilities: $600	If 10% of $2000 is $200, then 30% of $2000 is $3 \times \$200$.
• Food and Clothing: $400	20% is $2 \times \$200$.
• Health and Personal Care: $100	5% is half of 10%, which is $\$200 \div 2$.
• Transportation: $300	15% is 10% + 5%, so 15% is $200 + $100.
• Savings: $200	Since the last two categories are 10%, each is $200.
• Miscellaneous: $200	

A Checking

1. This table shows the amount of time that Canadians listen to different types of radio programs, by percent. Which set of data does each circle graph match?

Type of radio program	a) Listening time for ages 12 to 17 (%)	b) Listening time for all ages (%)
talk	2.3	11.4
sports	0.6	2.5
music	86.3	66.1
other	10.8	20.2

Circle Graph A

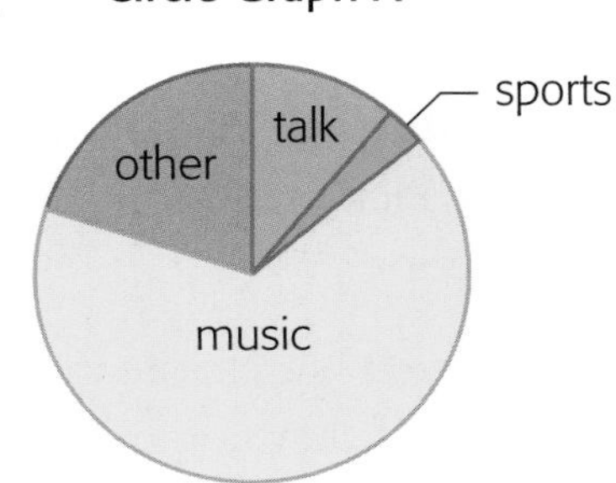

Circle Graph B

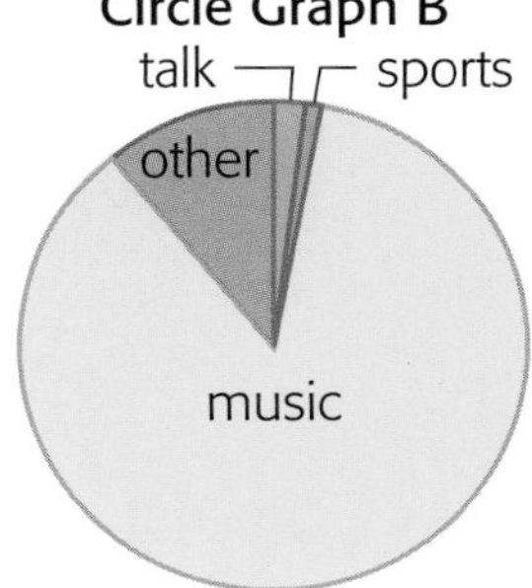

Reading Strategy

Write five statements about the circle graph. Share them with a partner. Ask your partner to agree or disagree with your statements.

2. Robert surveyed all 24 family members at his family reunion about their favourite kind of pie. Then he prepared the following graph. What advice can Robert give his family members when they are deciding which pies to serve at the next family reunion?

Favourite Kinds of Pie

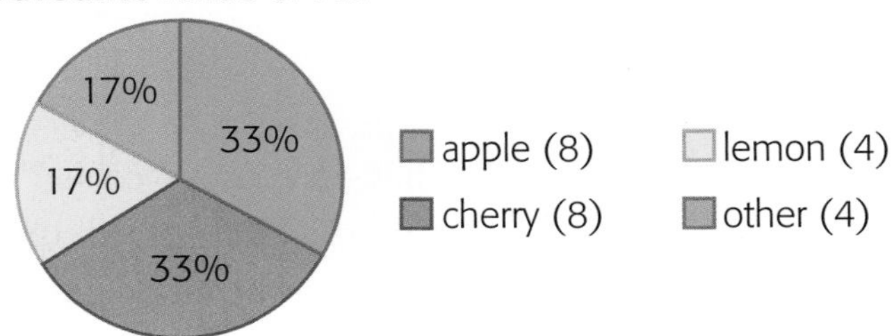

T-shirt Sizes Sold

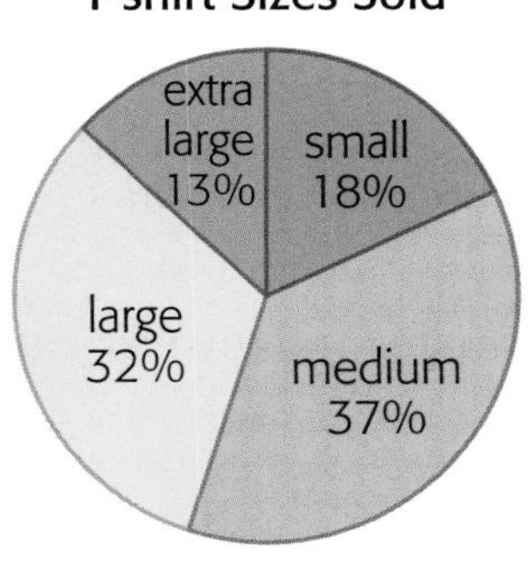

B Practising

3. Linda sold 200 T-shirts at her stall last weekend. The graph at the left shows what percent of each size was sold. How many medium T-shirts did Linda sell?

4. The following graphs show how much space two newspapers give to various sections.
   a) Why can't you tell which newspaper gets more income from advertising?
   b) Can you tell which newspaper has more sports pages? Explain.

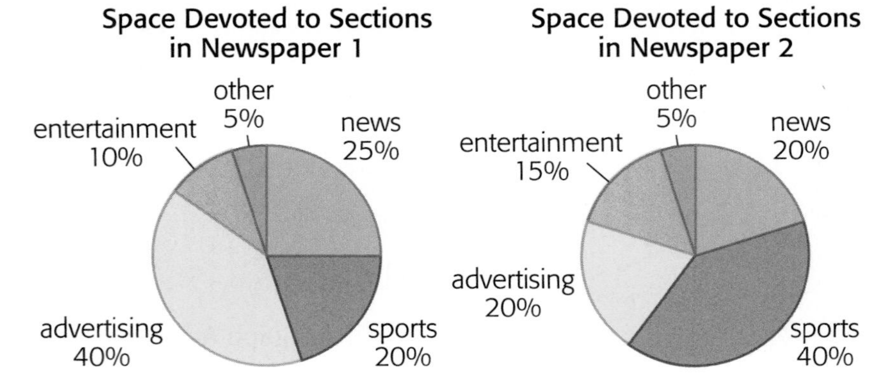

5. Today's editions of both newspapers in question 4 have 120 pages. Pick one of the newspapers. How many pages are in each section?

6. Erica surveyed her classmates about what superpower they would want if they could have only one.

Superpower	Percent of total (%)
power to fly	29
super strength	21
invisibility	20
power to read minds	13
power to control weather	7
other	■

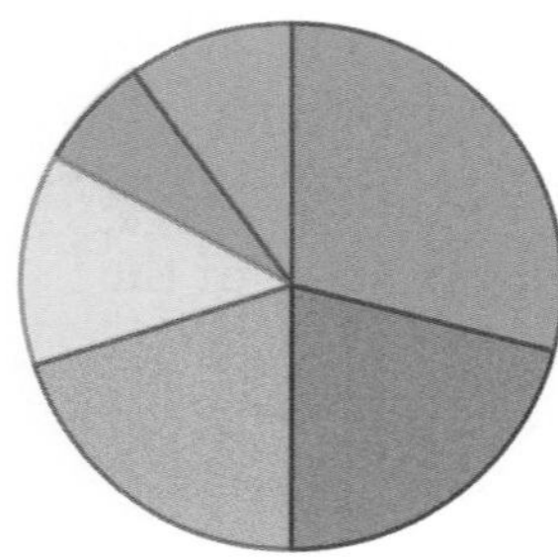

   a) What percent is "other"?
   b) Copy the circle graph into your notebook. Label each section in the circle graph with a name and the percent.

7. **a)** Write three questions you could ask about the data in question 6.
   b) Exchange your questions with a classmate, and answer each other's questions.

8. What information can you not get from a circle graph?

11.2 Exploring Circle Graphs

GOAL

Predict how data might be distributed.

EXPLORE *the Math*

Circle graphs are often a convenient way to display data.

Choose one of the circle graphs below. Think of some data you could collect about your class or school that might end up looking like the graph you chose. Collect the data.

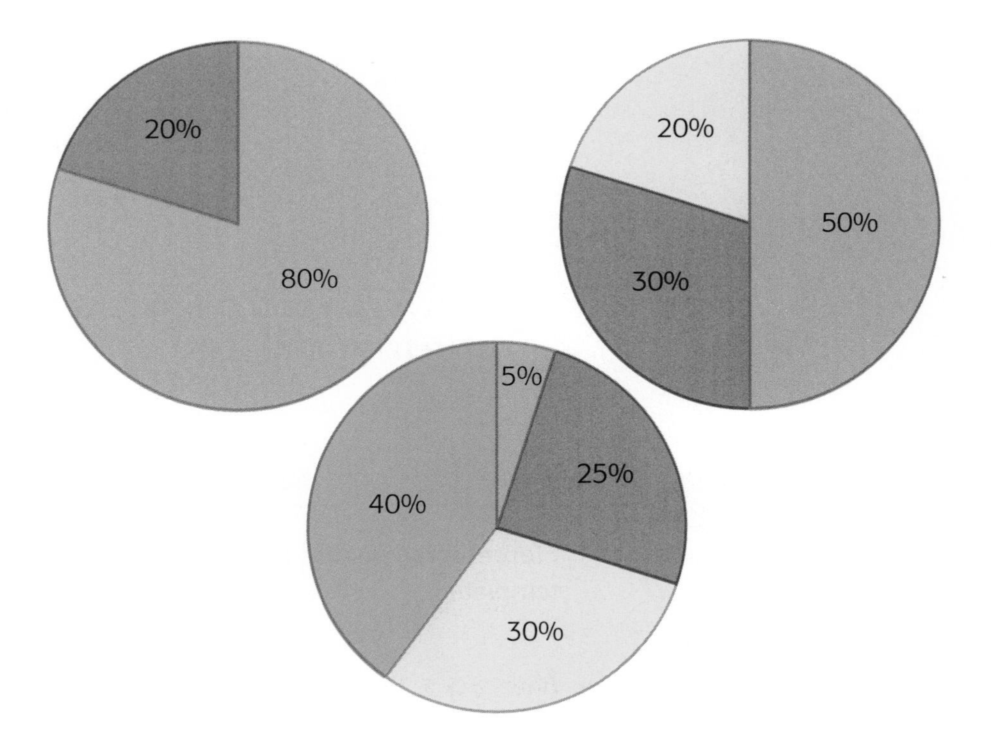

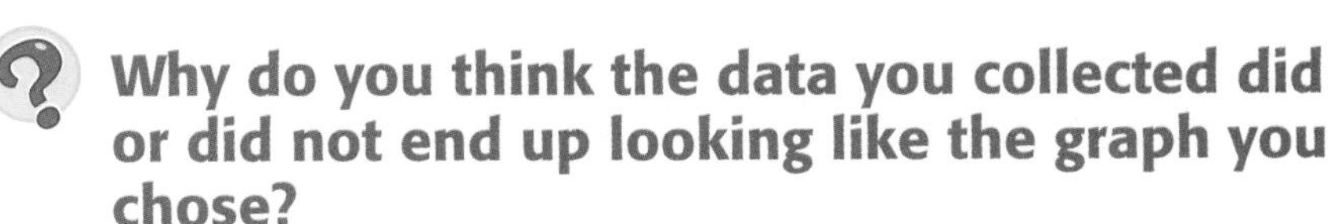

Why do you think the data you collected did or did not end up looking like the graph you chose?

11.3 Constructing Circle Graphs

YOU WILL NEED

- a 100% circle template (Blackline Master)
- a compass
- a protractor
- a calculator

GOAL

Create a circle graph for a data set.

LEARN ABOUT the Math

Sarah asked a group of people what their favourite outdoor exercise is. She recorded her results.

Favourite exercise	Number of people
cycling	16
skateboarding	10
skating	10
skiing	4

How can you represent Sarah's results in a circle graph?

Example 1 | Using a 100% circle template

I represented Sarah's results in a circle graph using a 100% circle template.

Megan's Solution

Favourite exercise	Number of people	Percent (%)
cycling	16	40
skateboarding	10	25
skating	10	25
skiing	4	10
Total	40	100

I wrote each number of people as a percent. There are 40 people in total.

16 out of 40 is like 4 out of 10, or 40%.

10 out of 40 is like 1 out of 4, or 25%.

4 out of 40 is like 1 out of 10, or 10%.

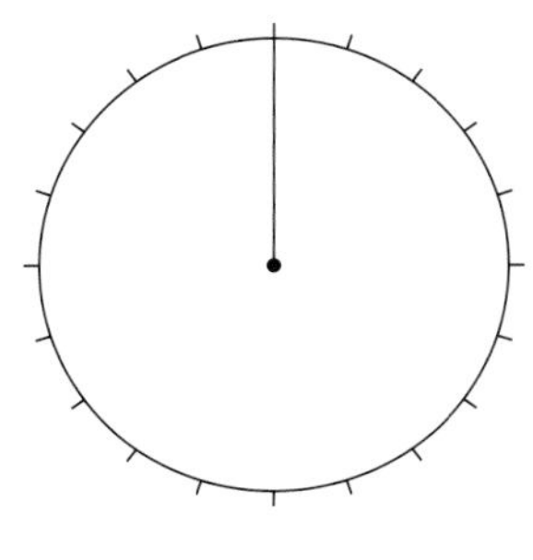

I drew a radius on the circle, from the centre to 0%, as a place to start.

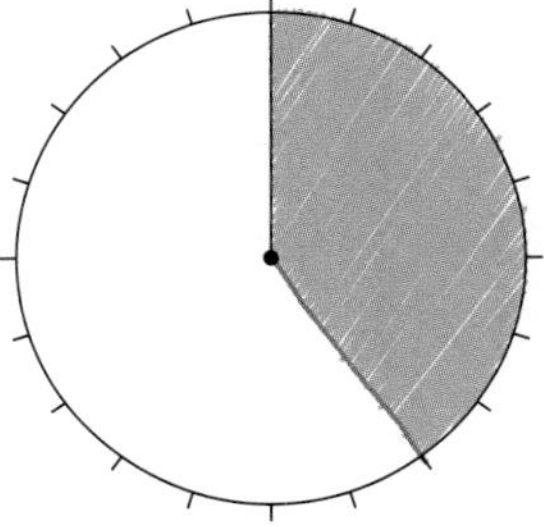

Each mark on the template represents 5%. For 40%, I counted 8 marks. I drew a radius to complete the first section.

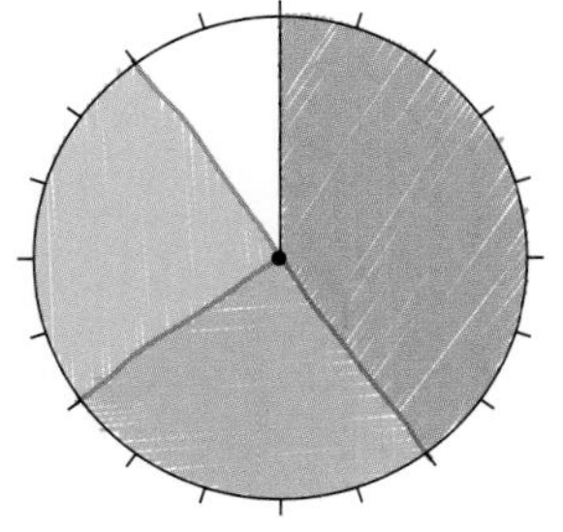

For 25%, I counted 5 marks and drew a radius. I did this twice. There were 2 marks left. They represented the last 10% of the data.

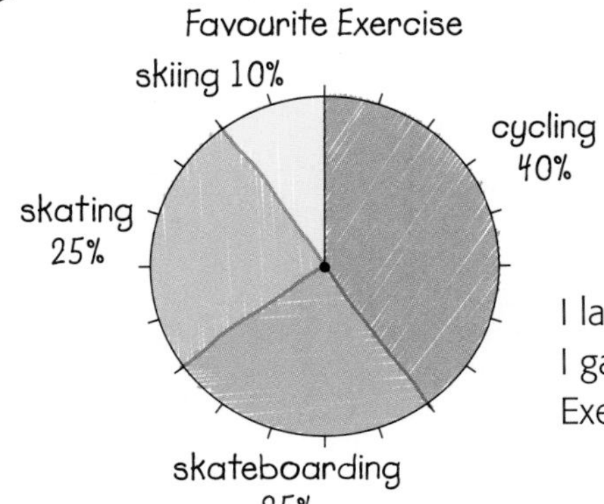

I labelled each section. I gave my circle graph the title "Favourite Exercise."

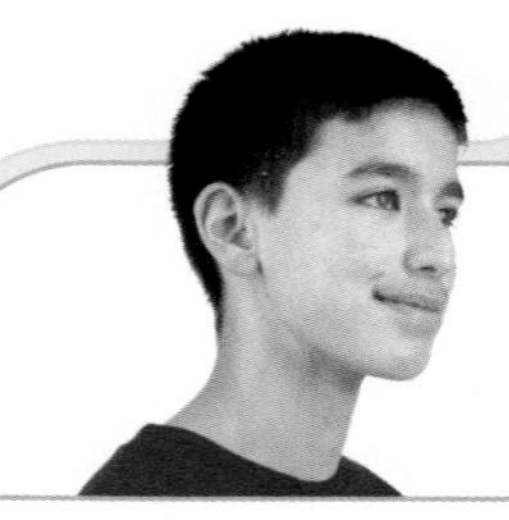

Example 2 | Using central angles

I represented Sarah's results in a circle graph using central angles.

Nolan's Solution

Favourite exercise	Number of people	Percent (%)	Central angle (°)
cycling	16	40	40% of 360 = 144
skateboarding	10	25	25% of 360 = 90
skating	10	25	25% of 360 = 90
skiing	4	10	10% of 360 = 36
Total	40	100	360

I wrote each number of people as a percent. Then I determined the central angle for each percent. There are 360° in a circle, so 100% of a circle is 360°.

I drew a circle and marked the centre. Since there are two sections with 90° angles, I drew a diameter and split it in half to represent these two sections.

Then I marked a 36° angle for the skiing section.

I checked the remaining section. It should have a 144° angle.

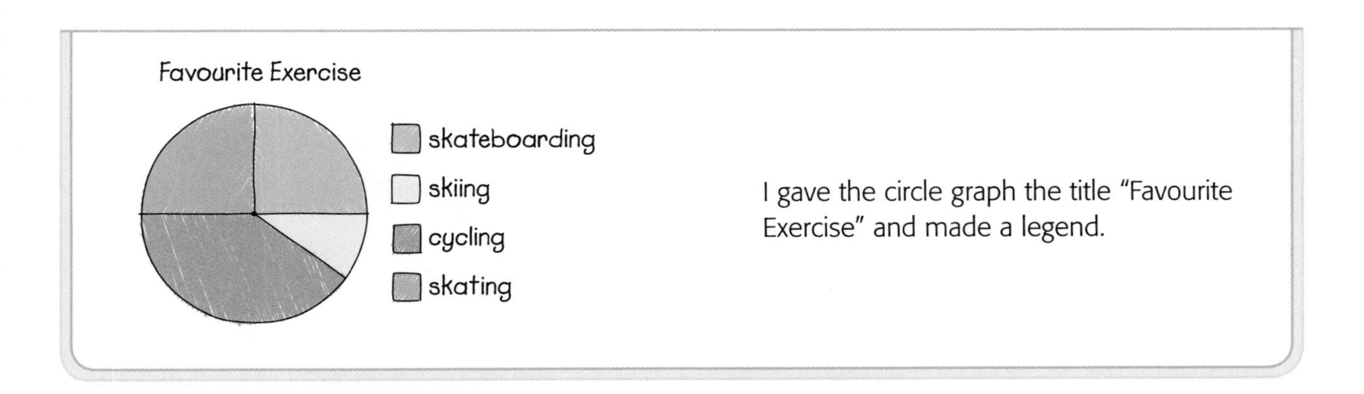

I gave the circle graph the title "Favourite Exercise" and made a legend.

Example 3 | Using a spreadsheet

I represented Sarah's results in a circle graph using a spreadsheet.

Nestor's Solution

	A	B
1	cycling	16
2	skateboarding	10
3	skating	10
4	skiing	4
5		

I entered Sarah's results in a spreadsheet.

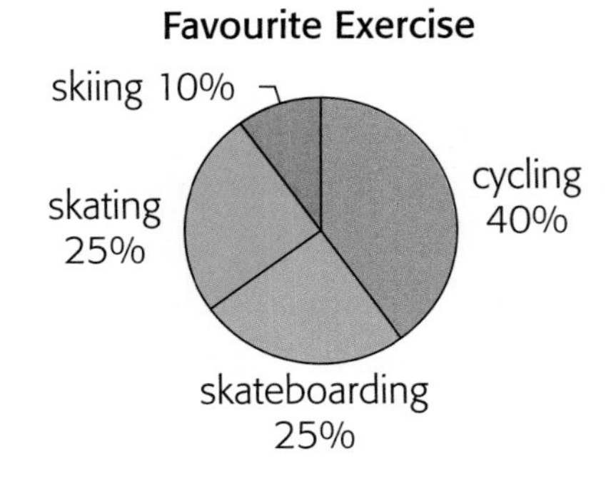

I generated a circle graph for the data using the spreadsheet program.

Reflecting

A. Why do you think circle graphs are sometimes called pie charts?

B. How are the three methods for constructing a circle graph alike? How are they different?

C. What kind of data would you use each method for?

WORK WITH the Math

A Checking

1. Two groups of people at a mall were asked, "What was the first thing you bought here today?"

Group A

Item	Number of people	Percent (%)
clothing	20	■
books	16	■
CDs or DVDs	40	■
other	4	■

Group B

Item	Number of people	Percent (%)
clothing	30	■
books	24	■
CDs or DVDs	36	■
other	30	■

a) Calculate the missing percents.

b) Display the data using a 100% circle template. Explain what you did.

c) Combine the two sets of data. Create a circle graph using a compass and a protractor to display the combined data.

B Practising

2. Charlotte surveyed 150 people. Write each number of people as a percent. How many degrees does the central angle of each section have?

a) 50 **b)** 75 **c)** 20 **d)** 5

3. Milk is 88% water, 5% carbohydrates, 3% fat, 3% protein, and 1% inorganic material. Represent the composition of milk in a circle graph.

4. The following table shows the flavours of ice cream that were sold at a school sports day.

Flavour	Percent sold (%)	Central angle (°)
vanilla	28	■
mint chocolate chip	6	■
chocolate	42	■
strawberry	12	■
bubble gum	12	■
Total	100	360°

a) Complete this table.
b) Display the data in a circle graph.
c) Create a question about the data. Answer your question.

Activity	Percent (%)
cards	8
board games	5
video games	45
arcade	12
movies	30

5. The table at the left shows activities that were organized for birthday parties. Display the data in a circle graph.

6. This table shows the results of a survey of Canadian adults.

Education	Number (in thousands)
0 to 8 years	2.2
some high school	4.0
high school graduate	4.9
some post-secondary	2.5
post-secondary certificate or diploma	7.5
university degree	4.4
Total	25.5

a) Enter the data in a spreadsheet.
b) Display the data in a circle graph using the spreadsheet.
c) What calculation do you think the spreadsheet program did to create the circle graph?

7. What are some ways you can check that your circle graph is correct?

11.4 Communicate about Circle Graphs

Use data and graphs to support conclusions.

LEARN ABOUT the Math

Jessica wants her mother to increase her allowance. She decides to convince her mother that she needs a larger allowance by putting together a report that shows her spending and saving habits. She makes a circle graph to display how she uses her allowance. She asks Ashley to comment on her report.

How can Jessica improve her report?

Jessica's Report

Allowance	Amount earned	Amount spent on entertainment	Amount spent on food	Amount spent on clothes	Amount spent on music	Amount saved
$40	$60	$29	$31	$14	$12	$14

My Spending Habits

I organized my data in a spreadsheet. Then I used the graphing program on my computer to construct a circle graph.

I chose a circle graph to show my spending and saving habits.

I gave my graph a title and labelled the sections of the graph with percents.

I showed that almost 31% of my allowance goes to food, which I need, so I really have only 69% of my allowance for other expenses.

From my graph, I can conclude that I spend more than I save.

Ashley's Comments

Is this a typical month?

How did you use the spreadsheet program?

Why did you use a circle graph?

You didn't say why you need more allowance.

Communication *Checklist*

- ✔ Did you include all the important details?
- ✔ Did you make reasonable conclusions?
- ✔ Did you justify your conclusions?

A. Which of Ashley's comments do you think is most important for improving Jessica's report? Why?

B. What additional suggestions can you make to help Jessica improve her report?

Reflecting

C. Do you think Jessica presented a convincing argument for increasing her allowance?

WORK WITH the Math

Example | Using a circle graph to support a conclusion

Nick surveyed 40 students after gym class about what kind of drink they like best after exercising. He prepared a report to show the kinds of drinks that should be sold in the school cafeteria. He asked Pavlo to read his report and make suggestions for improvements.

Pavlo's Editing

To gather information about the kinds of drinks that should be sold in the school cafeteria, I surveyed 40 students. ← Add "who were coming out of gym class, since they had just finished exercising and would be thirsty."

85% of these students preferred bottled water, lemonade, or iced tea.

Since 40% preferred bottled water, it should definitely be sold. ← I agree – it's the most popular.

A total of 45% preferred either iced tea or lemonade. This is more than the number of students who preferred water, so water should not be the only drink offered. ← Good point!

Juice should also be offered for students who want a nutritional choice.

← Add a conclusion: "I recommend that bottled water, lemonade, iced tea, and juice should be sold."

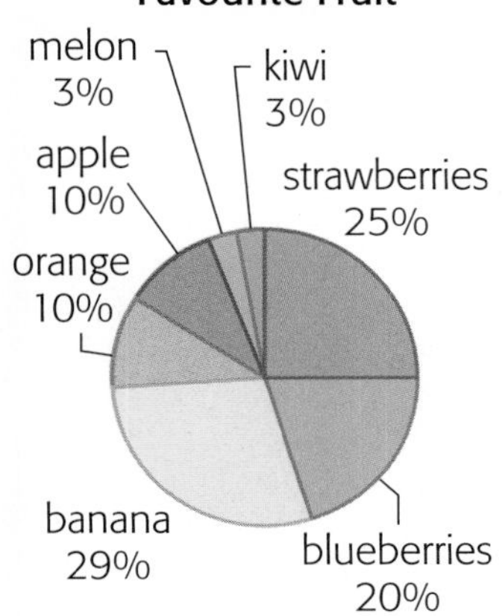

A Checking

1. Petra surveyed 40 students at the school picnic about their favourite fruit. She concluded that berries should not be served at the next picnic, since less than half of the graph is berries. What do you think about Petra's interpretation of the data?

B Practising

2. Kevin wrote a report about the food he ate in a week. He used a circle graph. What questions would you ask to help Kevin draw more conclusions in his report?

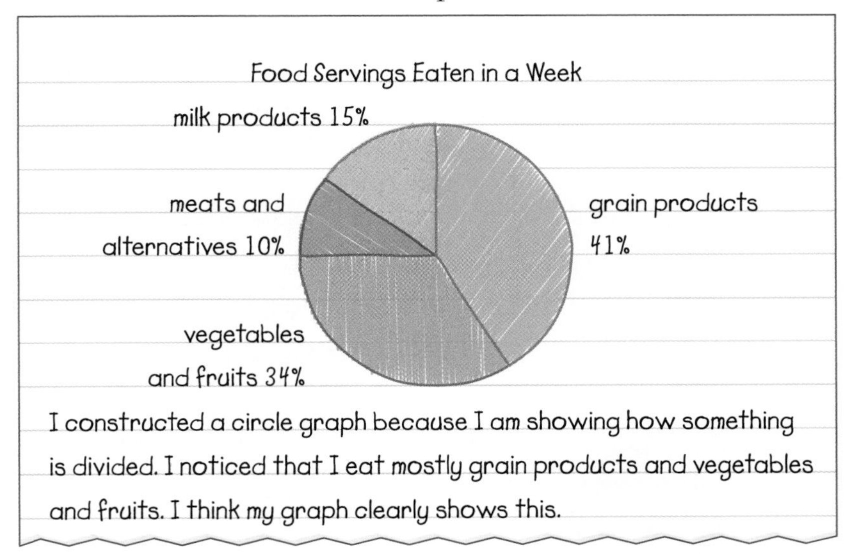

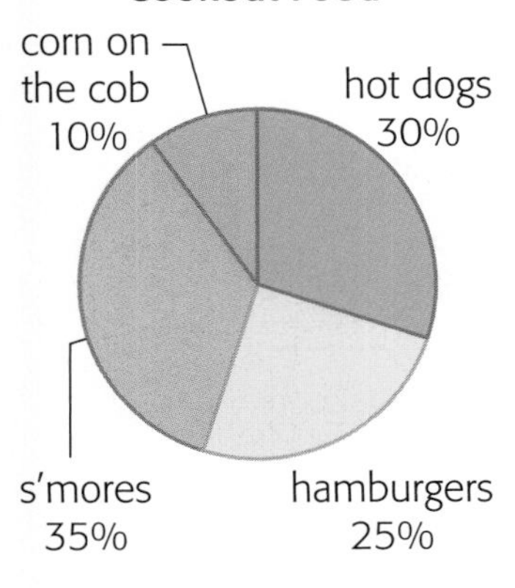

3. The circle graph at the left shows favourite foods at a campfire cookout. Write a report based on the data in the graph. Share your report with a classmate, and ask for ways to improve it.

4. Look on the Internet or in newspapers and magazines to find circle graphs that show similar information. Explain how the circle graphs are similar and how they are different.

5. When you are studying a circle graph, what kind of questions should you ask yourself about the information it shows?

MATH GAME

Race to 100%

Number of players: 2 or more

YOU WILL NEED
- a bag
- different-coloured counters
- a compass

How to Play

1. Assign each player a different colour of counter. Put all the counters in the bag.
2. One player reaches into the bag and pulls out a handful of counters. This player then draws a circle graph as follows:
   - Draw a circle and place the counters around it, equally spaced. Place all the counters of each colour together.
   - Draw line segments from the centre of the circle to the places on the circumference where the colours change. Label each section with its colour and percent, to the nearest 1%.
   - Record the percent for each colour in a table.
3. Players take turns pulling counters from the bag and drawing a circle graph. Players add the percents for each turn to the percents for the previous turn.
4. The first player to accumulate 100% or more wins.

Denis's Circle Graph

I had the second turn.
I pulled out three blues, one yellow, two reds, and two purples.
I drew the circle graph and recorded the percents.
Now I'm tied for first.

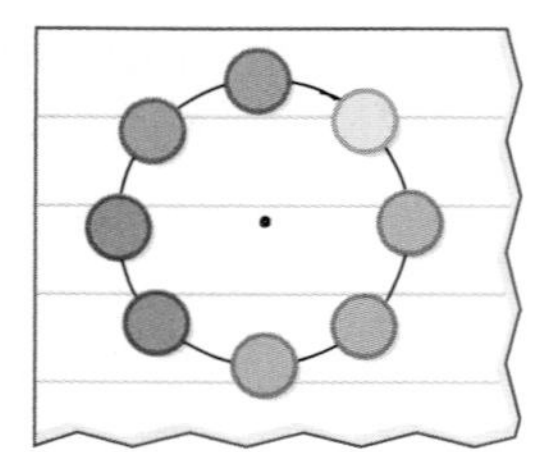

purple 25%
yellow 15%
red 25%
blue 40%

Chad:	Denis:	Jorge:	Akeela:
red	yellow	blue	purple
~~30%~~	~~40%~~	~~10%~~	~~20%~~
55%	55%	50%	45%

CURIOUS MATH

Graphs of Different Shapes

A circle graph is used to represent data as parts of a whole.

Could you use a triangle, a square, a rectangle, or any other shape to represent the same kind of data?

The following table and circle graph show the types of paper students bought for school at a local store on one day.

Type of paper	Number of packages
lined	64
plain	8
graph	8

Types of Paper Purchased

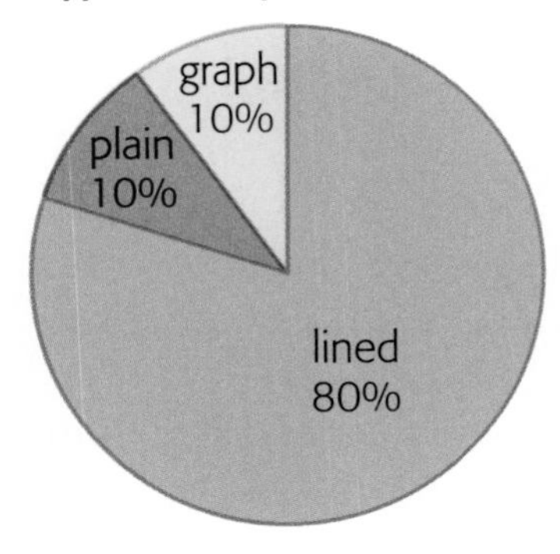

1. Draw a rectangle with 10 squares that are the same size. Colour the rectangle to represent the percents of types of paper bought.

2. Represent the same data using a different shape. Explain your choice.
3. Is one shape easier to use than the other for drawing a graph? Explain.

Chapter Self-Test

1. A Grade 7 class surveyed 500 students, asking which language their mother speaks. They displayed the data they gathered in the following table.

Language Mother Speaks at Home

Language	Number of mothers
Arabic	30
Chinese	90
English	100
French	90
Hindi	60
Ukrainian	80
other*	50

*includes Cree, Punjabi, Japanese, Korean, and more

a) Display these data in a circle graph.
b) What are some facts you can learn from your graph?

2. Suppose that you manage two movie theatres. The following circle graphs show the percents of different types of movies shown each year at your theatres. Theatre 1 is more successful than Theatre 2. What changes might you make to the movies shown at Theatre 2 to increase its audiences? Explain any assumptions you make.

Types of Movies at Theatre 1

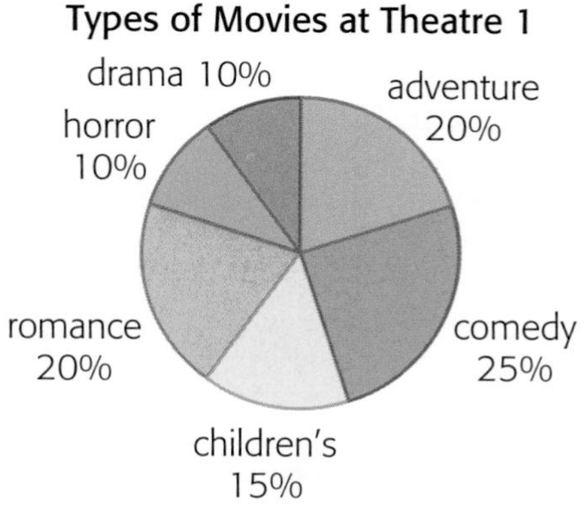

Types of Movies at Theatre 2

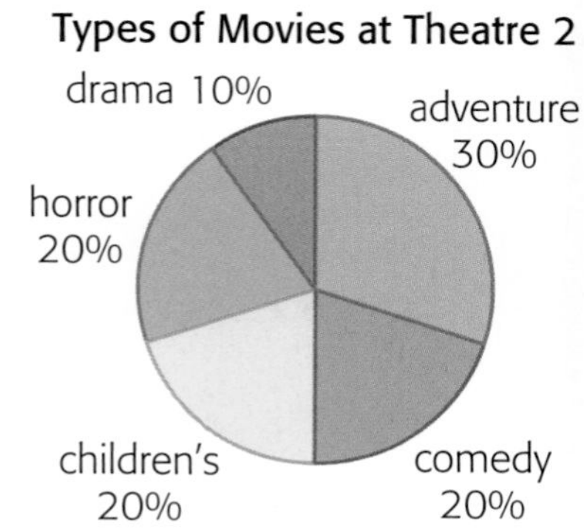

3. Gary's older brother weighs 80 kg. His body consists of 39.8 kg of muscle, 14.9 kg of fat, 14.2 kg of bone, and 11.1 kg of other tissue. Display the data in a circle graph.

4. A major league baseball player's record of outcomes for his first 600 times at bat is shown in the following graph.

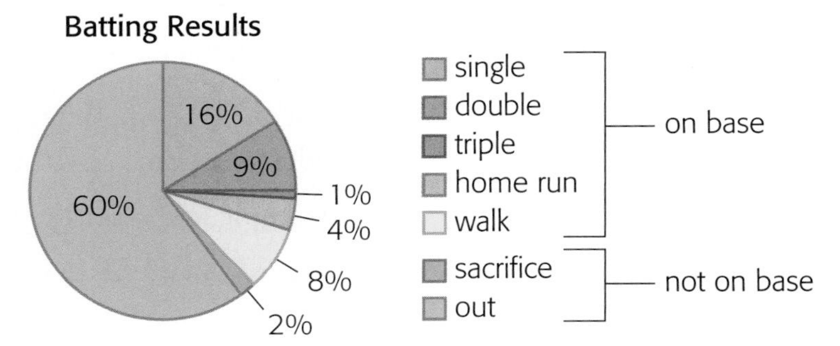

   a) How many times did the player get on base?
   b) How many home runs did he get?

5. For a probability experiment, Hoshi grabbed coloured counters from a bag three times.

Colour	First handful	Second handful	Third handful
blue	6	4	2
red	4	5	5
brown	2	3	4
green	5	4	3
orange	3	2	2
yellow	2	2	4

   a) Construct a circle graph for each handful.
   b) What is the central angle of each section in your third circle graph?

What Do You Think Now?

Revisit What Do You Think? on page 467. How have your answers and explanations changed?

Chapter **Review**

Frequently Asked Questions

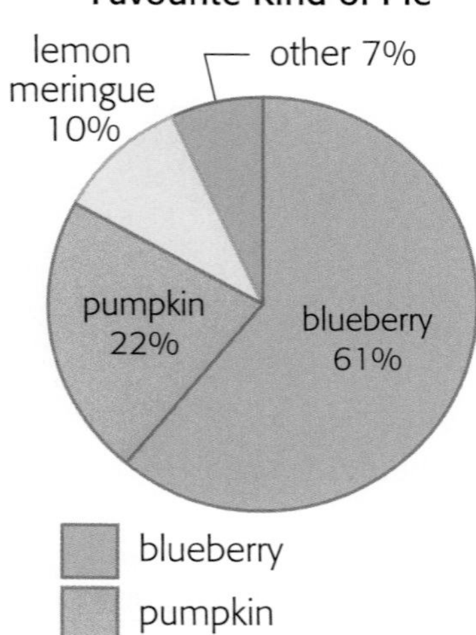

Q: How do you read a circle graph?

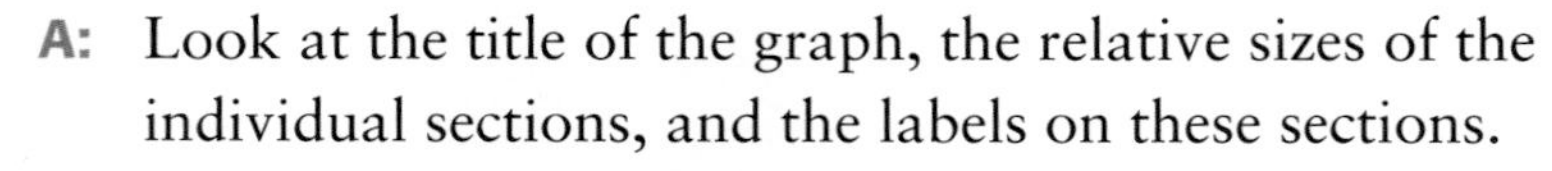

A: Look at the title of the graph, the relative sizes of the individual sections, and the labels on these sections.

For example, consider the graph at the left.

The title of the graph gives an overview of the information displayed in the graph.

Each section represents one part of the whole. The size of each section represents its fraction of the whole.

The label on each section gives the category name and a percent, so that you know the size of the section.

There may be a legend that identifies the categories by colour.

Q: How can you draw a circle graph?

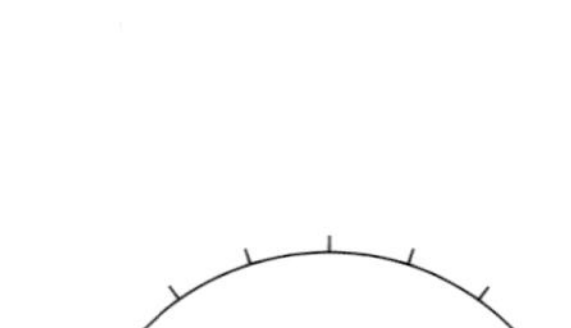

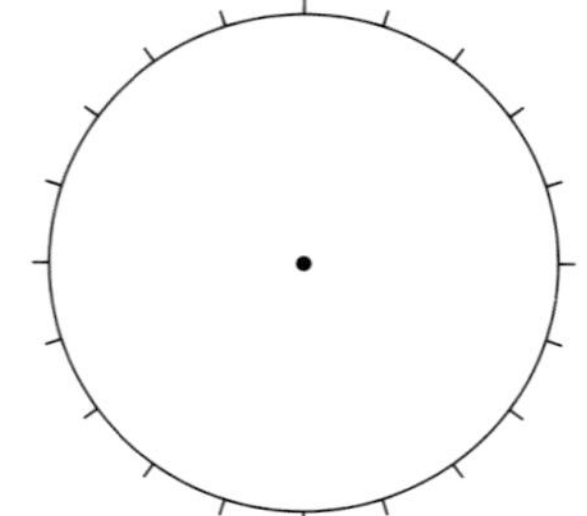

A1: Calculate the number of degrees the central angle for each section should be by multiplying the percent value, expressed as a decimal, by 360°. Then draw the sections using a ruler and a compass. Colour each section, label it with the category and percent, and give the graph a title.

A2: Convert each amount into a percent of the whole. Then use a 100% circle template with benchmark percents to draw sections based on the percents you calculated. Colour each section, label it with the category and percent, and give the graph a title.

A3: Enter the data into a spreadsheet program, and use the program to create a circle graph. Give the graph a title.

Practice

Lesson 11.1

1. A company surveyed 4000 employees about how they get to work. The data collected are shown in the following circle graph.

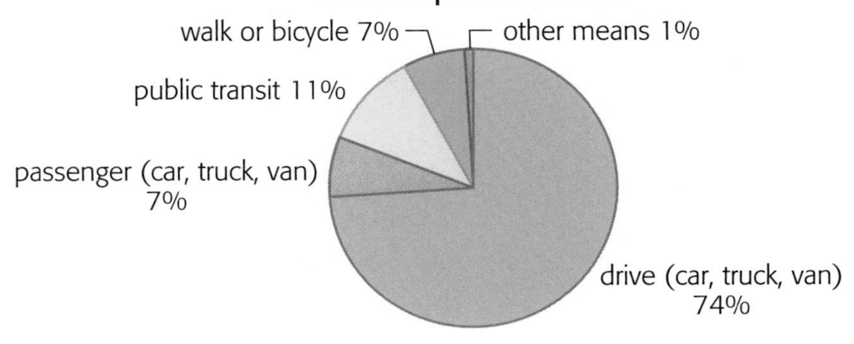

a) How many employees walk or ride a bicycle to work?

b) How many people use a car, truck, or van to get to work?

c) What could "other means" of transportation be?

Lesson 11.3

2. Anne recorded the colours of 100 cars in the parking lot of a supermarket.

Colour of car	Number of cars of each colour
white	20
silver	32
black	18
red	12
blue	18

a) Why would a circle graph be an appropriate way for Anne to display her data?

b) Display Anne's data in a circle graph.

3. A 300 g container of yogurt contains 228 g of water, 54 g of carbohydrates, 12 g of protein, and 6 g of fat.

a) Display the data in a circle graph.

b) Create a problem based on your graph. Exchange your problem with a classmate, and solve each other's problem.

Source	Revenue ($)
registration	25 000
dances	3 500
ticket sales	2 750
sponsors	6 000

4. The revenue of a local hockey team for a season is shown at the left.

a) What was the club's total revenue for the season?

b) Create a circle graph that displays the club's sources of revenue.

c) Approximately what percent of the club's revenue came from sponsors?

d) How do the revenues from ticket sales and sponsors compare?

e) What three sources provide about 85% of the revenue?

Lesson 11.4

5. The following database shows the lunchtime drink choices of the Grade 7 and 8 students in a school:

Type of drink	Grade 7	Grade 8
bottled water	12	20
milk	19	12
apple juice	11	13
orange juice	13	27
grapefruit juice	20	4
no drink	5	8

a) Which grade has a greater percent of students who prefer juice?

b) Which three drinks should be sold in the school cafeteria? Present your opinion in a letter to the principal. Include a circle graph to make your letter convincing.

6. a) Look on the Internet or in newspapers and magazines for data that can be displayed using a circle graph. Create a circle graph to display the data.

b) Write a statement that explains what the data suggests, and support your statement with your graph.

c) Trade statements with a classmate. Give each other suggestions on how to improve your statements.

Chapter Task

Task | *Checklist*

✔ Are your results in an appropriate form?

✔ Are your results easy to understand?

✔ Did you justify your conclusions?

Designing a Spinner

A game company wants to design a spinner that will work just like rolling two dice. In this game, there are three outcomes:

- If you roll a sum from 2 to 4, you get three counters and another roll.

- If you roll a sum from 5 to 8, you get two counters.

- If you roll a sum from 9 to 12, you get one counter.

How can you create a spinner that works just like dice?

A. Calculate the theoretical probability of each outcome.

B. Create a circle graph with three different sections. The sizes of the sections are determined by the theoretical probabilities you calculated in part A.

C. Use your circle graph to build a spinner. Label the sections.

D. Conduct an experiment to compare the outcomes on your spinner with the outcomes when rolling two dice. Record the data.

E. Does your spinner work just like rolling two dice? Write a report to the game company, explaining why the company should use your spinner.

Chapters 8–11

Cumulative Review

Note: Select ALL the correct answers to each question.

Cathie received the following marks on five quizzes: 93%, 76%, 85%, 93%, and 3%. Use these marks to answer questions 1, 2, 3, 4, and 5.

1. What is the range of Cathie's marks?
A. 3 **B.** 75 **C.** 90 **D.** 93

2. What is the mode of Cathie's marks?
A. 3% **B.** 76% **C.** 85% **D.** 93%

3. What is the median of Cathie's marks?
A. 3% **B.** 76% **C.** 85% **D.** 93%

4. What is the mean of Cathie's marks?
A. 70% **B.** 76% **C.** 87% **D.** 93%

5. What is the mean of Cathie's marks if the outlier is not included?
A. 70% **B.** 76% **C.** 87% **D.** 93%

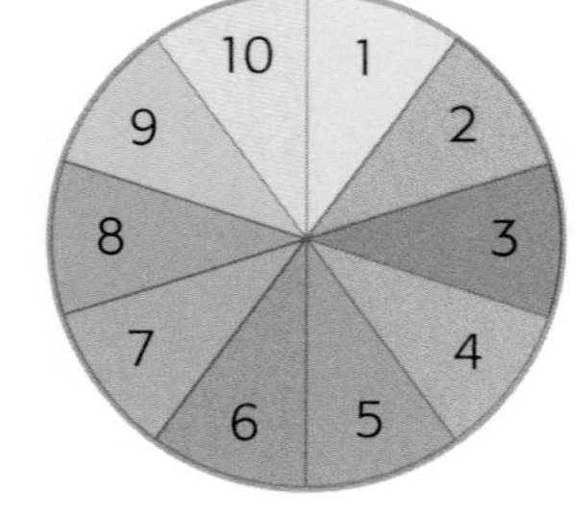

Questions 6, 7, and 8 refer to the spinner shown at the left.

6. What is the theoretical probability of spinning a 5?
A. 5% **B.** 10% **C.** 20% **D.** 50%

7. What is the theoretical probability of spinning a multiple of 3?
A. $\frac{1}{3}$ **B.** $\frac{3}{10}$ **C.** $\frac{1}{5}$ **D.** $\frac{1}{10}$

8. What is the theoretical probability of spinning an even number and tossing a tail with a coin?
A. 0.2 **B.** 25% **C.** 0.5 **D.** 50%

9. Which solutions are correct?
A. $7n = 84; n = 77$
B. $c - 9 = 79; c = 88$
C. $q + 14 = 40; q = 26$
D. $4z + 4 = 52; z = 13$

10. What is the value of p in $13 = p - 27$?
A. -40 **B.** -14 **C.** 14 **D.** 40

11. Kim is 10 years old. Which expression tells how old Kim will be y years from now?

A. $10 - y$ **B.** $10y$ **C.** $10 + y$ **D.** $\frac{y}{10}$

12. One pizza serves six people. Chris bought p pizzas for his party. Which expression tells how many people were served at Chris's party?

A. $p - 6$ **B.** $6p$ **C.** $p + 6$ **D.** $\frac{p}{6}$

13. Solve $\frac{n}{5} + 2 = 7$ using the graph below.

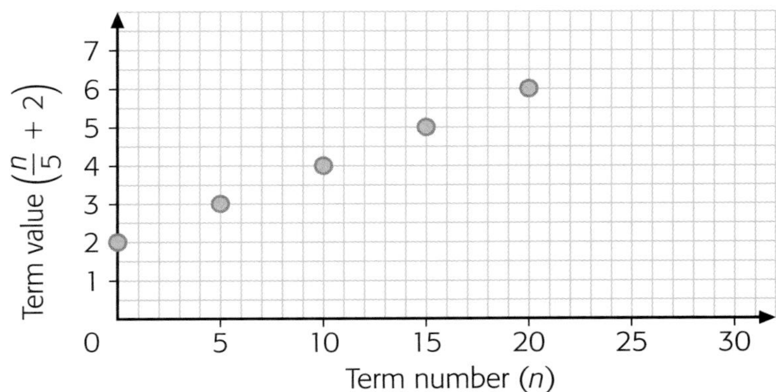

A. $n = 13$ **B.** $n = 5$ **C.** $n = 1$ **D.** $n = 25$

14. Kale sold 200 ice cream cones at his stand last week. The following graph shows the percent of each kind he sold. How many vanilla ice cream cones did he sell?

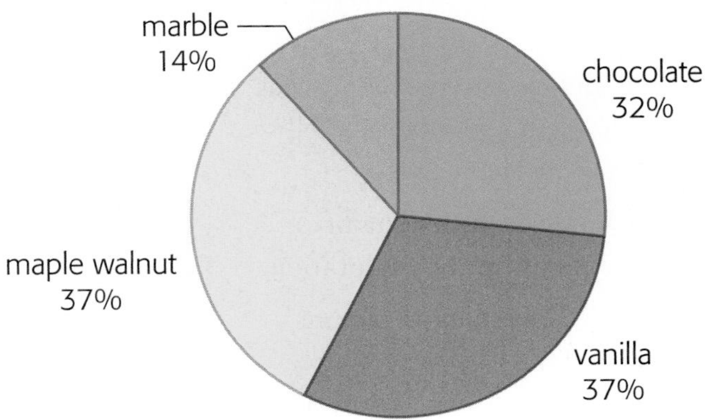

A. 32 **B.** 37 **C.** 74 **D.** 6

Glossary

Instructional Words

C

calculate [*calculer*]**:** Figure out the number that answers a question; compute

clarify[*clarifier*]: Make a statement easier to understand; provide an example

classify [*classer* ou *classifier*]**:** Put things into groups according to a rule and label the groups; organize into categories

compare [*comparer*]**:** Look at two or more objects or numbers and identify how they are the same and how they are different (e.g., Compare the numbers 6.5 and 5.6. Compare the size of the students' feet. Compare two shapes.)

conclude [*conclure*]: Judge or decide after reflection or after considering data

construct [*construire*]: Make or build a model; draw an accurate geometric shape (e.g., Use a ruler and a protractor to construct an angle.)

create [*inventer* **ou** *créer*]**:** Make your own example

D

describe [*décrire*]**:** Tell, draw, or write about what something is or what something looks like; tell about a process in a step-by-step way

determine [*déterminer*]**:** Decide with certainty as a result of calculation, experiment, or exploration

draw: 1. [*dessiner*] Show something in picture form (e.g., Draw a diagram.)
2. [*tirer*] Pull or select an object (e.g., Draw a card from the deck. Draw a tile from the bag.)

E

estimate [*estimer*]**:** Use your knowledge to make a sensible decision about an amount; make a reasonable guess (e.g., Estimate how long it takes to cycle from your home to school. Estimate how many leaves are on a tree. What is your estimate of 3210 + 789?)

evaluate [*évaluer*]**:** 1. Determine if something makes sense; judge
2. Calculate the value as a number

explain [*expliquer*]**:** Tell what you did; show your mathematical thinking at every stage; show how you know

explore [*explorer*]**:** Investigate a problem by questioning, brainstorming, and trying new ideas

extend: 1. [*prolonger*] In patterning, continue the pattern
2. [*généraliser*] In problem solving, create a new problem that takes the idea of the original problem farther

J

justify [*justifier*]**:** Give convincing reasons for a prediction, an estimate, or a solution; tell why you think your answer is correct

M

measure [*mesurer*]**:** Use a tool to describe an object or determine an amount (e.g., Use a ruler to measure the height or distance around something. Use a protractor to measure an angle. Use balance scales to measure mass. Use a measuring cup to measure capacity. Use a stopwatch to measure the time in seconds or minutes.)

model [*représenter* ou *faire un modèle*]: Show or demonstrate an idea using objects and/or pictures (e.g., Model addition of integers using red and blue counters.)

P

predict [*prédire*]: Use what you know to work out what is going to happen (e.g., Predict the next number in the pattern 1, 2, 4, 7, ...)

R

reason [*raisonner* ou *argumenter*]: Develop ideas and relate them to the purpose of the task and to each other; analyze relevant information to show understanding

relate [*établir un lien* ou *associer*]: Describe how two or more objects, drawings, ideas, or numbers are similar

represent [*représenter*]: Show information or an idea in a different way that makes it easier to understand (e.g., Draw a graph. Make a model. Create a rhyme.)

S

show (your work) [*montrer son travail* ou *présenter sa démarche*]: Record all calculations, drawings, numbers, words, or symbols that make up the solution

sketch [*esquisser*]: Make a rough drawing (e.g., Sketch a picture of the field with dimensions.)

solve [*résoudre*]: Develop and carry out a process for finding a solution to a problem

sort [*trier* ou *classer*]: Separate a set of objects, drawings, ideas, or numbers according to an attribute (e.g., Sort 2-D shapes by the number of sides.)

V

validate [*valider*]: Check an idea by showing that it works

verify [*vérifier*]: Work out an answer or solution again, usually in another way; show evidence of

visualize [*imaginer*]: Form a picture in your head of what something is like; imagine

Mathematical Words

A

algebraic expression [*expression* (n.f.) *algébrique*]: The result of applying arithmetic operations to numbers and **variables**; e.g., in one **formula** for the perimeter of a rectangle, $P = 2 \times (l + w)$, the algebraic expression $2 \times (l + w)$ shows the calculation (Also known as an **expression.**)

angle bisector [*bissectrice* (n.f.)]: A line that cuts an angle in half to form two equal angles

B

base [*base* (n.f.)]: The side of a shape that is measured for calculating the area or perimeter of a shape. Each base has a corresponding **height** that creates a 90° angle with the base. Any side of a shape can be the base of the shape.

C

Cartesian coordinate system [*système* (n.m.) *de coordonnées cartésiennes*]**:** A method (named after mathematician René Descartes) for describing a location by identifying the distance from a horizontal number line (the x-axis) and a vertical number line (the y-axis). The location is represented by an ordered pair of **coordinates**, (x, y). The axes intersect at (0, 0), which is called the **origin**.

centre of rotation [*centre* (n.m.) *de rotation*]**:** A fixed point around which other points in a shape rotate in a **clockwise (cw)** or **counterclockwise (ccw)** direction; the centre of rotation may be inside or outside the shape

circle graph [*diagramme* (n.m.) *circulaire*]**:** A graph that shows how the parts make up a whole

circumference [*circonférence* (n.f.)]**:** The boundary of a circle; the length of this boundary

clockwise (cw) [*dans le sens* (n.m.) *des aiguilles d'une montre*]**:** Turning in a sense similar to the hands of a clock; e.g., a turn from direction OP to direction OQ is a clockwise turn (Also see **counterclockwise.**)

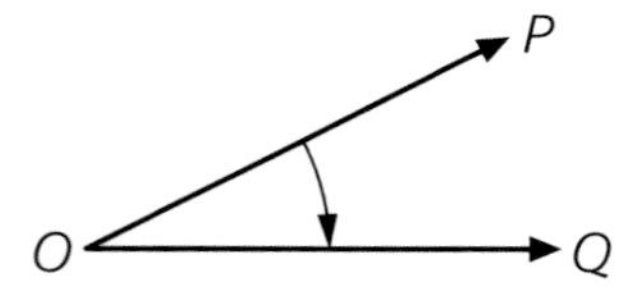

common denominator [*dénominateur* (n.m.) *commun*]**:** A **common multiple** of two or more denominators; e.g., for $\frac{2}{3}$ and $\frac{3}{6}$, a common denominator would be any **multiple** of 6. If you use the **least common multiple** of the denominators, the common denominator is called the lowest common denominator.

common factor [*diviseur* (n.m.) *commun*]**:** A whole number that divides into two or more other whole numbers with no remainder; e.g., 4 is a common factor of 12 and 24

common multiple [*multiple* (n.m.) *commun*]**:** A number that is a **multiple** of two or more given numbers; e.g., 12, 24, and 36 are common multiples of 4 and 6

constant term [*constante* (n.f.)]**:** A quantity that does not change; e.g., in $2 \times n + 5$, 5 is a constant term

convex [*convexe*]**:** A design where all interior angles measure no greater than 180°

coordinates [*coordonnées* (n.f.pl.) *d'un point* ou *coordonnées* (n.f.pl.)]**:** An ordered pair, used to describe a location on a grid labelled with an x-axis and a y-axis; e.g., the coordinates (1, 3) describe a location on a grid that is 1 unit horizontally from the **origin** and 3 units vertically from the origin

counterclockwise (ccw) [*dans le sens* (n.m.) *contraire des aiguilles d'une montre*]**:** Turning in a sense opposite to the hands of a clock, e.g., a turn from direction OQ to direction OP is a counterclockwise turn (Also see **clockwise.**)

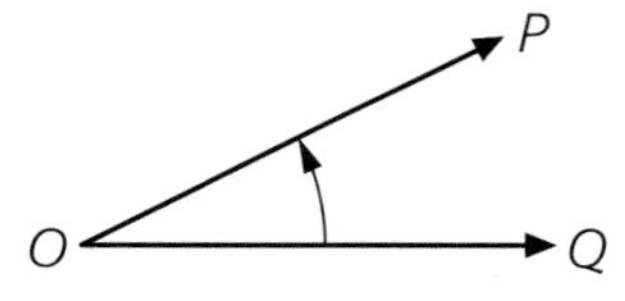

D

diameter [*diamètre* (n.m.)]**:** A **line segment** that joins two points on the **circumference** of a circle and passes through the centre; the length of this line segment

digital root [*racine* (n.f.) *numérique*]**:** The number obtained by adding the digits of a number, then repeating the digit addition for each new number found, until a single-digit number is reached, e.g., the digital root of 123 is $1 + 2 + 3 = 6$

divisibility rule [*règle* (n.f.) *de divisibilité* ou *caractères* (n.m.pl.) *de divisibilité*]**:** A way to determine if one whole number is a **factor** of another whole number without actually dividing the entire number

E

equally likely outcomes [***résultats*** (n.m.pl.) ***également probables***]**:** Two or more outcomes that have an equal chance of occurring; e.g., the outcome of rolling a 1 and the outcome of rolling a 2 on a 6-sided die are equally likely outcomes because each outcome has a **probability** of $\frac{1}{6}$

equation [***égalité*** (n.f.); ***remarque: en français, une équation comporte obligatoirement une inconnue***]**:** A statement that two quantities or **expressions** are **equivalent**; e.g., $4 + 2 = 6$ and $6x + 2 = 14$

equivalent [***équivalent***]**:** Equal in value; e.g., two equivalent fractions are $\frac{1}{2}$ and $\frac{2}{4}$, two equivalent **ratios** are 6:4 and 9:6, and the fraction $\frac{1}{2}$ is equivalent to the decimal 0.5

event [***événement*** (n.m.)]**:** A set of one or more outcomes in a **probability** experiment; e.g., the event of rolling an even number with a 6-sided die consists of the outcomes of rolling a 2, a 4, or a 6

experimental probability [***probabilité*** (n.f.) ***expérimentale***]**:** In a **probability** experiment, the **ratio** of the number of observed **favourable outcomes** to the number of **trials**, or repetitions, of the experiment

expression [***expression*** (n.f.) ***numérique***]**:** See **algebraic expression** [***expression algébrique*** (f)]

F

factor [***facteur*** (n.m.)]**:** One of the numbers you multiply in a multiplication operation

$$\underset{\text{factor}}{\underset{\uparrow}{2}} \times \underset{\text{factor}}{\underset{\uparrow}{6}} = 12$$

favourable outcome [***résultat*** (n.m.) ***favorable***]**:** The desired result in a **probability** experiment

formula [***formule*** (n.f.)]**:** A rule represented by symbols, numbers, or letters, often in the form of an **equation**; e.g., Area of a rectangle = length × width or $A = l \times w$

G

greatest common factor (GCF) [***plus grand diviseur*** (n.m.) ***commun*** ou ***PGDC***]**:** The greatest whole number that is a **factor** of two or more whole numbers; e.g., 4 is the greatest common factor of 8 and 12

H

height [***hauteur*** (n.f.)]**:** A **line segment** drawn to form a right angle with the side of a shape

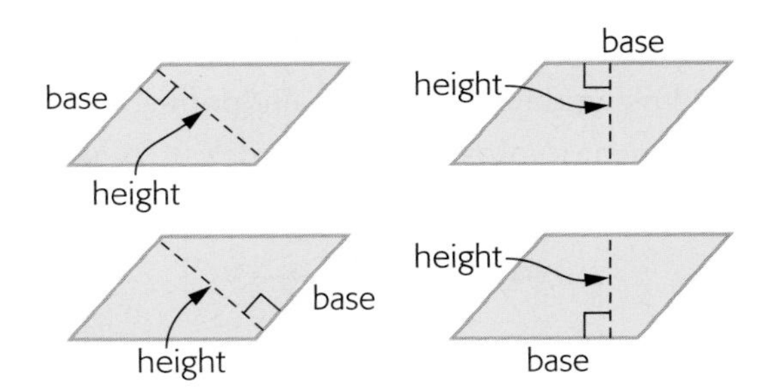

I

improper fraction [***fraction impropre*** (n.f.)]**:** A fraction in which the numerator is greater than the denominator; e.g., $\frac{4}{3}$

independent events [***événements*** (n.m.pl.) ***indépendants***]**:** Two **events** are independent if the **probability** of one is not affected by the probability of the other; e.g., if you toss a coin and roll a die, the events are independent. The result of rolling the die does not depend on the result of tossing the coin.

integer [***nombre*** (n.m.) ***entier*** ou ***entier*** (n.m.)]**:** the counting numbers (+1, +2, +3, ...), zero (0), and the opposites of the counting numbers (−1, −2, −3, ...)

intersection point [*le point d'intersection* (n.m.)]: The point where two lines or line segments cross each other; eg., QR intersects ST at intersection point E

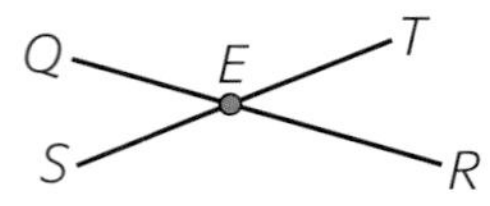

L

least common multiple (LCM) [*plus petit multiple* (n.m.) *commun* ou *PPMC*]: The least whole number that has two or more given whole numbers as **factors**; e.g., 12 is the least **common multiple** of 4 and 6

linear relation [*rapport* (n.m.) *linéaire* ou *relation* (n.f.) *de variation directe*]: A **relation** whose plotted points lie on a straight line

line segment [*segment* (n.m.) *de droite* ou *segment* (n.m.)]: Part of a line with two endpoints; it is named using the labels of the endpoints, e.g., the line segment joining points X and Y is called XY

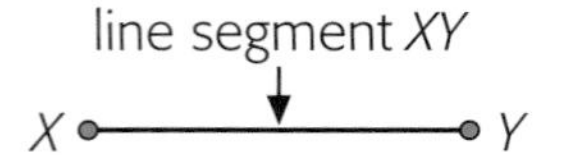

lowest terms [*sous forme* (n.f.) *irréductible*]: An **equivalent** form of a fraction with numerator and denominator that have no **common factors** other than 1; e.g., $\frac{3}{4}$ is the lowest term form of $\frac{12}{16}$ since $\frac{3}{4} = \frac{12}{16}$ and 3 and 4 have no common factors other than 1

M

mean [*moyenne* (n.f.)]: A representative value of a set of data; it is determined by sharing the total amount of the data evenly among the number of values in the set; e.g., consider the set of data 3, 6, 8, 14, 9. There are 5 values, and their sum is 40. The mean is 8 because 40 divided equally among 5 values would give each number the value 8. That is, $40 \div 5 = 8$.

median [*médiane* (n.f.)]: A representative value of a set of data; the middle value of the ordered data. When there is an odd number of values, the median is the middle value; e.g., the median of 2, 3, and 4 is 3. When there is an even number of values, it is the value halfway between the two middle values; e.g., the median of 2, 3, 4, 5, 6 and 6 is 4.5.

mixed number [*nombre fractionnaire* (n.m.)]: A number made up of a whole number and a fraction; e.g., $5\frac{1}{2}$

mode [*mode* (n.m.)]: A representative value of a set of data; the value or item that occurs most often in a set of data. A set of data might have no mode, 1 mode, or more than 1 mode; e.g., the mode of 1, 5, 6, 6, 6, 7, and 10 is 6.

multiple [*multiple* (n.m.)]: The product of a whole number and any other whole number; e.g., when you multiply 10 by the whole numbers 0 to 4, you get the multiples 0, 10, 20, 30, and 40

N

numerical coefficient [*coefficient* (n.m.)]: The multiplier of a **variable**; e.g., in $2 \times n + 5$, 2 is the numerical coefficient of n

O

opposite integers [*nombres* (n.m.pl.) *entiers opposés* ou *entiers* (n.m.pl.) *opposés*]: Two **integers** the same distance away from zero; e.g., +2 and −2 are opposite integers

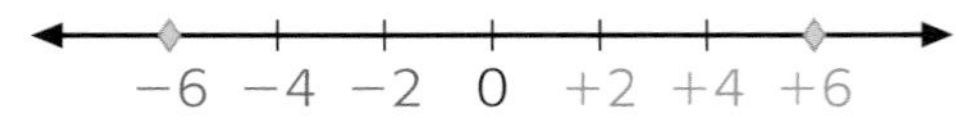

order of operations [*priorité* (n.f.) *des opérations*]: A set of rules people use when calculating to get the same answer. The rules for the order of operations are
Rule 1: Do the operations in brackets first.
Rule 2: Divide and multiply from left to right.
Rule 3: Add and subtract from left to right.
To remember the rules, think of "BDMAS": Brackets, Divide and Multiply, Add and Subtract.

origin [*origine* (n.f.)]**:** The point from which measurement is taken; in the **Cartesian coordinate system,** it is the intersection of the vertical and horizontal axes and is represented by the ordered pair (0, 0)

outlier [*observation* (n.f.) *aberrante*]**:** A data value that is far from the other data values

P

parallel [*parallèle*]**:** Always the same distance apart; e.g., line segments AB and CD are parallel

A ———— B

C ———— D

pattern rule [*règle* (n.f.) *de la suite*]**:** A way to describe a pattern that compares a characteristic of the figure to the figure number; e.g., a pattern rule for the pattern shown below is $b = 4 \times n + 1$, where b is the number of blocks in figure n

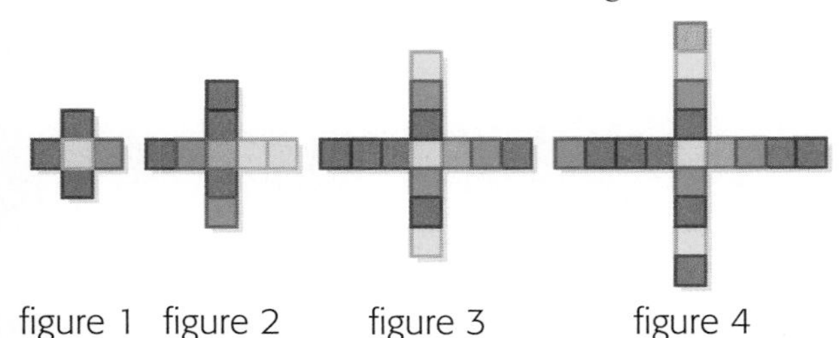

percent [*pourcentage* (n.m.)]**:** A part to whole **ratio** that compares a number or an amount to 100; e.g., $25\% = 25:100 = \frac{25}{100}$

perpendicular bisector [*bissectrice* (n.f.) *perpendiculaire*]**:** A line that intersects a **line segment** at 90° and divides it into two equal lengths; any point on the perpendicular bisector to AB is equidistant from endpoints A and B

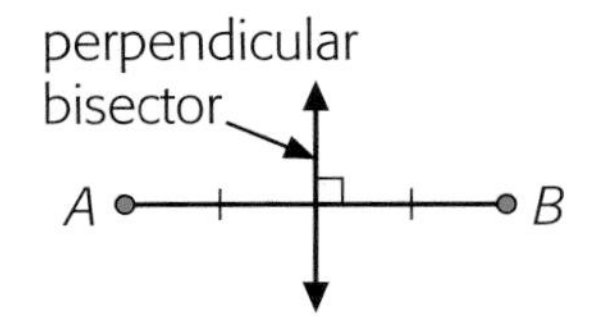

π (pi) [*(pi)* (n.m.) ou **π**]**:** The **ratio** of the **circumference** of a circle to its **diameter**; its value is about 3.14

prime number [*nombre* (n.m.) *premier*]**:** A number with only two **factors**, 1 and itself; e.g., 17 is a prime number since its only factors are 1 and 17

probability [*probabilité* (n.f.)]**:** A number from 0 to 1 that shows how likely it is that an **event** will happen

proportion [*proportion* (n.f.)]**:** A number sentence that shows two **equivalent ratios** or fractions; e.g., $\frac{1}{4} = \frac{5}{20}$

R

radius [*rayon* (n.m.)]**:** Half the **diameter** of a circle; the distance from the centre of a circle to a point on the **circumference**

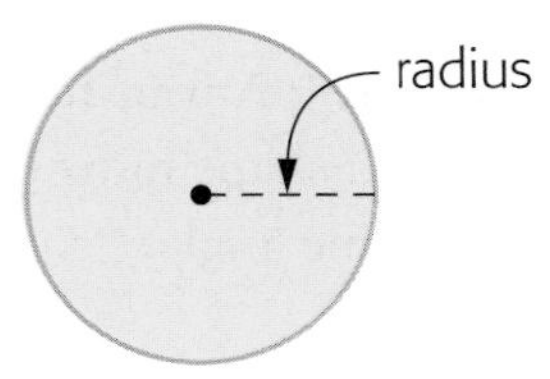

range [*étendue* (n.f.)]**:** The difference between the greatest and least number in a set of data; e.g., the range of 6, 7, 7, 8, 9 is 3, because $9 - 6 = 3$

ratio [*rapport* (n.m.)]**:** A comparison of two quantities with the same units; e.g., if you mix juice using 1 can of concentrate and 3 cans of water, the ratio of concentrate to juice is 1:4, or 1 to 4

reflection [*réflexion* (n.f.)]**:** The result of a flip of a 2-D shape; each point in a 2-D shape flips to the opposite side of the line of reflection, but stays the same distance from the line (Also see **transformation.**)

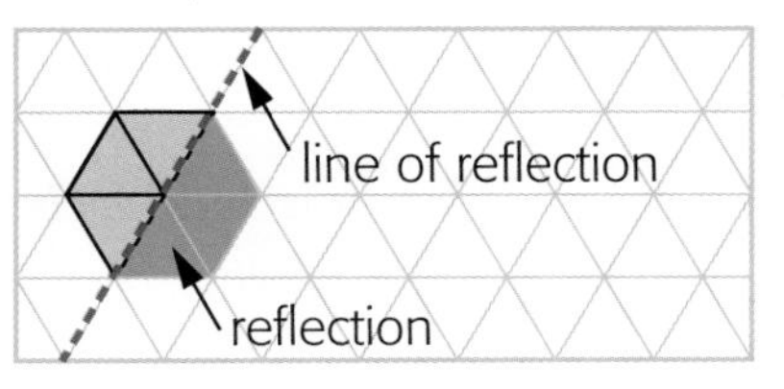

relation [*relation* (n.f.)]: A property that allows you to use one number to get information about another number; e.g., the perimeter of a square is 4 times the length of one side, so if you know the length of one side of the square, you can determine the perimeter. This relation may be represented by the **formula** $P = 4s$ or a table of values.

Side length (cm)	1	2	3	4
Perimeter (cm)	4	8	12	16

repeating decimal [*suite* (n.f.) *décimale périodique*]: A decimal in which a block of one or more digits eventually repeats in a pattern; e.g., $\frac{25}{99} = 0.252\ 525\ ...$, $\frac{31}{36} = 0.861\ 111\ 1\ ...$, $\frac{1}{7} = 0.142\ 857\ 142\ 857....$ These repeating decimals can also be written as $0.\overline{25}$, $0.86\overline{1}$, and $0.\overline{142\ 857}$

rotation [*rotation* (n.f.)]: A **transformation** in which each point in a shape moves about a fixed point through the same angle

S

sample space [*espace* (n.m.) *des échantillons*]: All possible outcomes in a **probability** experiment

scatter plot [*diagramme* (n.m.) *de dispersion*]: A graph that attempts to show a relationship between two **variables** by means of points plotted on a coordinate grid

solution to an equation [*solution* (n.f.) *d'une équation*]: A value of a **variable** that makes an **equation** true; e.g., the solution to $6x + 2 = 14$ is $x = 2$

statistics [*statistique* (n.f.)]: The collection, organization, and interpretation of data

T

terminating decimal [*fraction* (n.f.) *décimale finie*]: A decimal that is complete after a certain number of digits with no repetition; e.g., 0.777

theoretical probability [*probabilité* (n.f.) *théorique*]: The **ratio** of the number of **favourable outcomes** to the number of possible **equally likely outcomes**; e.g., the theoretical probability of tossing a head on a coin is $\frac{1}{2}$, since there are 2 equally likely outcomes and only 1 is favourable

transformation [*transformation géométrique* (f)]: The result of moving a shape according to a rule; transformations include **translations, rotations,** and **reflections**

translation [*translation* (n.f.)]: The result of a slide; the slide must be along straight lines, left or right, up or down (Also see transformation.)

tree diagram [*diagramme* (n.m.) *en arbre* ou *arbre* (n.m.)]: A way to record and count all combinations of **events**, using lines to connect the two parts of the outcome; e.g., this tree diagram shows all the combinations that can happen if you toss a coin twice

1st toss	2nd toss	1st toss	2nd toss
H	H (HH)	T	H (TH)
	T (HT)		T (TT)

trial [*essai* (n.m) ou *événement* (n.m.)]: A single **event** or observation in a **probability** experiment

V

variable [*variable* (n.f.)]: A letter or symbol, such as a, b, x, or n, that represents a number; e.g., in the **formula** for the area of a rectangle, the variables A, l, and w represent the area, length, and width of the rectangle

Z

zero principle [*principe* (n.m.) *de la somme des nombres opposés*]: When two **opposite integers** are added the sum is zero; e.g.,

(● ●) + (● ●) = 0
(−2) + (+2) = 0

Answers

Chapter 1, p. 1

1.1 Divisibility by 10, 5, and 2, p. 6

1. a) 10 no, R5; 5 yes; 2 no, R1
b) 10 no, R7; 5 no, R2; 2 no, R1
c) 10 no, R6; 5 no, R1; 2 yes
d) 10 yes, 5 yes, 2 yes

2. a) 0 **b)** 2, 4, 6, 8 **c)** 2, 7 **d)** 5

3. e.g., Every number is divisible by 1.

4. e.g., 1005; The ones digit is 5, so it is divisible by 5 but not by 10.

5. e.g., 1 kg or 5 kg bags; 1645 is divisible by 1 and 5, but not by 2 or 10.

6. a) 1 way, with 2¢ coins; 2 is a factor of 456, but 5 and 10 are not.
b) 3 ways, with 10¢, 5¢, or 2¢ coins; 10, 5, and 2 are factors of 1430.
c) 1 way, with 5¢ coins; 5 is a factor of 2455, but 2 and 10 are not.
d) 0 ways; 2, 5, and 10 are not factors of 6843.

7. a) e.g., I was born in 1994, which is divisible by 2 because it ends in an even number but not divisible by 5 or 10 because it does not end in 0 or 5.
b) e.g., The next year divisible by 10, 5, and 2 is 2010. I'll be 16.

8. a) 1000, 1020, 1040, 1060, 1080, 1100
b) e.g., If the last two digits are divisible by 20, the number is divisible by 20; 6860 is divisible by 20 because 60 is.

9. e.g., I am 13; $2 \times 13 = 26$; $26 \times 5 = 130$; 13Ø = 13. It works because multiplying by 2 and then by 5 is the same as multiplying by 10. Removing the last digit 0 is the same as dividing by 10. Multiplying by a number then dividing by it leaves the starting number.

10. 910, 990

11. Be specific about how the rules are alike and different.

1.2 Divisibility by 3 and 9, pp. 9–10

1. a) 3 yes, 9 yes
b) 3 no, 9 no; digits sum to 20, which has a remainder of 2 when divided by 3 and 9
c) 3 yes, 9 no; digits sum to 6, which has a remainder of 6 when divided by 9
d) 3 yes, 9 yes

2. a) 7 **b)** 6 **c)** 0 or 9 **d)** 6

3. a) No, the digits sum to 10, which is not divisible by 9, so there can't be 9 equal rows.
b) No, the digits sum to 21, which is divisible by 3.

4. a) 3 yes, 9 yes
b) 3 no, R2, 9 no, R8
c) 3 yes, 9 yes
d) 3 yes, 9 no, R6

5. 9999, 1008

6. If the number is divisible by 3, it could be 150, 450, or 750; if it is divisible by 9, it must be 450.

7. e.g., $1234 \div 9$ and $4321 \div 9$ both have a remainder of 1; rearranging the digits doesn't change their sum.

8. a) e.g., 1001
b) e.g., 3330 **c)** e.g., 3000 **d)** e.g., 4500

9. 3879; e.g., Add 3 to 3876 because both 3876 and 3 are divisible by 3 so the sum is too.

10. e.g., I'd divide 18 927 because each digit or pair of digits is divisible by 9. I'd use a divisibility rule for 17 658 because it's harder to divide.

11. Be specific about how the rules are alike and different.

1.3 Divisibility by 6, pp. 13–14

1. **a)** yes **b)** no **c)** no **d)** yes

2. **a)** 0, 6 **b)** 0, 3, 6, 9

3. **a)** no **b)** yes **c)** yes **d)** no

4. e.g., 3

5. **a)** No, 3258 is divisible by 2 (ones digit even) and by 3 (digits sum to 18, which is divisible by 3), so it's divisible by 6.
   b) No, 9355 is not even, so it is not divisible by 6.

6. **a)**

		2 is a factor: Yes	2 is a factor: No
3 is a factor	Yes	6, 12, 18, 24	3, 9, 15, 21
	No	2, 4, 8, 10, 14, 16, 20, 22	1, 5, 7, 11, 13, 17, 19, 23

   b) e.g., Each multiple of 6 is in the cell in which 2 and 3 are factors.

7. no, e.g., 1006 is not divisible by 6.

8. e.g., An odd number cannot be divisible by 6.

9. **a)** e.g., 7002 **b)** e.g., 2700 **c)** e.g., 3600

10. **a)** not always, e.g., 6, 18, and 30 are divisible by 2 and by 6 but not by 12
    b) yes, e.g., If a number is divisible by 12, you can form groups of 12, which you can arrange as 4 groups of 3 or 6 groups of 2. So both 2 and 3 must be factors of the number.

11. Use the divisibility rules for 2, 3, and 6.

1.4 Divisibility by 4 and 8, p. 18

1. **a)** 4 no, R2; 8 no, R2
   b) 4 yes, 8 yes
   c) 4 yes; 8 no, R4
   d) 4 yes; 8 no, R4

2. **a)** 2, 6
   b) 2, 6
   c) 0, 4, 8
   d) 0, 2, 4, 6, 8

3. **a)** yes **b)** yes, yes

4. **a)** 4 no, R2; 8 no, R6
   b) 4 yes, 8 yes
   c) 4 yes, 8 yes

5. no, e.g., 4 and 12

6. 98 760

7. **a)** e.g., The last 3 digits of 5320 are 320, and 320 is divisible by 8. 5320 is divisible by 8 because $3 \times 4 + 2 \times 2 + 0 = 16$, which is divisible by 8. Maddy's rule works for 5320.
   b) e.g., The thousands place value and greater place values are divisible by 8, so you only have to divide the number formed by the last 3 digits.
   c) e.g., If the last 2 digits of a number are divisible by 4, the entire number is divisible by 4; the rule makes sense because the hundreds place value and greater place values are divisible by 4.

8. e.g., Dividing by 2 a second time is like dividing by 4; dividing by 2 a third time is like dividing by 8.

9. Look for a pattern in the divisibility rules for 4 and 8, and exend that pattern for 16.

Mid-Chapter Review, p. 21

1. **a)** 10 no, R1; 5 no, R1; 2 no, R1
   b) 10 yes, 5 yes, 2 yes
   c) 10 no, R8; 5 no, R3; 2 yes
2. the height of 5 cubes, because 1405 is divisible by 5 but not by 2 or by 3
3. 990
4. 22 077
5. Yes, 2043 is divisible by both 3 and 9.
6. **a)** yes **b)** no, R3 **c)** yes **d)** yes
7. Yes, it is divisible by 6 because it is divisible by 2 (ones digit even) and by 3 (digits sum to 9, which is divisible by 3) and divisible by 9 (digits sum to 9, which is divisible by 9).
8. **a)** 4 yes, 8 yes
   b) 4 yes, 8 yes
   c) 4 no, R1; 8 no, R1
9. 9992; e.g., 10 000 is divisible by 8, and the greatest multiple of 8 less than 10 000 is 10 000 − 8 = 9992.
10. e.g., The last 2 digits, 48, are divisible by 4, and the last 3 digits, 048, are divisible by 8. Each place value greater than or equal to 1000 is divisible by both 4 and 8.

1.6 Determining Common Multiples, p. 25

1. **a)** 2, 4, 6, 8, 10
   b) 5, 10, 15, 20, 25
   c) 6, 12, 18, 24, 30
2. 30
3. e.g., 5 is a factor because the last digit is 0; 3 is a factor because the sum of the digits is divisible by 3.
4. **a)** 36 **b)** 12 **c)** 30 **d)** 60
5. e.g., 16 packages of buns, 12 packages of soy patties
6. **a)** no **b)** yes **c)** no **d)** no
7. **a)**

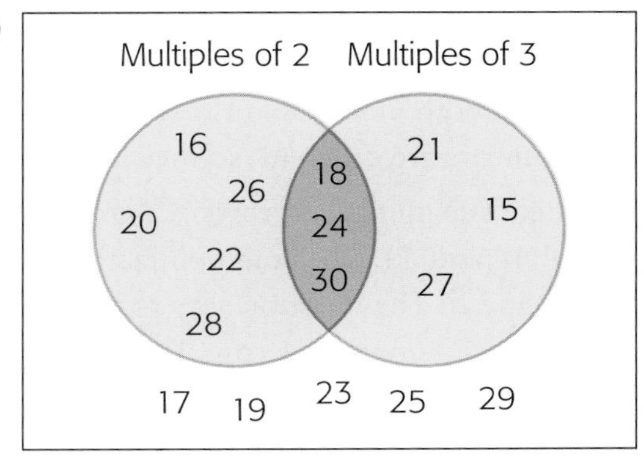

   b) e.g., common multiples of 2 and 3
8. once
9. not always correct

1.7 Determining Common Factors, p. 29

1. **a)** common factors: 1, 5; GCF 5
   b) common factors: 1, 2, 3, 6; GCF 6
   c) common factors: 1, 5; GCF 5
   d) common factors: 1, 2, 3, 4, 6, 8, 12, 16, 24, 48; GCF 48
2. 60 cm
3. **a)** e.g., 2, 3, 5
   b) e.g., 2, 4, 8
   c) e.g., 3, 5, 9
4. **a)** yes **c)** no **e)** yes
   b) yes **d)** yes
5. **a)** 150: 5, 15; 200: 100, 5, 20
   b) 50
6. 110, e.g., 5 is a factor, so the number ends in 0 or 5; it is divisible by 2, so its ones digit is even.
7. 1, e.g., The GCF must be a common factor of the two primes. The only two factors of a prime number are 1 and itself; the two primes are different so the only common factor and the GCF is 1.

8. 12 and 24, e.g., Since 24 is the LCM, both numbers are factors of 24; the factors of 24 are 1, 2, 3, 4, 6, 8, 12, and 24. Since the GCF is 12, both numbers are at least 12. The numbers are different, so they are 12 and 24.

9. e.g., The number of rows is a common factor of 48 and 54. The common factors are 1, 2, 3, and 6. The question says rows, so assume there is more than 1 row. The possibilities are 2 rows of $54 \div 2 = 27$ chairs, 3 rows of $54 \div 3 = 18$ chairs, and 6 rows of $54 \div 6 = 9$ chairs.

10. Explain how common factors can be helpful in determining the size of the tiles.

1.8 Solve Problems by Identifying and Extending a Pattern, p. 33

1. 8 numbers
2. 4986
3. 1001, 1011, 1021, 1031, ..., or 1091 beads
4. 9 numbers
5. 10 000
6. 0
7. 1
8. **a)** 9
   b) Determine the digital root of numbers multiplied by 3.

Chapter Self-Test, p. 35

1. 36 090 is divisible by 10 because the last digit is 0; therefore, it is also divisible by 2 and 5.
2. 8
3. e.g., 8 is a factor of 2232 because $2 \times 4 + 3 \times 2 + 2 = 16$, which is divisible by 8; since 8 is a factor, 4 is a factor too.
4. **a)** 43 210, e.g., The last digit has to be 0 if the number is divisible by 10, 5, and 2, so arrange digits in order from greatest to least to form the greatest possible number.
   b) 4320, e.g., It is not possible to use all the digits because the sum of the digits is 10, and 3 and 9 aren't factors of 10, so drop the digit 1 and use the others to create 4320.
5. **a)** true, if a number is divisible by 10, then last digit is 0, so it is divisible by 5 and 2.
   b) false, e.g., 12 is divisible by 4, but not by 8.
   c) true, e.g., 2 and 3 are factors of 6, so a number that is divisible by 6 must also be divisible by 2 and 3.
   d) true, 3 is a factor of 9, so a number that is divisible by 9 must also be divisible by 3.
6. **a)** 75
   b) e.g., 150, 225, 300
   c) 1, 5
   d) 5
7. **a)** e.g., If the rocks can be divided into 2, 3, and 5 equal groups, the number must be a common multiple of 2, 3, and 5.
   b) 30, e.g., 30 is the LCM of 2, 3, and 5

Chapter Review, pp. 37–38

1. 10 010, e.g., Add 10 to 10 000.
2. yes, e.g., The product of any number and 10 must be a multiple of 10, and 2 and 5 are factors of 10.
3. **a)** e.g., 3 is a factor of 9.
   b) no, e.g., 3 is a factor of 6, but 9 is not.
4. **a)** no, e.g., Each tricycle has 3 wheels, and 1035 is divisible by 3 because its digits sum to 9, which is divisible by 3.
   b) No, 1230 is not divisible by 9 because its digits sum to 6, which is not divisible by 9.

5. 1

6. 21 456 is divisible by 2 (last digit even) and by 3 (digits sum to 18, which is divisible by 3), so it is divisible by 6.

7. 0, 2, 4, 6, or 8 because □8 must be divisible by 4.

8. yes, 2232 is divisible by 8 and by 4

9. a) e.g., To calculate $0 \div 3$, think what number multiplied by 3 equals 0: $0 \times 3 = 0$ so $0 \div 3 = 0$. To calculate $3 \div 0$, think what number multiplied by 0 equals 3. No number multiplied by 0 equals 3 because 0 multiplied by any number is 0, so $3 \div 0$ has no solution.

b) e.g., To get multiples of a number, multiply it by 1, 2, 3, and so on. If you multiply 0 by 1, 2, 3, and so on, you always get 0. If you multiply other numbers by 1, 2, 3, and so on forever, you get an unlimited number of multiples.

10. a) 12th

b) 8, e.g., every 12th car is a green convertible, and there are 8 multiples of 12 less than 100: 12, 24, 36, 48, 60, 72, 84, and 96

c) e.g., Without common multiples, I would have to make a list or draw a diagram. That would take a long time and it would be easy to make a mistake.

11. a) 80; e.g., 160, 240, 320

b) 200; e.g., 400, 600, 800

c) 60; e.g., 120, 180, 240

d) 120; e.g., 240, 360, 480

12. D

13. 30 cm, e.g., The lengths must be the GCF of 90 and 120, which is 30.

Chapter 2, p. 41

2.1 Comparing Fractions, pp. 47–49

1. a) $\frac{12}{20}$ and $\frac{10}{20}$ **c)** $\frac{6}{30}$ and $\frac{2}{30}$

b) $\frac{5}{8}$ and $\frac{6}{8}$ **d)** $\frac{16}{24}$ and $\frac{3}{24}$

2. a)

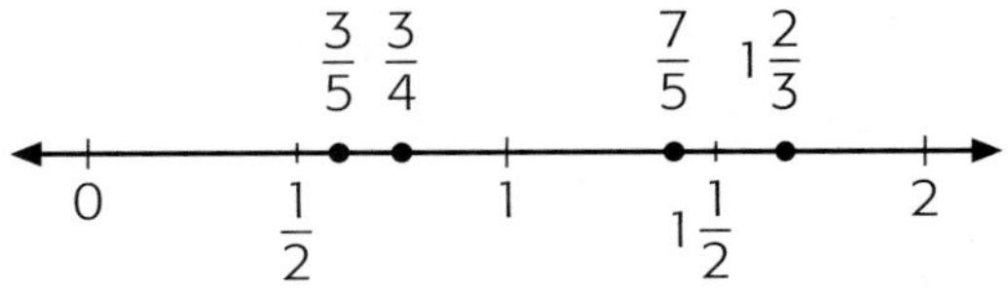

b) $\frac{3}{5}, \frac{3}{4}, \frac{7}{5}, 1\frac{2}{3}$

3. a) $\frac{3}{7} < \frac{2}{3}$ **b)** $\frac{2}{5} < \frac{1}{2}$ **c)** $\frac{8}{6} > \frac{4}{8}$

4. a) $\frac{1}{2}$ **b)** $\frac{2}{3}$ **c)** $\frac{5}{2}$ **d)** $\frac{5}{3}$

5. a)

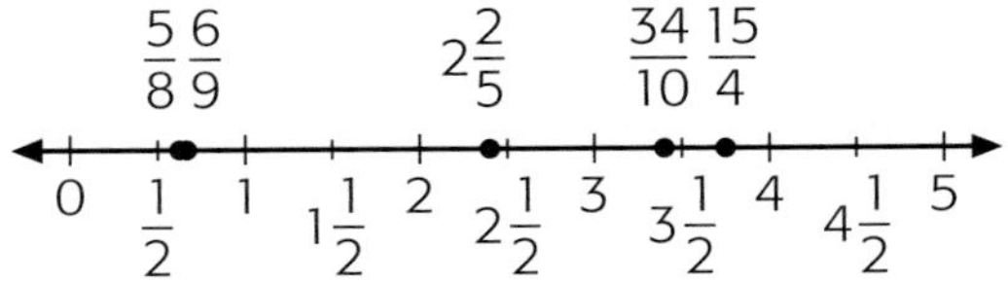

b) $\frac{5}{8}, \frac{6}{9}, 2\frac{2}{5}, \frac{34}{10}, \frac{15}{4}$

6. a)

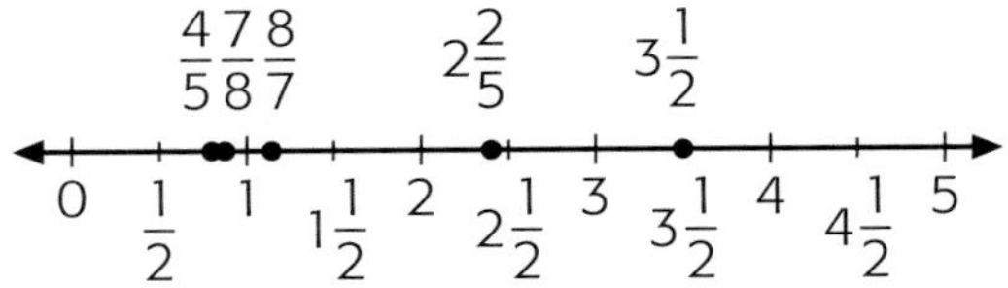

b) $3\frac{1}{2}, 2\frac{2}{5}, \frac{8}{7}, \frac{7}{8}, \frac{4}{5}$

7. a) $\frac{4}{9} < \frac{5}{6}$ **b)** $\frac{4}{5} > \frac{1}{6}$ **c)** $\frac{8}{3} > \frac{13}{15}$

8. a) $\frac{3}{8}$ **b)** $2\frac{1}{2}$ **c)** $\frac{2}{3}$ **d)** $\frac{2}{10}$

9. a) $\frac{8}{5}$ **b)** $\frac{3}{8}$ **c)** $\frac{21}{9}$

10. Quiz B

11. Yes, $\frac{6}{8} < \frac{8}{10}$

12. e.g., Alasdair $\frac{1}{3}$ or $\frac{1}{5}$, Briana $\frac{13}{24}$ or $\frac{7}{12}$, Lesya $\frac{5}{7}$ or $\frac{17}{24}$

13. e.g., It is often between the original two fractions; no, $\frac{4}{9}$ can be chosen for $\frac{3}{5}$ and $\frac{7}{10}$, but $\frac{4}{9} < \frac{3}{5}$ and $\frac{4}{9} < \frac{7}{10}$

14. e.g., if the numerator is more than half the denominator

15. Explain why it's easier to compare fractions when the numerators are the same than when they are different.

2.3 Adding Fractions with Fraction Strips, pp. 54–55

1. a) $\frac{3}{5} + \frac{1}{2} = \frac{11}{10}$ b) $\frac{1}{10} + \frac{1}{2} = \frac{6}{10}$

2. a) e.g., $\frac{1}{6}$ is less than $\frac{1}{4}$, and $\frac{1}{4} + \frac{3}{4} = 1$, so $\frac{1}{6} + \frac{3}{4}$ would be less.
   b) $\frac{11}{12}$

3. a) e.g., about $\frac{4}{5}$ c) e.g., about $1\frac{1}{4}$
   b) e.g., about $1\frac{1}{4}$ d) e.g., about $1\frac{1}{2}$

4. a) $\frac{4}{5}$ c) $\frac{5}{12}$ e) $1\frac{1}{6}$
   b) $\frac{4}{3}$ d) $\frac{11}{12}$ f) $1\frac{1}{12}$

5. $\frac{1}{2}$

6. e.g., $\frac{1}{2} + \frac{2}{4}$, $\frac{1}{3} + \frac{6}{9}$, $\frac{3}{4} + \frac{3}{12}$, $\frac{2}{5} + \frac{6}{10}$, $\frac{3}{7} + \frac{12}{21}$, $\frac{9}{11} + \frac{6}{33}$

7. $\frac{7}{12}$

8. e.g., 12 or 24

9. no, e.g., $\frac{1}{4} + \frac{1}{3} = \frac{7}{12}$; also, $\frac{1}{2} = \frac{6}{12}$ and $\frac{6}{12} + \frac{7}{12}$ is more than $\frac{6}{12} + \frac{6}{12}$, which is a whole pail.

10. Yes, because you add the second fraction onto the end of the first one, so it has to be greater. If you switched them around, you'd be adding the first onto the end of the second one, so it is greater than that one too.

11. Explain why it is faster to add two fractions with the same denominator.

2.4 Subtracting Fractions with Fraction Strips, pp. 58–60

1. a) e.g., Because if you have 4 fifths and take away 2 of them, you have 2 left.
   b) e.g., about $\frac{1}{2}$ c) $\frac{3}{10}$

2. $\frac{7}{12}$

3. a) $\frac{3}{6}$ b) $\frac{3}{8}$ c) $\frac{3}{12}$

4. e.g., All the numerators are 3, and all the denominators are the same as the denominator in the question; it makes sense since if you have 5 parts of something and take away 2 parts, you always have 3 parts left.

5. a) e.g., about $\frac{1}{3}$ b) e.g., about $\frac{1}{2}$
   c) e.g., about $\frac{3}{4}$

6. a) $\frac{1}{2}$ c) $1\frac{11}{12}$ e) $\frac{1}{10}$
   b) $1\frac{3}{4}$ d) $1\frac{1}{12}$ f) $\frac{5}{6}$

7. a) e.g.,

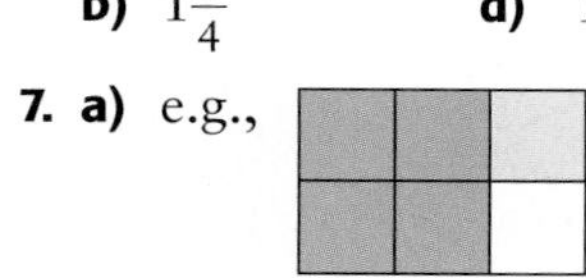

   b) $\frac{3}{6}$ or $\frac{1}{2}$ c) $\frac{1}{6}$

8. a) $\frac{3}{10}$
   b) e.g., I know the answer is less than $\frac{1}{2}$, which is $\frac{5}{10}$, but more than $\frac{1}{5}$, which is $\frac{2}{10}$, so $\frac{3}{10}$ makes sense.

9. e.g., yes

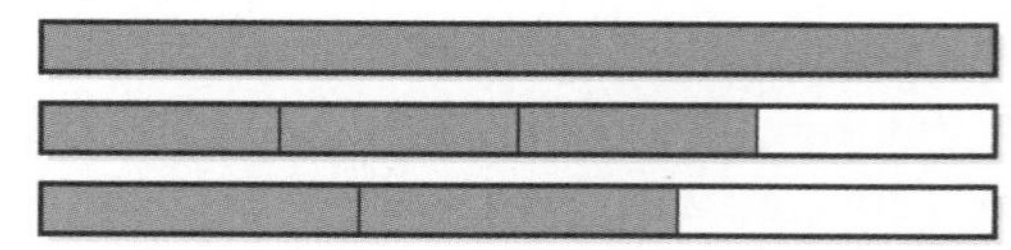

$1 - \frac{2}{3}$ is the white part of the $\frac{2}{3}$ bar. If you subtract the white part of the $\frac{3}{4}$ bar (which is $\frac{1}{4}$), what is left is the difference you were looking for.

10. a) $\frac{1}{12}$ **b)** $\frac{2}{12}$ **c)** $\frac{1}{12}$

11. a)

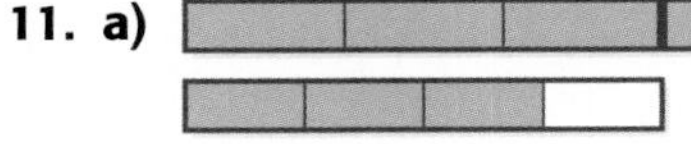

b) It takes $\frac{1}{4}$ to get from $\frac{3}{4}$ to 1 and another $\frac{1}{3}$ to get to $\frac{4}{3}$, so you add $\frac{1}{4}$ and $\frac{1}{3}$.

c) $\frac{7}{12}$

12. a) e.g., about $\frac{1}{3}$

b) e.g., about $\frac{1}{5}$

c) e.g., about $\frac{1}{8}$

13. e.g., between none of the performers and $\frac{1}{4}$ of them since the greatest fraction that will play music is $\frac{1}{4}$: $\frac{1}{4} + \frac{1}{2} = \frac{3}{4}$ and $1 - \frac{3}{4} = \frac{1}{4} + \frac{1}{2} = \frac{3}{4}$

14. a) e.g., Model $\frac{5}{12}$ and $\frac{1}{4}$.

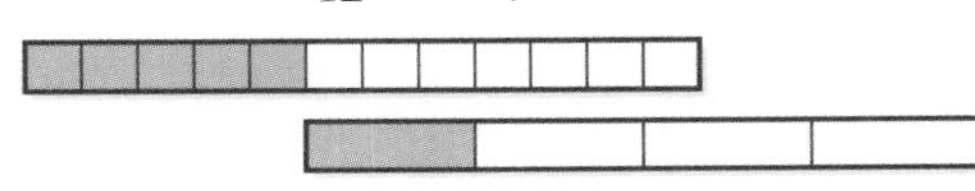

b) $\frac{8}{12}$ **c)** $\frac{2}{12}$ **d)** e.g., Yes

15. Explain how the use of common denominators makes addition and subtraction similar.

2.6 Subtracting Fractions with Grids, pp. 65–66

1. a) $\frac{7}{15}$ **b)** $\frac{14}{24}$

2. $\frac{3}{12}$ or $\frac{1}{4}$

3. a) $\frac{2}{15}$ **c)** $\frac{1}{21}$ **e)** $\frac{7}{20}$

b) $\frac{1}{12}$ **d)** $\frac{5}{24}$ **f)** $\frac{7}{20}$

4. a) e.g., Half of $\frac{1}{3}$ is $\frac{1}{6}$, and $\frac{1}{5}$ is more, so she phoned more on Saturday.

b) $\frac{2}{15}$

5. $\frac{5}{8}$, e.g., I know the answer is more than a half, and $\frac{3}{4}$ is $\frac{6}{8}$, so $\frac{5}{8}$ is reasonable.

6. e.g., The gas tank started at $\frac{7}{8}$ full. After the ride to his grandmother's, Jeff's gas gauge read $\frac{1}{2}$ full. How much of the tank did he use? $\frac{3}{8}$. It makes sense, since $\frac{1}{2}$ is $\frac{4}{8}$, and 4 eighths and 3 eighths should be 7 eighths.

7. A: e.g., always true since both are greater than $\frac{1}{2}$ but less than 1. B: e.g., sometimes true. I know $\frac{11}{12} - \frac{7}{12} = \frac{4}{12}$ and that's more than $\frac{1}{4}$, but $\frac{5}{6} - \frac{2}{3} = \frac{1}{6}$ and that's less than $\frac{1}{4}$.

8. e.g., an eighth note

9. Explain why you prefer one method over the other.

Mid-Chapter Review, p. 69

1. a) $\frac{18}{30}$ and $\frac{10}{30}$

b) $\frac{6}{10}$ and $\frac{2}{10}$

c) $\frac{9}{30}$ and $\frac{8}{30}$

2. a) $\frac{2}{3}$ **b)** $\frac{2}{3}$ **c)** $\frac{7}{5}$

3. $\frac{1}{9}, \frac{2}{3}, \frac{5}{6}, \frac{8}{5}, \frac{7}{3}, 3\frac{1}{4}$

4. a) estimate: about $1\frac{1}{2}$; calculation: $\frac{7}{5}$

b) estimate: a little more than 1; calculation: $1\frac{1}{12}$

c) estimate: a little less than 1; calculation: $1\frac{1}{10}$

d) estimate: a little less than $1\frac{2}{3}$; calculation: $\frac{19}{12}$

5. $\frac{5}{12}$

6. a) $\frac{3}{10}$ **b)** $\frac{16}{12}$ **c)** $\frac{3}{10}$ **d)** $\frac{8}{12}$

7. e.g., about $\frac{1}{2}$

8. A, C, D

A. e.g., Answer is more than $\frac{3}{4}$, so it's more than $\frac{1}{2}$. It's less than $1\frac{1}{2}$ since you'd have to add $\frac{3}{4}$ again, not just $\frac{1}{5}$ to get that high.

B. $\frac{3}{4} + \frac{3}{4} = 1\frac{1}{2}$, but $\frac{5}{6}$ is greater than $\frac{3}{4}$, so $\frac{3}{4} + \frac{5}{6}$ is greater than $1\frac{1}{2}$

C. It's more than $\frac{1}{2}$ since you are adding to $\frac{1}{2}$, and it's not $1\frac{1}{2}$ since you're adding less than 1 to the $\frac{1}{2}$.

D. It's more than $\frac{1}{2}$ since $\frac{2}{3}$ is already more than $\frac{1}{2}$, and it's less than 1 since you're adding less than $\frac{1}{3}$ to $\frac{2}{3}$.

9. a) 2 by 3 c) 3 by 5
b) 1 by 5 d) 2 by 4

2.7 Adding and Subtracting Fractions with Number Lines, pp. 72–73

1. a) $\frac{11}{12}$ b) $\frac{8}{15}$

2. a) $\frac{9}{20}$ b) $\frac{1}{20}$

3. a) $\frac{7}{6}$ b) $\frac{14}{12}$ c) $\frac{2}{9}$ d) $\frac{11}{21}$

4. $\frac{3}{8}$

5. $\frac{9}{35}$

6. $\frac{4}{15}$

7. a) yes, e.g., $\frac{2}{4}$ and $\frac{1}{3}$ b) yes, e.g., $\frac{4}{4} - \frac{1}{6}$

8. e.g., The part of the long arrows that isn't covered by the short arrows is the same, so the subtractions are the same too.

9. Explain why you find one method more convenient than another.

2.9 Adding and Subtracting Fractions, pp. 77–78

1. a) $\frac{2}{5}$ b) $\frac{7}{6}$ c) $\frac{1}{8}$ d) $\frac{20}{21}$

2. $\frac{2}{3} > \frac{1}{5}$; $\frac{7}{15}$ greater

3. C, D

4. a) e.g., about $\frac{1}{4}$

b) e.g., 20 since the fraction $\frac{1}{20}$ was used

5. e.g., $\frac{2}{3} + \frac{3}{5} + \frac{6}{15} = \frac{25}{15}$

6. B, C, D

7. Yes; the answers are equivalent.

8. a) $\frac{23}{21}$ b) $\frac{41}{35}$ c) $\frac{55}{36}$ d) $\frac{5}{12}$

9. $\frac{7}{12}$

10. A. false, e.g., The sum would be less than $\frac{2}{8}$, or $\frac{1}{4}$.

B. true, e.g., It could be $\frac{1}{5} + \frac{1}{20}$.

C. false, e.g., $\frac{2}{5}$ is already more than $\frac{1}{4}$.

D. true, e.g., $\frac{1}{10}$ and $\frac{3}{20}$

11. e.g., about $\frac{1}{3}$

12. B, $\frac{1}{30}$

13. e.g., if there was a $\frac{1}{2}$ can of paint you were adding to a $\frac{1}{3}$ can and a $\frac{1}{4}$ can

14. about $\frac{13}{24}$

15. Explain how to add fractions with different denominators and then subtract the result.

2.10 Adding and Subtracting Mixed Numbers, pp. 84–85

1. a) $5\frac{5}{8}$ b) $2\frac{5}{12}$ c) $1\frac{1}{4}$ d) $8\frac{17}{24}$

2. $5\frac{1}{2}$

3. a) $3\frac{11}{12}$ b) $5\frac{14}{15}$ c) $1\frac{4}{5}$ d) $1\frac{11}{12}$

4. a) $2\frac{1}{3}$ b) $1\frac{3}{5}$ c) $8\frac{17}{30}$ d) $9\frac{7}{20}$

5. $2\frac{1}{2}$ squares

6. $\frac{5}{6}$ hours, e.g., $1\frac{1}{2} + \frac{2}{3}$ is a bit more than 2, so there should be a bit less than 1 hour left and that's what I got.

7. $\frac{1}{4}$ boxes

8. e.g., A, C, B, D

9. **a)** $9\frac{3}{4}$ **b)** $1\frac{11}{12}$

10. $4\frac{7}{8}$

11. $3\frac{2}{3}$ pages

12. e.g., Suppose there are $3\frac{1}{4}$ pizzas left and people eat $1\frac{1}{2}$ of them, and you want to know how many pizzas are left.

13. e.g., when the two fraction parts add to 1

14. 7 or 8, e.g., depending on if the two fraction parts added to more than 1

15. e.g., because he was thinking of the difference on a number line. He needed $\frac{1}{3}$ to get up to 3 and then another $4\frac{1}{8}$ to get up to $7\frac{1}{8}$.

16. **a)** e.g., just estimate as $12 - 2$

b) e.g., add a bit too much since it's easier, and then take away the extra you added

17. e.g., $\frac{1}{6} + 1 + \frac{3}{6} = 1\frac{4}{6}$;

$\frac{27}{6} - \frac{17}{6} = \frac{10}{6}$;

$4\frac{1}{2} + \frac{1}{6} = 4\frac{4}{6}$; $2\frac{5}{6} + \frac{1}{6} = 3$; $4\frac{4}{6} - 3 = 1\frac{4}{6}$

2.11 Communicate about Estimation Strategies, p. 88

1. e.g., The distance from 3 to 4 is 1. So, the distance from $2\frac{1}{2}$ to 4 is $1\frac{1}{2}$. Therefore, a little more than $1\frac{1}{2}$ packages will be left.

2. e.g., $1\frac{5}{6}$ is close to 2. It is $3\frac{1}{2}$ from 2 to $5\frac{1}{2}$. Therefore, a little more than $3\frac{1}{2}$ packages are left. It doesn't say you need an exact answer, so an estimate should be enough.

3. e.g., $2\frac{1}{3} + 2\frac{1}{3} + 2\frac{1}{3} = 6\frac{3}{3}$ or 7; another $2\frac{1}{3}$ gets to $9\frac{1}{3}$, so about 4 batches; a whole number estimate is good enough because she probably won't make a fraction of a batch.

4. e.g., $3\frac{4}{5}$ bags are a little less than 4 bags.
$2\frac{3}{4}$ bags are a little less than 3 bags.
4 bags + 3 bags = 7 bags
9 bags − 7 bags = 2 bags
Therefore, a little more than 2 bags of straw will be left.

5. e.g., They probably have a little more than $1\frac{1}{2}$ boxes each. They each collected more than 1 box, but less than 2. If they each collected about $1\frac{1}{2}$ boxes, the total would be $3 + \frac{1}{2} + \frac{1}{2} + \frac{1}{2} = 4\frac{1}{2}$, which is close to 5. This estimate is as good as I can do, because the question says "almost" 5 boxes.

Chapter Self-Test, pp. 89–90

1. $\frac{4}{9}, \frac{3}{5}, \frac{8}{5}$

2. **a)** $\frac{1}{3}$ **b)** $\frac{3}{5}$ **c)** $\frac{12}{5}$

3. e.g., 2 and 9, or 6 and 18

4. **a)** green and blue **b)** $\frac{1}{2}$

5. **a)** $\frac{5}{8}$, e.g., $\frac{3}{8}$ is almost $\frac{1}{2}$, so adding $\frac{1}{4}$ should give just over a half, so $\frac{5}{8}$ is reasonable.

b) $1\frac{3}{20}$, e.g., $\frac{2}{5}$ is a little more than $\frac{1}{4}$, so the answer should be a little over 1, so $1\frac{3}{20}$ is reasonable.

6. $\frac{1}{2} + \frac{1}{4} = \frac{3}{4}$

7. **a)** $\frac{1}{8}$ **b)** $\frac{1}{20}$

8. $\frac{1}{5}$

9. **a)** $\frac{5}{12}$ **b)** $\frac{5}{24}$

c) e.g., How much time does Luke spend in school and sleeping altogether?

10. $\frac{31}{40}$, e.g., Write $\frac{3}{8}$ and $\frac{2}{5}$ as equivalent fractions with the same denominator and then add: $\frac{3}{8} + \frac{2}{5} = \frac{15}{40} + \frac{16}{40} = \frac{31}{40}$

11. a) $\frac{7}{18}$ **b)** $\frac{13}{40}$

12. a) $6\frac{23}{36}$ **b)** $3\frac{9}{10}$ **c)** $\frac{4}{5}$ **d)** $1\frac{4}{7}$

13. e.g., The fraction parts are the same.

Chapter Review, pp. 93–94

1. e.g., $\frac{2}{3}$, $\frac{5}{6}$, and $\frac{11}{10}$.

2. a) $\frac{1}{5}$ $\frac{2}{5}$ $\frac{2}{3}$ $\frac{8}{7}$ $\frac{15}{4}$

0 $\frac{1}{2}$ 1 $1\frac{1}{2}$ 2 $2\frac{1}{2}$ 3 $3\frac{1}{2}$ 4

b) $\frac{1}{5}, \frac{2}{5}, \frac{2}{3}, \frac{8}{7}, \frac{15}{4}$

3 a) $\frac{3}{5}$ **b)** $\frac{1}{3}$ **c)** $\frac{5}{3}$ **d)** $\frac{9}{4}$

4. a) $\frac{13}{12}$ **b)** $\frac{3}{8}$ **c)** $\frac{7}{8}$ **d)** $1\frac{1}{10}$

5. a) $\frac{5}{21}$ **b)** $\frac{3}{12}$ **c)** $\frac{1}{6}$ **d)** $\frac{3}{20}$

6. a) $\frac{11}{12}$ **b)** $\frac{1}{12}$

7. $\frac{2}{15}$

8. a) greater than 1, e.g., $\frac{5}{7}$ is greater than half and $\frac{2}{3}$ is only $\frac{1}{3}$ away from 1

b) not greater than 1, e.g., $\frac{5}{6}$ is $\frac{1}{6}$ away from 1 and $\frac{1}{7}$ is less than that, so you don't get all the way to 1

9. a) $1\frac{8}{21}$ **b)** $\frac{41}{42}$

10. a) $\frac{31}{35}$ **b)** $1\frac{5}{9}$ **c)** $\frac{1}{30}$ **d)** $\frac{1}{15}$

11. a) $2\frac{9}{10}$ **b)** $5\frac{2}{9}$ **c)** $3\frac{5}{7}$

12. $1\frac{1}{6}$ h

13. a) yes, e.g., since it's $2\frac{3}{4}$

b) no, e.g., because $\frac{1}{10}$ is really small

c) no, e.g., since $\frac{2}{3} + \frac{4}{7}$ is more than 1

d) yes, e.g., since $1\frac{9}{13}$ is greater than 1 but less than 2, and $\frac{3}{5}$ is less than 1

Chapter 3, p. 97

3.2 Adding and Subtracting Decimals, pp. 104–105

1. a) e.g., about 10 **b)** e.g., about 5

2. a) 7.94 **b)** 1.626

3. a) e.g., about 37 **b)** e.g., about 74 **c)** e.g., about 49 **d)** e.g., about 540

4. a) 23.776 **b)** 380.881 **c)** 3.039 **d)** 231.152 **e)** 625.742 **f)** 0.923

5. Yes, she has enough wire fence.
6.6 m + 2.1 m + 7.2 m = 15.9 m is greater than 14.6 m. She has
15.9 m − 14.6 m = 1.3 m more.

6. 14.81 s

7. a) e.g., 4.26 and 0.82
b) 5.08
c) 3.44
d) e.g., greatest 10.98, least 0.12

8. 0.48 L

9. e.g., a 200 m race

10. Explain when you might subtract to determine an exact answer and when you might estimate.

3.3 Multiplying by Numbers Less than 1, pp. 108–109

1. a) 0.24 **b)** 0.14

2. a) $0.36, estimate e.g., $0.40
b) $0.49, estimate e.g., $0.45

3. a) 0.68 **b)** 6.08

4. a) 0.18 **b)** 0.56

5. e.g., c), a), e), b), d), f); check: **a)** 1.04 **b)** 2.94 **c)** 0.3 **d)** 3.18 **e)** 1.12 **f)** 4.2

6. $0.6 \times 8.7 = 5.22$
7. $1.08\ m^2$
8. $1.61
9. $1.05\ m^2$ greater
10. e.g., When you multiply by 0.5, it's like taking half. It's easier to take half of 0.64 than to try to multiply 0.64×0.7.
11. Use your knowledge of what happens when a number is multiplied by a decimal less than 1.

3.4 Multiplying by Numbers Greater than 1, pp. 112–113

1. **a)** 6.80 **b)** 58.30
2. **a)** estimate e.g., 20; answer 16.2
   b) estimate e.g., 36; answer 35.467
3. **a)** 3.756 **c)** 57.184 9
   b) 49.44 **d)** 3627.978
4. e.g., a), c), e), f), b), d); check: **a)** 58.05 **b)** 1.17 **c)** 7.902 08 **d)** 0.066 **e)** 3.7067 **f)** 3.5665
5. **a)** 557.052; estimate e.g., 450
   b) 0.797 94; When a number is multiplied by a decimal less than 1, the product will be less than the number, so the product is less than 1.023.
   c) 33.4085, estimate e.g., $1 \times 30 = 30$
   d) 591.30, estimate e.g., $55 \times 10 = 550$
6. e.g., 0.4×5.0, 1.8×4.9, 4.562×2.120
7. $16.72\ m^2$
8. $1.88 or $1.87
9. $4.1\ m^2$
10. Miguel: 1.8 m
    Romona: 1.7 m
11. $46.25
12. e.g., yes, because $0.85 is less than $1
13. $7.65
14. e.g., No, she does not even have enough for one coat because the ceiling has an area of about 4 m by 4 m, or $16\ m^2$, which is more area than the can will cover.
15. $6890.00
16. Explain why Meagan's statement is incorrect.

3.5 Solve Problems Using Guessing and Testing, p. 117

1. 7 of width 20.3 cm, 7 of width 15.6 cm, and 8 of width 8.4 cm
2. **a)** e.g., 46.8 cm long, 46.8 cm wide or 50.0 cm long, 43.6 cm wide
   b) 46.8 cm long, 46.8 cm wide
3. 4 m long, 2 m wide
4. 31.2 m long, 31.2 m wide
5. **a)** e.g., 5 cm high, 8 cm long
   b) yes, e.g., 4 cm high, 10 cm length
6. e.g., Model A: 7.7 m long, 7.7 m wide; Model B: 10.8 m long, 5.4 m wide
7. e.g., 160 squares, each with side length of 11 cm; 40 squares, each with side length of 22 cm

Mid-Chapter Review, p. 119

1. e.g., d), a), b), c); check: **a)** 8.91 **b)** 87.282 **c)** 119.978 **d)** 2.133
2. e.g., by estimating
   a) e.g., about 12 **c)** e.g., about 240
   b) e.g., about 100 **d)** e.g., about 23
3. **a)** e.g., yes **b)** $1.82 left over
4. **a)** 0.18 **b)** 0.24
5. e.g., d), c), a), b); check: **a)** 2.952 **b)** 2.2869 **c)** 7.42 **d)** 13.23
6. $32.36
7. $12.3\ cm^3$

8. 7.400 cm
9. 4781.10 g

3.6 Dividing by Numbers Less than 1, p. 123

1. **a)** 20 **b)** 26
2. **a)** e.g., about 8 **b)** e.g., about 6
3. **a)** 5.5 **b)** 5.1
4. **a)** 9.0 **b)** 7.0 **c)** 5.0 **d)** 41.3
5. **a)** 6.00 **c)** 72.86 **e)** 6.75
   b) 62.00 **d)** 82.2 **f)** 2285.2
6. **a)** 12 pieces **b)** 17 pieces
7. 4 glasses, plus some more water left over
8. 7696.92 s
9. e.g., 11 full boxes plus one half box
10. 50 dice
11. e.g., Division is the reverse of multiplication.
12. Use your knowledge of what happens when a number is divided by a decimal less than 1.

3.7 Dividing by Numbers Greater than 1, pp. 126–127

1. **a)** 3.0 **b)** 5.5
2. **a)** 2.3, e.g., calculator
   b) 10, e.g., noticed that $5.050 \times 10 = 50.50$
3. $7.50
4. **a)** 3 **b)** 2.5 **c)** 15 **d)** 3.6
5. e.g., b), a), d), c), e), f); check: **a)** 3.5 **b)** 1 **c)** 6.8 **d)** 4.5 **e)** 22.2 **f)** 22.33
6. **a)** correct answer is 1.71
   b) correct answer is 5.93
   c) correct
   d) correct answer is 0.40
7. **a)** 115 dimes **c)** 46 quarters
   b) 230 nickels **d)** 1150 pennies
8. **a)** 14 pieces plus some left over
   b) 8 pieces plus some left over
   c) 16 pieces plus some left over
   d) 22 pieces plus rope left over
9. 22 L
10. 22.5 h
11. 12.5 g
12. **a)** 1.5 m **b)** 1.7 m
13. 8 min
14. 146.667 g
15. e.g., Problem: There are 3 identical pencils in a box. The total mass of the box is 142.4 g, and the empty box has a mass of 18.8 g. What is the mass of each pencil? Solution: Subtract $142.4 - 18.8 = 123.6$ to determine the mass of the 3 pencils. Divide by 3 to determine the mass of one pencil: $123.6 \div 3 = 41.2$ on my calculator. The mass of each pencil is 41.2 g.
16. Use your knowledge of what happens to a number when it is divided by a decimal greater than 1.

3.8 Using the Order of Operations with Decimals, pp. 130–131

1. 5.1
2. D
3. **a)** 8.02 **b)** 6.32
4. **a)** correct
   b) correct answer 14.4
   c) correct answer 34.26
   d) correct answer 18.7
   e) correct
5. e.g., yes
6. **a)** The numerical expression requires you to divide 5.8 by 2, then add the result to 6.2×2

b) $(6.2 \times 2 + 5.8) \div 2$
c) 9.1

7. **a)** 67 **b)** 8.8 **c)** 205.7 **d)** 1

8. **a)** 2.64 **b)** 12.7

9. **a)** $(5.2 + 8.6) \times 6.2$
b) $(5.24 + 8.6) \times 6 - 5.2$
c) $9.6 \div 3.2 \times 6.1 - 8.5$

10. Division and multiplication are each represented by a letter in BDMAS, but they are done in the same step. The same is true for addition and subtraction.

3.9 Expressing Fractions as Decimals, pp. 135–137

1. **a)** $0.\overline{5}$ **b)** $0.\overline{134\,56}$

2. **a)** $0.3125 > 0.\overline{2}$
b) $0.\overline{63} > 0.625$
c) $0.85 > 0.78\overline{5\,714\,28}$

3. **a)** terminates **c)** repeats
b) repeats **d)** terminates

4. **a)** $\frac{13}{80}$ **b)** $\frac{171}{200}$

5. **a)** 0.56 **c)** 0.0625 **e)** 0.95
b) 0.625 **d)** 0.8 **f)** 0.6875

6. **a)** $0.\overline{16}$ **c)** $0.\overline{63}$ **e)** not repeating
b) $0.\overline{8}$ **d)** $0.4\overline{6}$ **f)** $0.\overline{513}$

7. **a)** repeats **d)** terminates
b) terminates **e)** repeats
c) repeats **f)** terminates

8. **b)** $0.2\overline{7}$, $0.\overline{4}$, 0.593 75, 0.6, $0.8\overline{3}$, 0.9375

9. **a)** $\frac{8}{9999}$, $\frac{8}{99\,999}$, $\frac{8}{999\,999}$
b) $0.\overline{8}$, $0.\overline{08}$, $0.\overline{008}$, $0.\overline{0008}$, $0.\overline{000\,08}$, $0.\overline{000\,008}$
c) repeating decimal, with 8 as last digit

10. **a)** $0.\overline{142\,857}$ **b)** $0.\overline{285\,714}$ **c)** $0.\overline{428\,571}$

11. **a)** When the numerator increases by 1, add $\frac{1}{7}$.
b) $0.\overline{571\,428}$, $0.\overline{714\,285}$

12. **a)** $<$ **b)** $=$ **c)** $>$ **d)** $>$ **e)** $<$ **f)** $>$

13. **a)** $\frac{1}{8}$, 0.35, $0.\overline{39}$, $\frac{5}{7}$, $\frac{9}{10}$
b) $\frac{27}{50}$, $\frac{5}{9}$, 0.56, $0.\overline{56}$, $0.5\overline{6}$

14. **a)** $0.\overline{6}$ **b)** $0.\overline{1}$ **c)** $0.0\overline{3}$ **d)** $1.\overline{3}$

15. **a)** $0.08\overline{3}$ **c)** $0.02\overline{27}$
b) $0.03\overline{5\,714\,28}$ **d)** $0.01\overline{9\,230\,76}$

16. **a)** e.g., All the decimal equivalents have a repeating period that starts in the thousandths.
b) e.g., The denominators are all multiples of 4.

17. **a)** $\frac{1}{3}$
b) $0.\overline{3}$
c) 33¢, 33¢, 34¢, so total is $1
d) e.g., Three friends buy a toy that costs $2. How much should each pay? (66¢, 66¢, 67¢)

18. Explain how you can tell there is no equivalent fraction with a denominator that is a 10, 100, 1000, or so on.

3.10 Expressing Decimals as Fractions, p. 140

1. **a)** $\frac{81}{500}$ **b)** $\frac{7}{90}$ **c)** $\frac{27}{99}$

2. **a)** $\frac{3}{8} > \frac{1}{4}$ **b)** $\frac{23}{100} > \frac{1}{7}$ **c)** $\frac{211}{250} < \frac{22}{25}$

3. **a)** $\frac{14}{99}$ **c)** $\frac{7}{90}$ **e)** $\frac{27}{99}$
b) $\frac{273}{999}$ **d)** $4\frac{17}{99}$ **f)** $\frac{767}{999}$

4. **a)** $0.416 > \frac{1}{4}$ **c)** $0.\overline{6} = \frac{2}{3}$
b) $0.52 > \frac{1}{2}$ **d)** $0.6 < \frac{2}{3}$

5. **a)** C **b)** D **c)** A **d)** B

6. e.g., $\frac{9}{20}$ is equivalent to 0.45, which is less than $0.\overline{45}$

7. e.g., 0.729 is equivalent to $\frac{729}{1000}$

Chapter Self-Test, p. 143

1. **a)** 14.79 **b)** 18.37 **c)** 3.82 **d)** 786.63
2. **a)** $>$ **b)** $<$
3. 2 videos
4. $1.37
5. **a)** 3.726 **b)** 22.2345 **c)** 120.52 **d)** 2872.0905
6. $77.5¢/L
7. **a)** 4 **b)** 8.8
8. **a)** terminates **b)** terminates **c)** repeats **d)** repeats
9. **a)** 0.85 **b)** 0.6875 **c)** $0.\overline{67}$ **d)** $0.\overline{285\ 714}$
10. **a)** $\frac{33}{50}$ **b)** $1\frac{1}{3}$ **c)** $256\frac{179}{200}$ **d)** $73\frac{25}{99}$

Chapter Review, pp. 145–146

1. **a)** 374.1 **b)** 934.02
2. 10.15 m
3. **a)** estimate e.g., 27; calculation 27.2
   b) estimate e.g., 6; calculation 6.76
4. **a)** 18.29 **b)** 29.899
5. yes
6. **a)** 7.2, e.g., pencil and paper
   b) 129, e.g., calculator
   c) 22.8, e.g., calculator
   d) 0.54, e.g., hundred grid
7. **a)** e.g., Mariette has a bigger table even though it is 0.1 m shorter and 0.1 m wider. The fraction by which it is shorter is much smaller than the fraction by which it is wider.
   b) Mariette's table area 0.32 m^2; Julie's table area 0.27 m^2
8. e.g., The answer will be less than both the numbers.
9. **a)** e.g., Yes, because if she buys single fares it will cost $58.75, which is more than $45.75.
   b) e.g., No, because if he buys single fares, it will cost $42.30, which is less than $45.75.
10. 7.78 L
11. 13, including the top one
12. e.g., I estimated 100 pieces. The piece of string was about 25 m long, which is 100×0.25. An estimate of 100 pieces of string 0.25 m long seems appropriate.
13. e.g., c), d), b), a); check: **a)** 12.3 **b)** 10.0 **c)** 3.0 **d)** 3.0
14. 2850 sheets of paper
15. about 43
16. **a)** estimate e.g., 37; calculation 33.9
    b) estimate e.g., 3.3; calculation 3.4
17. **a)** $\frac{4}{5}$ **b)** $\frac{147}{200}$ **c)** $\frac{23}{25}$ **d)** $\frac{1}{4}$
18. **a)** terminates **b)** repeats **c)** repeats **d)** terminates
19. **a)** 0.44 **b)** $0.8\overline{3}$ **c)** $0.8\overline{6}$ **d)** 0.375
20. $\frac{2}{9}$, 0.25, 0.252 525 …, 0.2555 …, $\frac{13}{15}$
21. **a)** $\frac{63}{100}$ **b)** $\frac{7}{11}$
22. e.g., Martin is painting a wall that is 2.4 m high by 3.6 m wide. There is a window in the wall that is 1.0 m high by 1.4 m wide. One small can of paint covers 1.5 m^2. How many cans of paint does Martin need to paint the wall? Solution: Subtract the area of the window from the total area of the wall, and divide the result by the amount that a can of paint will cover. An expression for this is $((2.4 \times 3.6) - (1.0 \times 1.4)) \div 1.5 = 4.8$. Martin will need 5 cans of paint.

Cumulative Review: Chapters 1–3, pp. 148–149

1. C **2.** D **3.** D **4.** B **5.** C **6.** A, B **7.** A, B **8.** A **9.** A, C **10.** A, B, C, D **11.** B **12.** A **13.** B **14.** A **15.** A **16.** A, C, D **17.** C **18.** B **19.** B **20.** A

Chapter 4, p. 151

4.1 Percents as Fractions and Decimals, pp. 156–157

1. a) 12 **b)** 4 **c)** 10 **d)** 15

2. $\frac{9}{25}$

3. a) 1 **b)** 17 **c)** 33 **d)** 1

4. $\frac{7}{20}$

5. a) $\frac{11}{50}$ **b)** $\frac{1}{20}$ **c)** $\frac{3}{10}$ **d)** $\frac{18}{25}$

6. a) 0.03 **b)** 0.94 **c)** 1.00 or 1 **d)** 0.4

7. 60%, 0.6, $\frac{3}{5}$

9% 0.09, $\frac{9}{100}$

3%, 0.03, $\frac{3}{100}$

44%, 0.44, $\frac{11}{25}$

24%, 0.24, $\frac{6}{25}$

50%, 0.5, $\frac{1}{2}$

100%, 1.0, $\frac{1}{1}$

12%, 0.12, $\frac{3}{25}$

8. a) C **b)** D **c)** A **d)** B

9. wool $\frac{3}{5}$, polyester $\frac{3}{10}$, nylon $\frac{1}{10}$

10. a) = **b)** > **c)** > **d)** > **e)** = **f)** <

11. a) e.g., $\frac{1}{3}$ **b)** e.g., $\frac{1}{7}$ **c)** e.g., $\frac{2}{3}$ **d)** e.g., $\frac{1}{10}$

12. a) blue 20%, white 32%, black 24%, red 24%

b) blue $\frac{1}{5}$, white $\frac{8}{25}$, black $\frac{6}{25}$, red $\frac{6}{25}$

13. a) 20%, 80% **b)** $\frac{1}{5}$, $\frac{4}{5}$

14. a) 15% **b)** 38

15. Explain how to compare two fractions with the same numerator.

4.3 Estimating Percents, p. 162

1. e.g., $\frac{10}{20}$

2. a) e.g., 10 **b)** e.g., 20

3. e.g., $\frac{9}{38}$ is close to $\frac{10}{40}$, which is 25%

4. a) e.g., 10% of 27 is 2.7

b) e.g., $\frac{1}{3}$ of 60 is 20

c) e.g., 75% of 24 is 18

d) e.g., 90% of 50 is 45

5. a) e.g., greater **b)** e.g., about the same **c)** e.g., less **d)** e.g., greater

6. a) e.g., $\frac{12}{24}$ is $\frac{1}{2}$ or 50%

b) e.g., $\frac{20}{80}$ is $\frac{1}{4}$ or 25%

c) e.g., $\frac{60}{300}$ is $\frac{1}{5}$ or 20%

d) e.g., $\frac{30}{150}$ is $\frac{1}{5}$ or 50%

7. a) e.g., greater **b)** e.g., less **c)** e.g., less **d)** e.g., less

8. Not enough students have signed up.

9. e.g., about 300 people

10. e.g., $\frac{19}{26}$ is close to $\frac{20}{25}$, which is 80%, so you do not need an exact answer.

11. Provide examples as to when a percent can be estimated and when it needs to be calculated exactly.

4.4 Using Percents to Make Comparisons, p. 165

1. a) 40%, 40% **b)** equal records

2. first day

3. Tom's punch
4. second day
5. $\frac{47}{50}, \frac{28}{30}, \frac{37}{40}, \frac{23}{25}$
6. **a)** Tara \$2, Jolene \$2.10
   b) Tara $\frac{2}{25}$, Jolene $\frac{7}{100}$
   c) Tara
7. small chance of rain, but may still rain (less than 50%, more than 0%)
8. e.g., in days, 10% of 365 is 36.5
   $36.5 > 7$
9. The rates are the same.
10. $\frac{3}{5} = 60\%$
    $\frac{4}{6} = \frac{2}{3}$, about 66%
    $60\% < 66\%$;
    $\frac{3}{5} = \frac{18}{30}$
    $\frac{4}{6} = \frac{20}{30}$
    $\frac{18}{30} < \frac{20}{30}$

Mid-Chapter Review, pp. 166–167

1. **a)** 1¢ **b)** 72¢ **c)** 100¢ **d)** 40¢
2. **a)** $<$ **b)** $=$ **c)** $>$ **d)** $>$
3. **a)** 40% **b)** 60%
4. **a)** e.g., 80% **c)** e.g., 25%
   b) e.g., 40% **d)** e.g., 50%
5. **a)** reasonable **c)** not reasonable
   b) reasonable **d)** reasonable
6. **a)** 10% of 40 and 5% of 40; \$6
   b) 1% of 40; \$2.40
7. 12 kg
8. science test
9. Tracy
10. the phone cards that are now \$10

4.5 Calculating with Percents, pp. 172–173

1. **a)** $6 + 3 = 9$ **b)** $\frac{15}{100} = \frac{3}{20}; \frac{3 \times 3}{20 \times 3} = \frac{9}{60}$
2. **a)** 225 **b)** 450
3. **a)** e.g., \$4.05 **b)** e.g., \$1.95
4. **a)** 10 **c)** 9 **e)** 30
   b) 18 **d)** 6 **f)** 110
5. **a)** 30 **c)** 70 **e)** 160
   b) 88 **d)** 16 **f)** 125
6. 5%
7. 48
8. e.g., 3793
9. **a)** \$1500 **b)** \$7500
10. yes, 20% tip
11. O: 1125, A: 1025, B: 250, AB: 100
12. 250
13. 66%

4.6 Solve Problems that Involve Decimals, pp. 177–178

1. **a)** \$3.50 **b)** \$2.80 **c)** \$6.29 **d)** 240
2. **a)** \$0.90 **b)** \$3.60
3. **a)** \$20.03 **c)** \$1.26
   b) \$51.93 **d)** \$296.79
4. \$44 635
5. \$191.21
6. \$331
7. 8%
8. **a)** \$21.60 **b)** \$24.41 (PST, GST)
9. **a)** e.g., with \$49.99: \$52.99, \$53.49, \$53.99
   b) e.g., because 1% of something that costs more is greater
10. e.g., Give an example of how to calculate sales tax on an item.

4.7 Solve Problems Using Logical Reasoning, pp. 182–183

1. 25
2. $52
3. a) 3 b) 12
4. e.g., about 33.6 km each hour
5. 624 students
6. e.g., The computer that is 70% of $1499 is about 7 × $150 = $1050. The computer that is 60% of $1699 is about 6 × $170 = $1020; this is the lower price.
7. a) 15 L b) 165 L c) 24.75 L
8. 18 years
9. a) 18 b) e.g., 7
10. a) e.g., about 45 s
    b) e.g., more than 100 s
11. not the same price
12. No, the raise was 5% of a smaller amount than the 5% reduction, so more was subtracted from the salary than was added to it.
13. a) 14

Chapter Self-Test, p. 185

1. 82%, $\frac{41}{50}$, 0.82; 35%, $\frac{7}{20}$, 0.35; 7%, $\frac{7}{100}$, 0.07
2. a) 6; 18 b) 4; 36
3. a) 14 b) 70 c) 65 d) 20
4. e.g., 1200
5. $22.80
6. e.g., To determine 10% you just divide by 10; there are more calculations to determine 17%.
7. a) 68%, 70%, 76%, 85%, 80%, 80%
   b) $\frac{17}{25}$, $\frac{21}{30}$, $\frac{38}{50}$, $\frac{32}{40}$, $\frac{12}{15}$, $\frac{51}{60}$
8. a) $5.37 b) $2.40

Chapter Review, pp. 187–188

1. a) 11 b) 13 c) 33 d) 2
2. 70%, 0.7, $\frac{7}{10}$; 8%, 0.08, $\frac{2}{25}$; 75%, 0.75, $\frac{3}{4}$; 15%, 0.15, $\frac{3}{20}$; 25%, 0.25, $\frac{1}{4}$; 55%, 0.55, $\frac{11}{20}$
3. a) 20% b) 75% c) 90% d) 25%
4. a) 48% b) 71
5. a) e.g., 56 c) e.g., 200
   b) e.g., 190 d) e.g., 3
6. a) e.g., 80% of 70 c) e.g., 40% of 500
   b) e.g., 95% of 200 d) e.g., 30% of 10
7. e.g., greater
8. e.g., 5% is half of 10%, which is easy to calculate.
9. Sanjeev spent a greater percent: $\frac{18}{30} = 60\%$, $\frac{13}{20} = 65\%$.
10. a) > b) >
11. $574
12. a) 21 b) 50
13. 330
14. $1200
15. a) 15.8 c) $524.40
    b) 73.12 d) $52.98
16. 80%
17. a) e.g., Divide 284 by 4.
    b) e.g., 75% is 3 × 25%, so 75% of 284 is 3 × 71 = 213.
18. 60 t
19. e.g., Step 1: Find 10% because it's easy. Step 2: Multiply by 3 to find 30%. Step 3: Find 2% because it's easy. Step 4: Multiply by 2 to find 4%. Step 5: Add 30% and 4% to get 34%.

Chapter 5, p. 191

5.1 The Area of a Parallelogram, pp. 197–199

1. A: base 3 cm, height 3 cm; B: base 10 cm, height 6 cm; C base 16 cm, height 9 cm

2. $23.4\ cm^2$

3. They have the same height and base.

4. Depends on parallelograms created.

5. **a)** $20.63\ m^2$ **b)** $15.00\ m^2$

6. e.g., **a)** A: base 2 cm, height 2 cm; B: base 7 cm, height 2 cm; C: base 8 cm, height 1 cm
   b) A: $4\ cm^2$; B: $14\ cm^2$; C: $8\ cm^2$

7. **a)** 7 m **c)** 7 cm **e)** 7 m
   b) $220\ cm^2$ **d)** $4.4\ m^2$ **f)** $896.5\ cm^2$

8. e.g., one parallelogram with base 36 cm and height 1 cm, one with base 12 cm and height 3 cm, one with base 9 cm and height 4 cm

9. e.g., base 12 cm, height 3 cm
   a) e.g., base 6 cm, height 3 cm
   b) e.g., base 12 cm, height, 6 cm

10. e.g., If the base and the height are sides, then the parallelogram should have right angles. I drew a rectangle.

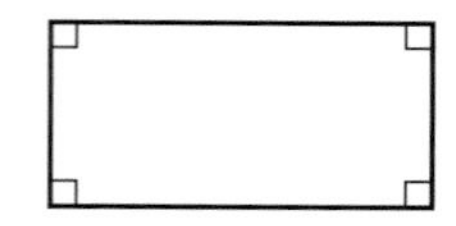

11. **a)** e.g.,

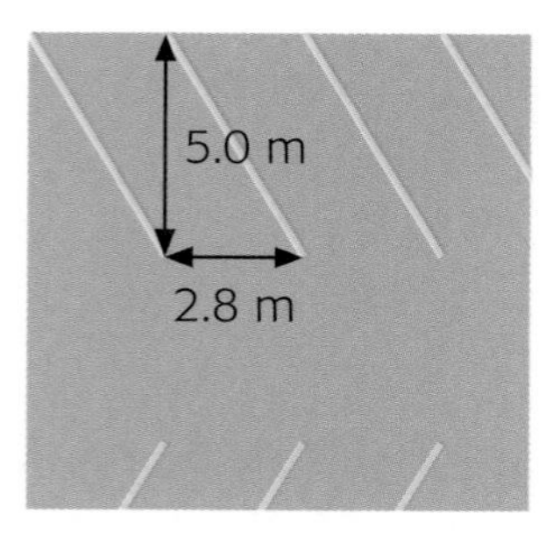

   b) 1 space: area $14\ m^2$, cost \$17.50
   5 spaces: area $70\ m^2$, cost \$87.50
   10 spaces: $140\ m^2$, cost \$175.00
   15 spaces: $210\ m^2$, cost \$262.50

12. Explain how determining the area of a rectangle is different from determining the area of a parallelogram.

5.2 The Area of a Triangle, pp. 204–206

1. **a)** $24\ cm^2$ **b)** $12\ cm^2$ **c)** $8\ cm^2$

2. **a)** $18\ cm^2$ **c)** $5.25\ m^2$
   b) $270\ cm^2$ **d)** $22.5\ m^2$

3. estimate, e.g., A: $2\ cm^2$, B: $4\ cm^2$, C: $2\ cm^2$, D: $2\ cm^2$; calculation, A: $2\ cm^2$, B: $4.5\ cm^2$, C: $2\ cm^2$, D: $2\ cm^2$

4. **a)** $4.5\ cm^2$ **b)** $1.9\ cm^2$

5. **a)** 24 cm **b)** 3.4 m **c)** $18\ cm^2$ **d)** 50 cm

6. **a)** $11.3\ cm^2$ **b)** $6.1\ cm^2$

7. $10\ m^2$

8. **a)** $9.0\ cm^2$ **c)** $4.5\ cm^2$
   b) $4.5\ cm^2$ **d)** $18.0\ cm^2$

9. **a)** $12.8\ m^2$ **b)** \$107.52 **c)** $128\ m^2$

10. **a)** 6 cm **b)** $12\ cm^2$

11. $144.5\ cm^2$

12. **a)** 27 cm **b)** 4 mm

13. e.g., This kite has an area of $2700\ cm^2$.

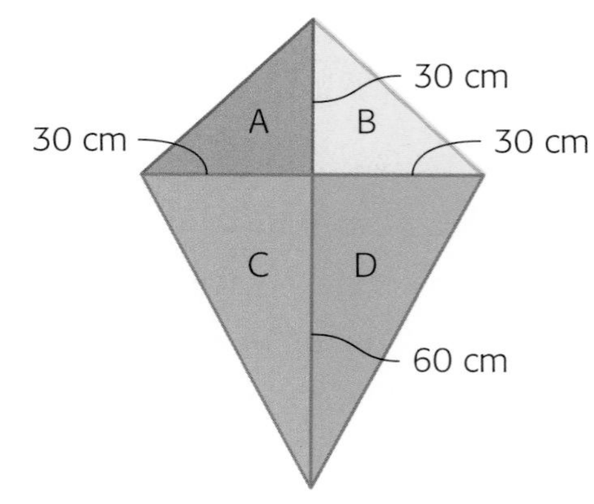

14. $2\ cm^2$

15. e.g., yes, triangle of height 4 cm, base 2 cm and parallelogram of height 2 cm, base 2 cm

16. e.g., If you use the 5 cm side as the base for triangle A, then its height must be less than 4 cm, so it must cover less area than triangle B.

17. Explain why each triangle has three pairs of bases and heights, but each combination of base and height gives the same value for the area of the triangle.

5.4 Calculating Circumference, pp. 211–213

1. **a)** 16 cm **b)** 14.8 cm
2. **a)** 20 cm, 63 cm **b)** 16 cm, 51.5 cm
3. **a)** 14.1 cm **c)** 20.1 cm **e)** 22 mm
   b) 5.3 cm **d)** 113.0 m **f)** 12.6 cm
4. **a)** 44 m **c)** 39.6 cm **e)** 145.1 m
   b) 122.5 cm **d)** 56.5 cm **f)** 0.31 m
5. 251 cm
6. **a)** 4.0 cm, 12.6 cm **b)** 5.0 cm, 15.7 cm
7. 9.6 cm
8. 34.5 m
9. clock: 18.0 cm, 56.5 cm; watch: 18 mm, 113 mm; tea bag: 3.8 cm, 11.9 cm; sewer cover: 31 cm, 195 cm; protractor: 11.8 cm, 37.1 cm; fan: 101 cm, 631 mm
10. 4396 m
11. 94.2 cm
12. about 141.3 m
13. about 10.5 cm
14. about 28.9 m
15. about 249.9 m
16. about 50 m
17. Explain the relationship between radius and circumference.

Mid-Chapter Review, pp. 214–215

1. **a)** 7 m^2 **b)** 6.0 cm^2
2. **a)** 7 cm^2 **b)** 8.1 m^2
3. **a)** 82 cm **c)** 54.0 cm
   b) 33.9 m **d)** 9.4 km
4. **a)** 47 cm **c)** 63 cm **e)** 138 cm
   b) 188 cm **d)** 53 cm **f)** 63 cm
5. 4.2 cm, 13.2 cm

5.5 Estimating the Area of a Circle, p. 219

1. e.g., penny about 3 cm^2, nickel about 3 cm^2, quarter about 4 cm^2, two-dollar coin about 6 cm^2
2. e.g., about 12 m^2
3. e.g., about 700 cm^2
4. about 20 m^2
5. **a)** e.g., about 5 m^2
   b) e.g., about 200 m^2
   c) e.g., about 80 mm^2
6. e.g., About 5 m^2 of the 12 m^2 mat is covered by circles. That means about $\frac{1}{2}$ of the mat is covered by circles.
7. Explain why you like one method for estimating the area of a circle better than another.

5.6 Calculating the Area of a Circle, pp. 223–224

1. **a)** 346.2 cm^2 **c)** 531 cm^2
   b) 154 cm^2 **d)** 6.2 cm^2
2. **a)** 41.8 cm^2 **c)** 22.9 cm^2
   b) 13 cm^2 **d)** 2.3 cm^2
3. e.g., estimate: about 37 squares in the circle, so area is about 37 cm^2; using a formula: radius is 3.5 cm, so area is $3.5 \times 3.5 \times \pi = 38.5$ cm^2
4. e.g., **a)** I would measure the area of a plastic flying disc to see if a sticker will fit on it.
   b) I would measure the circumference of a basketball to see if it will fit in my gym bag.
5. **a)** 4.2 cm^2 **b)** 2.1 cm^2
6. **a)** 52.8 cm^2 **b)** 17.6 cm^2

7. a) 1519.8 cm^2 b) 379.9 cm^2

8. a) 100.0 m^2 b) 78.5 m^2 c) 21.5 m^2

9. 89.3 cm^2

10. a) 251 015.6 m^2 d) $5300.63
b) $313 769.50 e) $319 070.13
c) 1927.5 m

11. e.g., The area will be 4 times larger.

12. e.g., Find the area of the big circle, find the area of the small circle in the middle, and subtract the area of the smaller circle from the larger.

13. Explain how to calculate the area of a circle (about 8.0 cm^2) using circumference.

5.7 Solve Problems Using Diagrams, p. 229

1. 3.7 m^2

2. 72 m^2

3. about 3.2 L

4. 295 cm^2

5. 24 ways

6. 12

7. 3 black cats with long hair, not short tails

Chapter Self Test, pp. 231–232

1. a) 22.5 cm^2 b) 21.0 m^2

2. a) 30 cm^2 b) 8.8 cm^2 c) 30 cm^2

3. a) 16 cm^2 b) 20 cm^2

4. a) area b) area c) circumference

5. a) 15.7 km c) 9.4 cm
b) 163 cm d) 66 cm

6. a) 3 cm^2 c) 25.5 cm^2
b) 95 cm^2 d) 120.8 cm^2

7. a) 225 m^2 b) 176.6 m^2 c) 48.4 m^2

8. the piece with the larger circles

Chapter Review, pp. 233–234

1. a) 5.4 cm^2 b) 17.5 cm^2 c) 49.5 m^2

2. $2.5 \times 3.2 = 8$ cm^2

3. a) e.g., △A: height 5 cm, base 5 cm;
△B: height 5 cm, base 3 cm;
△C: height 5 cm, base 7 cm
b) e.g., △A: 12.5 cm^2, △B: 7.5 cm^2,
△C: 17.5 cm^2

4. 4.6 cm^2

5. 11.9 cm

6. 22.0 cm

7. a circle with radius of 3.5 cm

8. 38.5 cm^2

9. a) 180° b) 125°

Chapter 6, p. 237

6.2 Adding Integers Using the Zero Principle, pp. 245–247

1. b) +2 d) +2 f) −10
c) −1 e) −6

2. a) 0 b) 0

3. a) (−5) c) (−3) e) (−3)
b) 0 d) (−2) f) (+1)

4. −1

5. By the zero principle, the sum of any two opposite integers is 0.

6. a) −5, −6, −7; add −1 to previous term
b) 1, 2, 3; add +1 to previous term

7. a) (−1), (−1) c) (−1), (+1), (−1), (−1)
b) (+1), (+1) d) (−1), (−1), (−1)

8. a) (+5) b) (−4)

9. a) $>$ b) $=$ c) $>$ d) $=$ e) $<$ f) $<$

10. e.g.,

a) $(+1) + (+1) + (+1) + (+1) + (-1) = (+3)$

b) $(-1) + (-1) + (-1) + (+1) = (-2)$

c) $(+1) + (+1) + (-1) + (-1) = 0$

d) $(+1) + (-1) + (+1) + (-1) + (-1) = (-1)$

11. e.g., $(-1) + (-2) + (-2) = (-5)$; $(-6) + (-1) + (+2) = (-5)$; $(3) + (-2) + (-6) = (-5)$

12. e.g., The three missing integers must add to zero, but with three integers you can get only +1 or −1.

13. a) (−6)

b) e.g.,

−3	−10	−5
−8	−6	−4
−7	−2	−9

14. a) 0 **b)** 0

15. a) true **b)** true **c)** false

6.3 Adding Integers that Are Far from Zero, pp. 250–251

1. a) 0 **b)** −27 **c)** −27 **d)** +7 **e)** +7

2. a) −70 **b)** −30 **c)** +30 **d)** −70

3. a) +8 **b)** −8 **c)** −40 **d)** −25 **e)** −5 **f)** +20

4. a) 10 **b)** 20

5.

−1	−2	+3
+4	0	−4
−3	+2	+1

6. Heidi +16, Rana +14, Sonya +12, Indu −1, Meagan −9

7. a) −4 **b)** −16 **c)** −8 **d)** +5 **e)** −9 **f)** +18

8. e.g., $(-20) + (+8)$ is the negative difference between 20 and 8, which is the opposite integer of $20 - 8$.

9. e.g., $(+20) + (-8)$ is the difference between 20 and 8, because it's taking 8 from 20, which is $20 - 8$.

10. Explain the addition of negative numbers (−28).

6.4 Integer Addition Strategies, pp. 256–257

1. a) −30 **b)** +2

2. e.g., The integers are the same, just in a different order.

3. +14

4. a) +6 **b)** +6

c) e.g., order of addition doesn't change sum

5. a) −15 **b)** +2 **c)** +5 **d)** +10

6. e.g., $(+12) + (-20) + (-14) + (+10) + (+16) = (+4)$; $(+15) + (+11) + (-16) + (-18) + (+12) = (+4)$

7. 345 m

8. a) +5, +9, +7, +8

b) e.g., $(+4) + (+1)$ and $(-2) + (-3)$ add to 0

c) e.g., order of addition doesn't change sum

d) e.g., +14, −12, +11, −13

9. Explain why you prefer one method of adding integers over another (+22).

Mid-Chapter Review, p. 260

1. a) (+3) **b)** (−7) **c)** (+1) **d)** (−1) **e)** (+5) **f)** 0

2. a) (+3) **b)** (−2) **c)** (+10) **d)** (+8)

3. a) e.g., Both are positive or, if one is negative, the other is positive, and it takes more counters to model the positive integer.

b) e.g., Both are negative or, if one is positive, the other is negative, and it takes more counters to model the negative integer.

4. 55 m

5. a) (+10) **b)** (−100) **c)** (−130) **d)** (−40)

6. a) (−30) **b)** (−41) **c)** (−44) **d)** (−34)

7. (+32)

8. step 3

6.5 Subtracting Integers Using Counters, pp. 264–266

1. a) (−6) **b)** (+1) **c)** (+5) **d)** (−1)

2. a) (−3)
b) e.g., There are enough blue counters on the left to allow subtraction.

3. a) (+3)
b) e.g., There are not enough blue counters on the left to allow subtraction.

4. (−4) − (−6) = (+2)

5. (+6) − (−4) = (+10), (−4) − (+6) = (−10)

6. A, B

7. a) (+2), (+3), (+4) **b)** (−9), (−8), (−7), (−6), e.g., If you subtract lesser and lesser integers from a positive or negative integer, then the answer gets greater and greater.

8. b) −9 **c)** +16 **d)** +10 **e)** −3 **f)** +7

9. a) +4 **b)** +5 **c)** +16 **d)** −18 **e)** −15 **f)** +5

10. a) (+3) **b)** (−5) **c)** (+1) **d)** (+7)

11. a) false, e.g., (−2) − (−3) = (+1)
b) false, e.g., (+2) − (+3) = (−1)
c) true, e.g., (+2) − (−1) = (+3)
d) false, e.g., (−2) − (+3) = (−5)
e) false, e.g., (−2) − (−3) = (+1)

12. Explain why subtracting an integer is like adding its opposite.

6.6 Subtracting Integers Using Number Lines, pp. 271–272

1. a) (−75) **b)** 0 **c)** −75

2. a) (+8) **b)** (−1)

3. a) (+70), (−70)
b) e.g., The arrows for the subtractions point in opposite directions, but they have the same length.

4. a) +20 **b)** −40 **c)** −2 **d)** +3 **e)** +20 **f)** 0

5. a) (−5) − (−15) **b)** (+15) − (+25) **c)** (−20) − (+35) **d)** (−100) − (−145)

6. e.g., One integer is 5 places to the left of the other.

7. a) −34 **b)** +7 **c)** −25 **d)** +23

8. b) −350 **c)** −130 **d)** +700 **e)** +55 **f)** −648

9. D

10. Explain why adding an opposite is like subtracting.

6.7 Solve Problems by Working Backward, p. 275

1. e.g., Start with 10. Add (+1). Subtract (−3). Add (−5). The result is 9. The quick way to figure out the original number is to add (−1), because (+1) − (−3) + (−5) = (−1).

2. Subtract (+2). Add (−1). Subtract (−2). The original number is 3.

3. −2

4. e.g., Start with the original number. Add (+5). Subtract (−2). Subtract (+4). Subtract (+3).

5. 64 kg

6. \$320.00

7. e.g.,

8. e.g., Janet is training for a race. Every week she runs 3 km more than the previous week. During her 7th and final week of training, Janet runs 24 km. How far did she run in the first week? (6 km)

Chapter Self-Test, p. 276

1. **a)** $(+1)$ **b)** (-2) **c)** $(+2)$ **d)** (-15)
2. **a)** $(+1)$ **b)** $(+1)$ **c)** (-7)
3. **a)** $(+2) - (+5)$ **b)** $(-10) - (-40)$
4. **a)** (-3) **b)** (-13) **c)** (-9) **d)** (-4)
5. Sam took out \$67.
6. **a)** The larger integer value is 12, and positive, so adding a smaller negative number will give a positive integer (right of 0) and the difference between 12 and 4 is 8, so 8 units to the right.

   b) Subtracting a positive number from a negative number always gives a larger negative number, to the left of 0, and the sum of 15 and 23 is 38.

Chapter Review, p. 278

1. e.g., $(-2) = (-4) + (+2)$,
   $(-2) = (-1) + (-1)$,
   $(-2) = (+7) + (-9)$
2. Polly took out \$10.
3. **a)** (-36) **b)** (-45)
4. ■ $+ (+1)$ is greater because a positive integer is added, so the value is increased, while ■ $- (+1)$ is less because a positive integer is subtracted.
5. C greatest, B least
6. e.g., Alike: both can be modelled with number lines or counters; subtracting an integer is like adding the integer with the opposite sign. Different: the order of the integers matters in subtraction but does not matter in addition; addition involves combining two amounts and subtraction involves determining the difference between two amounts.
7. **a)** $(+5)$ **b)** (-5) **c)** (-1) **d)** (-2)
8. (-9) and (-4)
9. -30 °C

Chapter 7 2-D Geometry, p. 281

7.2 Comparing Positions on a Grid, pp. 288-289

1. $A(-2, 3)$, $B(2, 2)$, $C(1, -4)$, $D(-2, 0)$, $E(-3, -4)$
2.

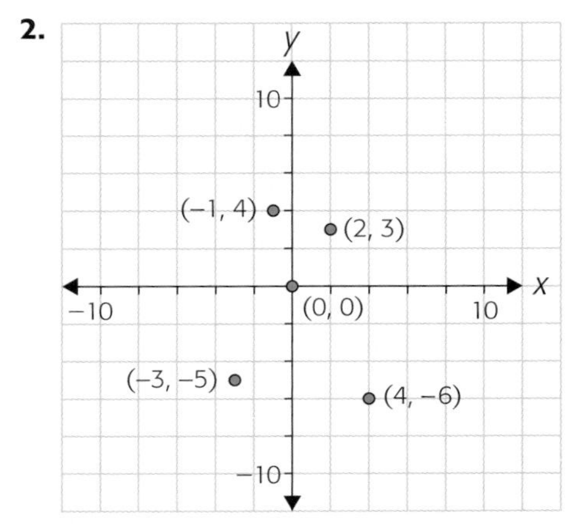

3. **a)** 3 units **b)** 10 units **c)** 7 units
4. **a)** right angle scalene triangle

   b) parallelogram
5. **a)** below, $-5 < -3$ **b)** above, $-1 > -3$
6. **a)** $(-11, 28)$ **b)** $(-15, -28)$
7. **a)** e.g., $(-3, 3)$, $(-2, 2)$, $(-1, 1)$, $(1, -1)$, $(2, -2)$

b)

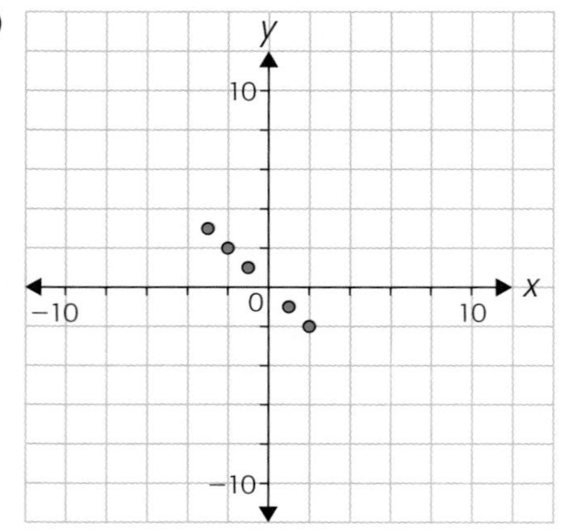

c) a line **d)** moves to right

8. e.g., $(-2, -3)$ and $(-8, 2)$

9. e.g., $(-8, -3)$, $(-9, -8)$, $(-6, -8)$

10. $(3, 2)$, $(3, -2)$, $(-3, 2)$, $(-3, -2)$

11. e.g., Point $(3, -4)$ is 7 units to the right of and 7 units lower than point $(-4, 3)$.

7.3 Translations and Reflections, pp. 293–295

1. a)

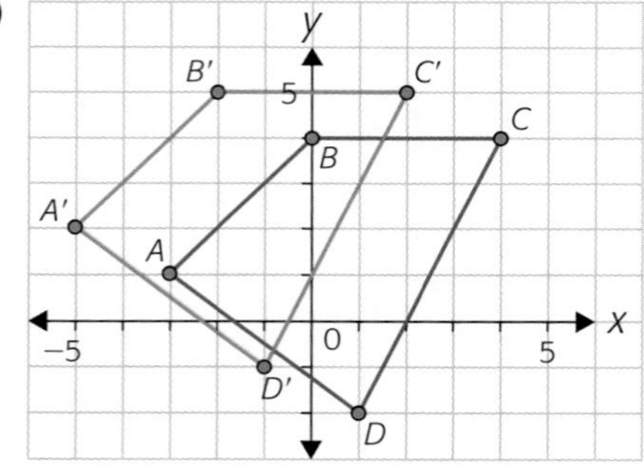

b) $A'(-5, 1)$, $B'(-2, 5)$, $C'(2, 5)$, $D'(-1, -1)$

2. $P'(6, 2)$, $Q'(4, 0)$, $R'(2, 5)$

3. a) $A'(-4, 1)$, $B'(1, -5)$, $C'(4, 3)$, $D'(-2, 3)$

b) $A'(4, -1)$, $B'(-1, 5)$, $C'(-4, -3)$, $D'(2, -3)$

4. yes

5. a) 2 units right, 5 units up

b) $B'(5, 5)$, $C'(4, 9)$

6. $X'(3, -6)$, $Y'(3, -2)$, $Z'(6, 1)$

7. a) 5 units to left, 4 units up

b) 4 units to left, 5 units down

c) 9 units to left, 1 unit down

8. $P'(2, 1)$, $Q'(6, 3)$, $R'(4, 6)$

9. a) right 2, down 3 **b)** $E(-10, -2)$, $F(0, 1)$

10. e.g., The directions that move B to B' are not the same that move A to A'.

11. a) e.g., $R(4, -2)$, $S(-2, -2)$ or $R(4, 10)$, $S(-2, 10)$

b) e.g.,

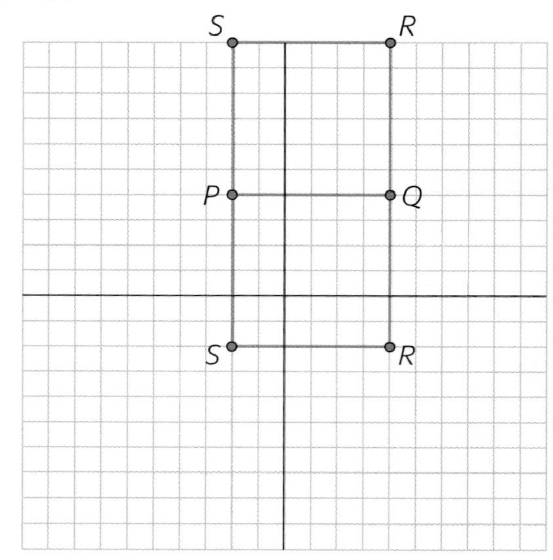

c) e.g., down 6

12. Explain where a figure could be after a transformation.

7.4 Rotations, p. 299

1. a) $(2, 0)$ **b)** counterclockwise, 90°

2. $D'(-3, 2)$, $E'(-5, 1)$, $F'(-1, -1)$

3. a), b)

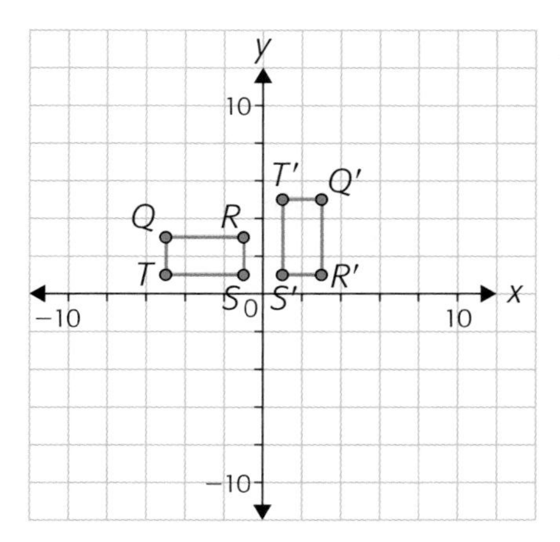

c) e.g., It was rotated 90°, not 180°.

4. 9:07:30, 180°

5. a) e.g., $X(2, 1)$, $Y(-1, 2)$, $Z(-1, -2)$
b) $X'(2, 1)$, $Y'(5, 0)$, $Z'(5, 4)$

6. a) $A'(4, -2)$, $B'(1, -2)$, $C'(-3, 1)$, $D'(0, 1)$
b) 180° clockwise

7. e.g., Label vertices, determine a centre of rotation, and choose a direction and degree of rotation; check the vertices all have negative coordinates.

Mid-Chapter Review, p. 301

1. e.g., $A(6, 6)$, $B(7, 3)$, $C(3, 1)$, $D(2, 5)$ translate left 4 and down 4 to $A'(2, 2)$, $B'(3, -1)$, $C'(-1, -3)$, $D'(-2, 1)$

2.

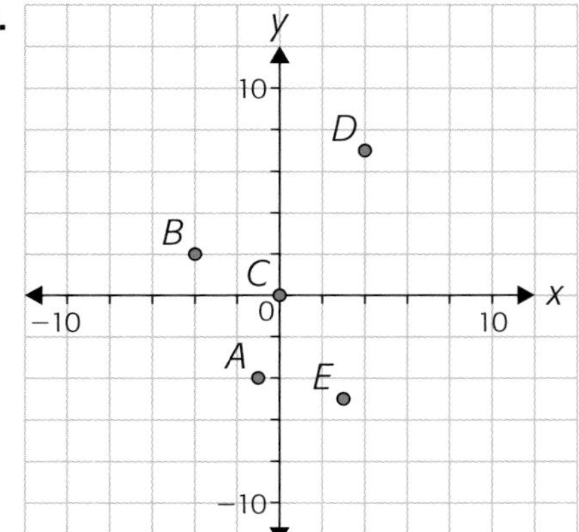

3. a) $C(0, 0)$ **c)** $D(4, 7)$
b) $B(-4, 2)$ **d)** $E(3, -5)$

4. a), b), c) $A'(-6, 2)$, $B'(-2, 2)$, $C'(-6, 5)$; $A'(0, 0)$, $B'(2, 0)$, $C'(0, -3)$

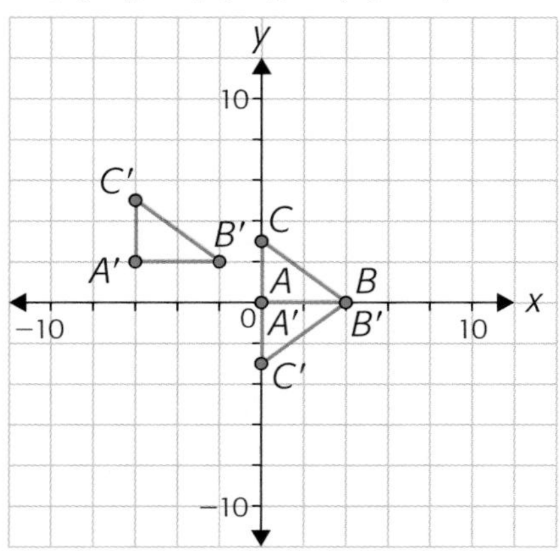

5. a) reflection about y-axis
b) 180° rotation about point (0, 0), translation of 7 to the right and 6 down

7.5 Communicate About Transformations, p. 305

1. a), b), c) e.g., $A(-4, 4)$, $B(-2, 4)$, $C(-1, 2)$, $D(-3, 2)$ was translated 5 units right and 1 unit down to create $A'B'C'D'$.

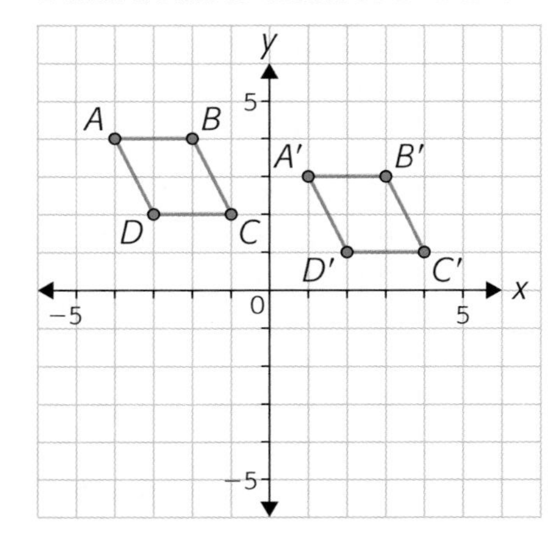

2. e.g., First, the shape was reflected in the x-axis, then it was rotated 90° ccw about the point $(0, -6)$.

3. e.g., reflect across y-axis, rotate 90° cw around point (0, 5), translate down 1 unit and right 1 unit

4. Use your knowledge of parallelograms and transformations, and use correct mathematical terminology.

7.6 Perpendicular Bisectors, pp. 313–314

1. Each perpendicular bisector will be at the midpoint of, and at right angles to, each line segment.
2. b)
3. Each perpendicular bisector will be at the midpoint of, and at right angles to, each line segment.
4. **c)** The circle goes through each vertex of the triangle.
5. **a)** when the construction is small enough to be done or modelled on paper or flexible material
   b) when the construction is on a large scale such as drafting or designing
   c) when a protractor is available for the application and the situation is small enough to use the protractor
   d) Use a transparent mirror when the construction is too large to use paper folding or a protractor
6. **c)** e.g., Fold the paper along the line segment. If point *A* is on top of point *B*, then it is the perpendicular bisector.

7.7 Parallel Lines, p. 318

1. *AB* and *XY* are parallel.
2. e.g., Draw line segment *AB*, 6 cm long. Draw lines that are at right angles from *A* and *B* using a protractor. Locate points *C* and *D* on these lines that are the same distance from *AB* using a ruler. Connect *C* and *D*. *CD* is parallel to *AB*.
3. **a)** It keeps the distance between the two lines equal.
   b) Use it to draw lines at right angles.
   c) It uses reflection to form perpendicular lines; the second is parallel to the original.
   d) Mark several points the same distance apart on a line using a ruler. Connect the points with the straight edge of the ruler.
4. **a)** e.g., The slanted lines in the window are parallel.
   b) The bars of the horse jump are parallel.
5. e.g., The opposite lines in the key of the court are parallel. The opposite outside boundaries of the court are made of two sets of parallel lines. The centre line is a perpendicular bisector to the long edge of the court boundary. The basketball hoop is placed on the bisector of the short edge of the court boundary. The sides of the wooden strips in the floor of the school gym are parallel.
6. e.g., Trace, then use a transparent mirror.

7.8 Angle Bisectors, pp. 319–322

1. b) and c)
2. The bisector will be at 40°.
3. e.g., an angle of 40° bisected at 20°
4. e.g., an angle of 120° bisected at 60°
5. **a)** e.g., an angle of 90° bisected at 45° with a protractor
   b) an angle of 160° bisected at 80° by folding
   c) an angle of 200° bisected at 100° using a compass and ruler
6. **c)** The angle bisectors intersect at the same point.
7. **a)** e.g., The lines running to the centre of the photograph bisect the vertices of the pentagon.
   b) e.g., In each blue parallelogram, the white lines bisect the small angles.
   c) e.g., Each spoke bisects the angle formed by the two neighbouring spokes.

8. Bisect a 60° angle in several ways.

Chapter Self-Test, p. 324

1. **a)** Brandon (−2, −4), Pine Dock (3, 3), Winnipeg (3, −4)

   b) 5 units **c)** 7 units

2. **c)** $X''(-5, 0)$, $Y''(-5, -1)$, $Z''(1, -1)$

3. **a)**

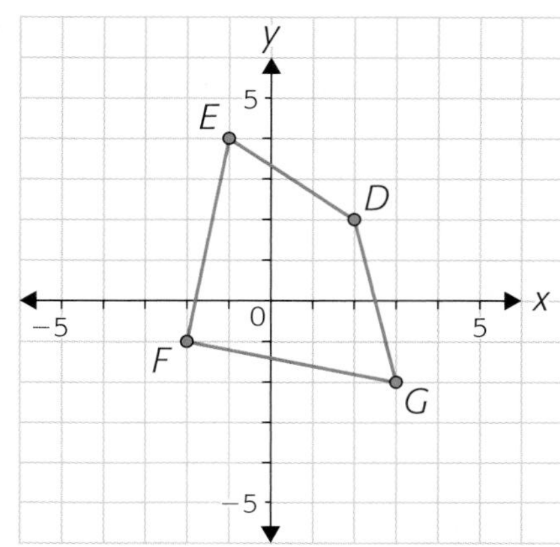

b)

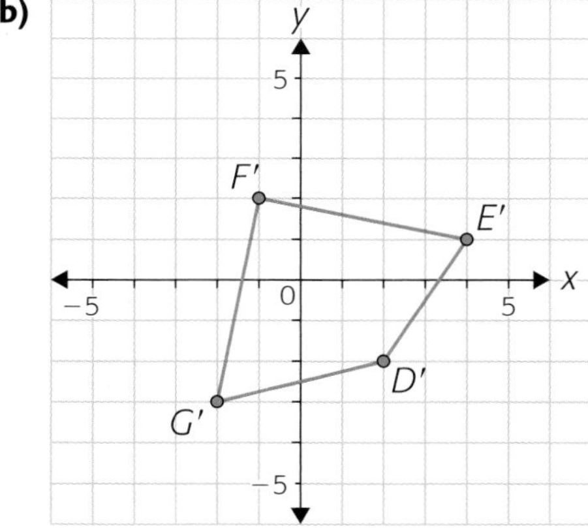

c) $D'(2, -2)$, $E'(4, 1)$, $F'(-1, 2)$, $G'(-2, -3)$

4. e.g., cw 90° about origin or ccw 270° about origin

5. e.g., Use a protractor and a ruler to determine lines at A and B perpendicular to AB and a ruler to determine points on those lines that are the same distance from AB.

6. e.g., an angle of 30° bisected at 15°, an angle of 90° bisected at 45°, an angle of 150° bisected by an angle of 75°

Chapter Review, pp. 327–328

1. **a)** (14, 0) has greatest 1st coordinate

   b) (−14, 0) has least 1st coordinate

   c) (0, −14) has least 2nd coordinate

   d) (0, 14) has greatest 2nd coordinate

2. **c)** $A'(0, 2)$, $B'(-3, 1)$, $C'(-3, -2)$, $D'(1, -1)$

   e) $A''(-2, 3)$, $B''(-5, 2)$, $C''(-5, -1)$, $D''(-1, 0)$

3. **a)** e.g.,

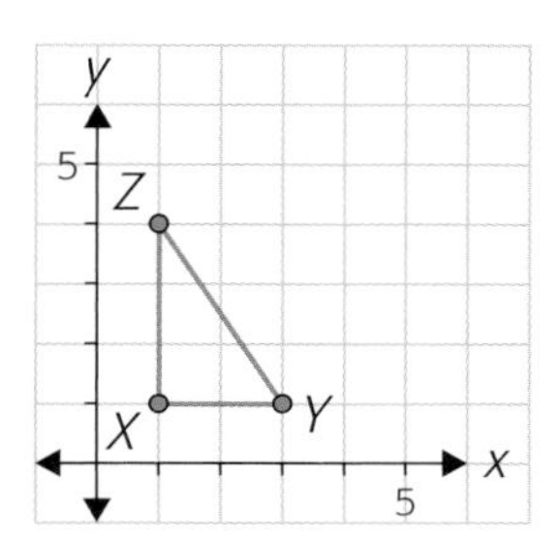

b) e.g., 6 units down, 6 units left; $X'(-5, -5)$, $Y'(-3, -5)$, $Z'(-5, -2)$

c) e.g., reflection in x-axis; $X''(-5, 5)$, $Y''(-3, 5)$, $Z''(-5, 2)$

4. **a), b)**

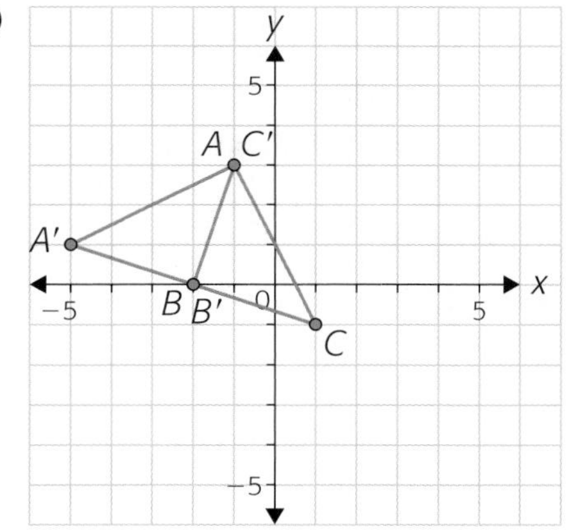

5. e.g., reflect in base of triangle, rotate 180° cw about centre of base, reflect in a horizontal line followed by a translation

6. **b)** e.g., translate left 1 unit, reflect in y-axis, translate down 4 units

7. Each perpendicular bisector will be at the midpoint of, and at right angles to, each line segment.

8. e.g., telephone poles, railroad tracks, gymnastic parallel bars
9. e.g., draw parallel lines using protractor and ruler
10. Each angle bisector will divide each angle in half.
11. e.g., Translations: The two red rectangles are translations of each other.

    Reflections: The two yellow triangles are reflections of each other across a vertical line through the centre of the square.

    Rotations: The blue shapes are rotations of one blue shape around the centre of the square.

    Perpendicular bisectors: The vertical line segment in the centre is the perpendicular bisector of the bases of the orange triangles.

    Parallel line segments: The horizontal line segment in the centre is parallel to the sides of the green rectangles.

    Angle bisectors: The diagonal line segments on the blue shapes bisect the 90° angles between the green and red rectangles.

Cumulative Review: Chapters 4–7, pp. 330–331

1. C	6. A	11. C	16. D
2. D	7. A	12. C	17. D
3. C	8. D	13. A	18. A
4. C	9. C	14. A, D	19. A, D
5. C	10. B	15. D	

Chapter 8, p. 333

8.1 The Range of a Set of Data, pp. 338–339

1. a) 18 b) 1435 c) 19.1 d) 130
2. 27.2 cents
3. e.g., 10, 12, 13, 15, 25
4. 15 days
5. a) 1694 g
   b) e.g., The size of an animal's brain is related to the size of the animal.
6. a) 747; 747
   b) The range for each class is the same.
   c) Describe what the range does and does not reveal about the sets of data.

8.2 The Median and Mode of a Set of Data, pp. 343–345

1. a) median 234.5, mode 230
   b) median 60.8, no mode
2. median 18, mode 18
3. e.g., 10, 10, 10, 14, 16, 18
4. a) 3 b) 54 c) 76% d) 268
5. a) 8 and 9 c) 7.1
   b) 18 d) F and G
6. a) 196 b) 125.5
   c) e.g., Gretzky scored more points for the Oilers than for the Kings. You would expect this because when you compare individual years, he mostly scored more for Edmonton.
7. e.g., mode, because data is non-numerical
8. a) 72 b) no, only that it is 19 or greater
9. one of 75, 82, 99, or 102
10. a) gold: modes 0, 2, 7, median 2; silver: mode 1, median 3; bronze: mode 1, median 3
    b) e.g., median, because modes are mostly not near most values
11. mode 5, median 10; explain which represents the data better

8.3 The Mean of a Set of Data, pp. 350–351

1. a) 19.9 b) 19.9
2. a) 6 b) 460
3. 108 790
4. a) 9.7 b) 9.3
   c) e.g., the two new ages were low
5. a) 130 b) 107
   c) e.g., median because it is in the middle of the data
6. e.g., mode tells which shoe size is most common; mean is likely to represent the temperature best
7. 7 values
8. 20 h
9. the student who read 12 books because the mean with 12 removed is 2
10. a) 20 167 new subscribers
    b) e.g., to know if its advertising is working
11. no, e.g., 48 is the mean of this set: 50, 22, 46, 55, 55, 60.
12. 74
13. e.g, Natalia's sales total is $2 more than the mean for Eric's class. When Natalia moves to Eric's class and you divide up the extra $2 over all of the other students, it raises the mean by that fraction.
    In Natalia's class, the mean was higher by $2 than her sales total. When you take away her sales, the total is less, but it is also divided over one less student. The result will be a mean that is a fraction of $2 greater.
14. yes

Mid-Chapter Review, p. 353

1. 16 kg
2. 342 m
3. B
4. median 4.5, modes 2.7, 4.9
5. 75 cm plant
6. a) mean 10.8 s, median 10.8 s
   b) e.g., No, times tend to get better as athletes improve.
7. 8 values
8. $67

8.5 Outliers, pp. 360–361

1. a)

```
                          X
                          XX   X
       X                  XXXXXX X
<-+----+----+----+----+----+----+----+->
  0    5    10   15   20   25   30   35
```

   b) 2
   c) mean 16, median 16, mode 14
   d) mean 17, median 16.5, mode 14
2. e.g., 257 g without the outlier mass of 54 g
3. a) e.g., $200 000
   b) mean $64 375, median $42 500, mode $35 000
   c) mean $55 333, median $35 000, mode $35 000
   d) e.g., Use the mean with the outlier to show the average salary is high.
   e) e.g., Use the mean with the outlier to show there is a big range between her salary and the average.
4. e.g., The low mark is not typical of his work.
5. a) 97, 89
   b) e.g., the mean without the outlier because it is a better indicator of his dad's usual score
6. mean with all values 138, mean without outlier of 25:150; median 150, mode 150; e.g., Mean without outlier, median, and mode all indicate goal is reached, but mean with outlier is lower; it indicates goal is not reached

7. e.g., The mean of all the lifespans is 2.7 years, but without the outlier of 12 it is 1.7 years, which is a better average because most of the lifespans are from 1 to 2 years.
8. Explain when it is appropriate to calculate a mean including an outlier, and when it is not.

8.6 Communicate about Data, pp. 364–365

1. e.g., If the school had ordered the median number of white milk cartons for each day last week, then there would have been two days when there wouldn't have been enough white milk. If the school had ordered the mean number of white milk cartons, there would have three days when there wouldn't have been enough milk. So it is better to use the median, 61, for white milk. If the school had ordered the median number of chocolate milk cartons for each day last week, then there would have been two days when there wouldn't have been enough chocolate milk. If the school had ordered the mean number of white milk cartons, it is the same; there would have two days when there wouldn't have been enough milk. So you can use either the mean or the median. I'd use the mean, 56, because it is higher.
2. **a)** mean 13, median 14, mode 14
   b) If Roger were to watch 2 h of TV each day, then he would be watching 14 h of TV each week. This is the median and the mode, so he is correct.
3. **a)** Asha's team: 85
   b) Peter's team: 86
   c) Winnie's team: 85
   d) Choose which value you think best represents the results and justify your choice.
4. **b)** e.g., Both the median and the mean are greater for Western and Northern Canada than they are for Eastern Canada.

Chapter Self-Test, p. 367

1. 45 cm, 138 cm
2. **a)** 44, no mode **b)** 153, 148
3. no, e.g., The median of 5, 6, 7, 8, 12, 13, 15, 21 is 10.
4. no, e.g., This set of values has no mode: 12, 15, 17.
5. 124
6. 1500; 499 is not an outlier, so it wouldn't affect the mean much; 1 is an outlier, but 1500 is much farther away from the data than 1 is, so it would affect the mean more.
7. **a)** median 25.5, mean 26, modes 27, 33
   b) one of the modes
   c) e.g., mean or median since the modes are greater than most of the temperatures

Chapter Review, pp. 369–370

1. **a)** 79 **b)** 6
2. **a)** 4, 4 **b)** 106.5, 115
3. **a)**

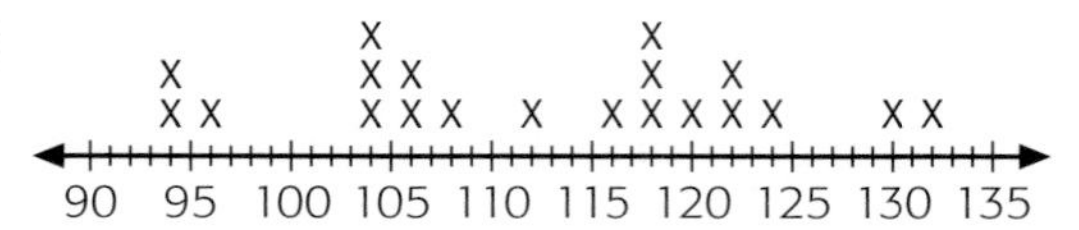

   b) 38 **c)** 112
4. means: 8, 11; medians: 8, 11; e.g., the means and medians are the same
5. **a)** median
   b) e.g., mean or median
   c) e.g., mode, median, or mean
6. mean, e.g., to compare this year's temperature with next year's; mode, e.g., stores need to know which size to order in greatest quantity

7. **a)** 99
   b) e.g., Use the mean without the outlier, because the outlier is unlikely to happen very often, and including it will have a strong effect on the mean.

8. **a)** e.g.,

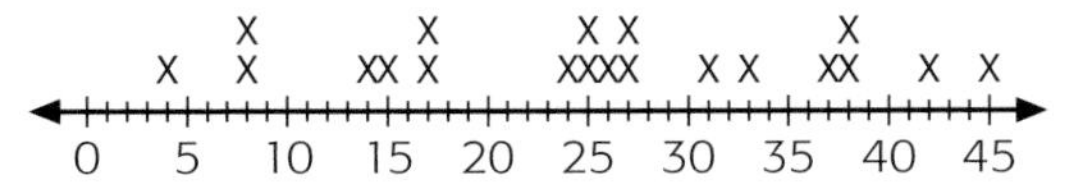

   b) e.g., mean or median both represent the typical middle value

9. **a)** mean: 100, mode: 92, median: 92
   b) Median or mode, because her scores were improving, and 92 represents her most recent scores better.

10. e.g., mode, because there are many more $5 cards than any other kind

Chapter 9, p. 373

9.1 Writing a Pattern Rule, pp. 380–382

1. e.g., $T = n + 4$

2. **a)** same: number of yellow squares; changes: number of blue squares
   b) Each figure has one yellow square; number of blue squares is twice the figure number.
   c) e.g., $2n + 1$ **d)** 2, 1

3. **a)** 6, 7, 8
   b) e.g., number of triangles in a figure is 3 more than the figure number
   c) e.g., $T = 3 + n$

4. Anne: In shape n, there are n blocks above the orange block and n blocks to the right of it; the orange block is 1, making $n + 1 + n$ blocks in total. Sanjay: In shape n, there are n green blocks placed vertically (up and down) and $(n + 1)$ orange placed horizontally (from side to side), making $n + (n + 1)$ blocks in total. Robert: In shape n, there are $2n$ green blocks placed in an "L" shape to the left of the only orange block, making $2n + 1$ blocks in total.

5. **a)** e.g., $T = (n + 1) + (n + 1) + 2$, where T represents the number of tiles in figure number n.
   b) e.g., $T = 2n + 4$
   c) 4 in both cases; 2 in both cases
   d) e.g., because the total number of tiles in each figure is the same

6. **a)**

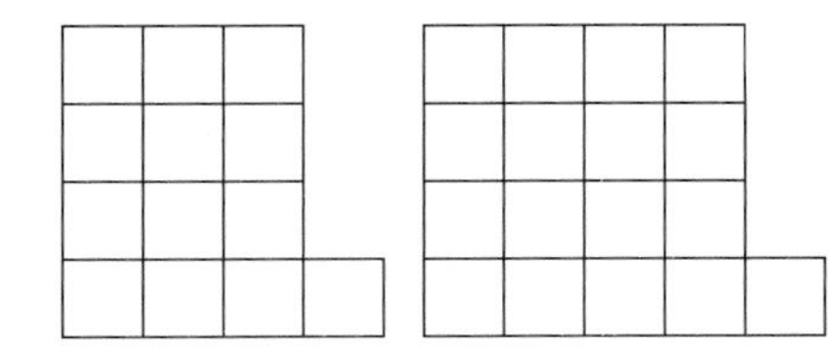

   b) e.g., $T = 4n - 3$
   c) -3, 4
   d) e.g., numerical coefficient: if figure number increases by 1, number of blocks increases by 4; constant term: pattern starts off with 3 fewer blocks than the figure number multiplied by the numerical coefficient

7. Substitute 257 for T and solve for n.
   a) yes, 128 **b)** no

8. **a)** e.g., The constant term describes the part of the pattern that stays the same.
   b) e.g., The numerical coefficient describes the part of the pattern that changes.

9.2 Evaluating an Expression to Solve a Problem, pp. 387–388

1. **a)** 30 **b)** 24 **c)** 6 **d)** 21

2. e.g., $12h + 35$

3. **a)** 9 **b)** 40 **c)** 27 **d)** 8

4. **a)** e.g., $8t - 2$ **b)** 30 reps

5. $6(b - 1) + 3 = 6((4) - 1) + 3 = 6(3) + 3 = 18 + 3 = 21$

6. **a)** e.g., $4p$ **c)** e.g., $2h + 5$
   b) e.g., $3h$ **d)** e.g., $10h$

7. **A.** blue tiles **C.** green tiles
B. purple tiles **D.** yellow tiles

8. **a)** $8h + 50$
b) \$170

9. **a)** \$25, \$27, \$29, \$31, \$33, \$35
b) e.g., $25 + 2t$
c) \$59

10. **a)** $56 - 3c$ **b)** \$41

11. **a)** 9, 11 **b)** $v = 2n + 1$ **c)** 17

12. $1000 + 30g$; explain why the pattern rule is useful.

9.4 Linear Relations and Their Graphs, pp. 395–397

1.

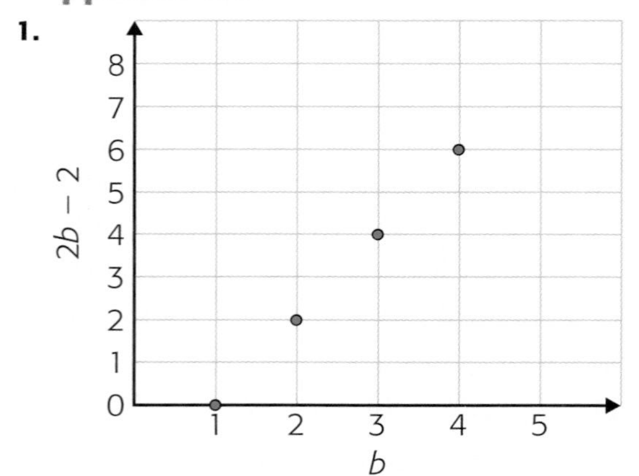

2. **a)**

n	1	2	3	4	5
$n + 3$	4	5	6	7	8

b)

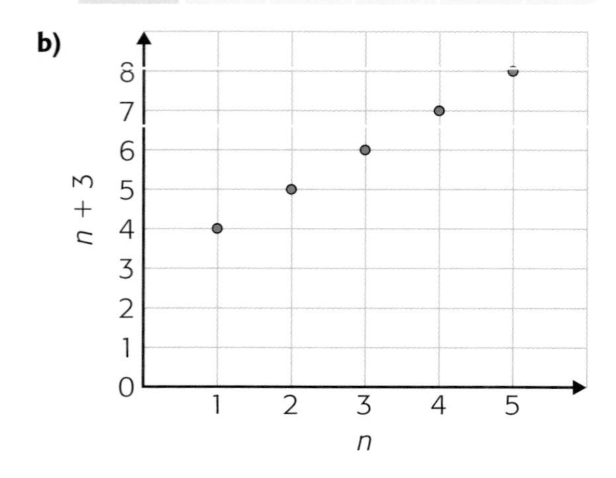

3.

	n	1	2	3	4	5
a)	$3n + 1$	4	7	10	13	16
b)	$5n + 3$	8	13	18	23	28
c)	$3n + 5$	8	11	14	17	20

4. For 3.a)

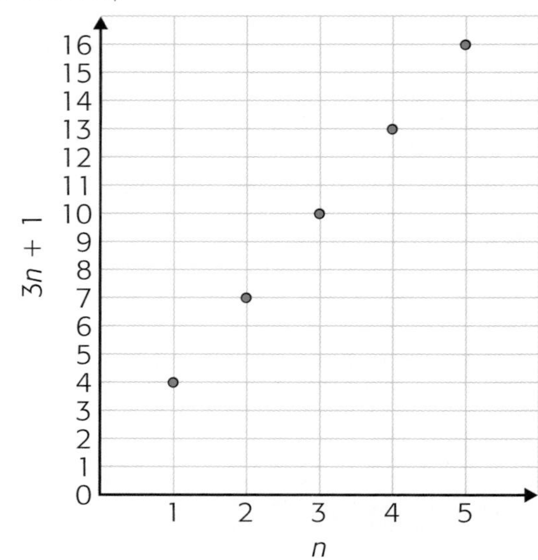

For 3.b)

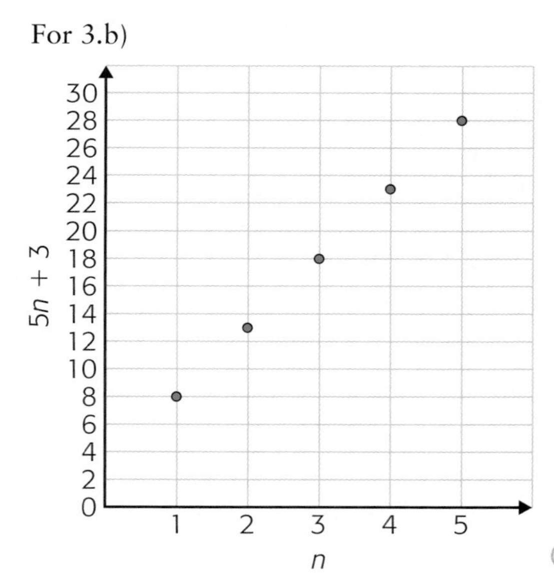

For 3.c)

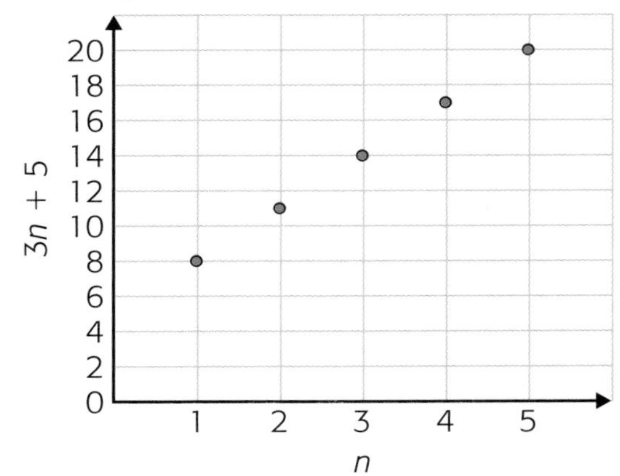

5.

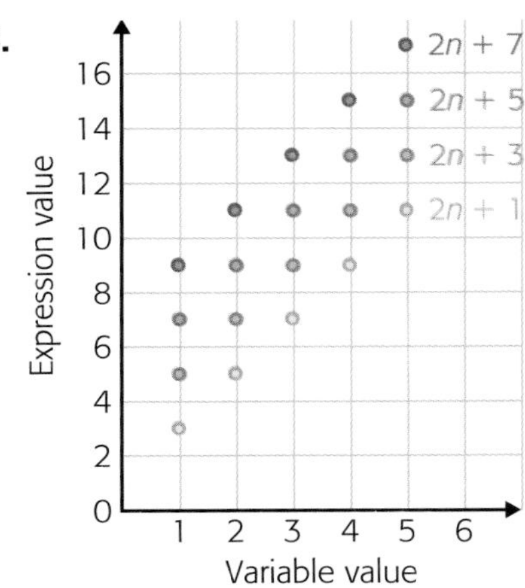

6. e.g., alike: parallel, or all go up the same way; different: at different heights

7.

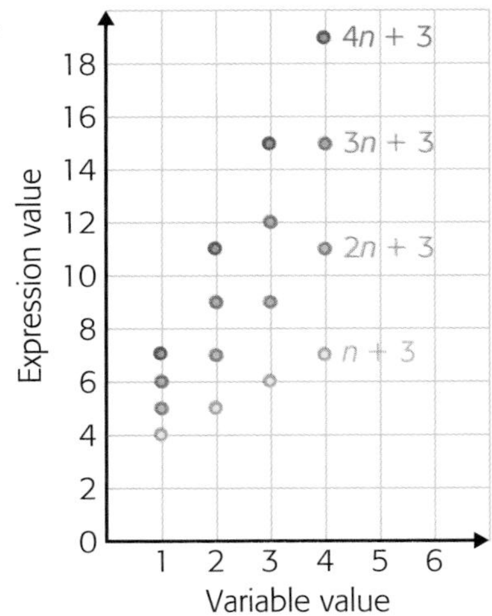

8. e.g., alike: all start at same variable value; all are linear; different: not parallel, they spread out

9. **A.** Graph B **B.** Graph C **C.** Graph A

10. **a)** e.g., $r = 3p - 3$

b)

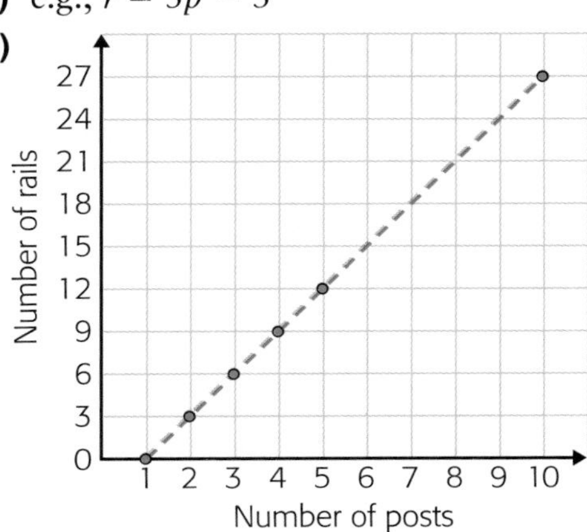

c) 27 rails

11. **a)** $r = 4p - 4$, coefficient and constant are both 4 in new fence, but 3 in old fence

b) e.g., graph for question 10 not as steep

12. **a)** e.g., $t = 3n + 1$

b)

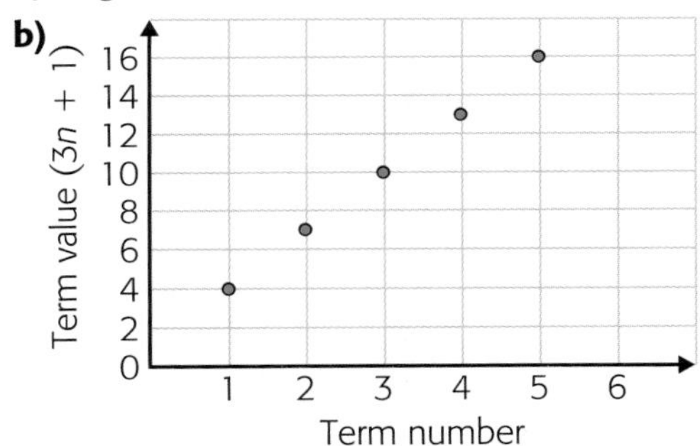

13. **a)** e.g., $v = 5p + 1$

b)

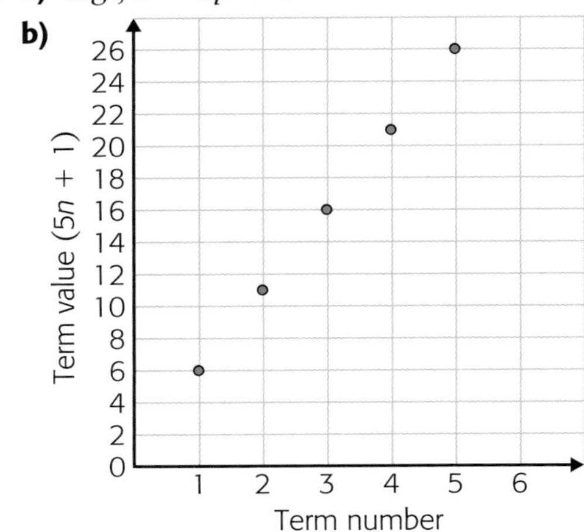

14. a) e.g., the relationship between number of paving stones and the number of border pieces

b) e.g., $b = 2t + 1$

c) e.g., the length of each border piece is equal to the length of a side of a paving stone

15. a) A. e.g.,

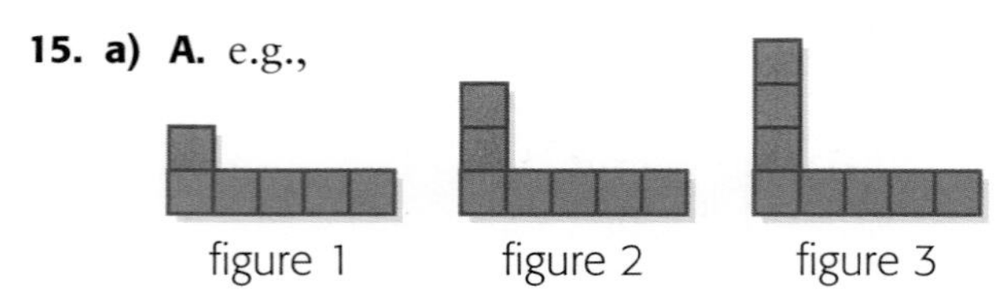

B. e.g.,

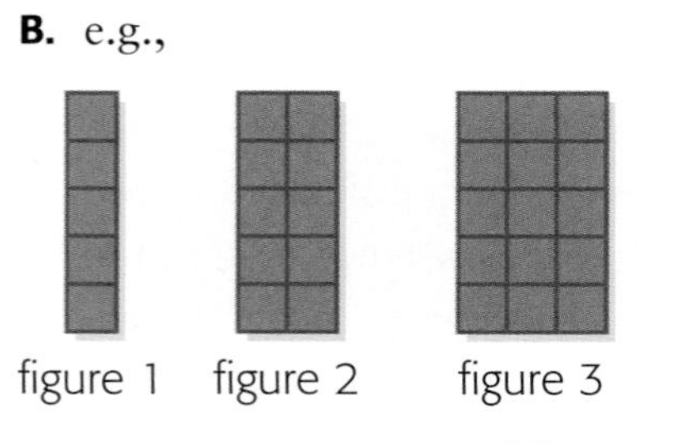

C. e.g.,

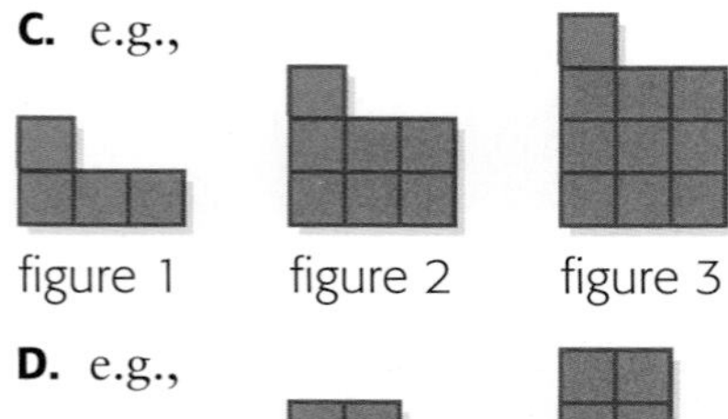

D. e.g.,

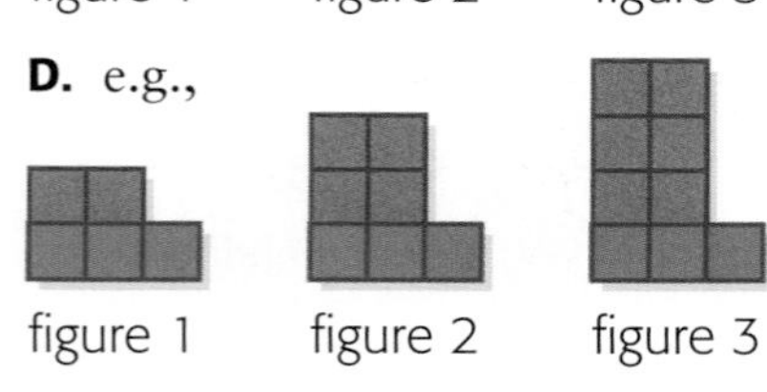

b) A.

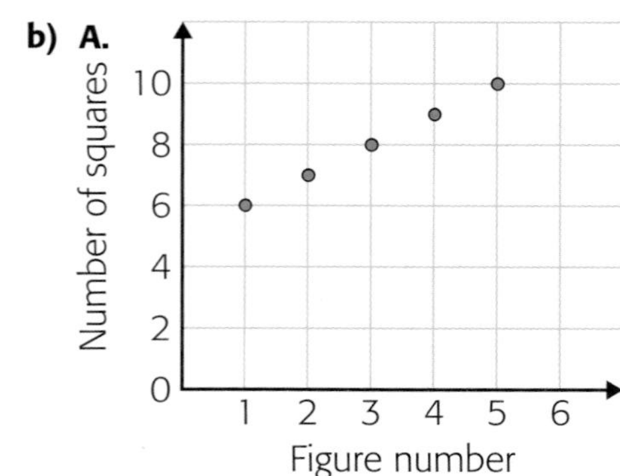

B.

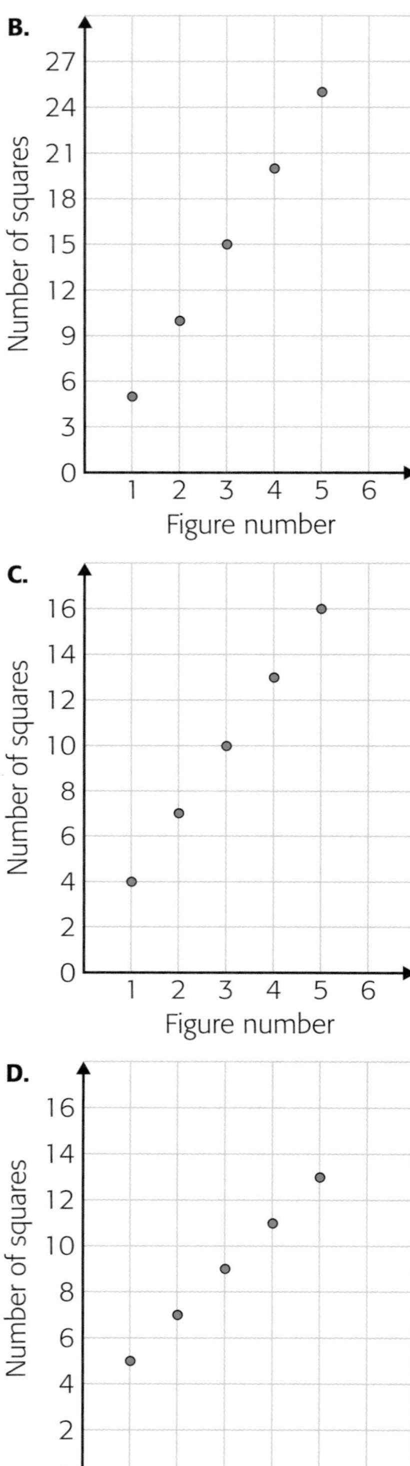

D.

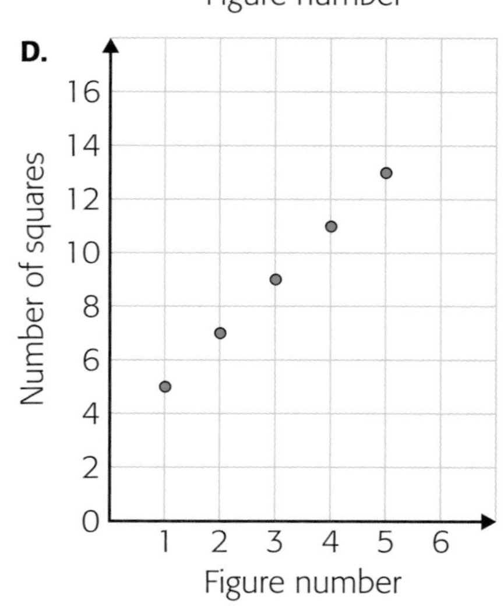

c) **A.** e.g., The numerical coefficient is 1, so each time the figure number goes up by 1, the graph goes up by 1 and the number of squares goes up by 1. The constant term is 5, the graph meets vertical axis at 5, and each figure in geometric pattern has 5 dark squares along the bottom.
B. e.g., The numerical coefficient is 5, so each time the figure number goes up by 1, the graph goes up by 5 and the number of squares goes up by 5. The constant term is 0, the graph meets the vertical axis at 0, and each figure in the geometric pattern does not have a constant number of squares at the bottom.
C. e.g., The numerical coefficient is 3, so each time the figure number goes up by 1, the graph goes up by 3 and the number of squares goes up by 3. The constant term is 1, so the graph meets the vertical axis at 1, and each figure in the geometric pattern has 1 dark square on the top.
D. e.g., The numerical coefficient is 2, so each time the figure number goes up by 1, the graph goes up by 2 and the number of squares goes up by 2. The constant term is 3, the graph meets the vertical axis at 3, and each figure in the geometric pattern has 3 dark squares along the bottom.

16. Explain what effect different parts of an expression have on the graph of the expression.

Mid-Chapter Review, pp. 399–400

1. e.g., $s = 3n$

2. a)

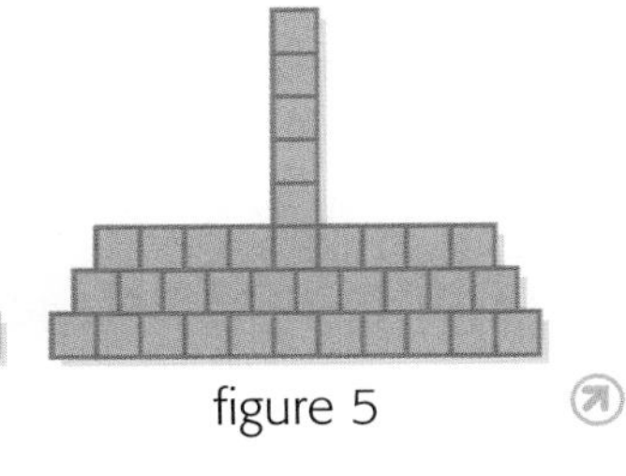

b) e.g., $7n$ **c)** 70

3. a) $s = 2n + 3$; $s = (n + 1) + (n + 1) + 1$
b) constant term 3, numerical coefficient 2
c) e.g., constant term says to add 3 to variable multiplied by the numerical coefficient; numerical coefficient says that each time the figure number goes up by 1, the number of tiles goes up by 2

4. a) e.g., $2h + 3$ **b)** \$19

5. Hours worked: 1, 2, 3, 4, 5, 6, 7, 8;
Dollars earned: 5, 6, 7, 8, 9, 10, 11, 12

6.

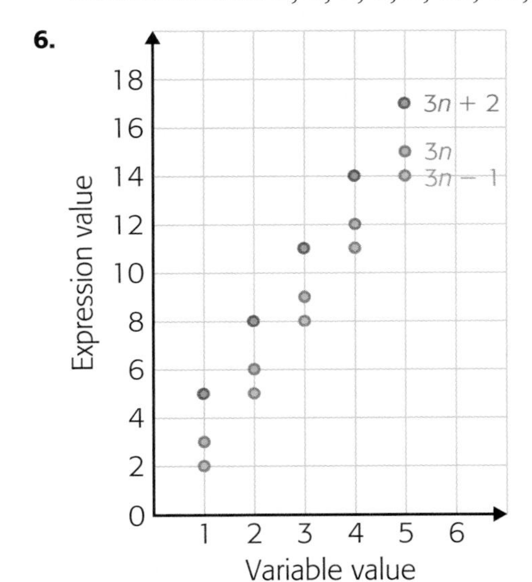

7. e.g., alike: parallel, all go up the same way; different: at different heights

8. a) e.g., $t = 12n - 8$
b)

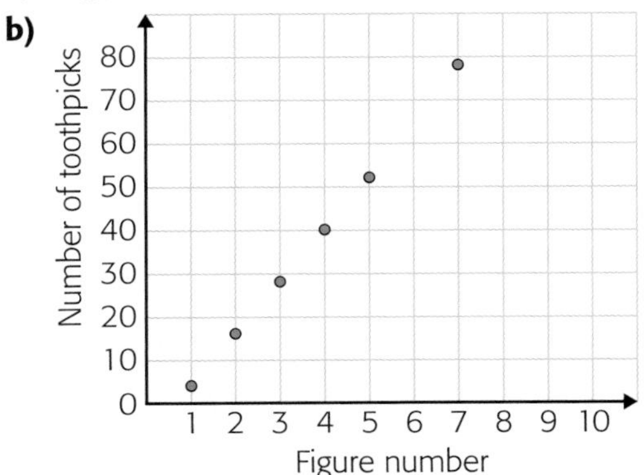

c) 76 toothpicks

9.5 Solving Equations Using Mental Math, pp. 403–405

1. a) $n = 7$ **c)** $P = 7$ **e)** $x = 27$
b) $w = 33$ **d)** $n = 6$ **f)** $y = 28$

2. a) $4n + 3 = 43$ **b)** $n = 10$
c) $4n + 3 = 4(10) + 3 = 40 + 3 = 43$

3. a) $b = 12$ **c)** $z = 22$ **e)** $m = 20$
b) $q = 15$ **d)** $w = 200$ **f)** $n = 40$

4. a) $m = 10$ **c)** $n = 4$
b) $a = 8$ **d)** $n = 7$

5. a) e.g., 6 plus what number gives 16? Subtract 6. What number multiplied by 5 gives 10? Divide by 5.
b) e.g., Substitute answer into original equation, and check that both sides are equal.

6. yes

7. a) $n + 2$ **b)** $24 = n + 2$ **c)** 22
d) 24 (two horizontally, 22 more vertically)
e) 21 (two horizontally, 19 more vertically)

8. a) $28 = 4 + 2n$ **b)** $n = 12$

9. a) $4 + 2n = 30$ **b)** $n = 13$

10. a) e.g., $c = 2 + d$ **c)** $d = 7$
b) $9 = 2 + d$

11. a) $25 = 4 + 3d$ **b)** $7 = d$

12. a) $2n - 1 = 7$
b) e.g., Zach could add 1 to 7 to get double the number. Next, to find the number, Zach must divide double the number by 2.

13. 33 squares

14. 49 triangles, with 1 toothpick left over

15. Explain how to solve for the variable.

9.6 Solving Equations Using Models and Drawings, pp. 409–410

1. a) $p = 24$ **b)** $w = 3$ **c)** $z = (+3)$

2. a) $p = 2$ **c)** $x = (+11)$ **e)** $x = (+4)$
b) $h = 3$ **d)** $c = 12$ **f)** $y = (+1)$

3. a) e.g., $c = 2n + 7$
b) $2n + 7 = 73$
c) figure 33

4. a) $n + 19 = 35, n = 16$
b) $8n = 192, n = 24$
c) $9n - 16 = 47, n = 7$

5. a) e.g., $a = 73 - 5w$
b) $58 = 73 - 5w$
c) 3 weeks

6. a) $C = 4n + 1$ **b)** 6 **c)** no

7. figure 12

8. a) e.g., $6i + 1$ **b)** $61 = 6i + 1$ **c)** 10

9. Explain when you would solve an equation using concrete materials and when you would use a drawing.

9.7 Solving Equations by Graphing, pp. 414–416

1. 7

2. a) Figure: 1, 2, 3; Number of tiles: 3, 4, 5
b) e.g., $s = n + 2$
c) $n + 2 = 22$
d) $n = 20$

3. a) Figure: 1, 2, 3; Number of counters: 5, 8, 11
b) e.g., $3n + 2$
c) $3n + 2 = 23$
d) $n = 7$

4. a) Week number: 1, 2, 3, 4, 5; Amount: $10, $15, $20, $25, $30
b) e.g., $5w + 5$ **e)** 19 weeks
c) $5w + 5 = 60$ **f)** $105
d) 11 weeks

5. a) figure 32 **b)** figure 48

6. a) 6 **b)** 5 **c)** 4

7. a) Mowing Earnings at \$15 for Each Lawn

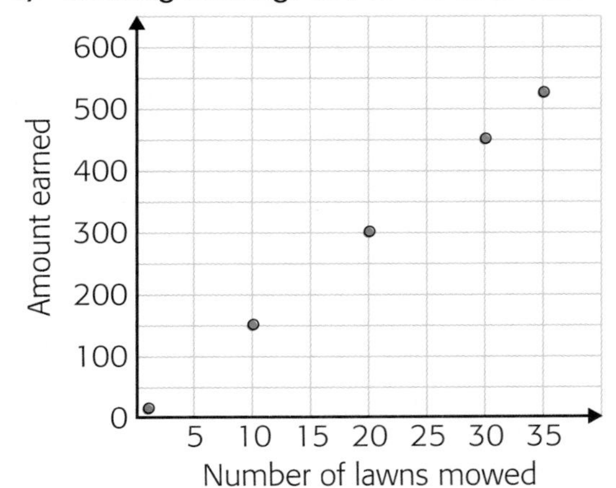

b) $15n - 100$ **c)** $n = 35$; 35 lawns

8. a) Packing Cans in Boxes

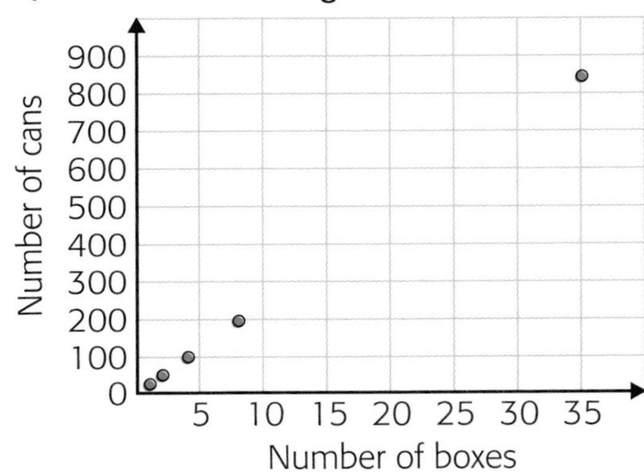

b) about 30 boxes

c) $24b$

d) 31 boxes

e) e.g., with counters or a diagram

9. Explain how to solve an equation by looking at the graph of the relation.

9.8 Communicate the Solution of an Equation, p. 420

1. e.g., Subtract 1 from both sides. There are 3 c's on one side and 3 groups of 3 on the other side, so one c is equal to 3.

2. e.g., Step 1: Start a pan balance with 4 containers on the left pan and 12 counters on the right pan. Step 2: Group the counters on the right into 4 groups of 3. There are 4 containers on the left pan and 4 groups on the right pan, so each container is worth 3.

3. a) $4c + 1 = 9$; 2 **b)** $3b + 2 = 14$; 4 **c)** $7 = 2c + 3$; 2

4. a) $x = 2$ **b)** $x = 4$ **c)** $z = 4$ **d)** $a = 50$ **e)** $b = (-11)$ **f)** $b = 4$

5. Discuss the importance of clarity.

Chapter Self-Test, p. 421

1. e.g., $s = 2n + 3$

2. a) e.g., $6p + 10$ **b)** $10 + 6p = 106$ **c)** 16 books

3. 52

4. $a = 3$

5. $n = 15$

6. figure 41

7. a) $x = 13$ **b)** $n = (+7)$ **c)** $p = 3$ **d)** $r = 50$

Chapter Review, p. 424

1. e.g., $t = 2n + 3$

2. a) e.g., $5h + 25$ **b)** \$70

3. a) e.g., $c = n + 4$

b)

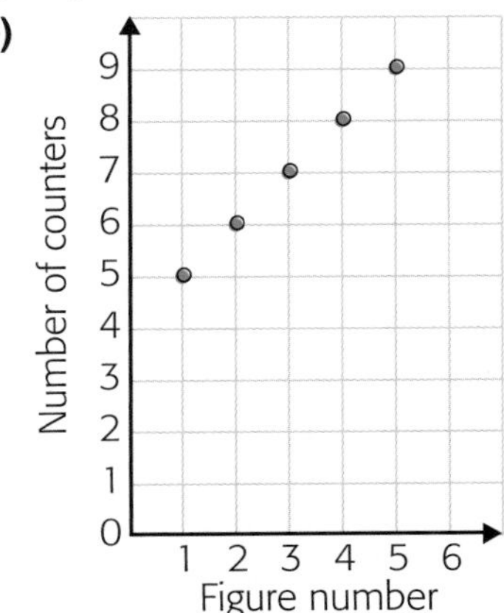

c) 9 counters

4. a) $25x + 300 = 900$ b) $x = 24$
c) Substitute 24 into original equation.

5. a) $x = 6$ c) $w = 3$ e) $w = 8$
b) $a = 5$ d) $c = -8$ f) $x = 5$

6. $n = 8$; e.g., I located the point with a vertical coordinate equal to 20.

Chapter 10, p. 427

10.2 Representing Probabilities as Fractions and Percents, pp. 433–435

1. $\frac{12}{30}$, 40%, 12:30

2. e.g.,
a) 3:20, $\frac{3}{20}$, 15% c) 11:20, $\frac{11}{20}$, 55%
b) 10:20, $\frac{10}{20}$, 50% d) 4:20, $\frac{4}{20}$, 20%

3. a) 30:100; $\frac{30}{100}$
b) impossible certain
less likely more likely
0 $\frac{30}{100}$ $\frac{1}{2}$ 1

4. e.g., a) prediction 90%; experimental probability 85%
b) prediction $\frac{1}{6}$; experimental probability $\frac{1}{5}$
c) prediction 50%; experimental probability 30%

5. a) $\frac{1}{2}$ b) $\frac{1}{2}$

6. a) $\frac{1}{4}$, 25% c) $\frac{0}{4}$, 0%
b) $\frac{2}{4}$, 50% d) $\frac{3}{4}$, 75%

7. a) $\frac{4}{11}$ b) $\frac{7}{11}$ c) $\frac{2}{11}$

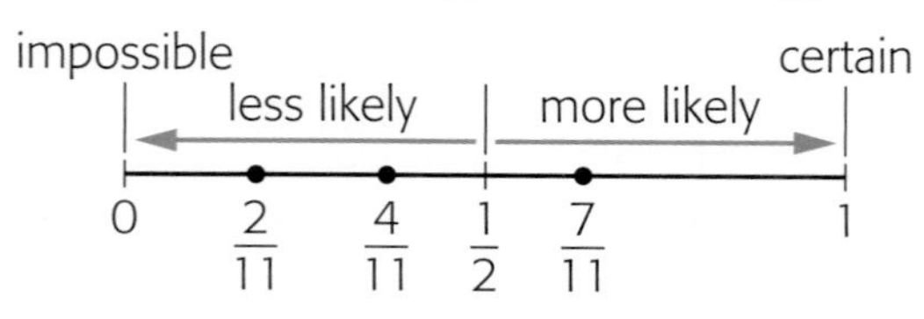

8. a) $\frac{1}{15}$, 1:15 c) $\frac{8}{15}$, 8:15 e) $\frac{3}{15}$, 3:15
b) $\frac{1}{15}$, 1:15 d) $\frac{7}{15}$, 7:15 f) $\frac{15}{15}$, 15:15

9. odd number, even number, number less than 20

10. a) 33% c) 42% e) 92%
b) 50% d) 25% f) 17%

11. e.g., a) a coin landing heads
b) a spinner that is divided into four equal parts, one of which is blue, landing on blue
c) selecting an even prime number from 1 to 31
d) selecting a marble that is not red from a bag with 1 red marble, 2 green marbles, and 3 blue marbles
e) selecting a green marble from a bag with only yellow marbles
f) rolling a number less than 7 on a regular die

12. a) $\frac{1}{10}$ c) e.g., ten 8s
b) 10% d) e.g., fraction form

13. a) Winning is impossible.
b) Winning is certain.
c) Winning and losing are equally likely.

10.3 Probability of Independent Events, pp. 438–439

1. Spinning a spinner and tossing a coin, because spinning the spinner and tossing the coin do not affect each other.

2. a) $\frac{5}{36}$ b) $\frac{6}{36}$ c) $\frac{2}{36}$

3. a) $\frac{6}{36}$ b) $\frac{10}{36}$ c) $\frac{6}{36}$

4. a) Yes; it lists the possible outcomes of each spin and all possible combinations of the two spins combined.
b) e.g., There are 3 rows and 3 possibilities in each row, so there are 3 groups of 3, or $3 \times 3 = 9$.
c) $\frac{5}{9}$ d) $\frac{8}{9}$

5. **a)** $\frac{4}{36}$ **b)** $\frac{26}{36}$
   c) The first roll does not affect the second roll.
6. **a)** $\frac{1}{24}$ **b)** $\frac{5}{24}$ **c)** $\frac{3}{24}$
7. **a)** e.g., Roll a die, then toss a coin.
   b) e.g., Roll a die, then toss a coin if the roll was even, or roll the die again if the roll was odd.

Mid-Chapter Review, p. 442

1. **a)** $\frac{1}{9}$, 11% **c)** $\frac{2}{36}$, 6% **e)** $\frac{36}{36}$, 100%
   b) $\frac{18}{36}$, 50% **d)** $\frac{16}{36}$, 44% **f)** $\frac{0}{36}$, 0%
2. **a)** rolling a number less than 4
   b) rolling an even number
   c) rolling a 6
3. **a)** $\frac{3}{12}$, 25% **b)** e.g., 13 times
4. **a)** yes–yes, yes–no, yes–maybe, no–yes, no–no, no–maybe, maybe–yes, maybe–no, maybe–maybe
   b) $\frac{3}{9}$ or 33% **c)** $\frac{4}{9}$ or 44%
5. **a)** 1–1, 1–2, 1–3, 1–4; 2–1, 2–2, 2–3, 2–4; 3–1, 3–2, 3–3, 3–4; 4–1, 4–2, 4–3, 4–4
   b) The outcome of the first roll does not affect the outcome of the second roll.
   c) $\frac{4}{16}$ or 25%

10.4 Solve Problems Using Organized Lists, p. 447

1. **a)** 10 combinations
   b) 5 combinations
   c) $\frac{5}{10}$
2. **a)** The following combinations of "win, tie, loss" all are worth 29 points:
   5, 1, 1; 5, 0, 4;
   4, 3, 0; 4, 2, 3; 4, 1, 6; 4, 0, 9;
   3, 4, 2; 3, 3, 5; 3, 2, 8; 3, 1, 11; 3, 0, 14;
   2, 6, 1; 2, 5, 4; 2, 4, 7; 2, 3, 10; 2, 2, 13;
   2, 1, 16; 2, 0, 19;
   1, 8, 0; 1, 7, 3; 1, 6, 6; 1, 5, 9; 1, 4, 12; 1, 3, 15; 1, 2, 18; 1, 1, 21; 1, 0, 24;
   0, 9, 2; 0, 8, 5; 0, 7, 8; 0, 6, 11; 0, 5, 14; 0, 4, 17; 0, 3, 20; 0, 2, 23; 0, 1, 26; 0, 0, 29
   b) The probability that Nathan's team had more losses than ties is 27 out of 37.
3. **a)** 100, 200, 300, 400, 600, 900
   b) $\frac{2}{6}$
4. $\frac{1}{16}$
5. Create a problem that can be solved with an organized list.

10.5 Using Tree Diagrams to Calculate Probability, pp. 450–451

(Note: for reasons of space, the tree diagrams are shown as combinations.)

1. $\frac{8}{36}$
2. **a)** purple-1, purple-2, purple-3, purple-4, purple-5, purple-6; orange-1, orange-2, orange-3, orange-4, orange-5, orange-6; yellow-1, yellow-2, yellow-3, yellow-4, yellow-5, yellow-6; green-1, green-2, green-3, green-4, green-5, green-6
   b) $\frac{23}{24}$
3. **a)** $50-$50, $50-$100, $50-$200, $50-$1000; $100-$50, $100-$100, $100-$200, $100-$1000; $200-$50, $200-$100, $200-$200, $200-$1000; $1000-$50, $1000-$100, $1000-$200, $1000-$1000
   b) $\frac{14}{16}$ **c)** $\frac{7}{16}$ **d)** $\frac{4}{16}$
4. **a)** 1-1, 1-2, 1-3, 1-4; 2-1, 2-2, 2-3, 2-4; 3-1, 3-2, 3-3, 3-4; 4-1, 4-2, 4-3, 4-4
   b) $\frac{6}{16}$ **c)** $\frac{3}{16}$ **d)** $\frac{2}{16}$
5. **a)** 6 outfits
   b) $\frac{4}{6}$
   c) yes, if it doesn't matter which shirt goes with which shorts

6. a) Doug's experiment: red-red, red-red, red-red, red-yellow, red-yellow, red-green; red-red, red-red, red-red, red-yellow, red-yellow, red-green; red-red, red-red, red-red, red-yellow, red-yellow, red-green; yellow-red, yellow-red, yellow-red, yellow-yellow, yellow-yellow, yellow-green; yellow-red, yellow-red, yellow-red, yellow-yellow, yellow-yellow, yellow-green; green-red, green-red, green-red, green-yellow, green-yellow, green-green

b) $\frac{6}{36}$

c) The events in Doug's experiment are independent because one does not affect the other; the events in Anna's experiment are not independent because the outcome of the second draw is affected by the outcome of the first draw.

7. a) 1-1, 1-2, 1-3, 1-4, 1-5, 1-6; 2-1, 2-2, 2-3, 2-4, 2-5, 2-6; 3-1, 3-2, 3-3, 3-4, 3-5, 3-6; 4-1, 4-2, 4-3, 4-4, 4-5, 4-6

b) $\frac{6}{24}$

8. Describe the relationship between the number of possible outcomes for the first event, the number of possible outcomes for the second event, and the total number of branches in the tree.

10.6 Comparing Theoretical and Experimental Probabilities, pp. 456–457

1. a) $\frac{10}{16}$

b) e.g., $\frac{15}{20}$, which is close to $\frac{10}{16}$

c) e.g., $\frac{53}{80}$, which is even closer to $\frac{10}{16}$

2. a) $\frac{3}{6}$ **b)** e.g., $\frac{42}{80}$, which is close to $\frac{3}{6}$

3. a) $\frac{4}{36}$ **b)** e.g., $\frac{6}{36}$

c) because the results of a die throw in an experiment are random

d) depends on class data

4. a) $\frac{6}{36}$ **b)** e.g., $\frac{7}{20}$

c) e.g., Use the spinner idea from example 3 but make each colour correspond to a number on a die, unless you can find a two-die probability program on the computer.

5. a) $\frac{1}{4}$

b) e.g., The outcome of the first draw does not affect the outcome of the second draw.

c) e.g., $\frac{2}{5}$, which is close to the theoretical probability.

6. e.g., Do not put each block back in the bag once it is removed, so the second outcome is now affected by the first outcome.

7. a) $\frac{16}{25}$ **b)** e.g., $\frac{15}{25}$

c) e.g., The experimental probability got closer to the theoretical probability.

8. a) $\frac{6}{24}$ **b)** e.g., $\frac{7}{24}$

c) e.g., They are close in value.

9. a) Mykola may have made an error in his calculation of theoretical probability.

b) Mae may have used a faulty model for her experiment; suggest one that should work.

Chapter Self-Test, pp. 459–460

1. a) $\frac{6}{10}$, 6:10, 60%

b) $\frac{15}{30}$, 15:30, 50%

c) $\frac{8}{20}$, 8:20, 40%

2. a) $\frac{7}{25}$ **b)** $\frac{2}{25}$ **c)** $\frac{8}{25}$ **d)** $\frac{10}{25}$

3. a) 25% **b)** 40% **c)** 5%

4. In experiment A, you return the first card to the deck before selecting the second card, so the first selection does not affect the second selection. In experiment B, the first card selected cannot be selected the second time, so the first selection affects the second selection.

5. a) $\frac{2}{36}$ **b)** $\frac{5}{36}$ **c)** $\frac{10}{36}$ **d)** $\frac{12}{36}$ **e)** $\frac{7}{36}$ **f)** $\frac{6}{36}$

6. **a)** 1-1, 1-2, 1-3, 1-4, 1-5; 2-1, 2-2, 2-3, 2-4, 2-5; 3-1, 3-2, 3-3, 3-4, 3-5; 4-1, 4-2, 4-3, 4-4, 4-5; 5-1, 5-2, 5-3, 5-4, 5-5
   b) $\frac{5}{25}$ **c)** $\frac{19}{25}$
7. e.g., It might be split into ninths with the numbers 1, 2, 3, 4, 5, 6, 7, 8, and 9. Tossing a coin has 2 possible outcomes and the spinner would have 9 possible outcomes. The number of combined outcomes would be $9 \times 2 = 18$.
8. **a)** e.g., $\frac{16}{20}$ or 80% **b)** $\frac{27}{36}$ or 75%
   c) e.g., The experimental probability is greater.
   d) e.g., The experimental rolls are random so it might just be that it was random chance that the probabilities do not match. Also, the dice might be bad, which would affect the outcome.
9. **a)** e.g., selecting an 11
   b) e.g., selecting a card less than 12
   c) e.g., selecting an even number
   d) e.g., selecting a 9 or a 10
   e) e.g., selecting a 2, 4, 6, or 8
   f) e.g., selecting a card greater than 3

Chapter Review, pp. 461–462

1. **a)** $\frac{1}{2}$, 50% **c)** $\frac{10}{100}$, 10%
   b) $\frac{90}{100}$, 90% **d)** $\frac{11}{100}$, 11%
2. **a)** e.g., selecting a multiple of 4
   b) e.g., selecting 120
   c) e.g., selecting a number less than 101
3. **a)** e.g., One spin doesn't affect the results of the other.
   b) e.g., They are not represented by an equal number of sections on the spinner.
4. **a)** $\frac{3}{30}$ **b)** $\frac{0}{30}$
5. **a)** 7% **b)** 29%
6. **a)** $\frac{15}{36}$, or 42% **b)** $\frac{12}{36}$, or 33%
   c) e.g., The experimental probability is based on actual results, while the theoretical probability is based on possible results.

Chapter 11, p. 465

11.1 Interpreting Circle Graphs, pp. 471–472

1. **A:** all ages, **B:** 12–17
2. e.g., Bring lots of apple pies and cherry pies, and half as many lemon pies and other flavours.
3. 74
4. **a)** e.g., don't know how much they charge
   b) no, total number of pages unknown, so can only compare the percents
5. e.g., Newspaper 1: news, 30; sports, 24; advertising, 48; entertainment, 12; other, 6
6. **a)** 10%
   b)

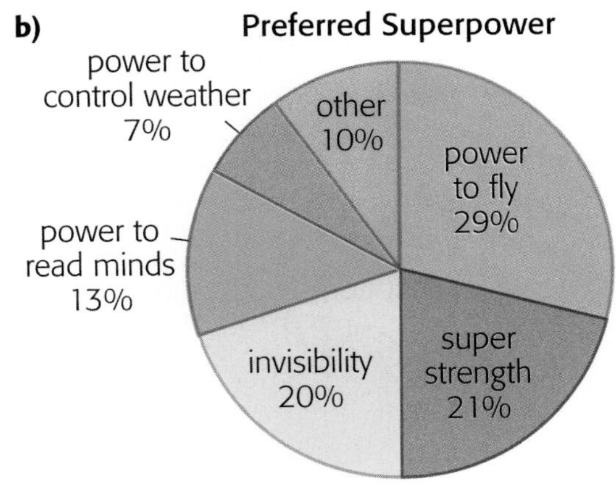

7. **a)** e.g., Which superpower was most popular? What two choices make up half of the responses? What percent of the graph do super strength and invisibility make up?
   b) e.g., power to fly; power to fly and super strength; 41%

8. Describe what circle graphs do and do not show.

11.3 Constructing Circle Graphs, pp. 478–479

1. a) Group A: 25%, 20%, 50%, 5%; Group B: 25%, 20%, 30%, 25%
   b) e.g., I created sections of the right sizes using the tick marks.

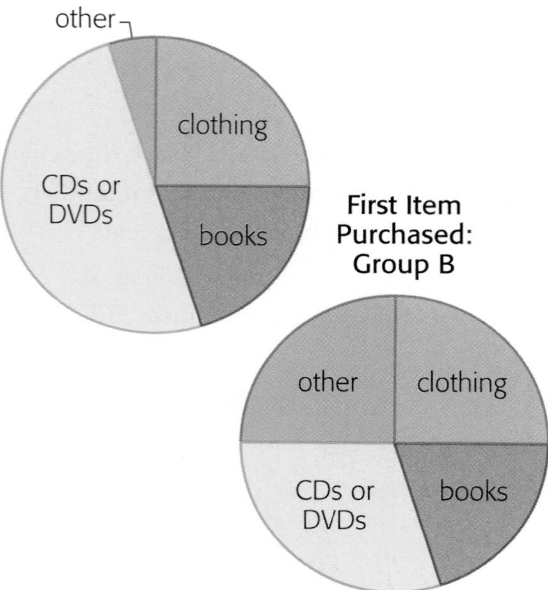

   c) e.g.,

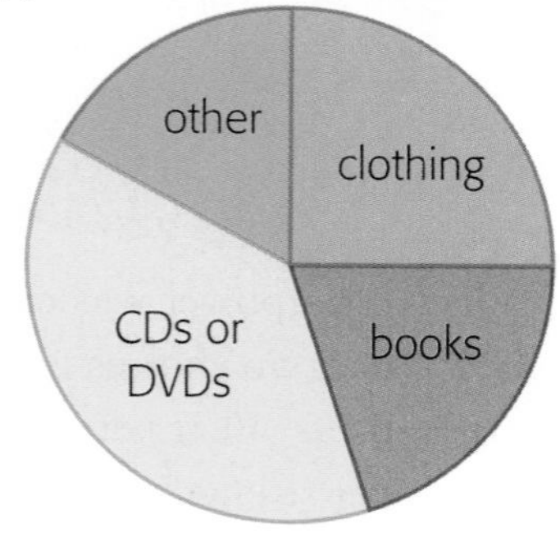

2. a) about 33%, 120°
   b) 50%, 180°
   c) about 13%, 48°
   d) about 3%, 12°

3. Composition of Milk

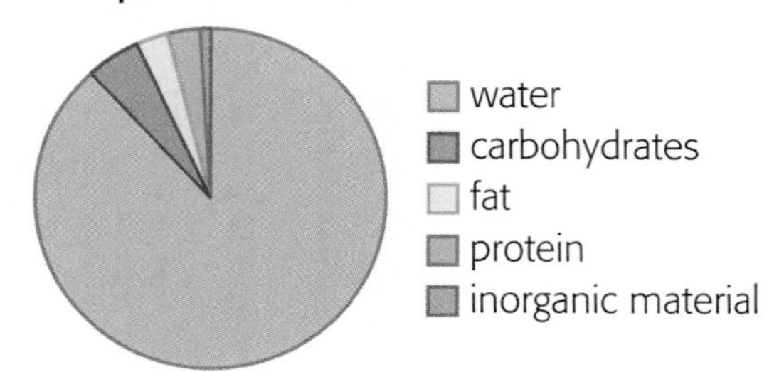

4. a) 101°, 22°, 151°, 43°, 43°
   b) Ice Cream Sales

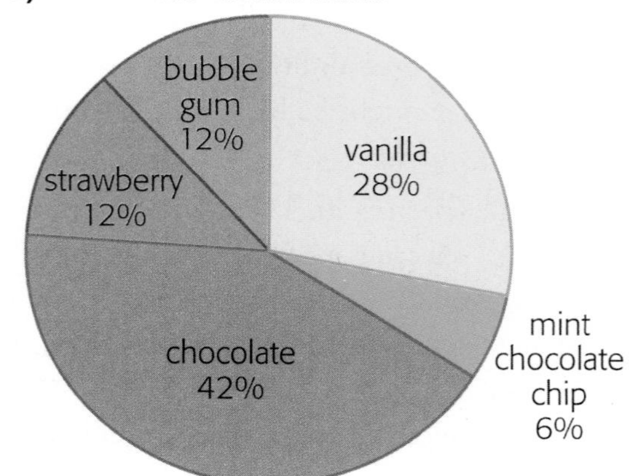

   c) e.g., What percent of ice cream sold had no chocolate in it? 52%

5. Birthday Party Activities

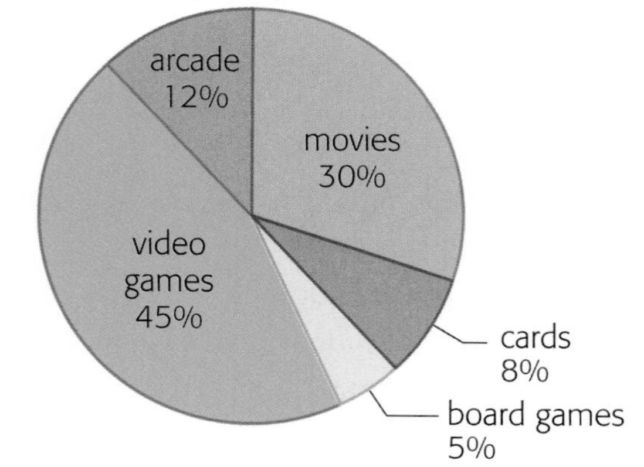

6. a), b)

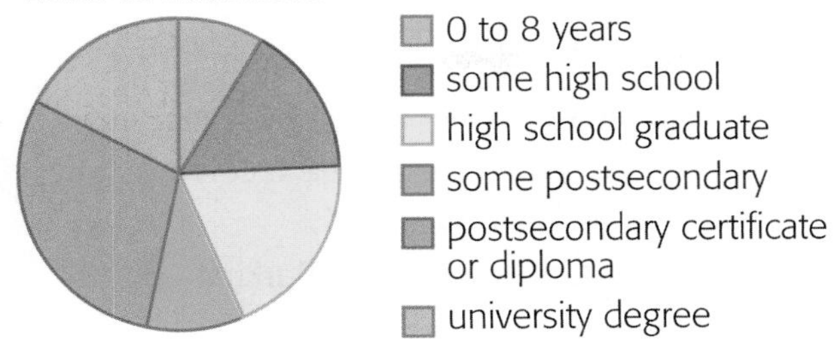

c) e.g., It probably calculated each value as a percent of the 25.5 thousand (by dividing each value by the total), and then calculated the central angle for each section (by multiplying the percent by 360°).

7. Explain how to check that your circle graph is correct.

11.4 Communicate about Circle Graphs, p. 483

1. e.g., disagree, because more of the class said strawberries or blueberries than any other fruit.

2. e.g., How many meals did you eat? What is the total number of servings of food you had?

3. e.g., Hot dogs and hamburgers make up half of the graph, so they are popular choices of food, but s'mores make up the largest section, and are the most popular choice of food at a cookout. If I were to plan a cookout, half the graph is hot dogs and hamburgers, so I would make sure there are lots of s'mores available. Since 9% said corn on the cob, I would bring a small amount so those people are happy, too.

4. e.g., I found these circle graphs of men's and women's favourite colours. Most men and women like blue best, and green the same amount, but more women like purple than men do.

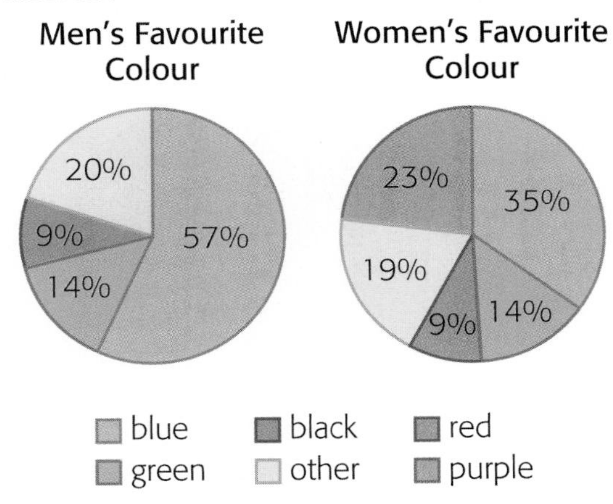

5. e.g., You could ask about the data, such as if any possible categories are missing, or how responses were grouped in categories, and about what the graph might mean in your life or someone else's.

Chapter Self-Test, pp. 486–487

1. a) Languages Spoken by Mothers

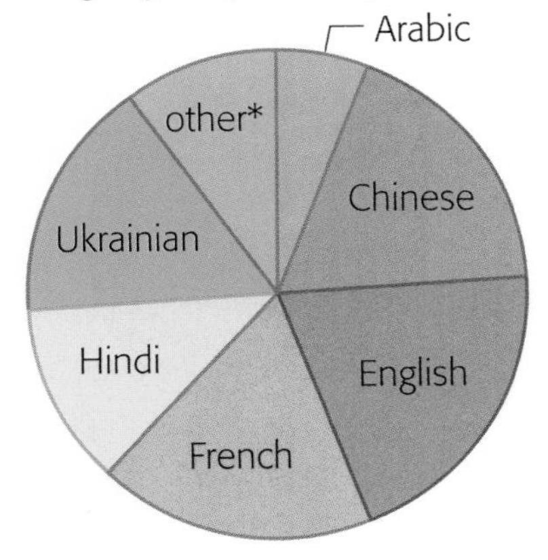

*Includes Cree, Punjabi, Japanese, Korean, and more.

b) e.g., English is the most widely spoken language, followed by Chinese and French, which are equal, and Ukrainian.

2. e.g., Comedies are the most popular type of show at Theatre 1, so there should be more of them at Theatre 2. Also, Theatre 2 should start showing romance films and cut down on the number of adventure and horror movies.

3. Human Body Mass

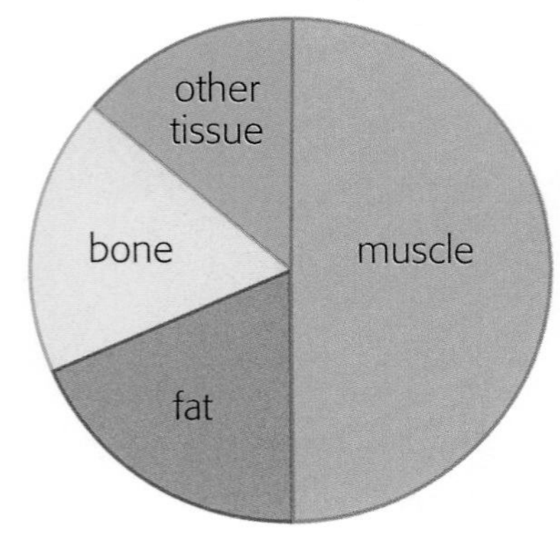

4. a) 228 b) 24

5. a) First Handful Second Handful

9%
27%
14%
23%
18%
9%

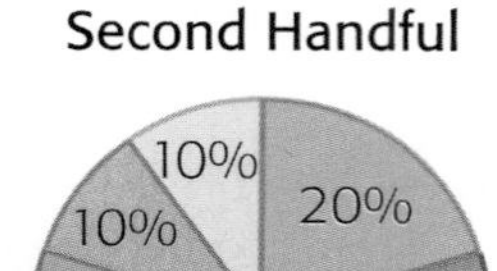

Third Handful

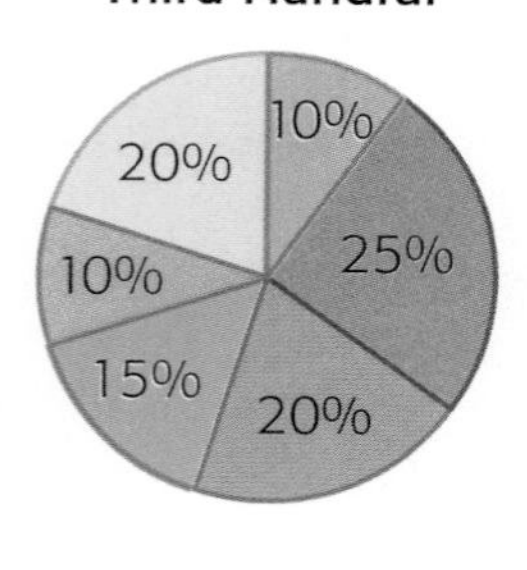

blue brown orange
red green yellow

b) blue: 36°, red: 90°, brown: 72°, green: 54°, orange: 36°, yellow: 72°

Chapter Review, pp. 489–490

1. a) 280 b) 3240
   c) e.g., motorcycle, scooter, skateboard, inline skates, working at home

2. a) e.g., It allows her to compare percents and see what fraction each colour is of the total number of cars.
   b) Car Colours in a Parking Lot

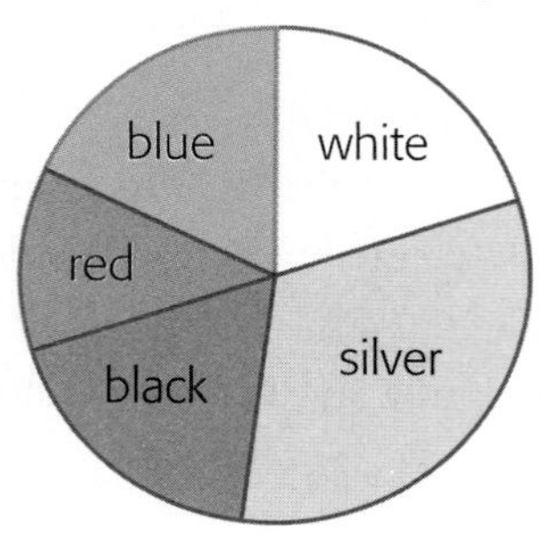

3. a) Yogurt Ingredients by Mass

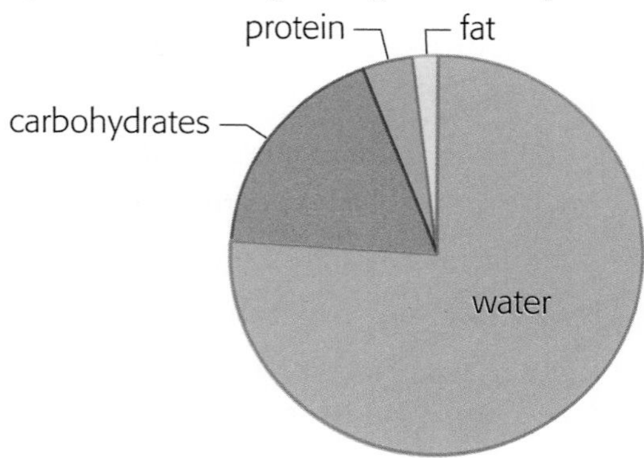

   b) e.g., About what fraction of the yogurt is water? $\frac{3}{4}$

4. a) $37 250
   b) Club Revenue for the Season

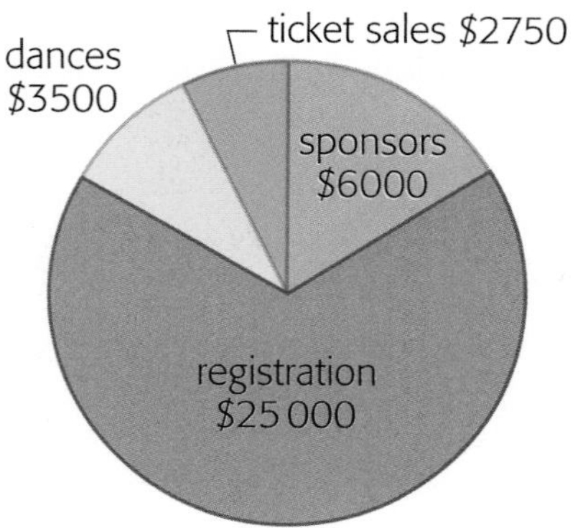

c) 16%

d) Revenue from ticket sales is a little less than half of the revenue from sponsors.

e) registration, dances, ticket sales

5. a) Grade 7

b) e.g., After a survey of the Grade 7 and 8 students in the school, I have learned that orange juice, water, and milk are the three most popular drinks for lunchtime. The circle graph shows that nearly $\frac{2}{3}$ of students prefer one of these drinks. So, I think these three drinks are the most important to offer at lunchtime.

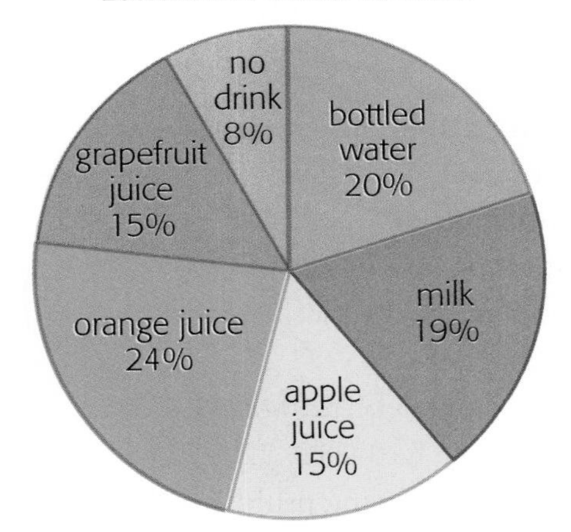

6. a) e.g., I read online that Winnipeg has 119 wet days (some rain or snow) and 246 dry days in a typical year.

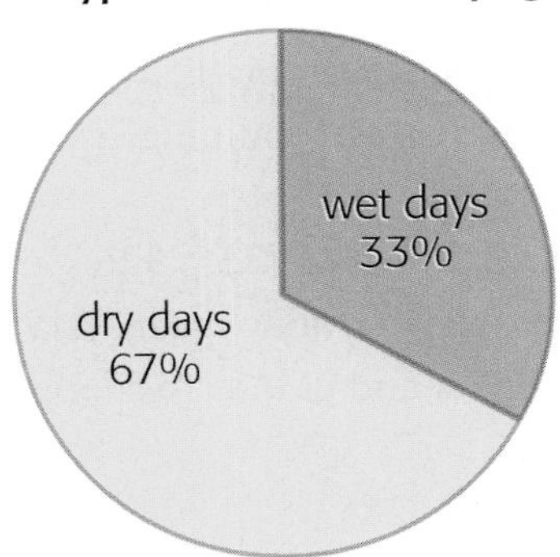

b) e.g., There are about twice as many dry days as wet days; the section in the graph showing dry days is twice the size of the section showing wet days.

c) e.g., I know this because the section in the graph is about twice as large and 67% is almost double 33%.

Cumulative Review: Chapters 8–11, pp. 492–493

1. C
2. D
3. C
4. A
5. C
6. B
7. B
8. B
9. B, C
10. D
11. C
12. B
13. D
14. C

Index

A

B

C

F

G

H

I

L

M

N

O

P

U

V

W

X

Y

Z

Credits

Chapter 1 Pages i–1: David Sailors/Corbis; page 2: Andrew Hampstead; page 6: Shutterstock; page 10: Cesar Lucas Abreu/The Image Bank/Getty Images; page 18: Terry Lusty; page 26: Courtesy of Invitation: The Quilt of Belonging; page 38: Rebecca Cook/Reuters/Landov.

Chapter 2 Pages 40–41: Jim Wark/Index Stock Imagery; page 60: Courtesy of Invitation: The Quilt of Belonging; page 62: Lisa Peardon/Taxi/Getty Images; page 70: © SC Photos/Alamy; page 72: Reprinted by permission of the Vancouver Symphony Orchestra; page 85: Richard Hutchings/Photo Edit; page 88: © Andrew Twort/Alamy; page 95: Peter J. Robinson/Firstlight.ca.

Chapter 3 Page 117: Shutterstock.

Chapter 4 Pages 150–151: Airphoto; page 153: © Jeff Greenberg/PhotoEdit; page 165: Pacific National Exhibition; page 178: © brt PHOTO/Alamy; page 180: Shutterstock; page 183: Shutterstock; page 188: Shutterstock; page 189: Shutterstock.

Chapter 5 Pages 190–191: MedioImages/Getty Images; page 192: © David Lee/Corbis; page 207: Cordelia Molloy/Science Photo Library; page 212: PhotoDisc/Getty Images; page 220: PhotoDisc Green/Getty Images; page 223 Clockwise: © SuperStock Inc./SuperStock, Shutterstock, Dave Mager/Index Stock, One Mile Up/Fotosearch.

Chapter 6 Pages 236–237: © Joseph Sohm; Chromo Sohm Inc./Corbis; page 242: Dave Sandford/Getty Images Sport; page 252: Reuters/Landov; pages 268–269: Daryl Benson/The Image Bank/Getty Images.

Chapter 7 Pages 280–281: Shutterstock; page 318 Left to right: Shutterstock, © Kit Houghton/Corbis; page 322 Left to right: Domespirit Geodesic Domes, © Gerard Degeorge/Corbis, Shutterstock.

Chapter 8 Pages 332–333: © Peter Hvizdak/The Image Works; page 340 Top to Bottom: © Neal Preston/Corbis, © Bettmann/Corbis; page 341: John Felstead/CP Picture Archive; page 342: Kyodo/Landov; page 345: Anja Niedringhaus/CP Picture Archive; page 350: Michael Dinneen/CP Picture Archive.

Chapter 9 Pages 372–373: Royal BC Museum #1189; page 384: © Brian Sytnyk/Masterfile; page 416: Aaron Harris/CP Picture Archive.

Chapter 10 Page 435: Jeff Greenberg/PhotoEdit Inc.

Chapter 11 Pages 464–465: Gloria H. Chomica/Masterfile.